D1088474

# Animal Geography

By the same author

ELEMENTARY GENETICS (*Macmillan*)

# Animal Geography

*by*

WILMA GEORGE, M.A.

*Fellow and Tutor in Zoology at Lady Margaret Hall and Lecturer in Zoology at Somerville College, Oxford*

HEINEMANN

LONDON

Heinemann Educational Books Ltd
LONDON MELBOURNE TORONTO
SINGAPORE AUCKLAND
IBADAN CAPE TOWN
HONG KONG



*First Published* 1962
*Reprinted* 1963, 1964

*Published by Heinemann Educational Books Ltd*
15-16 *Queen St, Mayfair, London W.*1
*Phototypeset by Filmset Limited*
*Printed in Great Britain for the Publishers*
*by Morrison & Gibb Ltd, London and Edinburgh*

To GEORGE CROWTHER

# Preface

*Animal Geography* has been written for all those who have ever wondered why animals are not the same all over the world, why for example there are elephants and rhinoceroses in Africa and in India but not in any part of the New World. It provides an introduction to the study of the distribution of animals round the world, for those who are starting zoology at school and for those whose knowledge has progressed further but who require a brief survey of the subject of zoogeography. I hope it will be of interest to those who travel from continent to continent and who would like to know how the fauna varies over such long distances and how this has come about. I hope it will be read by all those who are interested in animals and maps.

Because the representation of the distribution of animals round the world is a problem of mapping and because maps are visual reproductions of the shapes of the land, I have made animal geography a visual study. Representational animals of the zoogeographical regions of the world have been given pictorial expression, and an attempt has been made at a visual reconstruction not only of the continents during the more recent geological ages, but also of the distribution of a few important terrestrial mammal and other vertebrate families during that time. I believe that this method will give an idea of past land movements and past animal movements in a more easily understood form than can be done by words alone. It involves a certain arbitrariness. Where words can modify a statement to make plain a point of doubt, a drawing, unless it is to be complicated to a state of uselessness, has to make a decision.

There is little agreement amongst paleogeographers over the state of the land in past ages and whatever picture is drawn there will be some who do not approve of it. At best only a rough indication can be given of continental coastlines and land connexions millions of years ago so that although I have based my maps on recent authorities they should not be considered to be either accurate or definitive. Similarly the outer form of the fossil animals as I have drawn them is necessarily imaginary, but their time and place of occurrence is based on up to date evidence and in particular on the fundamental work of G. G. Simpson.

In describing the present day distribution of vertebrates by regions I have enumerated in full only the families of land mammals which occur (excluding the bats), picking out for further description those which seemed to me to be of special interest for my purpose. Anyone who wishes to plot the distribution of those mammalian families which I have not discussed in detail can do so from the information I have provided.

The animals chosen for illustration are not drawn to scale nor are they labelled, but are to be regarded as symbols of the different regions and different epochs. The text makes clear the type of animal that is depicted, but for those who require more precise information on regional animals a list of their scientific names is given at the back of the book.

I would like to thank D. L. Ride for his encouragement and for reading the manuscript at an early stage.

# Contents

## Part One
## PRESENT


| | PAGE |
|---|---|
| 1. Introduction | |
| *Maps* | 3 |
| *Animals* | 5 |
| 2. Animal Maps | |
| *Simple Maps* | 11 |
| *Compound Maps* | 13 |
| 3. Zoogeographical Regions | |
| *Palearctic* | 16 |
| *Nearctic* | 18 |
| *Neotropical* | 21 |
| *Ethiopian* | 24 |
| *Oriental* | 28 |
| *Australian* | 30 |
| 4. Dispersal | |
| *Creation* | 33 |
| *Limitation* | 33 |
| *Spread* | 35 |
| *Regional Aspects* | 38 |


## Part Two
## PAST


| | |
|---|---|
| 5. Paleogeography | |
| *Rocks* | 43 |
| *Continents* | 47 |
| 6. Evolution of Animals | |
| *Paleozoic and Mesozoic* | 51 |
| *Cenozoic* | 53 |
| *Summary of Mammal Evolution* | 60 |

## Part Three
## PAST TO PRESENT


7. Northern Regions
    *Cenozoic Distribution* 65
    *Nearctic and Palearctic* 66

8. Southern Regions
    *Intermigration* 74
    *Neotropical* 74
    *Ethiopian* 78
    *Oriental* 82
    *Australian* 84

9. Land Bridges
    *Gondwanaland* 88
    *South Atlantic Bridge* 89
    *Lemuria* 91
    *Antarctica* 92

10. Continental Drift 94


## Part Four
## ISLANDS


11. Island Patterns
    *Wallace's Line* 101
    *Classification of Islands* 104

12. Oceanic Islands
    *St. Helena* 107
    *Galapagos Islands* 108
    *Krakatau* 111

13. Continental Islands
    *British Isles* 115
    *Great Britain* 117
    *Ireland* 119

14. Ancient Islands
    *New Zealand* 123
    *Madagascar* 126

Conclusion 130
Book List 131
Index to Regional Illustrations 133
Index 136

# Part One

# PRESENT

# 1

# Introduction

## *Maps*

Animal geography, or zoogeography, combines animals with maps.

Maps represent pictorially the surface of the earth. The best guide to the physical characteristics of the world is a sphere, but because of the necessity of representation on a flat page, various methods have been devised for spreading out the sphere so that it can be looked at in two dimensions. The best known method is Mercator's projection which is the flattest looking of all and which is useful for seeing the main features of the world drawn compactly into a rectangle. Because of its obvious utility, it is a projection which is frequently used in spite of its great fault, which is to exaggerate the area of the polar regions. The lines of longitude are drawn as parallels, with the poles at infinite distance, so it is impossible ever to show the poles themselves on a Mercator projection.

Among many other methods, conic projections give some indication of the roundness of the world and the smallness of the polar regions by projecting the lines of longitude on to a cone in such a way that only one parallel touches the surface of the sphere and the apex of the cone is above the surface. The parallels are drawn as circles, the meridians are projected to meet the apex

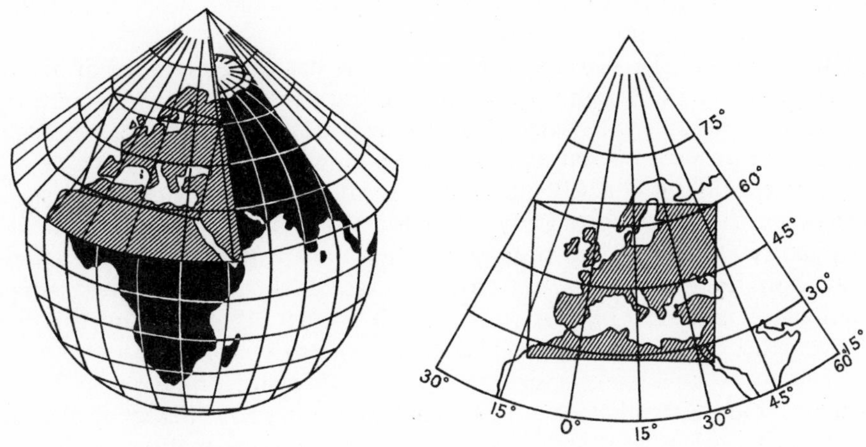

of the imaginary cone. Conic projections are useful when a picture of only a small area of the world is required at any one time. The whole world cannot be represented in continuous view in a conic projection. But a modification of this projection is particularly useful for depicting polar regions. Here the pole becomes the centre of a circle instead of the apex of a cone, the meridians radiate from the centre and the lines of latitude form concentric circles.

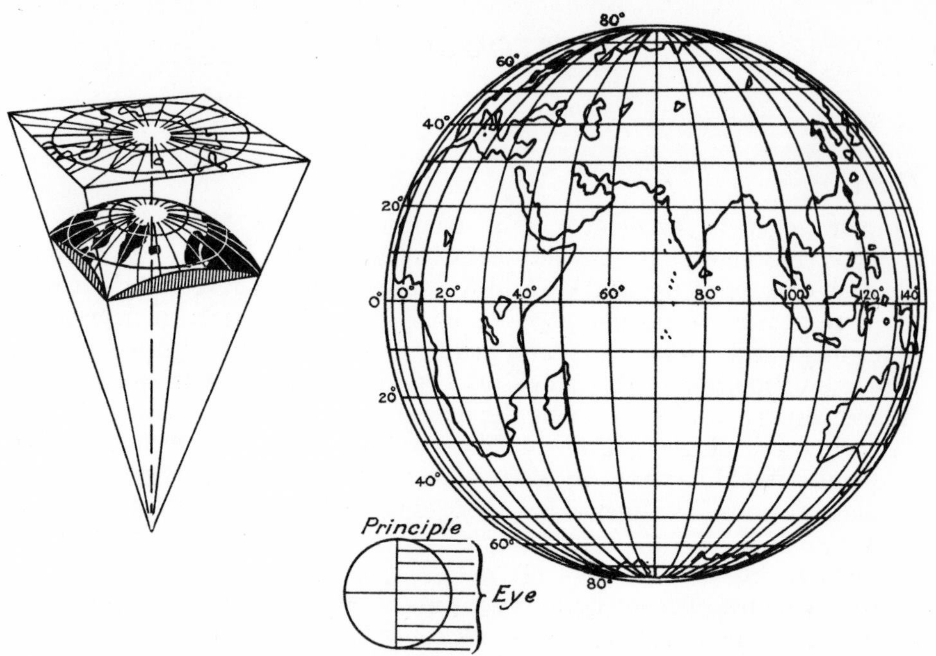


Orthographic projections represent the world in a circle. The plane of projection is the centre of the earth and, in the simplest type, the eye is supposed to be looking at the earth from an infinite distance. This projection suffers like the conic from the impossibility of showing more than half the world in one continuous picture.

Others picture the world within an oval. It has the advantage of bringing the polar regions to a point and of presenting the whole world in one view, but the representation suffers from serious angular distortion of the edges.

All these projections have been used in zoogeography, and have been the cause of considerable confusion and misunderstanding, Mercator's projection being the most commonly used and the most misleading. But as no satisfactory alternative has been found that fits the printed page neatly and shows both the whole world at one time as well as accurately representing the relations of its parts, no one projection has been adhered to in this book. Convenience of fitting the greatest area of land into as small a space as possible has had to be balanced against the possibility of misunderstanding. Convenience and its familiarity have frequently tipped the balance in favour of Mercator's projection, particularly when a continuous picture of the whole world has been required. For smaller areas and where Mercator is positively misleading, conic or orthographic projections have been used.

In all cases where the spherical world is represented on a flat page, some piece of the world is in the middle of the picture and other pieces on the edges. The choice of the midline is arbitrary, depending often on the country of origin of the map, though conventionally it is usually either the 0° meridian or the 180°. The choice of an unsuitable midline may on the one hand confuse by its unfamiliarity and on the other mislead the zoogeographer. It cannot be emphasized too strongly, therefore, that in the study of animal geography a globe is the best guide, and the only working model that cannot be misleading.

## *Animals*

Land covers about 29 per cent of the earth's surface and is unequally distributed. There is more than twice as much land in the northern hemisphere as in the southern. Most of the land in fact forms a nearly continuous mass, all the main continents being linked either by continuity of the land or by archipelagos and islands.

On this land and in its rivers live both vertebrate and invertebrate animals.

Theoretically animal geography is concerned with all animals, the invertebrates and the vertebrates, the terrestrial animals and the aquatic. There are some 1,000,000 species of animals and therefore any one book is by necessity selective. Only the geography of land and freshwater vertebrates, about 2 per cent of all animals, is discussed here and even amongst these there has been further selection to bring the emphasis on to mammals. For an account of the seas, the reader is referred to Ekman (1953) and for maps showing the geography of invertebrates to Bartholomew, Clarke and Grimshaw (1911). All land and freshwater vertebrates are dealt with in detail in Darlington (1957).

Animals are grouped into units and this grouping is the basis of classification, the giving of names to different sorts of animals and the indication of their relationships. Vertebrates are classified as a large group of the phylum Chordata. The vertebrates themselves are divided into five classes, the fish, the amphibia, the reptiles, the birds and the mammals. Each class is divided into orders. The class Amphibia, for example, has three living orders, the Anura (no tail) frogs and toads, the Urodela (tail visible) newts and salamanders, and the Apoda (no feet) worm-like caecilians of the tropics.

The orders are further subdivided into grades, one of which is the family. The family is further divided into sub-families, genera and species. Thus the giraffe belongs to the class Mammalia, the order Artiodactyla (even toes), the family Giraffidae, the sub-family Giraffinae, the genus *Giraffa* and the species *camelopardalis*. According to the binomial convention the scientific name for a giraffe is *Giraffa camelopardalis*. Often there is more than one species in a genus, genus in a family and so on. For instance *Okapia johnstonii*, the okapi, is in the same family as the giraffe, Giraffidae, but belongs to a different sub-family, Paleotraginae, and genus, *Okapia*. To take another example, in the horse genus *Equus* (family Equidae), *Equus asinus* is the African species of wild ass, but *E. caballus* is the domestic horse.

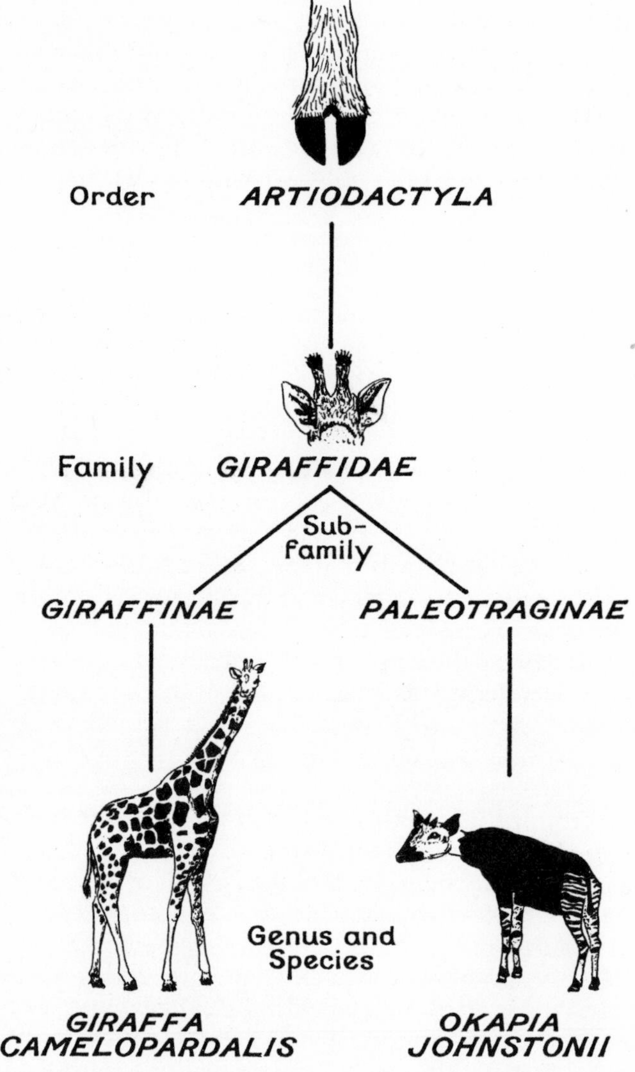


In the account of animal geography that follows the emphasis is on families of animals rather than on orders or species. This is an arbitrary choice but it has been used often and is convenient. The families are the units of classification which best show how vertebrates are spread through the world and there are frequently well-known names to describe them. Thus the word cats is generally recognized to refer to the cat family Felidae, dogs to the family Canidae.

For similar reasons, convenience and limitation, the theories outlined in later chapters make reference mainly to mammals. Mammals are familiar, well classified, well collected, have a well-documented history, and are mainly confined to the land.

The living mammals of the world are classified into families in the following way:

## Class Mammalia

*Order Monotremata:* egg-laying mammals; two living families.
F. Tachyglossidae: spiny anteaters
F. Ornithorhynchidae: duckbilled platypuses

*Order Marsupialia:* pouched mammals; eight living families.
F. Didelphidae: opossums
F. Dasyuridae: 'mice', 'cats' and 'anteaters'
F. Notoryctidae: pouched 'mole'
F. Peramelidae: bandicoots
F. Caenolestidae
F. Phalangeridae: phalangers, Australian 'opossums'
F. Phascolomidae: wombats
F. Macropodidae: kangaroos, wallabies

*Order Insectivora:* insect-eaters, archaic placental mammals; eight living families.
F. Solenodontidae: alamiqui
F. Tenrecidae: tenrecs
F. Potamogalidae: otter shrew
F. Chrysochloridae: golden moles
F. Erinaceidae: hedgehogs
F. Macroscelidae: elephant shrews
F. Soricidae: shrews
F. Talpidae: moles

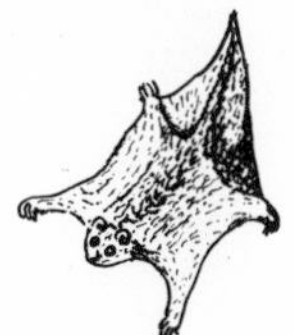

*Order Dermoptera:* gliding arboreal mammals; one living family.
F. Cynocephalidae: colugo

*Order Chiroptera:* flying mammals; seventeen living families, including fruit bats, vampire bats and the more numerous insectivorous bats.

*Order Primates:* arboreal omnivorous mammals; eleven living families.

F. Tupaiidae: tree shrews
F. Lemuridae: lemurs
F. Indridae: woolly lemurs
F. Daubentonidae: aye aye
F. Lorisidae: lorises, galagos
F. Tarsiidae: tarsiers
F. Cebidae: New World monkeys
F. Callithricidae: marmosets
F. Cercopithecidae: Old World monkeys
F. Pongidae: apes
F. Hominidae: man

*Order Edentata:* American mammals with simple or no teeth; three living families.

F. Myrmecophagidae: South American anteaters
F. Bradypodidae: sloths
F. Dasypodidae: armadillos

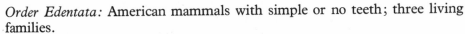

*Order Pholidota:* scaly anteaters of the Old World; one living family.

F. Manidae: pangolins

*Order Lagomorpha:* gnawing mammals with two pairs of upper incisors; two living families.

F. Ochotonidae: pikas
F. Leporidae: rabbits, hares

*Order Rodentia:* gnawing mammals; thirty-two living families, variously grouped into suborders (Wood 1955).

S.O. Sciuromorpha: the squirrel-like forms.
F. Aplodontidae: sewellel
F. Sciuridae: squirrels, prairie dogs
F. Ctenodactylidae: gundis

S.O. Castorimorpha
F. Castoridae: beavers

S.O. Theridomyomorpha
F. Anomaluridae: African flying 'squirrels'
F. Pedetidae: spring haas

S.O. Myomorpha: the mouse-like forms.
F. Cricetidae: hamsters, voles, rice rats, lemmings
F. Spalacidae: mole rats
F. Rhizomyidae: bamboo rats
F. Muridae: modern rats and mice
F. Geomyidae: pocket gophers

F. Heteromyidae: pocket mice, kangaroo rats
F. Gliridae: dormice
F. Platacanthomyidae: spiny dormice
F. Seleviniidae: selevinia
F. Zapodidae: jumping mice
F. Dipodidae: jerboas

S.O. Hystricomorpha: Old World porcupines and African rats
F. Hystricidae: porcupines
F. Thryonomyidae: cane rats
F. Petromuridae: rock rats

S.O. Caviomorpha: twelve South American rodent families, including tree porcupines, capybaras, guinea pigs and chinchillas.

S.O. Bathyergomorpha: sand burrowing rodents.
F. Bathyergidae: blesmols

*Order Cetacea:* whales; nine living families, all aquatic.

*Order Carnivora:* flesh-eaters; ten living families.
F. Canidae: dogs
F. Ursidae: bears
F. Procyonidae: raccoons, pandas
F. Mustelidae: weasels, otters, badgers, skunks etc.

F. Viverridae: civets
F. Hyaenidae: hyenas
F. Felidae: cats
and three families of seals.

*Order Tubulidentata:* tube-toothed mammal; one living family.
F. Orycteropidae: aardvark

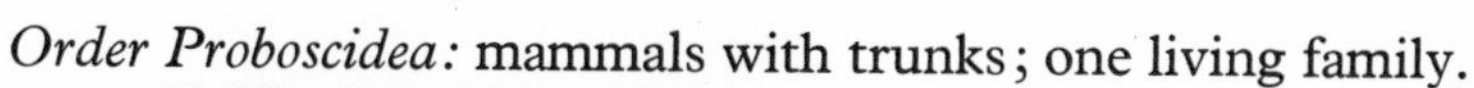

*Order Proboscidea:* mammals with trunks; one living family.
F. Elephantidae: elephants

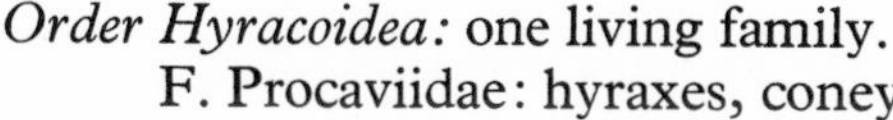

*Order Hyracoidea:* one living family.
F. Procaviidae: hyraxes, coney

*Order Sirenia:* two living aquatic families.

*Order Perissodactyla:* odd-toed ungulate mammals; three living families.
F. Equidae: horses
F. Tapiridae: tapirs
F. Rhinocerotidae: rhinoceroses

*Order Artiodactyla:* even-toed ungulate mammals; nine living families.
F. Suidae: pigs
F. Tayassuidae: peccaries
F. Hippopotamidae: hippos
F. Camelidae: camels, llamas
F. Tragulidae: chevrotains
F. Cervidae: deer
F. Giraffidae: giraffes, okapi
F. Antilocapridae: pronghorns
F. Bovidae: cattle, antelopes, sheep, goats

These are the orders and families of mammals that will be recurring throughout the book and which have, therefore, been set out so that they can be referred to at any time. Certain fossil orders and families will be described as they occur. A complete classification of the mammals can be found in Simpson (1945).

Only comparatively few families of the other vertebrate classes occur constantly and these too are described as they become important. For a comprehensive classification of these other groups, the reader is referred to Romer (1945).

When the geography of animals leaves the broadly geographical level, on the world scale, and turns to what may be called local distribution, in a consideration of islands for instance, the family unit loses some of its usefulness. At this point a few selected genera and species are mentioned. They are described in their place.

2

# Animal Maps

## *Simple Maps*

On a map of the world can be marked the area where any family of animal occurs. Such a map shows the range of the family in question, or its geographical distribution, and the map is called a distribution map.

The distribution of family units through the world varies greatly, but when the range of one particular family unit is mapped the simple pattern that emerges falls into one of two main groups. The first illustrates continuous distribution, the second discontinuous distribution. Within both these groups there are gradations from maps of animals with wide ranges to those with restricted ranges.

Of animals that have both a continuous distribution and a wide range there are the rat and bat families amongst the mammals, hawks and cuckoos amongst the birds. These families are world-wide and represent the one extreme of continuous distribution. Less extensive in range though still continuous is the crow family which is absent from New Zealand. Restriction

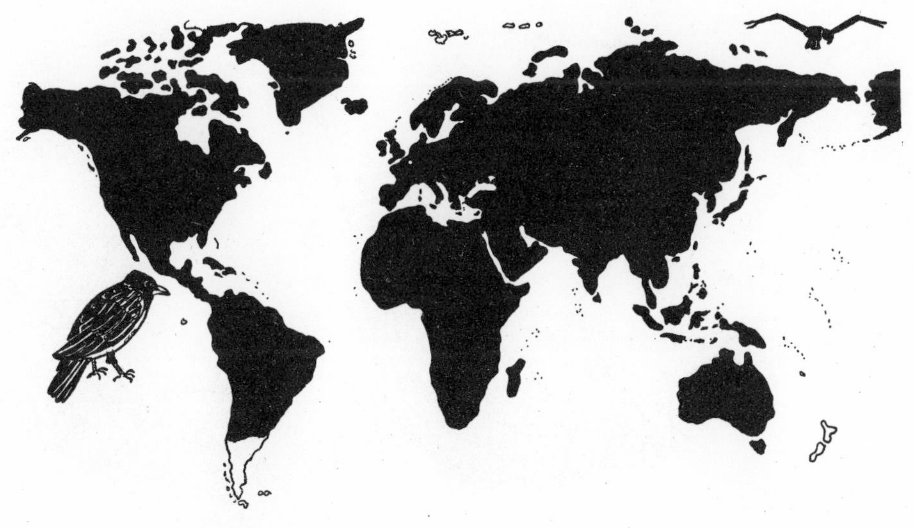

of range may be in an east-west or a north-south direction and many families have a continuous distribution restricted in one of these two ways. Thus the orioles are restricted to the eastern hemisphere, being abundant in the warmer regions of the Old World and Australia but absent from both North and South America. Beavers are restricted in the north-south direction; northern forms, they are absent from South America, Africa, southern Asia and Australia. The simple pattern of carp distribution does not make a clear-cut distinction between these north-south or east-west restrictions. Although it is mainly northern and absent from Australia and South America, it is found in Africa. All these examples illustrate families with a range extending across several continents, but the other extreme of continuous distribution is found in families that are confined to one continent or part of a continent. The giraffe family is confined to Africa and marmoset monkeys to South America. Otter shrews are found only within the equatorial forest belt of Africa. Pronghorns are confined to the north-western prairie land of America.

The next map illustrates discontinuous distribution, and again the range may be wide or restricted. The tapir family is discontinuously distributed, occurring in the Malayan area and otherwise only in South America where it ranges widely over the continent. The two discontinuous populations are separated from one another, either by the greater part of the land area of the world, or by the Pacific Ocean, depending on the point that is chosen for the

middle of the map. More restricted in their local range, but also discontinuously distributed over the world, are the liopelmidae a family of primitive frogs. One genus of the family is restricted to a few mountain streams of northwest America and the other occurs locally in New Zealand.

## *Compound Maps*

When the distributions of all animals are added together, the dissimilarities in individual ranges mark out the world into distinct regions. These regions are differentiated from one another by the different mixtures of animals which they contain, as well as by the fact that they may also contain a family which is uniquely found there. For instance one region is characterized by the co-existence of tapirs and members of the camel family even though neither family is itself confined to the region. No other region has this particular combination. In addition this same region has within its confines several families of vertebrates that are found nowhere else in the world.

The world was first divided into these zoogeographical regions on the evidence of its bird fauna. In 1857 Sclater named six avifaunal regions. These regions were only little modified when Wallace (1876) included all the land animals whose ranges were then known, both vertebrate and invertebrate.

Wallace's zoological regions correspond roughly with the continents, each region being separated from its neighbours by some obvious geographical feature, an ocean or a mountain range. The six regions have special names because they do not correspond precisely with political or cultural areas. They are:

Palearctic
Nearctic
Neotropical
Ethiopian
Oriental (Sclater's Indian)
Australian

These regions are generally accepted today because they best combine reality and usefulness.

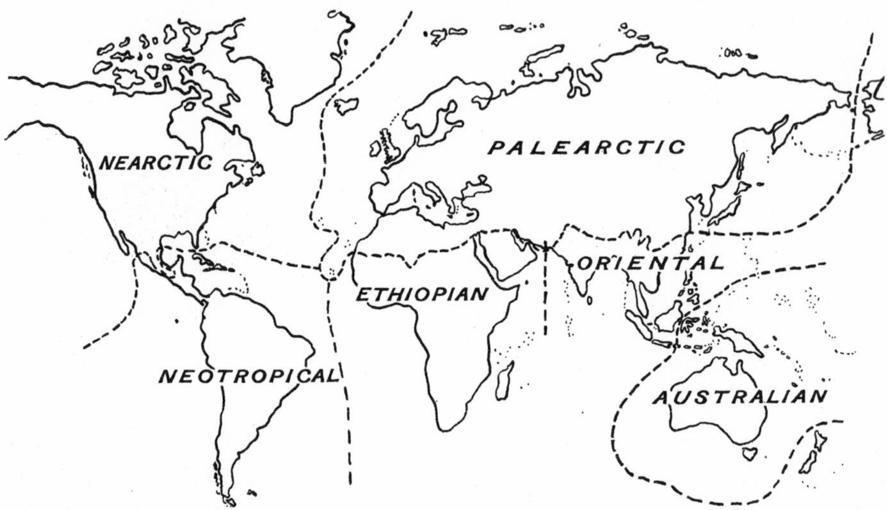


Many other regional classifications have been made, however, some based on the irregularities of distribution of one particular class of animals for which Wallace's regions may not be ideal, others based on the distribution of temperature variations and similar climatic factors. None of these has been found as generally satisfactory as the classification established by Sclater and Wallace in the nineteenth century.

But although generally acceptable, many modifications have been made to the status of the six regions. Some authors have considered the Neotropical and Australian regions to be zoologically so different from the rest of the world and from one another as to rank as regions equivalent to the remaining four put together. In this classification there are three realms, Neogea (Neotropical), Notogea (Australian), and Arctogea (the rest of the world). This grouping of the regions has been found to have some advantages and the names of the three realms are in common use.

Another commonly used modification was suggested by Heilprin in 1887. He proposed that the Palearctic and Nearctic did not merit separate regional status and should be combined into one region, the Holarctic. Many modern authors have accepted this amalgamation of the two northern regions. But, as Wallace himself maintained, it is almost impossible to divide the world into zoological regions all of which have exactly equal status. Some discrepancy can always be found because the regions are the result of natural processes. It is not the purpose of this account to decide on the validity of a region or the suitability of its name, but to outline briefly the zoological characteristics of different parts of the world and to look into the natural processes which have brought them into being. The six regions have therefore been used as the basis and possible differences in status ignored.

In the regional descriptions, the mammal families are listed in full, and these, with a few selected examples of other vertebrates, are used to indicate the general characteristics of each region.

# 3

# Zoogeographical Regions

## *Palearctic*

The Palearctic region is the northerly part of the Old World. It extends over the whole of Europe and the U.S.S.R. to the Pacific coast and south to include the Mediterranean coastal strip of Africa and part of the north of Arabia. It is bounded by the sea to the west, north and east, and by the Sahara and Himalayas to the south. The Palearctic is, therefore, in continuous land connexion with two of its neighbours, the Ethiopian and the Oriental regions, from which it is separated by a desert in the one case and a high mountain range in the other. From its other neighbour, the Nearctic, it is cut off by sea.

The climate is on the whole temperate. The region includes both wet forest lands and dry open steppe land as well as large areas of coniferous forest and a fringe of tundra. The fauna in these various climatic and vegetational subdivisions of the region also varies. All six regions vary within themselves according to the physical and vegetational differences encountered within their boundaries, but in considering only broad geographical classifications these differences are ignored.

Within the Palearctic there are representatives of twenty-eight families of land mammals, excluding the numerous bat families. This is not as large a number as some of the other regions have, nor does it include any very spectacular animals. But amongst them are families which have a wide con-

tinuous range, a restricted continuous range, a discontinuous range, and two families that are unique. Of Palearctic mammals, rabbit, murid mouse and dog families as well as several bat families are world-wide in their distribution; there are shrews, squirrels, cricetid mice, mustelids and members of the cat family in every other region except the Australian. Other Palearctic families are more restricted and occur in only four of the world's regions. The Palearctic shares bears and deer with Nearctic, Neotropical and Oriental regions, and bovids with the Nearctic, Ethiopian and Oriental. Restricted to the Old World are the families of hedgehogs, hystricid porcupines, civets, hyenas and pigs which occur in the Palearctic, Ethiopian and Oriental regions. In contrast the procyonids (pandas and raccoons) are otherwise known only from the New World. Dormice, jerboas (Dipodidae), coneys and wild horses occur in the Palearctic and in the Ethiopian region, whilst moles, pikas, beavers and jumping mice (Zapodidae) have a northerly distribution and are confined to Palearctic and Nearctic regions.

From this it can be seen that nearly a third of the twenty-eight Palearctic families have a wide range, whilst at the other extreme four families are shared by the Palearctic and Nearctic alone, and another four exclusively with the Ethiopian.

The camel family is the only mammal family occurring in the Palearctic which has a discontinuous distribution. The relatives of the camel, vicunas and guanacos, live in the Neotropical region. It is doubtful whether Palearctic camels are any longer genuinely wild, although some of the two-humped animals from central Asia may be so.

The two families of mammals that are restricted to the Palearctic are both myomorph rodents. They are the Spalacidae or mole rats and the Seleviniidae. Each family is represented by only one genus. *Spalax* is a brownish-yellow burrowing animal with no tail but typical rodent gnawing incisors. *Selevinia* is mainly remarkable for not having been discovered until 1938. Even then the first specimens were of skeletons left by vultures in Kazakhstan, and it was only after this discovery that the living animals were found.

Almost all the birds of the Palearctic belong to families which are of very wide distribution. There are pheasants, wrens, blackbirds, finches, warblers, sea birds, geese and birds of prey amongst the very large total number of families. There are no parrots. The only family that is restricted to the region is the hedge-sparrow family. The Palearctic shares its bird families, like its mammal families, with one or more of the neighbouring regions, in the main either with the Nearctic or with the Old World tropical regions, the Ethiopian and the Oriental.

As for the reptiles, the Palearctic region is more conspicuous for the absence from it of those which are found in other regions, than for the presence of distinctive forms. There are a few lizards, snakes and tortoises, and an alligator in China. No family is confined to the region.

In contrast, the Palearctic has a large number of tailed amphibia, ranging from the common newt, through the black and yellow European salamander,

and the blind white *Proteus* of the Adriatic caves, to the giant salamander from eastern Asia which is $5\frac{1}{2}$ feet long. Indeed most of the tailed amphibia (Urodela) are found either in the Palearctic or the Nearctic regions, across which the families are spread. Of the tailless amphibia (Anura) the common frogs and toads are widespread and there are a few tree frogs of both the hylid and polypedatid (rhacophorid) families.

Carp, salmon, pike, perch and sticklebacks are all common in Palearctic fresh waters. The carp family is the dominant family although it is not restricted to the region but occurs also in the Nearctic and Ethiopian regions.

The vertebrate fauna of the Palearctic is not then very rich. The characteristics of its fauna can be summarized as a complex of Old World tropical families and New World temperate. There are few endemic families.

## *Nearctic*

The Nearctic region covers the whole of North America and extends south as far as the middle of Mexico. It includes Greenland in the east and the Aleutian islands in the west. Except for the narrow strip of Central America it is cut off from all the other regions by sea, although the sea that separates it from the eastern Palearctic is very narrow.

The range of climate and vegetation in this region resembles that of the Palearctic.

Like the Palearctic, comparatively few families are represented in the Nearctic, and of these the largest proportion is made up of those with a wide range such as shrews, rabbits, squirrels, cricetid mice, dogs, mustelids, cats and bats. Bears, procyonids, deer and bovids also have a considerable, though not identical, range. Of the rest of the Nearctic mammals, four families are found otherwise only in the Palearctic. These are the families with a northerly range, moles, pikas, beavers and zapodidae jumping mice. With its other neighbour, the Neotropical, another four families are shared, families which have a westerly or New World range. In each case, only one genus of the shared family occurs in the Nearctic. There is an opossum, an armadillo, a tree porcupine and a peccary. The opossum and armadillo are considered to be comparatively recent immigrants from the Neotropical region, together with the tree porcupine, whereas the peccaries are primarily of northern origin.

Of the twenty-four families of Nearctic land mammals none has a discontinuous distribution. In other words the Nearctic does not share a family exclusively with either of the Old World tropical regions or with Australia.

The fauna of a region is characterized not only by the animals that it contains but also by the absence from it of otherwise widespread or neighbouring families. In the case of the Nearctic, many Palearctic and Neotropical families are not represented. There are, for instance, no hedgehogs, hyenas or pigs from the Palearctic, no tapirs from the Neotropical and,

rather surprisingly, no camels which are represented in both the neighbouring regions.

But although the total number of mammal families is less than that of the Palearctic and so many families are unexpectedly absent, the Nearctic has four endemic families. Like the two endemic families of the Palearctic, three of these families are rodents, the other an artiodactyl. All four live primarily in the west of the region, the pocket gophers and pocket mice living mainly in the arid areas of the west and south of North America, the sewellel near water in mountainous areas of the Pacific coast, and pronghorns on the prairies of western and central North America. The pronghorn family is an interesting group of artiodactyls related to both the deer and the bovids, but differing from both of them in the construction of the short, branched horns. The horns have a boney core and, like the deer, a soft skin covering, but unlike the deer only the covering of the horns is shed each year. Sewellels are superficially like muskrats but seem to be related to squirrels, whereas gophers and pocket mice form closely allied families of the myomorph rodents. These two live mainly in the Nearctic and are counted as endemic Nearctic families, but they have in fact spread southwards into the intermediate region where the Nearctic and Neotropical faunas overlap. Intermixture of faunas in this way is common between regions that have land connexions with one another.

To add to the native families of the Nearctic, murid mice and horses, along with domesticated pigs, have been introduced into the region by man.

Nearctic birds are even less differentiated from the neighbouring regions than the mammals. Wood-warblers extend over the whole of temperate North America, and there are several distinctive genera of grouse. Bright red cardinals, tanagers and humming birds are abundant, but they also live in the Neotropical region which is probably their original home. Only the wild turkeys can really be considered to belong exclusively to the Nearctic, and even they have a few stragglers into the Central American parts of the Neotropical.

In contrast to the Palearctic, the Nearctic is the home of many reptiles. Most of the snapping turtles and musk turtles are found there, as well as terrapins. Harmless garter snakes and poisonous rattlesnakes are typical of the Nearctic though not confined to it. There are geckos, horned iguanid lizards and skinks. The gila monster, the only poisonous lizard, belongs to a family exclusive to the region.

Tailed amphibia are abundant, some of them shared with the Palearctic, others more or less confined to the region. Among them are American salamanders, ambystomid axolotls and several of the neotenous forms of urodeles with reduced limbs and, like *Siren*, gills retained into adult life. In mountain streams of the north-west U.S.A. lives the frog *Ascaphus*. Like other frogs and toads it has no tail, but it has tail-wagging muscles, suggesting descent from some tailed ancestor. It shares this peculiarity with only one other frog, *Liopelma*, of New Zealand. The two are therefore considered to be closely related and are included in the same family, liopelmidae. In addition there are common frogs and toads and hylid tree frogs.

A few of the freshwater fish also belong to ancient and isolated families. The garpike and the bowfin are the only living members of a group of fish, the Holostei, which were much commoner millions of years ago than they are today. The garpikes of this group still have the covering of thick scales which was characteristic of all early fish, but which has been lost in modern forms. In addition, the mooneye and bass families are confined to the region and there are many carp and perch.

Compared with the Palearctic, the Nearctic is richer in reptiles and has more endemic families, but in other respects shows considerable resemblance

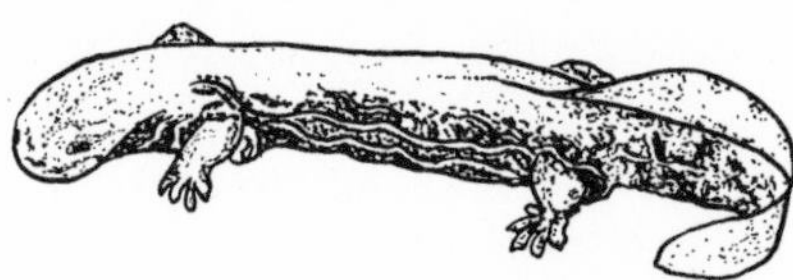

to it. Like the Palearctic its fauna is a complex of tropical and temperate families, but in contrast to the Palearctic, its fauna can be described as a combination of New World tropical and Old World temperate. Since both Palearctic and Nearctic are north temperate and have land connexions with tropical regions, and are the only regions which have these characteristics, their similarities are hardly surprising.

## *Neotropical*

The whole of South America, most of Mexico and the West Indies make up the Neotropical region. It is joined to the Nearctic by the Central American isthmus and separated from all other regions by sea.

The region is mostly tropical, only the southernmost part extending into the south temperate zone. From the west to the east runs the river Amazon with its hundreds of square miles of evergreen forests. Further south the rain forests give place to extensive grassy plains and small semi-desert areas, whilst in the west the long range of the Andes has high mountain forests, plateau land and gentle slopes.

The fauna of the Neotropical region is both distinctive and varied. Excluding bats, thirty-two families of mammals are represented in the region, of which seven are of wide distribution and sixteen are unique. This is the highest number of endemic families for any region.

Like the two preceding regions, the Neotropical has shrews, rabbits, squirrels, cricetid mice, dogs, bears (but only one genus), procyonids, mustelids, cats and deer. It shares with its northerly neighbour, the Nearctic, the opossum, armadillo, tree porcupine and peccary families.

Two Neotropical families show discontinuous distribution, the camel family and the tapirs. The camelids which are otherwise only Palearctic are represented in the Neotropical by one endemic genus, *Lama*, of which there are two species guanaco and vicuna, which live wild on the plateaux of the Andes and on the open grasslands. Two domesticated varieties, llamas and alpacas, have been derived from the guanaco. Differently, but still discontinuously distributed is the tapir family. Although separated by such a great distance, the Neotropical population is considered to belong to the same genus as the Oriental. Three species of this genus, heavily built animals with short tusks and small trunks, live in the forests of the Andes. Tapirs are related to rhinoceroses and more distantly to horses.

Many of the commonly occurring mammalian families have no representatives in the Neotropical region. There are no hedgehogs, moles, beavers, hyenas, native bovids or native horses. The absence of horses is curious for only a few thousand years ago they existed both here and in North America.

But in spite of the absence of common families, the Neotropical makes up its fauna by an abundance of exclusive families. Three families together form

an order of mammals, the Edentata, which is almost confined to the region. Only two other regions, the Ethiopian and Oriental have the distinction of containing unique mammal orders. In the latter cases the orders are small and the animals neither important nor numerous members of the fauna, but in the Neotropical the Edentata are rich in number and variety. Three families, anteaters, sloths and armadillos make up the order, and of these only one genus *Dasypus* the nine-banded armadillo has left the region to colonize successfully the Nearctic. There are three distinct types of anteater, ranging from the large bushy-tailed ground living animal to the tiny prehensile-tailed anteater of the forest trees. They are the only family of the Edentata which conform to the definition implied in the name: without teeth. There are two genera of sloths, both committed to an upside-down life in the trees, and a great variety of armadillos all of which have an armour of small bones covered with a layer of horny material. In spite of this covering armadillos are active burrowing and running animals.

Of the rest of the Neotropical endemic families there are marsupials, two families of monkeys, eleven of caviomorph rodents and, in addition, five families of bats.

Two families of marsupials occur in the Neotropical, but only one of them, the mouse-like Caenolestidae, is confined to the region. Didelphidae, or opossums, are found also in the Nearctic. Apart from these two families, the only other living marsupials occur in the Australian region where there are a further six families.

South American monkeys are diverse; douroucoulis, spider monkeys, capuchins, squirrel monkeys and howlers in the cebid family, and tamarins and marmosets in the callithricid family. The two families have in common the flat-nose feature, which separates them both from the downward-nose Old World monkeys. In other ways they differ greatly from each other. The small bushy-tailed marmosets and tamarins have clawed fingers and toes in contrast to the cebids, more typically monkey with flat nails and prehensile tails.

Eleven specialized families of rodents make the Neotropical the home of the caviomorph suborder of rodents. The New World porcupines are the only caviomorphs that are not confined to the region, occurring elsewhere only in the Nearctic. The porcupines are mainly arboreal and some of them have prehensile tails. Prehensile tails are common in Neotropical trees. The endemic caviomorph families include the largest of all rodents, the capybara which is four feet long, the guinea pigs, spotted pacaranas, pacas, agoutis, chinchillas, nutrias, burrowing degus and tucotucos, the rat chinchilla and the spiny rats.

Finally there are five indigenous families of bats of which the vampire bats are the best known. They are a serious pest of cattle herds, carrying diseases such as rabies, and it has been suggested that it was they who caused the extinction of the native horses of America.

As if this mammalian fauna were not striking enough, the birds equal it in their diversity and strangeness, so much so that South America has been called the Bird Continent. Nearly half the bird fauna is composed of restricted families, and two orders are confined to the region, the rheas or American ostriches and the partridge-like tinamus. Amongst the restricted families are crested toucans with enormous coloured beaks, trumpeters and hoatzins. Cracids to which the curl-crested curassows belong are almost restricted to the region and so too cotingids which include the flaming cock-of-the-rock and the black umbrella bird. On the forested slopes of the Andes

hover brilliantly coloured humming-birds, and in the Amazon forests live macaws, large variegated parrots with long tails. The only conspicuous lack in the bird fauna is a scarcity of song birds, and except for quails, there are no members of the pheasant family.

Snakes, lizards, crocodiles and turtles abound, many of them shared with the Nearctic but others, primarily tropical, with Africa and the Oriental region. Snakes include both constrictors and biters; anacondas, boa constrictors, pit vipers and coral snakes. New World iguanid lizards are numerous and varied, and the small tegus are almost confined to the region. Alligators and caimans are found in South American rivers, but only the caimans are restricted to the region. The Neotropical shares a family of mud-turtles (Pelomedusidae) with Africa, and snake-neck turtles (Chelyidae) with Australia. Both these families are pleurodires, or side-necks, so-called because of the way they bend their necks into the shell. They form a separate suborder from the commoner cryptodire turtles.

Amphibians of the Neotropical are almost all anurans in marked contrast to the two northern regions. There are hylid tree frogs as well as the commoner frogs and toads. The pipid family which is here represented by *Pipa* the Surinam toad, and *Protopipa*, is absent from all other regions except the Ethiopian and its distribution resembles that of the pelomedusid side-neck turtles. *Rhynophrinus*, the sole representative of its family, though related to the pipids, occurs in Central America. It is a pink and brown burrowing toad that feeds on termites. Only one tailed amphibian, *Oedipus*, is widespread through the region but a few axolotls have spread from the Nearctic as far as Mexico.

There are no carp in the region and the fish fauna is dominated instead by the characin fish, gymnotids and cat-fishes. Gymnotids, the electric eels of the Amazon are confined to the region but characins which include the vicious carnivorous piranhas, are, like the pipid toads and pelomedusid side-neck turtles, found also in the Ethiopian region. Less abundant, but equally curiously distributed, is the lungfish, of the Amazon, *Lepidosiren*, related in the same family to an African form. A third occurs in Australia and these three genera are the only members of the lungfish order, the Dipnoi. They have in common, lungs and internal nostrils additional to the gills of other fish, two pairs of lobed fins and a distribution which restricts them to the southern hemisphere.

In sum, the Neotropical is rich in endemic families of vertebrates of all classes, and, of the more widely distributed families, it shares many with the Nearctic and several with other tropical regions of the world.

## *Ethiopian*

The Ethiopian region covers the continent of Africa south of the Atlas mountains and the Sahara, and includes the southern corner of Arabia. Like the Neotropical it has land continuity with its northern neighbour but is otherwise isolated by sea. Also like the Neotropical, it has big rivers and tropical evergreen forests, as well as mountains and grassy plains, but it does not reach as far into the southern temperate zone. The large island of Madagascar with its smaller neighbours is often included in this region but for reasons that will be discussed later it is here treated separately.

The Ethiopian mammal fauna is the most varied of all the regions consisting of thirty-eight families, excluding bats. In number of unique families it ranks second only to the Neotropical.

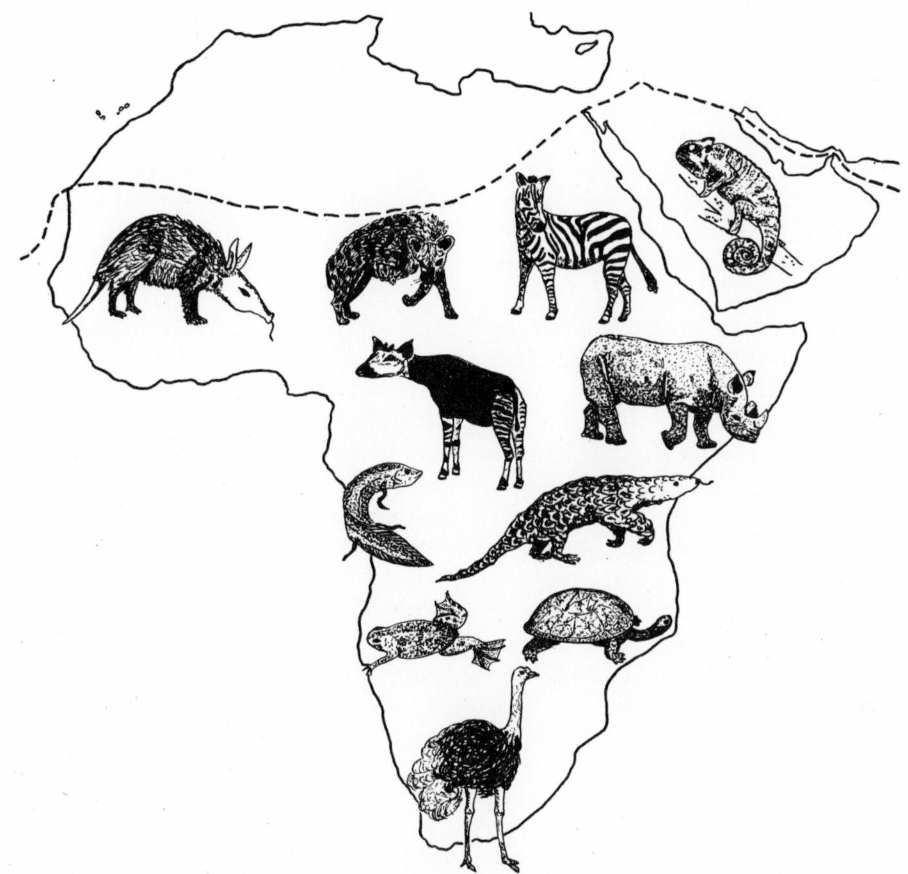

Only the shrews, rabbits, squirrels, cricetid mice, murid mice, dogs, mustelids, cats and bovids have a wide distribution. Apart from the twelve exclusive families the rest of the mammals are shared with either the Palearctic or the Oriental regions, or, as in the case of the hedgehogs, porcupines, civets, hyenas and pigs, with both.

Thus the Ethiopian shares with the more northerly Palearctic, families of dormice, jerboas (Dipodidae), coneys and wild horses. But it also differs markedly from this region in being without moles, beavers, bears and camels.

With the Oriental region the Ethiopian shares eight of its mammal families, three of which are primates and two, large ungulates. Lorises, Old

World monkeys, apes, pangolins, bamboo rats, elephants, rhinoceroses and chevrotains are all confined to the Old World tropical regions. The pangolins or scaly anteaters looking like large fircones, belong to only one genus, shared by both regions, but all the other shared families are different at the generic level in the two regions. Thus *Loxodonta*, the African elephant, with its huge ears and long tusks is differentiated from *Elephas* the Indian elephant which is an altogether smaller animal. White and black rhinoceroses, each with two nasal horns, represent the Ethiopian genera in contrast to two Oriental genera, only one of which is two-horned. Of the primate lorisidae, pottos and galagos live in Africa, whilst slender lorises are inhabitants of the Oriental region. The abundant Old World monkeys of the Ethiopian region are diverse, and more varied than their relatives of the Oriental. In Africa there are macaques, drills, baboons, mangabeys, guenons and geladas in contrast to a smaller number of Oriental langurs. In the forests of western and central Africa live two of the four great apes of the world, the gorilla and the chimpanzee. The other two orang utan and gibbon are Oriental.

The Ethiopian region has no mammal families exclusively in common with either the Nearctic or the Neotropical.

The African scene is pictured with herds of large herbivorous animals on open plains, zebras, loping giraffes, leaping and springing antelopes, rhinoceroses, elephants and, hidden, waiting for an endless supply of food, lions and other members of the cat family. In fact, of all these African mammals only the giraffe family is confined to the region, although the antelope subfamily of the bovids has reached a diversity in Africa which is found nowhere else.

Including the giraffes, there are twelve unique families of Ethiopian mammals: hippopotamuses and aardvarks; three families of insectivores; and six families of rodents, making an interesting comparison with the Neotropical whose rodents are also diverse and restricted. Like the giraffe family the amphibious hippo family contains only two genera, and the aardvarks, forming on their own the order Tubulidentata, only one genus. The aardvark, or cape anteater, is the size of a small pig with a highly curved back, long snout and long tongue. On the four digits of its front feet and the five of its hind there are sharp hoofs for digging through termites' nests.

Endemic insectivores are otter shrews, golden moles and elephant shrews, and the remaining six endemic families are rodents, whose relationship with the rodents of other parts of the world is obscure. The Anomaluridae and the Pedetidae may be allied to the sciuromorphs although there is no unanimity of opinion on this. Some of the anomalurids are squirrel-like but others are more like mice, some are gliders like the gliding-mice *Idiurus* and the African flying squirrel *Anomalurus*, but some are not. Probably allied to them is the Spring Haas, the sole representative of its family Pedetidae. Of the remaining rodents the cane rats and the rock rats probably have affinities with the Old World porcupines, whereas the gundis and blesmols seem to stand on their own.

Birds are numerous in the Ethiopian region having, like the mammals, strong affinities with the Oriental region and only six exclusive families. There are cuckoos, woodpeckers and hornbills as well as sunbirds, orioles and many birds of prey, but only comparatively few pigeons, parrots and pheasants. Exclusive to the region are ostriches, secretary birds, hammerheads, crested touracos, mousebirds and helmet shrikes. The ostrich is the only member of a unique order, doubtfully related to other large flightless birds in other parts of the southern hemisphere.

Many snakes, including constricting pythons and biting poisonous vipers occur in the region, and amongst the lizards the Cordylidae, or spiny lizards, are restricted, and the chameleon family nearly so. Only four of the fifty species of chameleon are found outside Africa and only one of these lives as far away as India. There are a few agamid and lacertid lizards but no iguanids. Crocodiles and turtles abound, amongst them the Neotropical pelomedusid family of the side-necks.

Amphibians are less distinctive but amongst them, in addition to widespread frogs and toads, is the pipid family represented by *Xenopus*, the clawed toad, which like its Neotropical relatives is aquatic. Hylid tree frogs are absent, their place being taken by another family of tree frogs, the polypedatids. Like other southern regions, the Ethiopian has no tailed amphibians.

The fish fauna, in contrast, is diverse and includes carp, Old World catfishes, characins, lungfish and several endemic families, amongst them the mormyrids. From electric organs in their tails the mormyrids generate an electric field and they are made aware of prey in their muddy pools when this field is distorted. Mormyrids are not related to the electric eels of the Amazon, but the characin fish are a family shared by Ethiopian and Neotropical. Similarly, the lungfish *Protopterus* of Africa is related to the Neotropical lungfish *Lepidosiren.*

The vertebrate fauna of the Ethiopian region is the most varied of all the regions, and in number of endemic families is second only to the Neotropical. In its fish, amphibia and reptiles it resembles both the Neotropical and the Oriental in several ways but in its birds and mammals has overwhelming affinities with the Oriental. Thus the Ethiopian has certain similarities with both Neotropical and Oriental regions because all three have a tropical climate, but its similarities are much stronger with the tropics of the Old World than with those of the New.

### *Oriental*

The Oriental takes in India, Indochina, south China and Malaya as well as the westerly isles of the Malay Archipelago. It is bounded by the Himalayas in the north and the Indian and Pacific oceans on its other sides, but there is no definite physical boundary in the south-east corner where the islands of the Malay Archipelago string out until they reach Australia. The big islands, Sumatra, Java and Borneo, with the Philippine group, certainly belong to the Oriental region, but the other islands are more difficult to place.

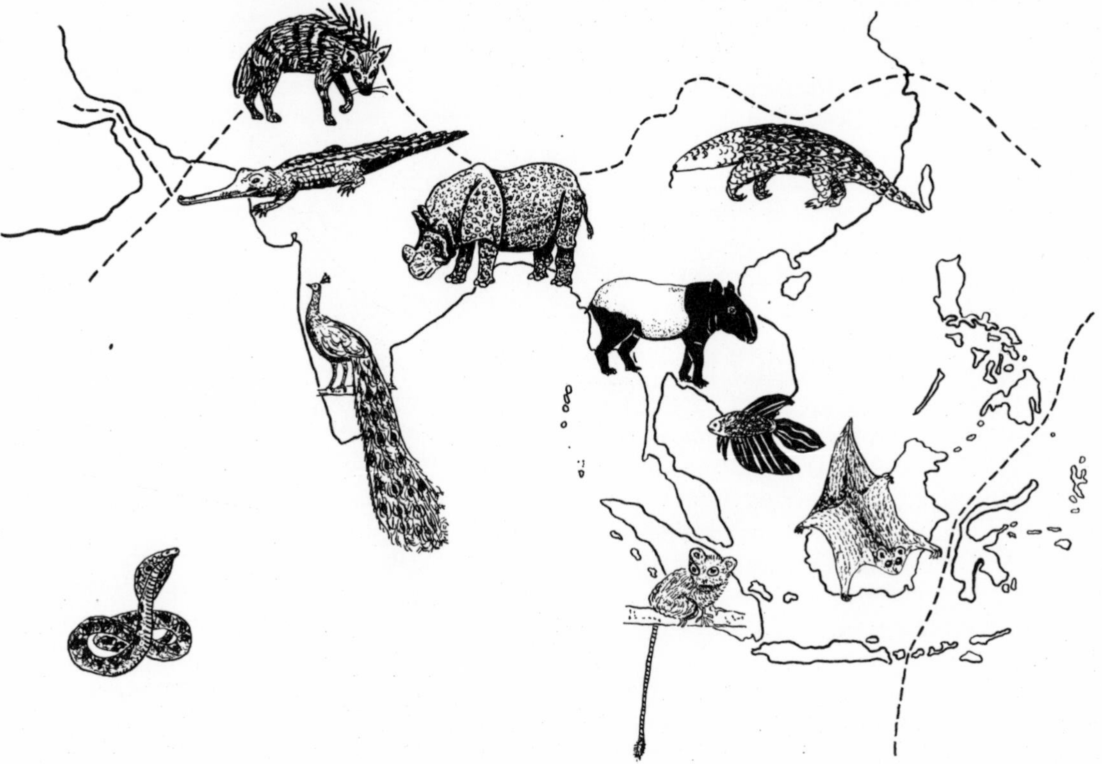

The climate of the Oriental region is mainly tropical.

Although the fauna resembles that of the Ethiopian region it is neither so rich in endemic families nor does it exhibit the same variety of widespread families. Of its thirty mammalian families, excluding bats, only four are endemic, like the Nearctic. One of the four belongs to an endemic order and in this the Oriental resembles both the Neotropical and the Ethiopian.

There are shrews, rabbits, squirrels, cricetids, murid mice, dogs, mustelids, cats and bovids. It shares hedgehogs, porcupines, civets, hyenas and pigs with both Palearctic and Ethiopian regions, but a quarter of its mammal families it shares exclusively with Africa. These are lorises, Old World monkeys, apes, pangolins, bamboo rats (Rhizomyidae), elephants, rhinoceroses and chevrotains. In spite of this considerable resemblance to the Ethiopian fauna, there are striking differences between the two regions.

Unlike the Ethiopian, the Oriental region has moles, bears, tapirs and deer in its fauna. In contrast, it is without jerboas (Dipodidae), coneys and horses. Furthermore it has its four unique families.

The family Cynocephalidae forms by itself the order Dermoptera. There is only one genus *Cynocephalus* (= *Galeopithecus*) the colugo. The affinities of the order are difficult to determine but it is likely to have been derived from the insectivores, diverging from them early in their history. The colugo is a gliding mammal, being aided in its leaps through the trees by a softly furred membrane which stretches from its neck to the tip of its tail and includes both the fore and hind limbs. Only the fingers and toes are excluded from the membrane. At rest on a tree the colugo spreads its membrane and thus, by elimination of its shadow, becomes nearly invisible.

Two primate families are confined to the Oriental region. They are tree shrews and tarsiers, of particular interest in evolutionary studies because they represent crucial stages in the primate story. The tree shrews lie near the base of the primate stock, having links with their insectivore ancestors through the African elephant shrews. Tarsiers represent a more advanced stage of primate evolution belonging to a group which was ancestral to the monkeys. Both these primate families contain small purely arboreal animals, living on an omnivorous diet and using their hands to bring food to their mouths. With these two families and representatives of lorises, Old World monkeys and apes, the Oriental region has half of all primate families, the largest proportion of this order anywhere.

Like the primate families and the colugo, the other unique Oriental family, the spiny dormouse, is also arboreal, but a rodent. Belonging to the myomorph suborder, the spiny dormice live in tall trees in India, boring their own holes in the wood.

Many brilliantly coloured birds live in the Oriental region. Most of them are common to other regions like the widespread woodpeckers or the tropical barbets, but many like sunbirds and hornbills show affinities with the Ethiopian region. Like Africa, the Oriental region has few parrots, but in contrast there are many pigeons and an abundance of pheasants. Indeed the Oriental with the Palearctic is the main home of pheasants. It is the native home of the peacock, the magnificent Argus pheasant and the jungle fowl, from which modern domestic poultry have been bred. With the Australian the Oriental region shares four bird families and has only one exclusive family, the fairy bluebirds.

Lizards, snakes and turtles are plentiful. There is a particularly large number of biting poisonous snakes, vipers and pit vipers, as well as constricting pythons. Lizards include cosmopolitan geckos and skinks as well as Old World agamids and varanids. Crocodiles are widespread and in addition there are gavials, slender-nosed crocodiles, an exclusive fish-eating family confined to India and Malaya. A freshwater turtle, the bigheaded turtle, is also confined to the region and there are many land turtles.

Very few tailed amphibia reach the northernmost parts of the region only, from the Palearctic, but anurans are common. Again like the Ethiopian region the tree frogs of the Oriental belong to the polypedatid family, hylids

being absent from all but a small area of northern Indochina. Pipid toads, however, do not occur, but common frogs and toads range widely.

The Oriental fish fauna is dominated by carp and catfishes.

The many similarities between the Oriental fauna and the Ethiopian arise largely because they are both tropical regions and both situated in the Old World. Although similarities can be found in all groups of vertebrates, they are more pronounced among the mammals and birds.

### *Australian*

The Australian region covers Australia, Tasmania and New Guinea and a few of the smaller islands of the Malay Archipelago, but New Zealand and the islands of the Pacific are not included. The region is unique in having no land connexions with any other region.

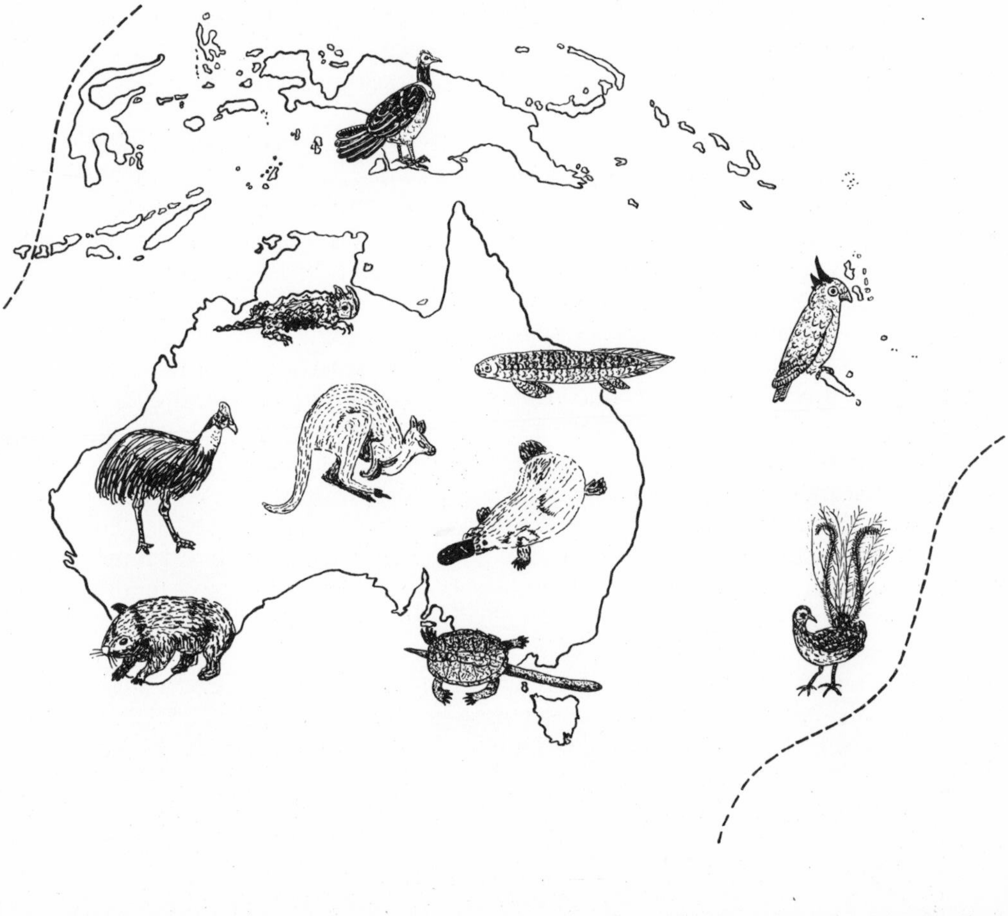

The northern part of the region, north Australia and New Guinea, lies within the tropics with high summer temperatures and much of the area is covered by rain forest. The interior of the Australian continent is also hot, but dry, while further south the climate becomes mainly temperate.

The most striking characteristic of the vertebrate fauna of the Australian region is its paucity. But what it lacks in variety and number of families, it makes up for in the uniqueness of many. Apart from bats, there are only nine families of mammals, and eight of these are unique. In addition to these there are rabbits, foxes, rats and mice which are recent introductions into Australia from the Palearctic, and dingo dogs and pigs which are probably also human introductions but dating from prehistoric times.

Of the nine feral families only one is a placental mammal and this, the murid mouse family, is of wide range in the Old World, but Australian murids are of distinct genera and the Hydromyinae water rats an exclusive subfamily.

The dominant mammal fauna is marsupial, made up of six families none of which occurs in the New World, where are found the only other living marsupials.

In a continent which has few placentals, none of them carnivores, the marsupials have become diverse and have taken to ways of life which in other parts of the world are followed by placentals. There is thus a striking parallelism in superficial structure between some Australian mammals and their counterparts in other regions. The marsupial mole, from the family Notoryctidae, resembles placental moles with its paddle-shaped feet and strongly clawed fingers.

The Tasmanian wolf, now probably extinct, looked like a hyena and lived a similar predatory life. In the same family, Dasyuridae, there are pouched 'mice', pouched 'jerboas', 'cats' and 'anteaters'.

The Peramelidae, bandicoots, can be considered the rabbits and insectivores of the marsupial world, whilst the Phascolomidae, wombats, parallel the large rodents.

In the phalanger family there are Australian 'opossums', 'squirrels' and flying phalangers equivalent in all superficial respects to flying placental squirrels.

Finally there are the kangaroos and wallabies which have no exact structural parallels. But although their looks are distinctive, their herbivorous diet and speed of travel in open country, suggest parallels with the ungulates of other parts of the world.

This parallel radiation of the marsupials is not, however, perfect. There are no marsupial bats, seals or whales. Placental representatives of these orders occupy the air and seas of Australia.

The remaining two families of Australian mammals belong to a separate sub-class of mammals, Monotremata. They are the egg-laying mammals and

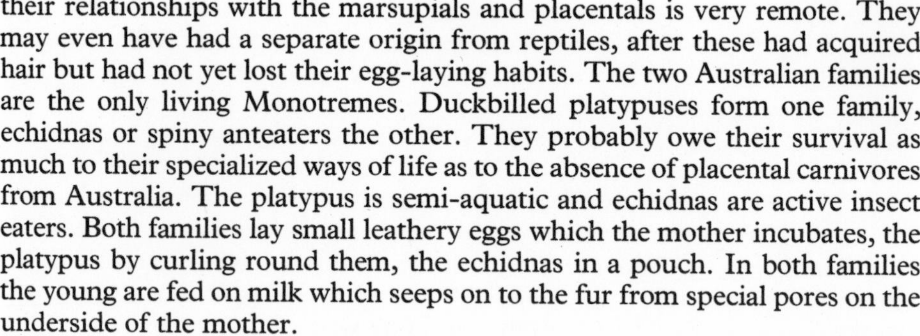

their relationships with the marsupials and placentals is very remote. They may even have had a separate origin from reptiles, after these had acquired hair but had not yet lost their egg-laying habits. The two Australian families are the only living Monotremes. Duckbilled platypuses form one family, echidnas or spiny anteaters the other. They probably owe their survival as much to their specialized ways of life as to the absence of placental carnivores from Australia. The platypus is semi-aquatic and echidnas are active insect eaters. Both families lay small leathery eggs which the mother incubates, the platypus by curling round them, the echidnas in a pouch. In both families the young are fed on milk which seeps on to the fur from special pores on the underside of the mother.

The bird fauna of Australia does not equal the mammals in peculiarity, for the vast majority of the birds belong to families with a wide range. Trogons and kingfishers, hawks and cuckoos all occur in the region together with pigeons and parrots both of which reach their greatest diversity there. So diverse are the Australian parrots that they are recognized as three exclusive subfamilies, cockatoos, lories and pygmy parrots. Four bird families are shared with the Oriental region; frogmouths, woodswallows, flowerpeckers and megapodes; but there are no pheasants which are so abundant in the Oriental, no finches, no barbets and no woodpeckers. Ten families are unique and include two of flightless birds (cassowaries and emus), honeysuckers, lyrebirds, bowerbirds and the legendary birds of paradise, known to the Portuguese as birds of the sun and thought by them to have no feet.

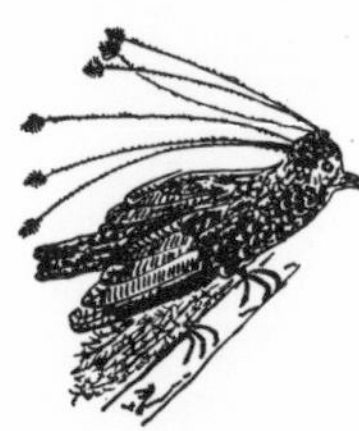

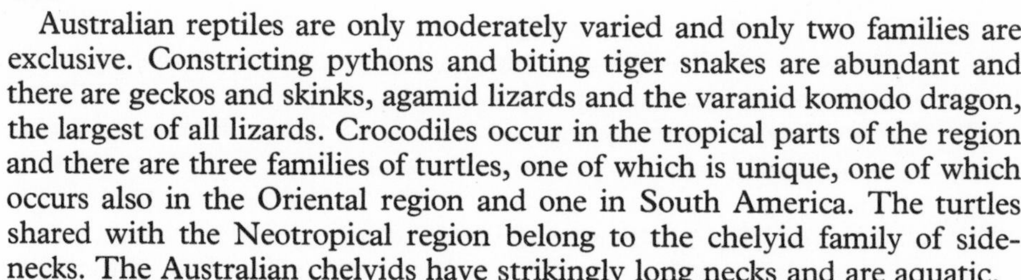

Australian reptiles are only moderately varied and only two families are exclusive. Constricting pythons and biting tiger snakes are abundant and there are geckos and skinks, agamid lizards and the varanid komodo dragon, the largest of all lizards. Crocodiles occur in the tropical parts of the region and there are three families of turtles, one of which is unique, one of which occurs also in the Oriental region and one in South America. The turtles shared with the Neotropical region belong to the chelyid family of side-necks. The Australian chelyids have strikingly long necks and are aquatic.

Amphibians are few, Australia being the only region from which common toads are absent. A few common frogs have reached the region and there are hylid tree frogs, found also in the New World and Palearctic, but absent from the Oriental and Ethiopian regions. There are no tailed amphibia.

The freshwater fish fauna is equally poor, but the third lungfish is found in the rivers of Queensland. *Neoceratodus* differs from the other two lungfish in the more obvious development of its lobed fins.

The Australian vertebrate fauna is remarkable for the poverty of its freshwater fish, amphibia and reptiles and for the uniqueness of its mammals. Some part of the fauna, a few frogs, turtles and marsupials, resembles that of South America. But another part, made up of the terrestrial reptiles, many birds and the placental mammals, shows close affinities with the Oriental region. The Australian region has little in common with the Ethiopian, for although they both have lungfish and side-necks, they do not share the same families of either of these groups.

# 4

# Dispersal

### *Creation*

Before Darwin and Wallace announced the theory of natural selection it was generally assumed that each species lived in the region best suited to it because it had been especially created for that place. Sloths were created for South America, elephants for Africa and India, and rats presumably for the whole world. Creation determined the location and the number of any group of animals. Creation explained both continuous and discontinuous distribution.

Certain facts however do not fit the theory of creation satisfactorily. The rapid spread of the rabbit in Australia after its introduction by man has proved that there was no obvious reason why the rabbit should not have lived there before, if congenial surroundings were all that was required. House sparrows have spread widely through North and South America; frogs which were once absent from the Azores attained plague proportions; the grey squirrel of America has proved more successful than the native British red squirrel and is slowly supplanting it.

Creation does not provide an answer either to the question why animals are limited or why they spread.

### *Limitation*

There are four main causes of limitation of range on land, three of which are closely interdependent. The first three are climate, vegetation, and other animals; the fourth, physical barriers. An animal may be limited by any one of these causes, by a physical barrier for instance, or it may be and usually is, limited by more than one. The causes of limitation form a complex network round the animal. The way in which these factors interact are discussed in detail in Allee and others (1949), Hesse, Allee and Schmidt (1951) and Elton (1958). Here limiting factors are only outlined briefly.

Climate can be thought of as composed of temperature and rainfall.

Low temperature prevents animals adapted to tropical conditions spreading to the poles. Reptiles which are primarily tropical, being numerous and varied where temperatures are high, decrease both in number and variety towards the poles. Crocodiles are hardly known outside the tropics and the most northerly occurrence of a turtle, the European pond tortoise, is $57\frac{1}{2}°$, and this is exceptional for the order. Conversely, high temperature prevents animals adapted to a cold climate spreading to the tropics. Dalliid blackfishes are limited in this way to northern polar regions. Penguins, too, are limited to cold water but, because cold currents flow north from the Antarctic, they have in one case reached the equator.

On mountains, temperature falls with increase in height. This can restrict the passage of an animal over a mountain range or, conversely, can restrict the spread of a high-mountain animal through the warmer lowlands. Parrots are rarely found in mountain regions where temperatures are low.

The other component of climate, rainfall, has a less obvious effect on animal spread. Vegetation is very sensitive to changes in rainfall and it is through its effects on the plant life of the land that rainfall is principally instrumental in limiting the spread of animals. Even so, most animals are prevented from living in or crossing deserts as much because they cannot survive long periods without water as because of the scarcity of vegetation. Animals that are specialized for living in deserts often have exaggerated powers of water retention in their tissues. At the other end of the scale, amphibia are more numerous in wet parts of the world than in dry because the majority are dependent on water for reproduction and their outer skins are not impermeable.

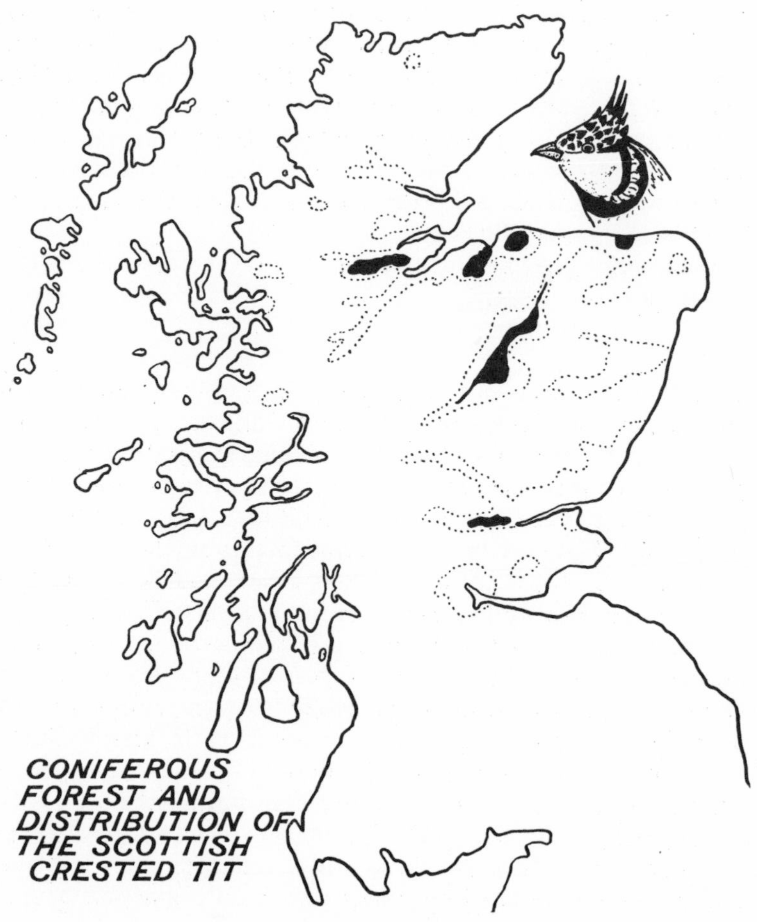
CONIFEROUS FOREST AND DISTRIBUTION OF THE SCOTTISH CRESTED TIT

The distribution of the vegetation of the world depends in a large degree on the climate, on both the temperature and the rainfall. Some animals can survive in many types of vegetation but the majority are limited. Tapirs and vicunas are both mountain-living animals, but the tapirs frequent the forests, vicunas open plateau land. The European crested tit nests in coniferous forests and its range in the British Isles is therefore limited to the central highland area of Scotland. The koala bear lives in the Australian region where there are eucalyptus leaves to eat, and the giant panda in China where there are bamboo shoots.

The third factor in animal limitation is the interaction between all the animals themselves. This is a complex problem. Animals prey on one another, animals parasitize one another, animals compete with one another for food, nesting sites, or just for space to live. When a new animal moves into an area it upsets the balance of the native population. If the population is sparse the newcomer may be able to move in with little upset. If the newcomer is a carnivore it may destroy much of the old population, as the fox is in danger of doing in Australia. In other cases, an animal which neither preys on nor parasitizes any member of the population may move in and oust one or more of the original population. This seems to happen when two animals have identical requirements for food, shelter and reproduction, and is known as replacement. The increasing limitation in range of the British red squirrel before the advances of the American grey squirrel may be a case of replacement. Amongst carnivores, the dingo dog may have replaced the Tasmanian wolf in Australia.

The fourth limiting factor is the presence of physical barriers. On land these barriers may be rivers, mountains or deserts. The last two of these differ from the first in that the limitation may be due to climate and vegetational factors more than to the actual physical barrier. Climate and scarcity of vegetation are probably more important in preventing animals crossing deserts than, for instance, the inability to walk on sand or stones. Mountains may be too high for an animal to cross but again it is more likely to be climate and vegetation that are limiting factors. Water is the least complex physical barrier. The river Amazon provides a barrier for many animals including monkeys and butterflies. But rivers are not a serious barrier to the average land vertebrate and they form a ramifying highway for freshwater fish. It can be assumed, therefore, that vertebrates spread across land unless they are prevented by one of the terrestrial limiting factors. Limitation by these factors is of major importance in determining the extent of range of an animal within a continent.

## *Spread*

Land vertebrates spread across land if conditions are favourable, but even if conditions are ideal some animals will spread faster than others. It may be a matter of size, psychology, the relative rates of birth and death, or it may depend simply on locomotion. Flying vertebrates should disperse faster and further than ground-living forms, but there are so many limiting factors operating everywhere, that even their potential spread is considerably reduced.

If powers of dispersal on land are not normally important limiting factors for vertebrates, differential powers of dispersal across water lead to many apparent anomalies of distribution. Fresh water limits but it is often small in extent. Therefore the main obstacle to wide spread is sea water.

Freshwater fish are variable in their response to sea water. Some, like the lungfish and perch, are unable to tolerate salinity for more than a short time, others, like salmon and eels, are as much at home in sea as in fresh water. For these last, the crossing of the sea is not a serious problem. These two extremes grade into one another. There are some minnows that are moderately salt-tolerant and could probably survive a sea journey, and sticklebacks appear to tolerate fresh and salt water equally.

Amphibia can swim, but they cannot tolerate salt water. Only one species of *Rana* is known to enter salt water normally and survive. Their permeable skins, and their reproductive habits are adapted to life in fresh water or damp terrestrial surroundings. Amphibia could not swim through the sea. Some might be carried through the air by birds, but the same characteristics that make them intolerant of sea water make them susceptible to drying out in the air. They cannot swim in the sea and they cannot be exposed for long periods to dry air. The only possible method for them to cross the sea seems to be provided on rare occasions when what is virtually a small island is swept into

the sea by exceptionally heavy rains and winds. In general then, amphibia do not normally spread across salt water barriers. Only on rare occasions do they seem to have 'rafted' a short distance. Although rafts have often been sighted, no one has studied the fauna of a raft, its place of origin nor its subsequent arrival. Driftwood from distant shores has been found washed up in some parts of the world, on some occasions with wood-boring animals in it, but no one has been able to study the whole process, and rafts must, therefore, remain a hypothetical means of transport.

Reptiles are much more versatile. The physiological limitations of amphibians do not apply to reptiles. It has been claimed that land and fresh water turtles when closed tightly inside their carapace, can float unharmed in the sea for long periods, and certainly they have colonized many islands hundreds of miles out in the ocean. Adult reptiles of all sorts and their eggs may be swept across stretches of sea on natural rafts. As neither the adults nor their eggs are as susceptible to drying as the amphibians, the rafts or islets may not need to be as large and leafy as those on which amphibians are supposed to travel, and they may, therefore, occur more often. Sea water is not, therefore, an insuperable obstacle to reptiles.

Birds because they can fly are able to overcome many of the barriers to dispersal which prevent other animals from spreading. Theoretically there is no limit to the spread of birds, but some birds fly further afield than others for reasons which are not always clear. Many birds are prevented from spreading for 'psychological' reasons, and the more usual limiting factors are as important in bird dispersal as in other cases. Furthermore, just because birds can fly, they can fly back to their starting point.

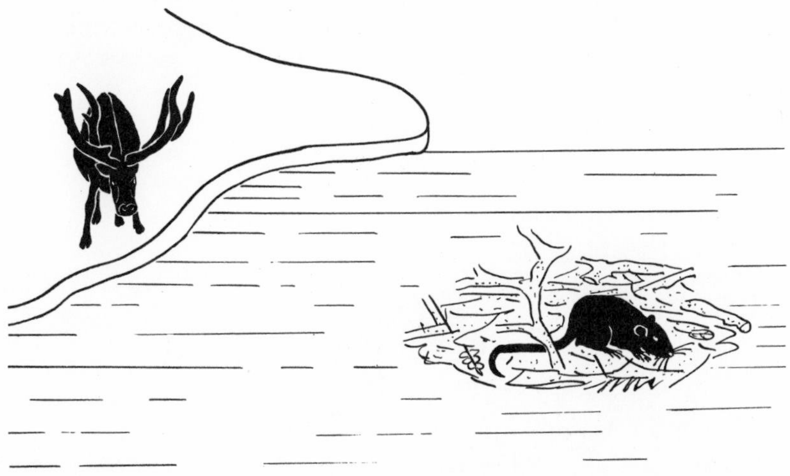

Land mammals vary in their response to sea water. The amphibious hippos and otters for instance are good swimmers and can probably survive long periods in the sea. Pigs, too, swim well and far. Bats, like birds, can fly over the oceans. Rats seem to be the most accomplished of all rafters if their world-wide dispersal and universal presence on ships is taken as evidence.

Spread across the seas is easier for some land vertebrates than it is for others. Amphibians are the most confined to land. Mammals are nearly as restricted, with the exception of bats and rats. Fresh water fish vary greatly amongst themselves. Birds and reptiles are the least confined.

It has been assumed that animals are always tending to spread and that they go on spreading until the limiting factors become intense enough to stop them. Having stopped they have been presumed to keep the range they had attained. This is not always true. The range of an animal can contract. The range of the red squirrel is gradually contracting before the spread of the grey.

## *Regional Aspects*

Land vertebrates spread across land and with varying success across the sea. The complex interaction of factors which limit this spread goes some way to explain the faunal differences between zoogeographical regions. Climatic conditions may be the main reason why urodele amphibians are absent from the southern continents but widespread through the north temperate regions. The vegetation may be the main reason for the small range of the giant panda. The success of flightless rails in New Zealand has been due mainly to the absence from that island of carnivorous mammals. Sea water accounts for the absence from the Azores of native frogs.

Other differences between the regions are not so easily accounted for. It is not clear on these grounds alone why tapirs should be absent from the Ethiopian region. Inability to spread in itself would not seem to be an explanation, since they have somehow spread between South America and Malaya. Climate and vegetation do not seem to explain the distribution either. Climatic and vegetational features similar to those in which they live can almost certainly be found in Africa. Again, these factors do not seem

adequately to account for the presence of marsupials in Australia and the Americas and their absence from all other regions.

The same sort of problems arise when the faunas of characteristic vegetational or climatic zones in different parts of the world are studied. Although the conditions of life may be almost identical, the fauna is unlikely to be so. The fauna of the great deserts of North America and Africa though superficially similar is not identical. The kangaroo rats of Arizona and the jerboas of the Sahara are superficially alike. Their hind legs are long, the feet furred, tails long and tufted and their hair silky. Close anatomical inspection reveals however, that the structure of their skulls is different, the kangaroo rats, therefore, belong to the family Heteromyidae, and the jerboas to the family Dipodidae. Similarly the horned lizards of Arizona, though strikingly similar to the spiny-tailed lizards of the Sahara, belong to separate reptile families, to the Iguanidae and to the Cordylidae. There are antelopes in the African desert, Gila monsters in the American. The differences are extensive but not complete. The vipers of the Sahara and the rattlesnakes of North America both belong to the same snake family, the Viperidae. The ground-squirrels of the Sahara and the prairie-dogs of the Nearctic desert are both Sciuridae.

Animals then do not live wherever climatic and vegetational conditions are suitable for them, nor are they only absent from land surrounded by salt water. Although some of the faunistic differences between the zoogeographical regions can be explained in these terms, others seem to require a different approach to the problem. The vertebrate fauna of the regions has been described as it is today; the means of dispersal and the limiting factors are those which are operative today. But today is an arbitrary moment. Behind it in time stretch millions of years of animal life, and behind that many more millions since the beginning of the earth. At all times animals have spread and been prevented from spreading, but they have not always been the same animals as today, nor have the limiting factors had the same spatial distribution. What has been happening over the years has affected the patterns of distribution that are seen today. An explanation of the anomalies of today must be sought in the conditions of the past.

# Part Two

# PAST

# 5

# Paleogeography

### *Rocks*

The earth is very old. It had its beginning some 4,000 million years ago. In its beginning it was a whirling mass of matter which gradually condensed into a sphere, and a crust was formed. As the surface of the crust cooled, water vapour from the cloud of gases surrounding the planet condensed to give rise to the oceans. It is not known how the land and sea were distributed at this early time. The oldest rocks are 2,000 million years old, and they are found on every continent, but their extent is impossible to estimate.

The land rose and fell many times during the succeeding years, mountains were thrown up and were worn away by the wind and the rain, the ocean invaded new areas and left others high and dry so that the face of the earth was changed considerably. But in spite of all this rising and falling, crumpling

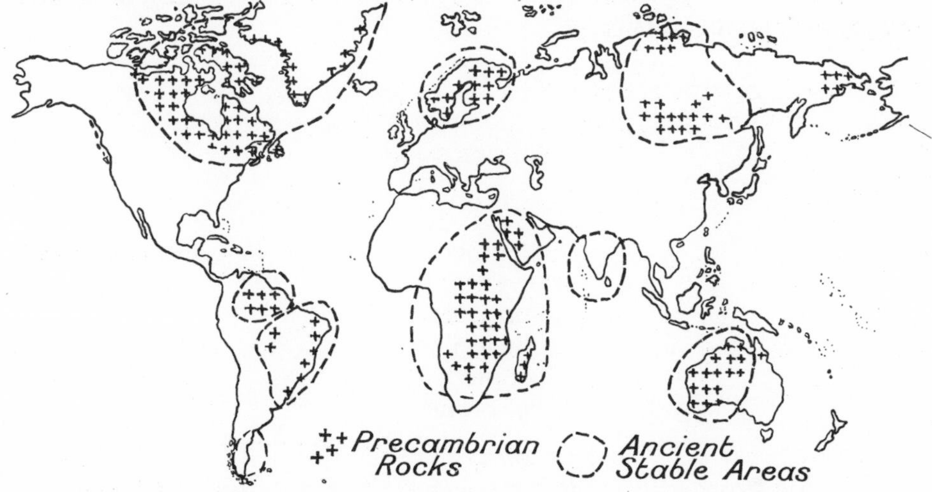


and faulting, it is possible that parts of the main continents had some sort of existence through this time. Furthermore, the presence of the oldest rock formation, the precambrian shields, on each of the six continents, suggests that none is much newer or older than any other. Unfortunately it is not known whether rocks of similar age and characteristics lie on the bottom of the oceans, the remains of lost continents.

Coming to epochs less remote in geological time, more precise statements can sometimes be made. Sediments accumulating on a sea floor or lake bottom are the source of rocks which are the most useful in the interpretation of past changes in the land. The sediments may be of fine sand or silt or the shells and skeletons of aquatic plants and animals. In time the lower layers are compacted by the pressure of the layers above and form into hard rock. An upheaval of the sea bottom, the draining away of water from a lake or a tilting of the land, may uncover such sedimentary rocks and bring them to the surface. Once above the surface, the rock is subject to the forces of erosion and thus succeeding layers become exposed. The nature of the inorganic sediments which have built up the rock may provide a clue to a former coastline, river bed or delta. But mainly the clues in the rocks are sought from the animals and plants that went to make them. Deposits of marine animals in a layer of rock indicate that the particular area was below the sea at the time when the animals were alive. Remnants of land plants or land animals can indicate dry land, but they do not always do so. An animal is rarely preserved unless it falls into water and although a land animal may remain in the fresh water into which it first fell it is frequently swept by rivers away from the place where it lived and even into the sea before it is fossilized.

The succession of plants and animals in stratified rocks determines the relative age of the strata. The presence of closely similar animals and plants in rocks in different parts of the world is taken as evidence of the contemporaneity of the strata. As a result of paleontological studies, and studies of different types of rock, the following time scale has been drawn up, dating from some 600 million years ago when the rocks contain for the first time a number of recognizable animal fossils.

GEOLOGICAL TIME SCALE, IN MILLIONS OF YEARS SINCE THE BEGINNING OF EACH EPOCH (Holmes 1960)

| | | |
|---|---|---|
| | 0 recent | |
| | 1 pleistocene | first fossils of man |
| | 10 pliocene | |
| | 25 miocene | |
| Cenozoic | 40 oligocene | |
| | 60 eocene | |
| | 70 paleocene | |
| | 135 cretaceous | |
| Mesozoic | 180 jurassic | first bird fossils |
| | 225 triassic | first mammal fossils |
| | 270 permian | |
| | 350 carboniferous | first reptile fossils |
| Paleozoic | 400 devonian | first amphibian fossils |
| | 440 silurian | |
| | 500 ordovician | first vertebrate fossils |
| | 600 cambrian | |

Both plants and animals, invertebrates and vertebrates are used in such studies. Obviously some animals are more likely to be fossilized than others, some more easily identified, land animals more useful for determining former land, marine animals for former seas. For remote epochs the geologist or the paleogeographer relies on the well-preserved invertebrates for his evidence. The skeletons, shells, of molluscs for instance, may be preserved intact in the rocks, or more frequently the substance of the living organism may be replaced by mineral silica or calcite, and leave a cast or impression of itself. Ancient invertebrates can show that the limestone rocks running across southern England in a narrow band from the Dorset coast to Lincolnshire were below the sea some 150 million years ago.

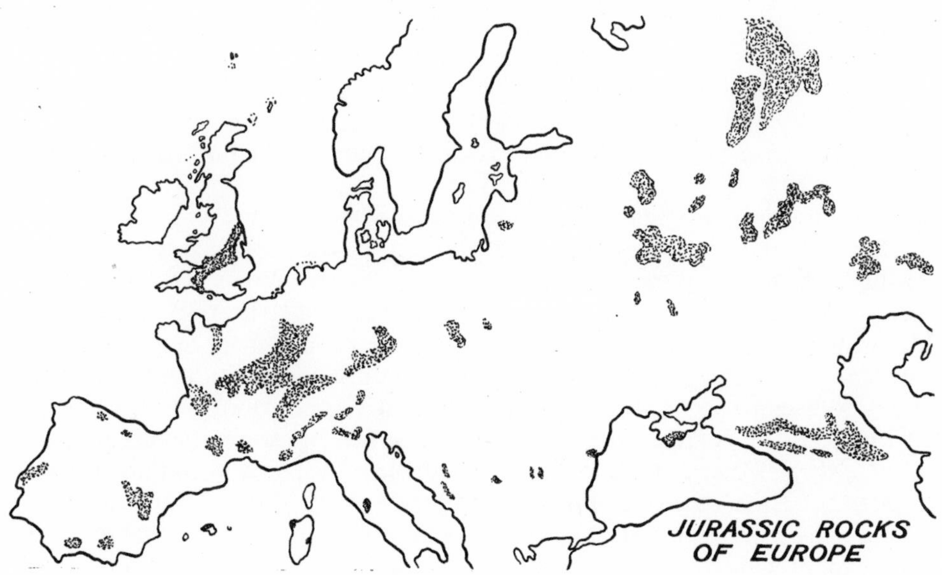

JURASSIC ROCKS OF EUROPE

To locate former sea on present-day land masses is not then very difficult. To identify the extent of the land in the past is less easy. Explorations of the sea bottom are in their early stages. Land animals are not preserved in exactly the place where they lived, and they are not very likely to be preserved at all. If they are fragile their skeletons are crushed or disintegrate before reaching the sedimenting waters of lake or sea, if they lie on land which is acid they are eroded. Such factors as these have led to a scarcity of insect fossils. Those preserved in the resin of Baltic coniferous trees date only from

30 million years ago. Amphibians are fragile and very few Mesozoic amphibians are known. The skeletons of birds too are easily destroyed before fossilization can take place and they are also difficult to piece together when they are found. The most useful fossils for identifying ancient land masses are those of terrestrial reptiles and mammals. This sets a limit in time below which it is unprofitable to go: a time before either reptiles or mammals were abundant on the land. But because reptiles cross sea barriers more easily than mammals, they give less useful evidence of land continuity in the past. In the present state of knowledge, world paleogeography depends to a large extent on a knowledge of mammal fossils.

There is another aspect which affects the reliability of fossil distribution as a guide to former land masses. This is the chanciness of finding fossils. Most are found by accident and depend on excavations that are carried out for other purposes, railway, road and factory building. Their density is therefore to some degree a measure of the industrial development of a country. Other fossils are found because paleontologists go to look for them. These tend to measure the distribution of paleontologists as much as that of the fossils themselves.

Positive evidence provided by a particular fossil in a particular place is valid, but, for the reasons given, negative evidence, that no fossil has been found in a particular place, is open to doubt. That fossil could turn up some time.

This is the sort of evidence on which maps of the ancient world have been built up. Considering the fragmentary nature of the evidence it is not surprising that there are many versions of these maps. There are also several different theories to account for the supposed past distribution of the land. The geographer can discuss their relative merits in terms of present-day geography, but the zoogeographer must argue from prejudiced evidence. When he tries to account for past and present distribution in terms of past land patterns he is arguing in a circle if those land patterns have been surmised largely from a study of past and present distribution. The zoogeographer needs independent physical evidence of the state of the continents through the ages to fit his plants and animals to, but unfortunately such independent evidence is usually not available. Each of the best known theories about the land in the past (from whatever arguments they have been derived) must therefore be considered. The decision to adopt one or the other will depend on which fits the facts the best and which is the simplest, always remembering that the theory is only a guess and that the facts at present available are not final.

The three best-known theories of paleogeography are those of the permanence of the continents, land bridges, and continental drift.

Because it is the simplest of the theories and because it fits a great many of the facts adequately, the first of these theories will be assumed to be the most likely, and the biological consequences of accepting it considered. This does not, however, mean that it is the correct theory but only that it forms a useful model to work with. The other two theories will be discussed later in relationship to the biological findings of the first.

## Continents

The theory of the permanence of the continents was put forward by Lyell in 1830–33. He argued that the great continents have always had some sort of existence and have occupied the same relative positions as they do today, but he also argued that these continents have changed in detail, have evolved through the geological ages as a result of the same sort of physical forces that are at work today. On the basis of this theory, world paleogeographical maps have been made. Some stretch back into cambrian days (see Wills 1951 and Dunbar 1949) but these are usually confined to limited areas. Maps of the whole world in these remote times are too indeterminate to be of much help to zoogeography. They take on more definite shape only in the middle of the Mesozoic.

Some 180 million years ago some part of all the continents and the main

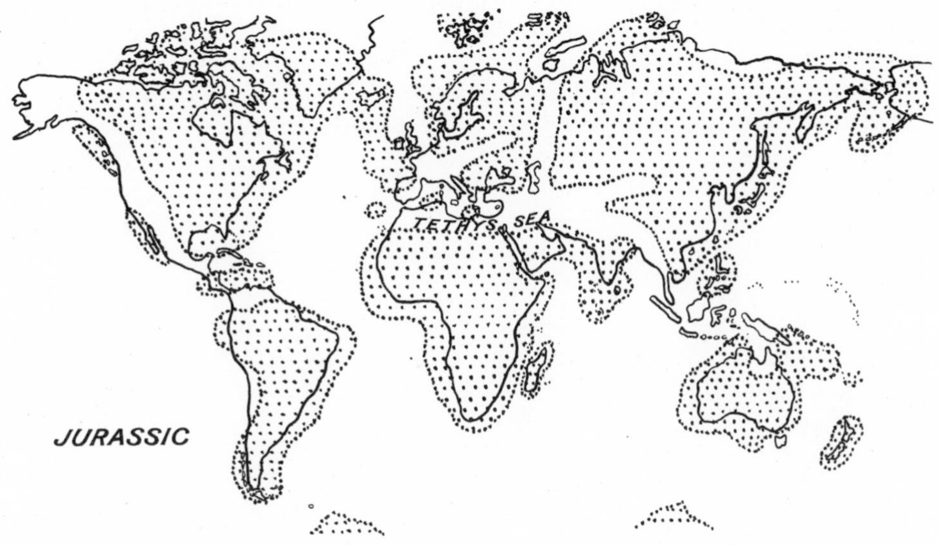


oceans are recognizable but they are not joined up in the same way as they are today, and they are only roughly the same shape. The most obvious difference between then and now is that the northern and the southern land masses were almost entirely separated from one another by a vast sea, the Tethys Sea. The northerly and westerly parts of the British Isles formed part of a North America-Greenland continent. Most of what is now Europe was below the Tethys Sea.

Several lines of evidence then suggest that by the cretaceous, South America and Africa had gained connexions with the northern continents by corridors of dry land. These connexions were of comparatively brief duration. Africa may have been isolated again before the end of the cretaceous, and South America only a few million years later, losing its North American connexion in the early paleocene. For the rest of the paleocene and eocene, neither of these continents had any connexion with the northern land masses.

Africa was the first to regain contact with the north, possibly in oligocene days, and only much later, in the pliocene, did the isthmus of Panama once again connect South America with North America.

During this later period when the African and South American connexions were being made with the north, the British Isles became part of Europe and ceased to be an outlying strip of the America-Greenland continent.

During the Cenozoic, too, changes took place along the shallow sea area between Alaska and Siberia. Several times there seems to have been land across what are now the Bering Straits and at some times this land may have included the more southerly islands of the area. The land was not stable in this part of the world however, and was as many times below the sea.

At different periods during the history of the earth there have been times of great movements when mountain ranges have been thrown up. The Caledonian mountains were formed as early as the silurian, the Appalachians of North America in the permian, the Andes and Rockies in the late cretaceous. The Eurasian mountains are mainly young. The Himalayas which cut off the Oriental region from the rest of Asia were formed as late as the middle of the Cenozoic, at the same time as the Alps and Pyrenees.

All this time too there was volcanic activity over parts of the world, probably even more widespread than it is today. An area that is volcanic still, has probably been an unstable part of the world through many epochs. Melanesia and the Malay Archipelago northwards through Japan and the Aleutian Islands have long been changeable owing to volcanic movement. There are volcanic areas also in the west of Central America and South America, and again in the Mediterranean.

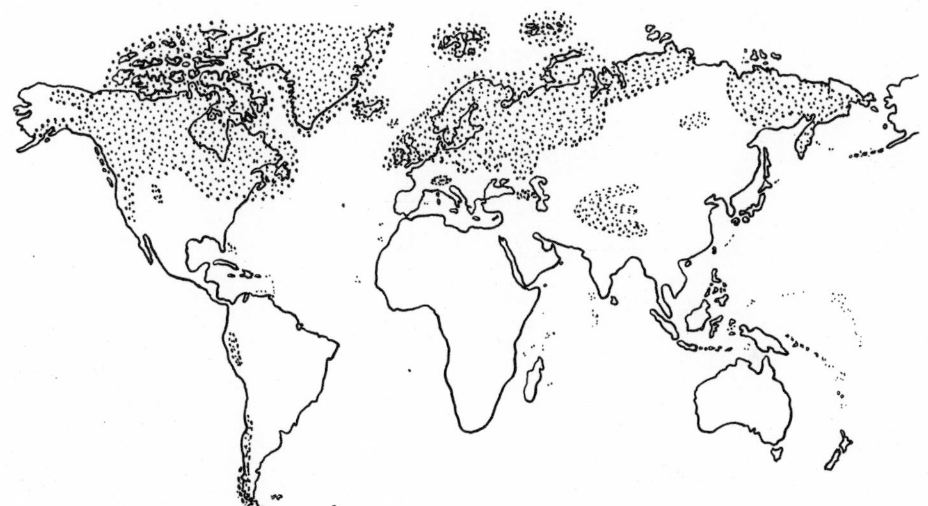

*Maximum extent of Pleistocene Glaciations*

In the last epoch of the Cenozoic yet another physical event had a profound effect on the world. Less than a million years ago, in the pleistocene, great sheets of ice covered areas of the northern hemisphere, advancing and retreating several times. Ice-covered areas were uninhabitable except for a very few species of animals and plants, and south of the ice itself the climate was cold. The general effect of the ice was to lower the temperature all over the world, pushing the edge of the temperate zone further south and reducing the extent of the tropical areas of the world. The accumulation of ice, lowered the level of the sea so that many areas that are now shallow seas were dry land during the pleistocene.

Over the past 180 million years, then, according to the theory of permanence, the main changes in the look of the world had been the shrinking of the Tethys Sea, the making and breaking of narrow connexions between the two northern continents and of their connexions with South America and Africa. Australia had been isolated most of this time.

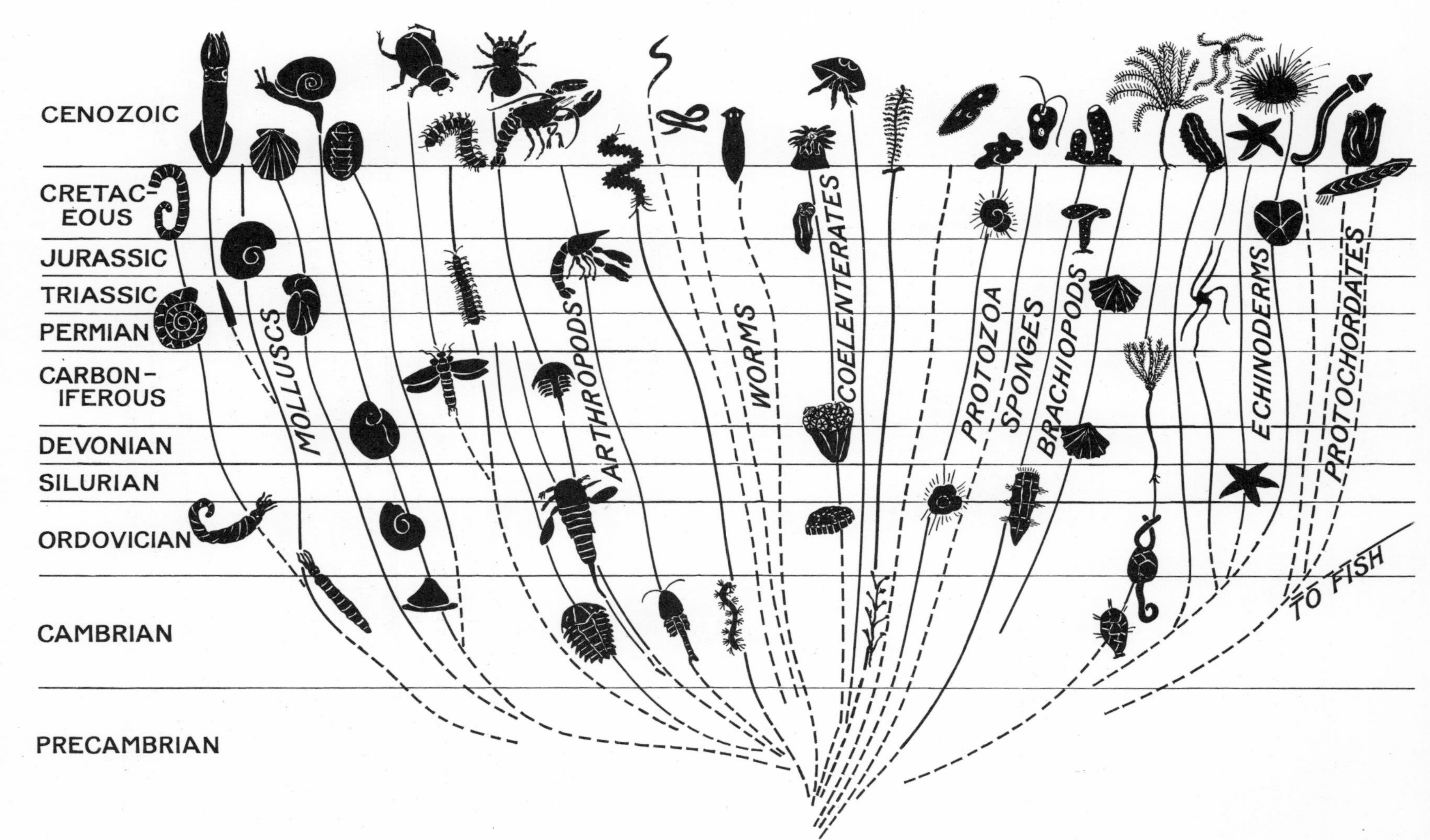
CENOZOIC
CRETAC-
EOUS
JURASSIC
TRIASSIC
PERMIAN
CARBON-
IFEROUS
DEVONIAN
SILURIAN
ORDOVICIAN
CAMBRIAN
PRECAMBRIAN
MOLLUSCS
ARTHROPODS
WORMS
COELENTERATES
PROTOZOA
SPONGES
BRACHIOPODS
ECHINODERMS
PROTOCHORDATES
TO FISH

# 6

# Evolution of Animals

## *Paleozoic and Mesozoic*

Living organisms have a long history, extending back possibly over 1,500 million years. It is not known what the first forms of life were, nor when plants and animals diverged from the common stock. It is presumed that the first recognizable animals resembled the Protozoa of today. The early forms may have been like the amoeba of the rain-water puddles, or like the plant-animals that move by the lashing of their whip-like flagella. After these came the sponges, coelenterates (jellyfish, corals and sea anemones) and flatworms. Gradually other forms of life came into being, other worms, molluscs (bivalves, snails and cephalopods), arthropods (crustacea, spiders, insects) and echinoderms (starfish, sea urchins, sea cucumbers). Almost nothing is known of the early evolutionary history of these invertebrate groups, for they had already a long history behind them by the cambrian. Cambrian is the name given to the earliest rocks in which recognizable fossils are normally found. The main groups of invertebrates are found in these rocks but they are represented by animals very different from modern forms. The most abundant cambrian animals are the trilobites, arthropods which looked like aquatic woodlice. They all lived in the sea, mostly on the bottom. There were no land animals in the cambrian. Trilobites lived on, becoming less abundant but not dying out until the permian. Besides worms, coelenterates like *Obelia*, and jellyfish, there were in cambrian seas eurypterids and king crabs, both relatives of modern scorpions. The extensively armoured eurypterids, some measuring six feet, dominated the seas and fresh waters as the trilobites declined. There were several sorts of molluscs, snail-like forms whose shells were not twisted, early bivalves, and shelled cephalopod ancestors of the nautilus and modern octopuses. All cambrian echinoderms were fixed to rocks by stalks and were covered over by thick calcified skeletons. According to the fossil record, in the early years of the Paleozoic, heavy armouring was the rule, but it should be remembered that forms with hard skeletons are more likely to have been preserved than those without so that the balance would be in favour of armoured forms. Even so, when the first known vertebrates appeared in the ordovician they too were heavily armoured.

The first vertebrates, fish without jaws, lived in the fresh waters of the period. Later still, life began to colonize the land. In the devonian the earliest known land plants, club-mosses, ferns and seed ferns came into being, and

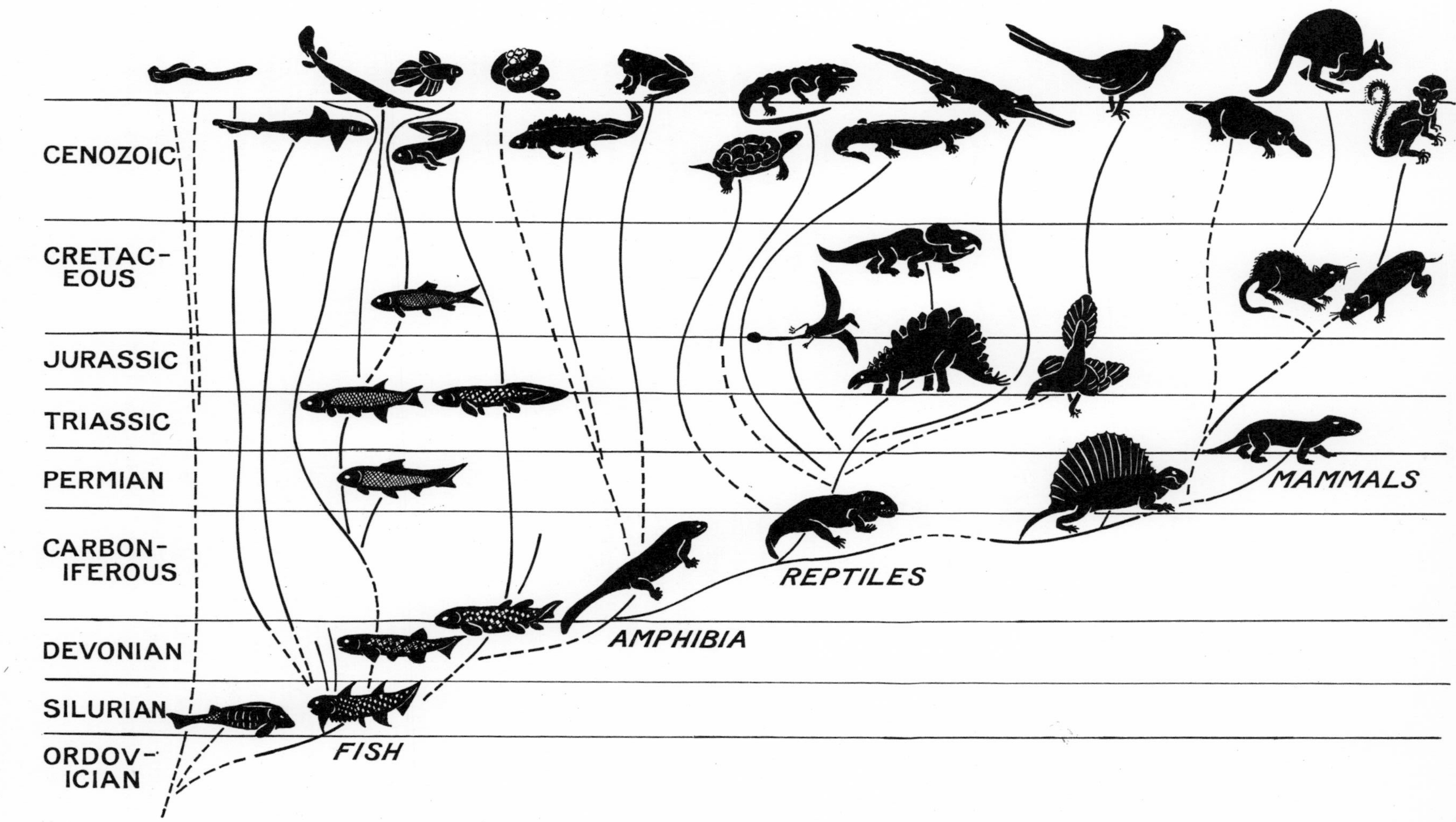
CENOZOIC
CRETAC-
EOUS
JURASSIC
TRIASSIC
PERMIAN
CARBON-
IFEROUS
DEVONIAN
SILURIAN
ORDOV-
ICIAN
FISH
AMPHIBIA
REPTILES
MAMMALS

shortly afterwards the earliest scorpions, spiders, centipedes and insects. The insects had not yet evolved into flying forms. Fish had become abundant by this time, radiating out into different forms, many of them still heavily armoured. The devonian forms died out eventually, but not before the ancestors of all modern fish had been derived from them. As the cambrian was the Age of Trilobites, the ordovician and silurian the Age of Eurypterids, so the devonian can be called the Age of Fish.

In the next geological epoch, the carboniferous, the vertebrates came out on to the land in the form of amphibia and reptiles. Insects were numerous by now and the carboniferous has been called the Age of Cockroaches. For some time to come, however, the land was to be dominated by the reptiles which evolved into many strange forms. There were small reptiles, large reptiles, quadrupedal reptiles, bipedal reptiles, herbivorous reptiles, carnivorous reptiles, land-living reptiles, aquatic reptiles and flying reptiles. The reptiles reached their peak in the jurassic and then lost their superiority. The abundant dinosaurs both large and small, and the flying reptiles died out suddenly in the cretaceous. It is not clear why this happened and many different theories have been put forward to explain it. It may have been too cold, or too dry, the vegetation may have become unsuitable as food, or some disastrous disease may have killed them or their eggs. It was most probable that it was some change in the climate of the cretaceous which was responsible because other groups of plants and animals were seriously affected at this time. Many of the cycad-like plants and the ginkgos died out on the land, and from the sea the big marine reptiles and the ammonites and belemnites (two groups of cephalopod mollusc) disappeared.

Whatever the cause of the reptile catastrophe, the birds and mammals were able to take advantage of it. Both these groups, the only two that are warm-blooded, were evolving whilst the reptiles were still the most successful land animals. By the cretaceous, birds and several groups of early mammals were in existence. They seem to have found suitable conditions for their way of life at the end of this period possibly provided by the newly evolving flowering plants and higher insects, for they diverged rapidly and started evolving into all the groups that are known today. Mammals, birds and insects have dominated the land since the beginning of the Cenozoic.

The Paleozoic and Mesozoic record is the story of succeeding groups rising to dominance and gradually dying away, from the Age of Trilobites through the Ages of Fish and Cockroaches to the Age of Reptiles. The Cenozoic is the Age of Mammals.

### *Cenozoic*

By the jurassic, then, most of the main groups of animals had already a considerable evolutionary history behind them. The five classes of vertebrates, the fish, amphibia, reptiles, birds and mammals had already been established.

Since the jurassic no new orders of fish, amphibia or reptiles have come into being, but within the orders already established there has been divergence into the families which survive today. Birds and mammals have diverged into families as well as orders since the jurassic. Families were used as the units in describing geographical distribution, so to be consistent it is also the family that must be considered as the evolutionary unit.

Ideally all modern families could be traced in detail from their first appearance in the rocks to the present day. This is possible for some mammal and a few reptile families. For the others, adequate fossil evidence is still lacking.

The main fish orders were already well established long before the beginning of the Cenozoic, and in fact many of the modern families of freshwater fish were already differentiated by the cretaceous. For instance, ancestors of the Australian lungfish were already similar to their modern descendants by this time. Holostean ancestors of the Nearctic garpike and bowfin, and the first characin fish were also marked off by the cretaceous. The carp family was a later development, not appearing until the eocene.

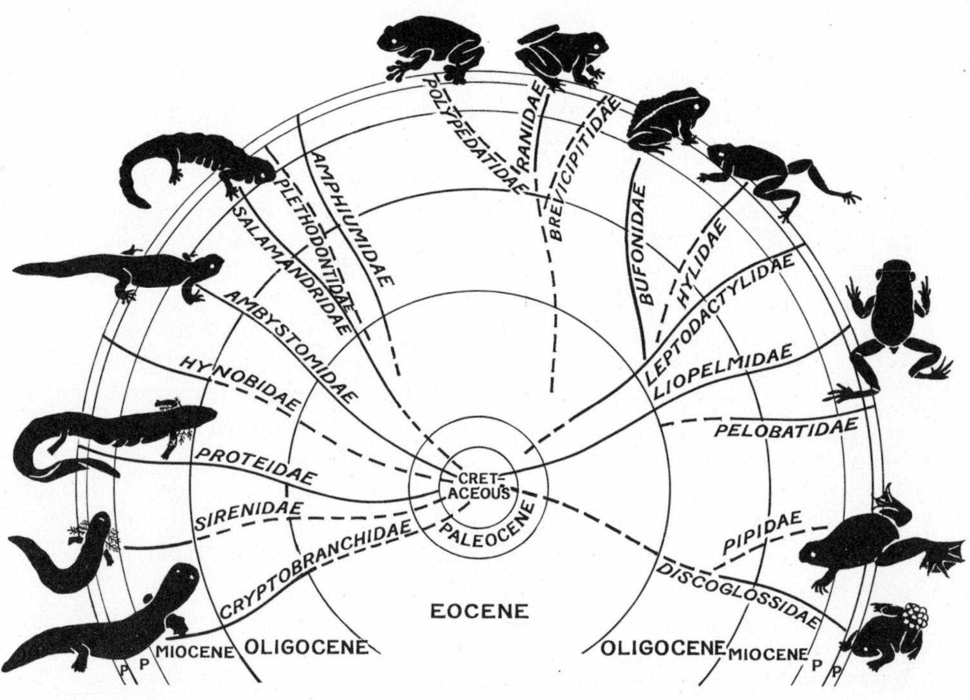


Almost nothing is known about the history of the modern amphibia. The three orders, apoda, urodela and anura are difficult to trace and difficult to relate to one another because of the scarcity of fossils. When the first anura appear in the rocks they are already well differentiated from other amphibians and show little signs of their derivation. It is therefore from the comparative anatomy of modern families that a hypothetical scheme of their Cenozoic evolution has been worked out. On this basis it seems that the liopelmids

(*Liopelma* and *Ascaphus*) were the first of the modern anurans, in the late jurassic, followed by pipid toads (*Pipa* and *Xenopus*) and, in the oligocene, hylid tree frogs and the common toads. The differentiation of the common frogs and polypedatid tree frogs may have been as late as the miocene. The ancestry of the urodeles is equally obscure. The ambystomid family (axolotls) is found in the cretaceous, salamanders in the eocene and giant salamanders in the oligocene. Their relationships to one another are not easy to determine. Nothing can be said about the evolution of the apodans.

Of the reptiles, only four orders persisted through the Cenozoic after the great Mesozoic orders had become extinct. These were the turtles, crocodiles, snakes and lizards, and *Sphenodon*. The turtles were recognizable by the triassic and during the jurassic differentiated into the two groups that are known today: the pleurodires (side-necks) and the cryptodires (vertical-neck turtles). Both groups had split up into their modern families by the cretaceous. Crocodile families too were firmly established before the beginning of the Cenozoic and this is also probably true of lizard and snake families. The varanid and iguanid families may be the oldest, and both they and the agamids (possibly derivatives of the iguanids) are known from the cretaceous. Teiids, lacertids and chameleons may be later offshoots, together with the snakes which almost certainly derive from varanid-like lizards. The *Sphenodon* family is the oldest of the surviving reptiles being already abundant in the early Mesozoic.

Birds left the main reptile stock, probably in the jurassic, and continued to evolve along independent lines, leaving little trace of their subsequent history in the rocks.

It was for the mammals that the Cenozoic was so important. It was their great evolutionary moment. Before this mammals had been scarce but in a comparatively short time they became the dominant land animals.

In many cases their fossil history is well known and some families can be traced without a break from their first appearance to the present day. But it is just this completeness which itself raises a difficulty. In theory all mammals could be traced back along converging lines to one common ancestor amongst the reptiles of early Mesozoic days. In theory the lines should be continuous from the earliest forms to the most modern. This hardly ever happens, however, and groups are separated from one another because their ancestors are not known. In practice, therefore, it is possible to talk about the duckbilled platypus family because it is cut off from its nearest relative the spiny anteater by certain morphological characteristics and there are no fossils earlier than the pleistocene to make the two families merge into one another. It is a good deal more difficult to decide when an elephant becomes an elephant. Ancestors of all elephants, mastodons and mammoths are known in the eocene and an evolutionary tree can be drawn giving off families of mastodons and the elephant family by continuous branching. Who is to decide in such cases when the elephant family has started, when it has ceased to be a pre-elephant or a paleomastodon and become an elephant? Unfortunately no word exists to describe this process in terms of classification and the decision to stop calling the fossils paleomastodons and to start calling them elephants at a particular moment in geological time is an arbitrary one. The better known the fossil history of a family the more acute is this problem. Bearing in mind

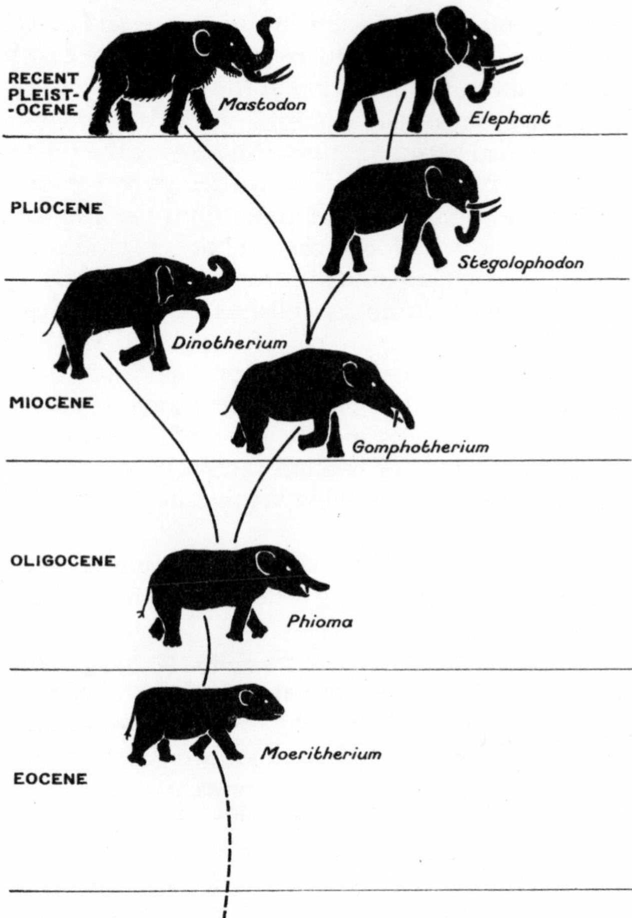


this arbitrariness of saying when a particular family has started, an outline of cenozoic mammalian evolution can be traced.

The first marsupials and first placentals appear in the rocks at the same time, in the cretaceous, giving no indication of their relationships to one another. From then on the fossil record is good.

Fossils of the main orders appear in the following sequence: marsupials and insectivores, edentates, condylarths and carnivores, primates, lagomorphs and rodents, followed by bats, perissodactyls, artiodactyls and proboscids.

Thus the Insectivora were the first of all placentals, differentiated in the cretaceous and contemporary with the first marsupials. They were ancestral to the later placental orders. Of insectivore families, hedgehogs and moles were the earliest fossil representatives of modern families.

No other mammal orders are known as early as the cretaceous.

In the next stratum however, the paleocene, several orders are found, distinct from the insectivores from which they were derived and distinct from one another. These are edentates, condylarths, carnivores, primates, lagomorphs and rodents. Of these the condylarths and primitive carnivores, creodonts, are more nearly alike at this time than the others, and show clear signs of derivation from the insectivores. They were both clawed animals with long tails, but whilst creodonts were probably still mainly insect-eaters, the condylarths were herbivores. From these generalized paleocene ancestors have evolved modern carnivores and the hoofed (ungulate) herbivores of the world. Condylarths became extinct during the eocene, unless the modern aardvark be considered a member of the order.

Creodonts, the earliest of the carnivores, radiated widely until they were replaced by modern carnivore families in the oligocene. By this time dog, civet, weasel and cat families were clearly distinct, the cat family having already sabre-tooth tigers amongst its members. Later came the raccoon family; and the bear family had differentiated from the dogs by the miocene. These were followed by hyenas which were the last of all the carnivore families to evolve, being derived as late as the pliocene from the civet family.

Of the other paleocene orders, edentates were represented by the paleanodonts, early derivatives of the insectivore stock. They gave rise rapidly to armadillos, and much later to anteaters and sloths.

Primates, whose affinities with the insectivores were very close in the paleocene, became common in the eocene and by the oligocene both Old World monkeys and apes had become distinguishable, to be followed closely by the New World monkeys and lorises.

The remaining two paleocene orders, the Lagomorpha and the rodents can be presumed to have arisen, like the others from the insectivores; but whether they were independent derivations from the start or whether they shared a common ancestor in late cretaceous days is not known. The Lagomorpha were at first rare, expanding in the eocene but not becoming really common until the oligocene by which time both the rabbit and pika families had differentiated.

The story of the rodents is more difficult to follow, for the relationships of even the modern families have not been satisfactorily worked out. They occur as rare fossils (probably sciuromorphs) in the late paleocene, expand in the eocene when ancestors of the sewellel family were already found, and by the oligocene the main groups had been sorted out. The sciuromorphs were giving rise to the beaver family, the myomorphs to the cricetid mice and gophers, and the caviomorphs to tree porcupine, cavy and chinchilla families. The squirrel family itself did not appear until the miocene to be followed, as late as the pliocene, by murid rat and mouse family and the spalacid mole rats.

Perissodactyla and Artiodactyla were in existence in the early eocene

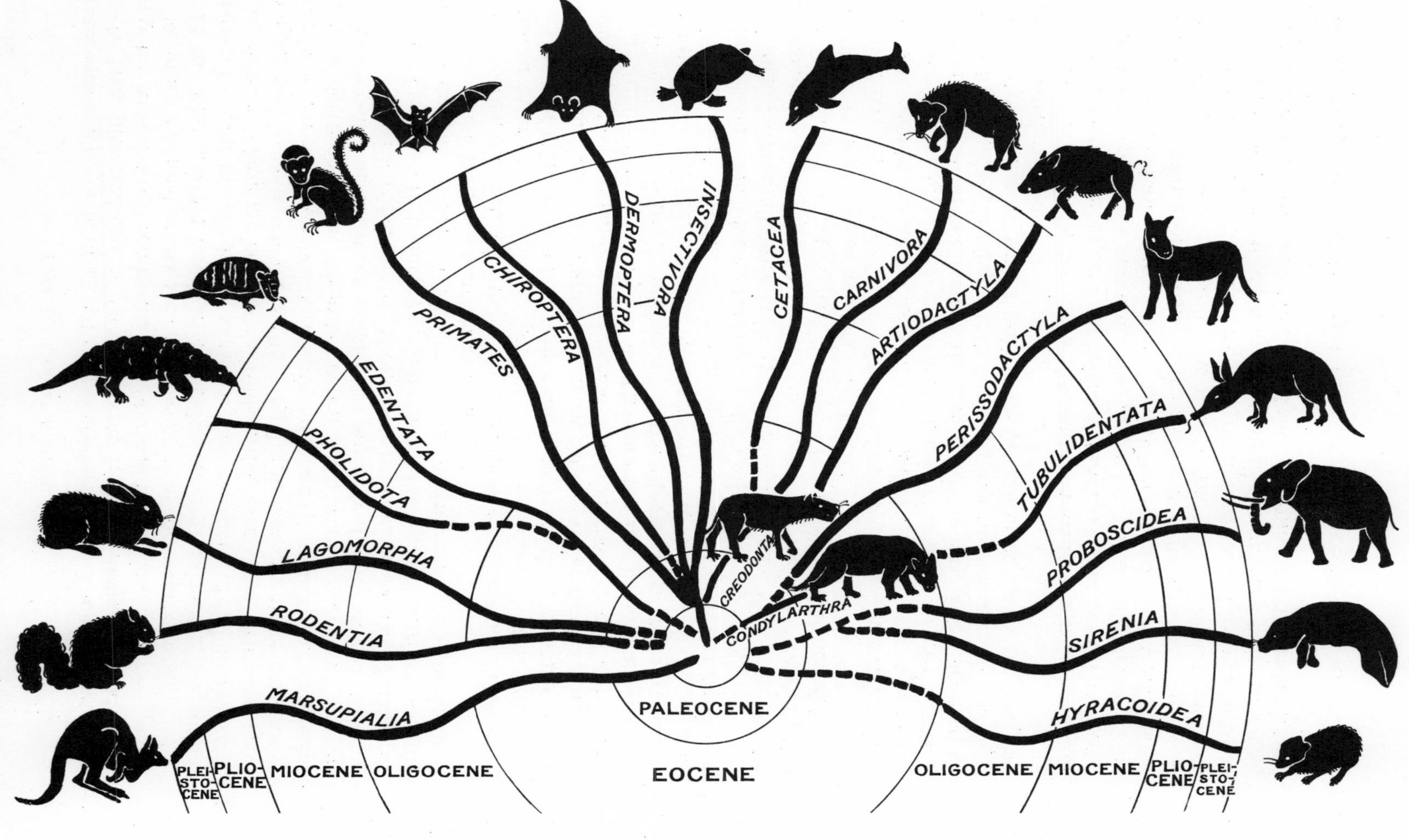

EDENTATA
PHOLIDOTA
LAGOMORPHA
RODENTIA
MARSUPIALIA
PRIMATES
CHIROPTERA
DERMOPTERA
INSECTIVORA
CETACEA
CARNIVORA
ARTIODACTYLA
PERISSODACTYLA
TUBULIDENTATA
PROBOSCIDEA
SIRENIA
HYRACOIDEA
CREODONTA
CONDYLARTHRA
PALEOCENE
PLEI-STO-CENE
PLIO-CENE
MIOCENE
OLIGOCENE
EOCENE
OLIGOCENE
MIOCENE
PLIO-CENE
PLEI-STO-CENE

derived from the condylarth-creodont stock. Already the horse, tapir and rhinoceros families were distinct. Of the artiodactyls, the camel family was one of the first to evolve, in the eocene, followed by pigs, peccaries and deer in the oligocene. The miocene saw giraffes, pronghorns and bovids, but the hippo family has not been traced further back than the pliocene although this cannot be the whole story as its differentiation from the pigs must have taken place much earlier. Amongst the bovid family, the antelopes appeared later than the rest.

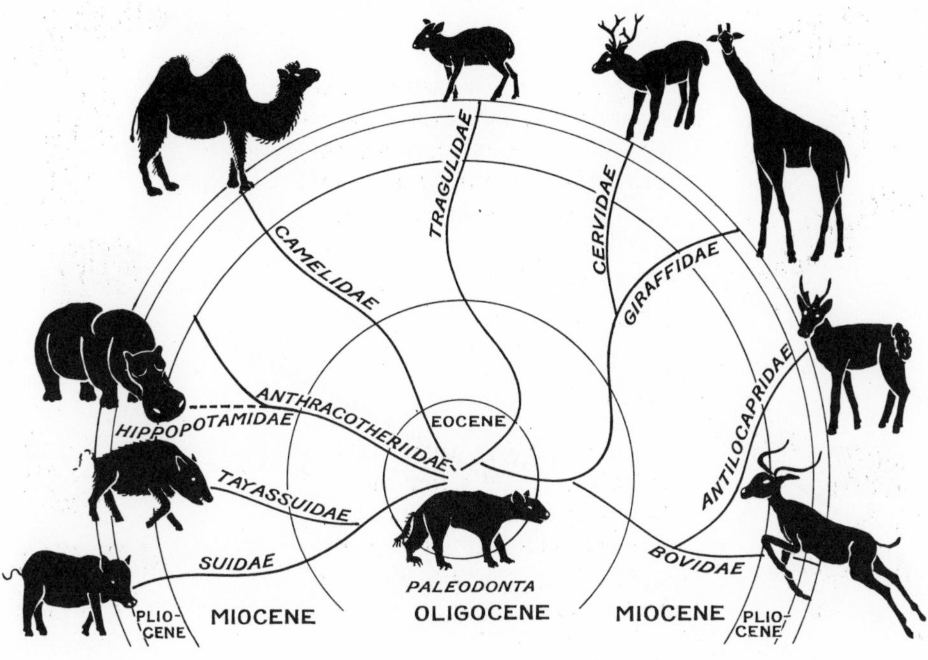


Finally the elephants, whose ancestors were of eocene and possibly condylarth origin, were not differentiated as a definite family distinct from the mastodons until the pliocene.

By the pliocene all the modern families of mammals had evolved, from the early insectivores to the latest of all, the murid mice and the hyenas.

## *Summary of Mammal Evolution*

*Cretaceous:* earliest mammal orders: marsupials and insectivores.

*Paleocene:* a few more orders established: edentates, carnivores (creodonts), condylarths, primates, lagomorphs (rare) and rodents (rare).

*Eocene:* all the main orders established and a few modern families: bats, perissodactyls, artiodactyls (camels), proboscids. Lagomorphs, primates and rodents expand.

*Oligocene:* a large number of modern families established: Old World monkeys; dog, cat, weasel and civets among the carnivores; beavers, cricetid mice, gophers, porcupines, cavies and chinchillas; sloths; pigs, peccaries and deer.

*Miocene:* a few late modern families differentiated from the earlier modern families: raccoons, bears, squirrels, giraffes, pronghorns, bovids and anteaters.

*Pliocene:* the last of the modern families appear: hyenas, murid mice, spalacid mole rats and elephants.

# Part Three
# PAST TO PRESENT

# 7

# Northern Regions

## *Cenozoic Distribution*

Mammals differentiated and spread during the Cenozoic from small beginnings to today's diversity and range. Fossils of mammal families are abundant enough in the rocks for a reasonable estimate to be made of their range at different geological periods. Thus a distribution map of miocene tapirs can be drawn. This can be compared with the modern distribution map on page 13. In miocene days there were no tapirs in South America, but in contrast to present-day distribution, tapirs lived in North America and Europe.

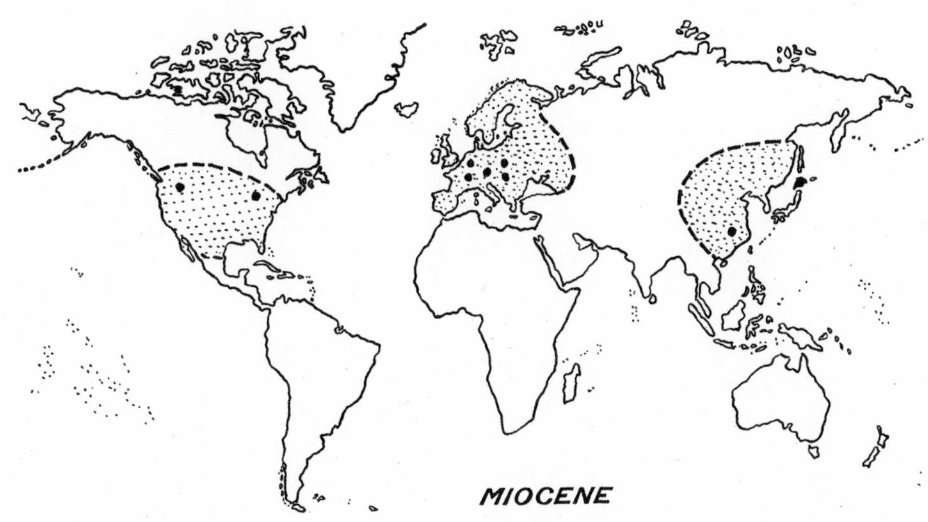


Just as simple Cenozoic distribution maps for individual families can be drawn, so also can the compound maps of zoogeographical regions of different Cenozoic epochs be delineated. Zoogeographical regions are not modern phenomena; they existed in the past, but they were not necessarily the same as they are today either in continental area or in the composition of their fauna. There are certain unfortunate gaps in parts of the mammal record, but on the whole the changes in range of the main families through the Cenozoic are reasonably well known.

With the theory of the permanence of the continents as a base, a picture can be built up of the evolution of mammal families, their spread, and their colonization of different parts of the world.

The general picture that emerges is one of mainly northern evolution and subsequent spreading from west to east or from north to south. Spread was compensated for by limitation however. Sometimes a family spread widely and then contracted, like the horses, or spread and became extinct in the middle of its range like the tapirs, or like the pronghorns never spread beyond the confines of the continent where it originated.

Whatever the propensities of the families, the direction and the distance of their spread was determined to some extent by the state of the land at the relevant period in Cenozoic history. Their spread was determined by the geographical location of their place of origin and by the connexions that place had with other parts of the world. Thus mammals originating somewhere in north-eastern Asia would first have to spread westwards into mid-Asia or Europe before they were available as migrants to Africa. But they were only able to make this final southerly migration if Africa had a suitable land connexion with the north at the time. The earliest continental connexions therefore provided a migration route for the earliest mammals, the latest connexions for the most modern.

## *Nearctic and Palearctic*

Towards the end of the Mesozoic, the modern Nearctic and Palearctic regions seem to have had a uniform fauna, and for this reason are thought to have comprised one land mass. It is from the northern hemisphere that the earliest mammals are known. By the cretaceous there were both marsupials and insectivores in the continents. There were holostean fish and lungfish; there were crocodiles and side-neck turtles. There were probably also liopelmid frogs, pipid toads and perhaps some of the more advanced frog families spread through the north. But already towards the end of the cretaceous the uniformity of the northern fauna was being modified. Some modern fish and amphibian families were not spreading through the area. Ambystomid urodeles (axolotls) and characin fish are known as fossils from the Nearctic strata of this epoch but not from those of the Palearctic. Marsupials appear to have been more abundant in the Nearctic than the Palearctic. But the differences were not all due to additions in the Nearctic. *Sphenodon* which had earlier been widespread was dying out at the end of the cretaceous and its only northern relic was in the Palearctic.

By the paleocene more orders of mammals had appeared in the north, descendants of the insectivores. There were creodont carnivores, condylarths and lemurs, the first recognizable primates. With the earlier marsupials and insectivores all these orders were spread through the northern lands. But there had also been a loss in the north: lungfish had disappeared. Differences between the Palearctic and Nearctic were becoming more definite. The first lagomorphs were found in Asia. In contrast, the most ancient of all edentates, the paleanodonts, had appeared in the North American continent. There were also a few rodents there. Unlike the rodents and lagomorphs which were to become widespread, the edentates remained

in the New World. It is not clear why edentates were restricted in this way, for it is thought that there was plenty of opportunity for faunal exchange between the two northern continents during the paleocene and into the early part of the eocene, judging from the way other groups of animals spread.

Eocene days saw new forms in the northern fauna, and there were no losses of already established groups. The number of mammalian families increased generally. Such is the crudeness of measuring time on the geological scale that several of these families appear simultaneously in both continents. Yet it is unlikely that they could have had such a wide centre of origin. Wherever they originated however, they must have spread rapidly. Such were the horses, rhinoceroses, ancestral artiodactyls and bats. The lagomorphs and

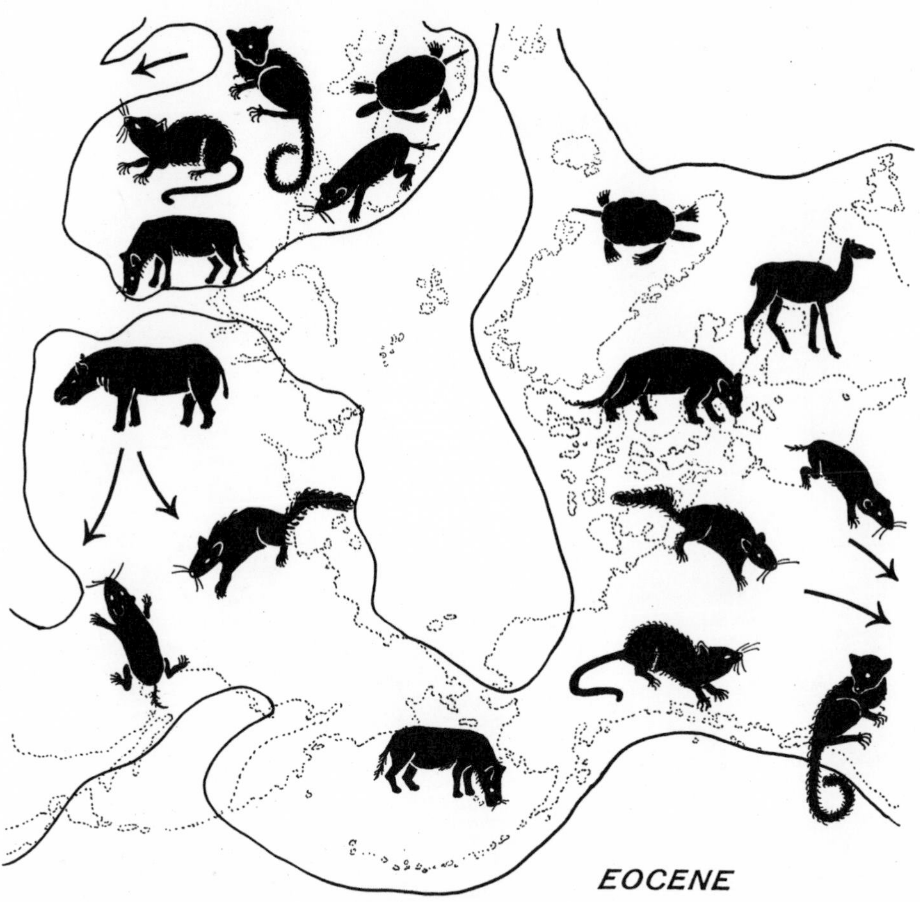


rodents had increased in number and had also spread, the lagomorphs from their original home in the Palearctic and the rodents from the Nearctic. Amongst other vertebrates, characin fish had colonized the Palearctic by the eocene and the holosteans were still flourishing. In contrast to the wide dispersal of these families, even of those which were new to the fauna, others were restricted. They may have been restricted because they were not yet numerous or they may have been restricted because by the late eocene the northern continents had lost their land connexions with one another. Whatever the reasons, there were differences in the late eocene faunas. The Palearctic and Nearctic could be considered as separate zoogeographical regions. The carp and salamander families and a bird, probably ancestral to ostriches, are known from European fossil beds of the epoch. These represented families which were unique to the Palearctic, if only temporarily so. The Nearctic was still characterized by its paleanodont edentates and to these had been added ancestors of the camels.

By the next epoch, the oligocene, further changes had taken place in the fauna. More new families had evolved, but some had also died out from the northern hemisphere. There were no longer any condylarths or lemurs. The other ancient orders, however, were still abundant, marsupials, insectivores, rabbits and rodents. The hedgehog and mole families were already recognizable amongst the insectivores; herbivores could be distinguished as peccaries and widespread tapirs. Carnivores, too, were becoming modern; dogs, weasels and sabre-tooth tigers roamed over the north. The mammalian fauna was becoming complex. All these new families were widespread at their first appearance in oligocene rocks so that their exact place of origin is not known, but only that they spread widely and rapidly. There must therefore have been a restoration of the continental connexion which had been presumed broken in late eocene days, to permit this large-scale faunal interchange. But not all groups travelled widely; some of both old and new were confined to one region or another. The paleanodonts and the camels were still characteristic of the Nearctic and they had been joined by the pocket gophers. In the Palearctic the first pigs and deer had arrived. There were also civets, parrots, trogons and ancestors of modern giant salamanders. Because of this differentiation between Palearctic and Nearctic in the later years of the oligocene it has been supposed that after inter-communication had been restored in early oligocene days, a new break had occurred. Not all the differences can be accounted for in this way, however, because the non-migrating paleanodonts and camels had already had an opportunity to spread and had not taken it. They appear to have been restricted by limitations other than sea barriers. However this may be, the zoogeographical regions were becoming more distinct. The fauna of both had similar components, marsupials in the trees, insectivores on the ground, rabbits, rodents and ungulates living on a herbivorous diet, dogs, tigers and mustelids to eat them, birds in the air and amphibia and fish in lakes and rivers. The two regions however, differed in their herbivores. Whilst tapirs and peccaries were common to both, there were browsing camels and gnawing gophers in the Nearctic, grazing deer and rooting pigs in the Palearctic. There were paleanodonts in the Nearctic and the Palearctic had an extra family of carnivores, the civets. Of the other vertebrates, there were axolotls in the Nearctic to correspond with the salamanders of the Palearctic. The parrots and carp had still not spread.

15 million years later, in the miocene with the exception of the paleanodonts these same families were flourishing and becoming more modern in appearance. The differences between Nearctic and Palearctic were increasing

because there was probably little interchange until well on into the miocene when a land connexion was once more established across some part of the

Bering Straits between Alaska and Siberia. Deer, carp and parrots spread to the Nearctic and squirrels were found throughout the north. New families appeared in both regions; bovids, giraffes and bears in the Palearctic, pronghorns in the Nearctic. There were Old World monkeys in the Palearctic for the first time. In many ways the Nearctic and Palearctic had already taken on their modern characteristics by the miocene. Already axolotls, gophers and pronghorns were typical of the Nearctic fauna. Holostean fish contracted to their modern, Nearctic, distribution. Pigs were typically Palearctic and only spread to the Nearctic in historic times. In other respects the differences that existed between the regions in miocene days were differences that did not last. Neither the camels of the miocene Nearctic, nor the beavers, giraffes and bovids of the Palearctic were to remain typical of their original regions.

By the pliocene the Palearctic was cut off by the Himalayas from the Oriental region, but it seems to have had a connexion with the Nearctic during part of the period because there was migration between the two. Bears and giant salamanders spread to the Nearctic, camels which had been restricted to the Nearctic since their first appearance in eocene days migrated

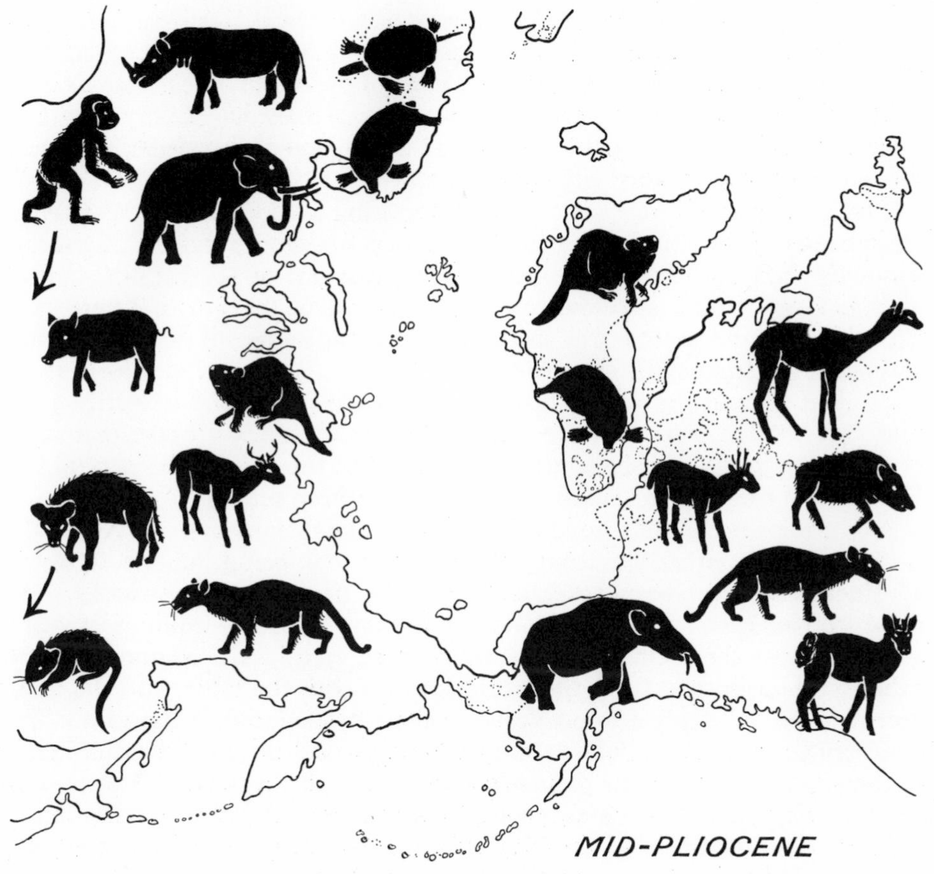


to the Palearctic for the first time. But the pliocene north also lost some of its earlier fauna. Neither side-neck turtles nor marsupials were any longer to be found there. But in spite of these interchanges and extinctions which increased the uniformity of the two northern regions, many of the old differences persisted and new ones came into being. These differences were due both to extinctions and new arrivals. Thus rhinoceroses which had been widespread, now vanished from the Nearctic; their continuous range was contracting. Hyenas, aardvarks and spalacid mole rats were new to the fauna when they appeared in the Palearctic. None of them ever colonized the New World. And so at the end of the pliocene the two northern zoogeographical regions were still distinctly different. Their differences were not the same as they had been in the previous epoch, nor were they the same as they are today, but they were gradually coming to resemble more closely the modern regions than they had done in earlier days.

The next epoch, the pleistocene, is not long ago in terms of mammalian evolution and most of the modern forms had evolved by then. The most notable events of this time were the ice ages. At the beginning of the Cenozoic it was probably warm and equable over most of the world, but by the pleistocene much of the land of the north was covered by ice. Many northern mammals had already migrated south and by the end of the pleistocene were the only survivors of once widespread groups.

The pleistocene is a particularly interesting period in the records of mammalian evolution. On the one hand many apparently flourishing forms suddenly died out and on the other, giant versions of several well-known mammals made their appearance in various parts of the world. There were giant beavers and mammoths in the north, giant moose in North America and the huge Irish elk in the Palearctic. Throughout the New World there were giant ground sloths; in Australia a giant kangaroo, and in Africa giant pigs. Yet another feature of the pleistocene was the thick fur coat that some of the northern mammals acquired. There were the woolly rhinoceroses of Eurasia and the woolly mammoths of both northern regions.

As the pleistocene ice spread south, many animals unable to survive in the new conditions either died out altogether or took refuge in the southern continents. Mammoths and elephants as well as tapirs and sabre-tooths, most of which had been typical of the northern fauna for many millions of years, were amongst those that suffered from these conditions. Mammoths and sabre-tooths vanished from the world for ever, but the tapirs and the more recently evolved elephants had already established colonies in the south. The southern colonies of the tapirs were at the extreme western and eastern ends of their range, so that their pleistocene extinction in the north left them with their modern pattern of widely spaced discontinuous distribution. Elephants although also members of the Nearctic and Palearctic in the pliocene were only established southwards in the Old World. Other families which suffered the same fate of northern extinction in the pleistocene were already restricted to the Old World. Thus monkeys, rhinoceroses and aardvarks disappeared from the north of their range. Camels on the other hand which were shared by Nearctic and Palearctic disappeared only from the Nearctic. For three Cenozoic epochs they had been typical of the Nearctic, only spreading south and west in late pliocene times. But in the pleistocene they vanished from their region of origin, from the centre of their range and so became discontinuously distributed. In contrast, the differential extinction of the peccaries, confined them in the pleistocene to the New World. In spite of the large-scale extinction in the north, a few families extended their range. Bovids and salamanders spread from Palearctic to Nearctic. Other families retained their place in the northern fauna amongst which were many of the regionally characteristic families. The holosteans, axolotls, gophers and pronghorns remained in the Nearctic; spalacids, hyenas and pigs in the Palearctic. No new families except the Hominidae appeared in the pleistocene. By the end of the last glaciation the faunas of Palearctic and Nearctic had taken on the characteristics that distinguish them today.

Gradually then through the Cenozoic what was a uniform northern fauna separated into Nearctic and Palearctic. As new animals evolved, some like the bears, salamanders and carp spread throughout the north, others like the pronghorns and axolotls remained in the region of their origin, whilst others like the camels and parrots spread from one region to the other and then died out in the region they had come from. Present day distribution depends not only on factors operating today but also on these same factors operating in the past when both the animals of the world and the continental connexions of the world were different.

# 8

# Southern Regions

## *Intermigration*

The Cenozoic evolution, spread and contraction of modern vertebrate families in the north had its effect on the fauna of the southern continents. Assuming that most land vertebrates only rarely cross sea to establish themselves in new places, the newly evolving northern families could only migrate into the southern continents at times when these had land connexions with the north. This led to differences in colonization of the southern continents, for they did not all have northerly connexions at the same time. Furthermore, differences were caused by differences between Palearctic and Nearctic. At times when regional differences between these two were marked, different faunas would be available for southwards migration from them. Thus South America could only receive animals that were already in the Nearctic, Africa only those that were in the Palearctic. Connexion with the north only, but at different times accounts for most of the distributional characteristics of the southern continental faunas.

In contrast to the general theory that land vertebrates require land by which to travel from one continent to another, some animals seem able to migrate along a chain of islands if the sea between them is not too wide. This applies in particular to reptiles, birds, bats, rats and some of the small arboreal mammals. Several instances of this type of colonization are suspected.

Although it is assumed that the majority of mammal families originated in the north, this is known not to be true of all. Several have originated in South America and others in Africa and Australia. Sometimes the southern families spread successfully into the north, when given the opportunity, more often they remained in their southern homes, or became extinct when new northern forms arrived.

## *Neotropical*

At the end of the Mesozoic and for a short period of the paleocene, South America was joined to North America by a thin neck of land in much the same place as the one that joins them today. At this time there were marsupials in the northern hemisphere and a few early placentals. Some of these mammals migrated into the southern continents probably with some of the birds, reptiles, amphibia (pipid toads perhaps) and fish (characins for example) typical of the time. Lungfish, side-neck turtles and crocodiles were already there by the cretaceous.

Shortly after this early invasion, some time in the paleocene, South America was cut off from the north by the submergence of the narrow connecting corridor. South America could no longer receive migrants from the north. Those it had already received evolved in isolation to fill the available habitats.

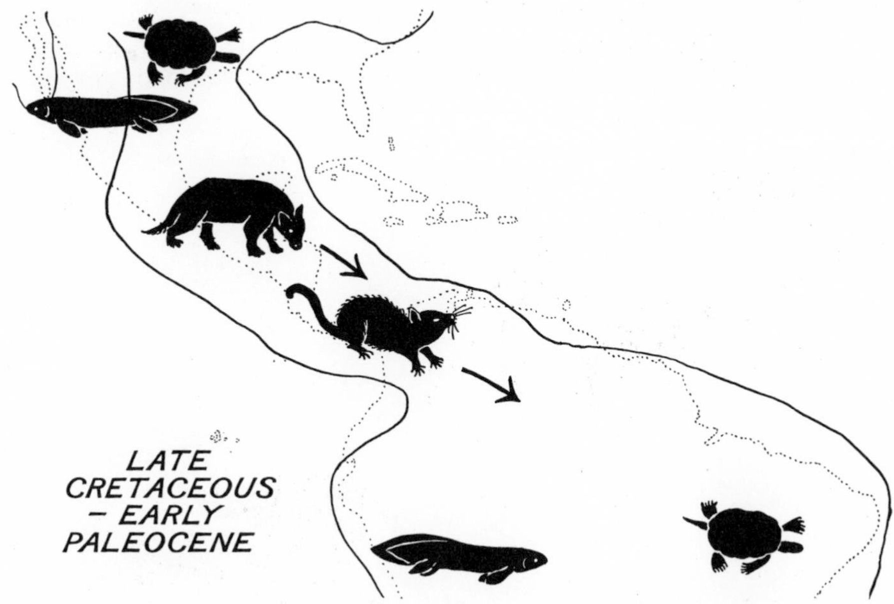


These earliest of South American mammals were representatives of only three groups from the north, the widespread marsupials and condylarths and the Nearctic paleanodonts. Once isolated in the Neotropical region, the marsupials diverged widely, not only into the tree-living and mouse-like forms of the modern region, but also into a large group of carnivorous animals, ranging in size from that of an opossum to that of a bear. One of the later of these marsupial carnivores was like a sabre-tooth tiger. Marsupials in fact were occupying many of the carnivore places in the fauna in ways parallel to their placental counterparts which were absent from the Neotropical at this time. The condylarths and paleanodonts were the only placentals present in the Neotropical at this time and neither group was carnivorous; the paleanodonts were insectivorous and the condylarths herbivorous. The paleanodonts evolved subsequently into some of the most typical of present-day Neotropical animals, armadillos, sloths and anteaters. But they too were more diverse in some epochs than they are today. For instance in the pleistocene there were giant ground sloths, giant armadillos and glyptodons. The condylarths also differentiated widely, but unlike the other two early immigrant groups, they have left no modern descendants. Some became strikingly similar to other lines of mammals. There were amongst them a 'horse' and good imitations of a rhinoceros and a hippopotamus, as well as many rat-like forms. This extensive group of early placental herbivores only reached this degree of diversity in South America. South America was isolated from the north just at the right time for these forms to diversify widely. Isolation kept out the placental carnivores who would have eaten them, and the northern herbivores who might have ousted them.

It was a little later in time, after these first mammalian groups had become established, that the ancestors of the South American monkeys and rodents arrived. It is possible that they joined the ancient immigrants in the oligocene, and may, therefore, have arrived by island-hopping across the sea channel. Being small and arboreal they would have been more suited to this type of

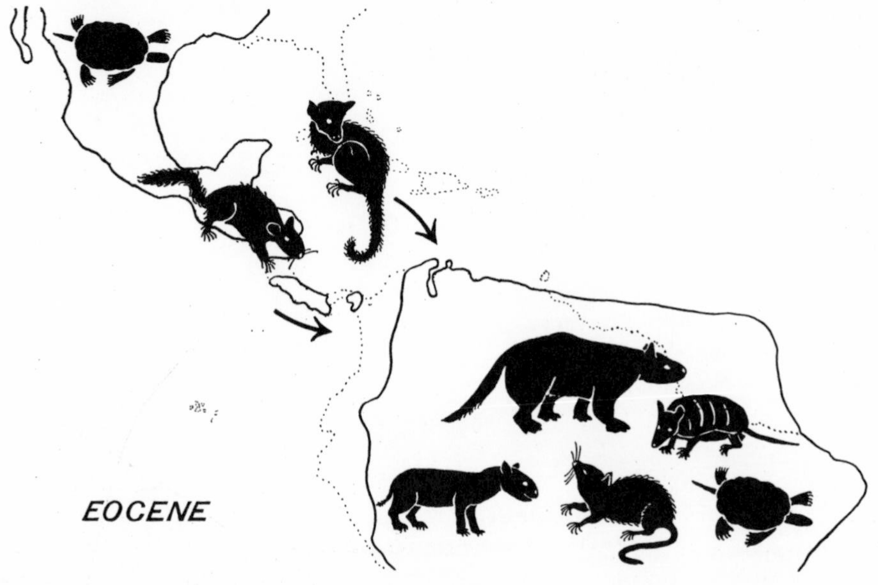


spread than other northern animals of the time. But whatever the date of their first arrival, and by whatever means they effected it, by late Cenozoic days they too had evolved into many different types.

The Neotropical fauna of mid-Cenozoic days was therefore composed of recently arrived placental rodents and arboreal primates, ancient paleanodont insectivores, large herbivores of ancient condylarth stock and a multitude of carnivorous, arboreal and rodent marsupials. Already, therefore before the pliocene, the Neotropical had many of its modern faunistic features, families of marsupials, edentates, monkeys and rodents.

Towards the end of the pliocene the Americas were once more joined by dry land and remained connected until the cutting of the Panama canal in recent times. At first the connexion was probably no more than closely lying islands and the invasion by modern placentals from the north was slow. The raccoons may have been the first to make the journey south. But as the land connexion became continuous there was a speeding up of the southerly flow. Once again, only those animals that had already established themselves in the Nearctic were available for this southerly dispersal. Thus, although many modern carnivores went south at this time, there were no hyenas amongst them because hyenas had not spread over from the Palearctic, and there are therefore no hyenas in the Neotropical today. Cats and bears spread south and because they were more successful than their marsupial counterparts, gradually supplanted them. Gradually, too, the special South American herbivores disappeared, falling prey to these new carnivores. With their disappearance, there was an empty place for the new northern herbivores to fill. Peccaries, deer, camelids and horses were available in the Nearctic for this take over, but there were no rhinoceroses for they had already gone from the Nearctic. No giraffes were available because they had never lived in the

New World, and neither bovids nor elephants had yet spread across from the Palearctic to the Nearctic. At the end of the pliocene therefore the Neotropical had acquired a further batch of characteristic animals, amongst them camels and peccaries.

By the pleistocene, otters, dogs, weasels and sabre-tooths as well as many of the smaller mammals had come to join the first invaders, and tinamus were already established. Even as late as this, another characteristic Neotropical animal had arrived, the tapir. But neither beavers, bovids, nor elephants spread south from the Nearctic although mastodons had by this time reached northern South America. The pleistocene fauna was soon complete and has persisted to the present day with only one or two exceptions. At the end of the pleistocene, horses, sabre-tooths, giant edentates, mastodons and the last survivors of the marsupial carnivores and of the South American herbivores died out. The elimination of the marsupials in the pliocene and the camels and tapirs in the pleistocene from the northerly end of their ranges, left colonies of these animals isolated in the Neotropical.

Although most of the migratory movements had been southwards during the Cenozoic, a few animals made their way north during the pliocene and pleistocene when there was a corridor of dry land to use. Of these, giant

armadillos, glyptodons and giant ground sloths had only a short evolutionary life in North America, but the later arrivals in the north, the opossum and the nine-banded armadillo, colonized the Nearctic successfully and survived. So, too, humming birds and tanagers went north from their Neotropical home, but the majority of the Neotropical animals which had evolved during the period of Cenozoic isolation, stayed where they were.

Thus the modern fauna of the Neotropical region can be accounted for by its early isolation when it contained only a few mammals, represented today by marsupials and edentates; the diversification of this fauna, together with rodent and primate immigrants, during the Cenozoic; and the acquisition of a number of modern mammals from the Nearctic during the pliocene, some of which subsequently became extinct at their northern source.

### *Ethiopian*

Fossils of cretaceous and early Cenozoic strata of Africa are rare, and for this reason it has proved difficult to reconstruct the story of the Ethiopian region. Much has depended on guesswork and deductions from what is known of the present-day distribution of families that inhabit Africa. What follows is one possible scheme of the sequence of events which led to the establishment of the modern zoogeographical region. Much may need to be changed when further fossil evidence becomes available.

Cretaceous Africa resembled cretaceous South America and the northern hemisphere in many ways. There were lungfish, crocodiles and side-neck turtles and probably also pipid toads. But beyond this the fossil record reveals little. Some early placental mammals may have been living in the Ethiopian region at this time; insectivores and condylarths were likely inhabitants.

At the end of the cretaceous, Africa probably lost land connexion with the north and became an isolated continent surrounded by sea. The basic fauna could evolve in isolation just as it would do a little later in the Neotropical, but the basic Ethiopian mammal fauna differed from that of the Neotropical. Ethiopian insectivores and condylarths contrasted with Neotropical marsupials, paleanodonts and condylarths.

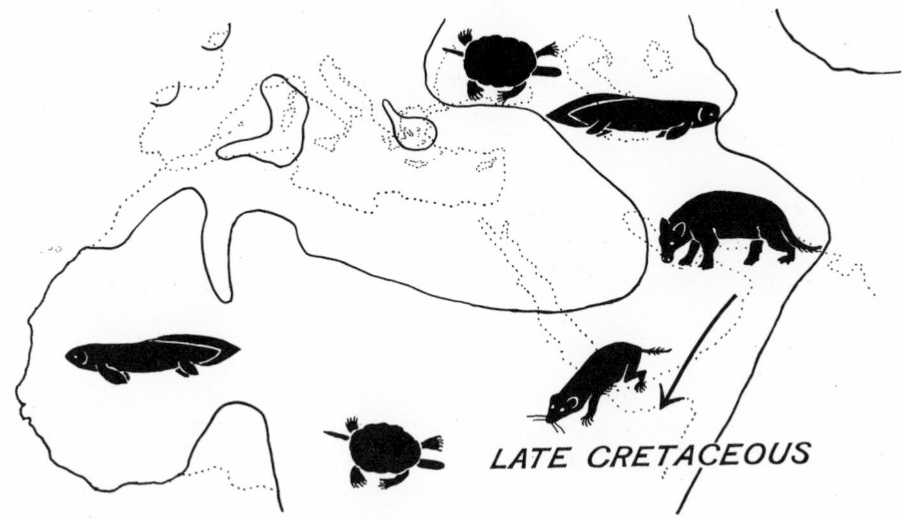


During the period of isolation, which lasted at most until the late oligocene, lemur-like members of the primate stock may have crossed the sea from the Palearctic. Lemurs being small and arboreal and the distance short, this is not improbable. It has already been suggested as an explanation for the arrival of primates in South America. It will later be put forward as a reason for the presence of lemurs in Madagascar.

During the early epochs of the Cenozoic, then, there were insectivores, condylarths and primates in Africa. The sequence of insectivore evolution is unknown, but at some time the modern African families must have diversified. The golden moles, the elephant shrews and the otter shrews may have originated in the continent in which they are found today. By the oligocene the condylarths had differentiated into several sorts of large herbivore as they had been doing in South America at the same time. But the results were different. Amongst the Ethiopian herbivore stock there were already elephant and mastodon ancestors, and a relatively huge animal, *Arsinoitherium*, with paired horns on the end of its nose. Old World monkeys were becoming distinct, differentiating from their lemur-like ancestors. Thus it seems that they preceded in time the monkeys of the Neotropical, although they may both have been derived from similar northern ancestors.

By the end of the oligocene Africa had gained a connexion with the Eurasian continent by way of a tract of forested land through what is now Arabia. There may have been an additional connexion further west. Late

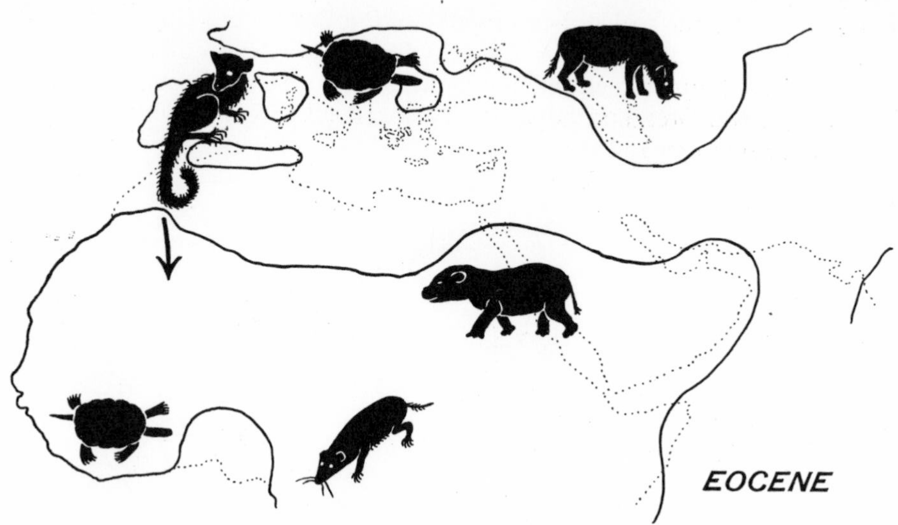


oligocene and miocene placentals from the Palearctic could invade Africa. Modern carnivores and rodents poured south. Cricetid mice, cats and dogs and the aardvarks occupied Africa at this time. Later on, towards the end of the miocene and through the pliocene, the corridor between Africa and Asia lost its forests and became dry. Whilst the corridor was changing in this way there was an influx of antelopes and many other animals that are typical of the plains of modern Africa. Palearctic giraffes, rhinoceroses, hyenas and murid mice made their way to Africa. Bears did not evolve in time to get into Africa before the corridor became too dry for them, but it is not easy to see why the deer failed to make the journey. Presumably they had a too northerly range during the crucial period before the land between Africa and Asia became unpleasantly arid.

Whilst the southerly invasion was going on, some of Africa's own products spread northwards. Mastodons and elephants left Africa and spread first into the Palearctic and then made their way into the Nearctic and Oriental regions. Much later, in the pleistocene, man-like apes may have gone north from Africa and spread round the world. In spite of their African origin, modern elephants had to recolonize Africa from the north. The early African forms died out. And the same story may apply to modern man.

Many of the original inhabitants of Africa must have found it hard to survive when the new mammals came down from the north after the mid-Cenozoic corridor had been made, and it is probable that many were considerably reduced in number. Some of the insectivores and primates may have suffered this fate.

As the Asia-African corridor became more arid it formed an effective barrier for almost all further exchange of fauna. By the pleistocene, Africa was isolated again from the rest of the world and her fauna evolved into the typically African forms of today.

The Ethiopian fauna can be accounted for then by colonization from the Palearctic during the cretaceous and the late oligocene to pliocene, with differentiation of the native fauna during the periods of isolation. The fauna is composed of insectivores, the results of Cenozoic isolation, and of a large number of northern families of which some are widespread but others remnants of families that were left in the south when the ice sheets descended. It is in these southern remnants that the Ethiopian resembles so markedly the Oriental region; the rhinoceroses, monkeys and elephants for example. Although these families have today an identical distribution, restricted to the Old World tropical regions, their distribution histories varied. Elephants, sprung from African stock, went north to the Palearctic and Nearctic and then south again to the Ethiopian and Oriental. Their extinction in the north in the pleistocene left them with their Ethiopian and Oriental colonies. Surprisingly their southern migration never took them to the Neotropical.

Monkeys, following the same route, never even got to the Nearctic. Their extinction in the Palearctic left them too with only Ethiopian and Oriental populations. Rhinoceroses were originally northern animals, but as they spread south in the Old World, their range contracted away from the Nearctic, and subsequent Palearctic extinction led to the same result once more.

There are similarities between the Ethiopian region and the Neotropical, both in climate and some of the verterbrate fauna, but the major part of their faunas is different. Many of the differences can be accounted for by the fact that in the cretaceous the two regions had received different components of the northern fauna, by the fact that they later regained connexions with the north in different epochs, and by the fact that when they did regain these connexions the connexions were with different northern regions both of which had already taken on some of their modern characteristics.

The fauna of the Ethiopian region differs from that of its Palearctic neighbour both in climate and because it was not in continuous connexion with it through the Cenozoic.

## Oriental

The Oriental region has a less complex history than most of the other regions. Once it had become part of the Asiatic mainland towards the end of Mesozoic times when the Tethys Sea dwindled away, it shared its fauna with the north.

Well on into Cenozoic days there was no differentiation of an Oriental fauna. Unfortunately the story of the Oriental region suffers like that of the Ethiopian from lack of fossils during the early epochs of the Cenozoic. Although it can perhaps be presumed that there were a number of frog and toad families, side-neck turtles, crocodiles, marsupials and insectivores in the Oriental cretaceous, as there were in the Palearctic at the time, there is no confirmation of this in the rocks. As a knowledge of the range of these families during the cretaceous is crucial for an interpretation of the colonization of Australia this is doubly unfortunate.

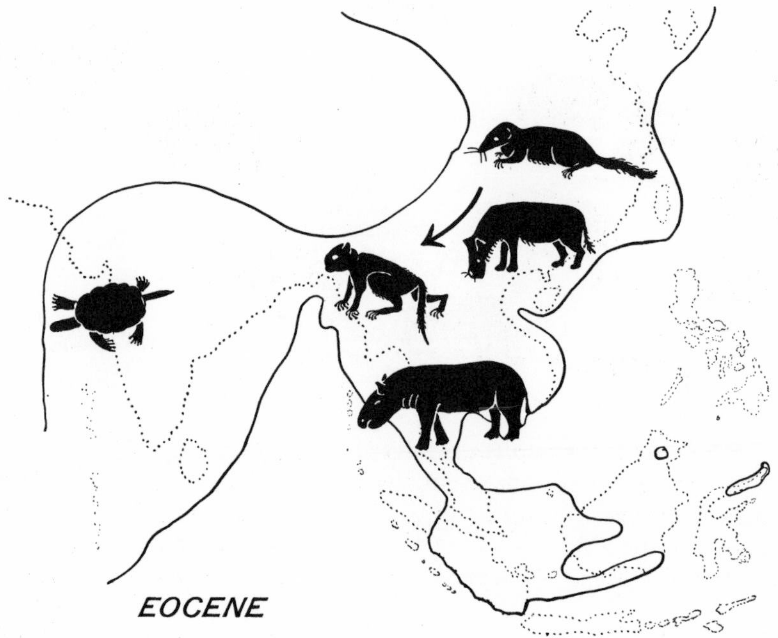


Assuming that the Oriental did indeed share its fauna with the north until the end of the oligocene, it would have had primates, lagomorphs, rodents, tapirs, rhinoceroses, deer and pigs. Of the northern rodents the beavers, however, never spread south as far as the Oriental region.

Ancestors of the Oriental tarsier lived in the eocene north, and a little later, oligocene, a primitive tree shrew inhabited the Palearctic. This is all that is known of two of the most characteristic modern Oriental families. They must have spread to the Orient at some time during the first part of the Cenozoic, eventually dying out in the north. Spread from the north, followed by extinction in the north is the explanation of most of the Oriental fauna.

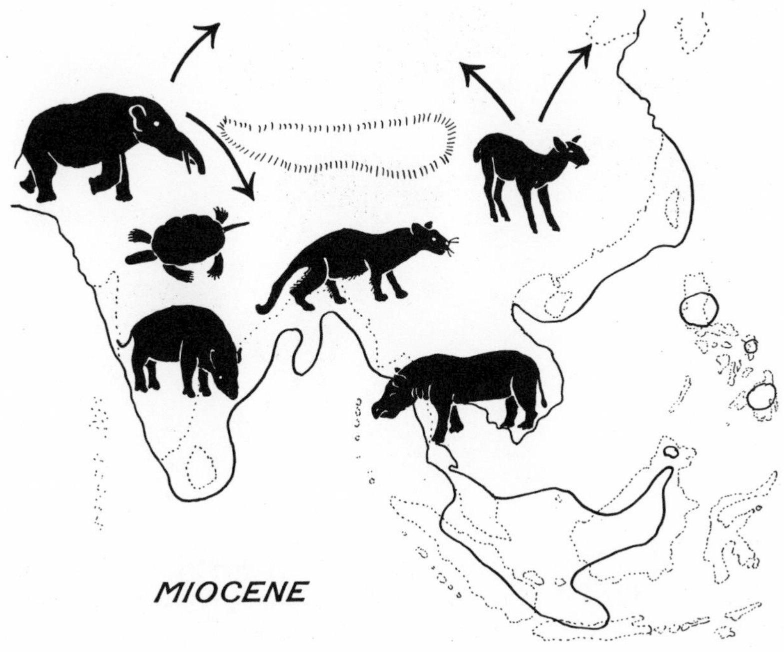


In miocene days great earth movements had initiated a period of mountain building which was to last well on into the pliocene. During this upheaval the Himalayas were built up. At first they lay as a comparatively small range between the Palearctic and the Oriental. At this time they cannot have hindered the free interchange of animals between the north and south. Elephants which had only recently spread north from Africa found their way to the Oriental in the miocene, and it is possible that the Old World monkeys followed the same course. Gavial crocodiles which had been inhabitants of the Palearctic spread southwards to both Africa and India, but for unknown reasons they did not maintain themselves in Africa. Giraffes too spread from the north into both of the Old World southern regions, but they did not survive in the Oriental.

By the end of the pliocene two events had occurred, which were the most significant of all for the modern Oriental fauna. The building of the Himalayas was complete, providing a barrier between Palearctic and Oriental, and the climate of the north was cooling.

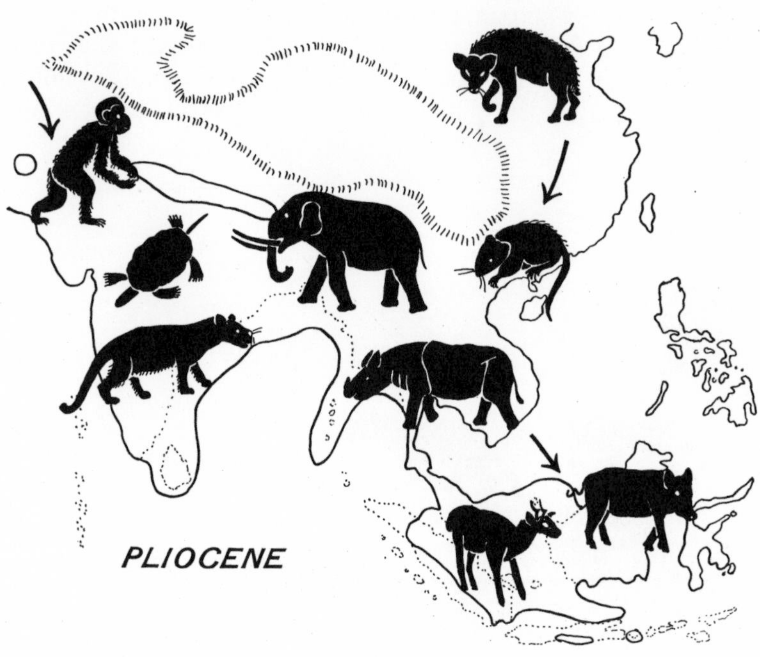


As a result of these two physical changes, the Oriental fauna was isolated and could differentiate from the Palearctic, and many of the families formerly with an extensive range became extinct in the north. Thus the Oriental, like the Neotropical and Ethiopian, came to contain the surviving tropical elements of once widely distributed animals. The disappearance from the north of the tapir family left colonies in the Oriental and Neotropical, but in most other respects the Oriental retained mainly Old World elements and in this resembled the Ethiopian, with rhinoceroses, monkeys and elephants for instance. This extinction of families in the pleistocene north and their continued existence in the south of their range provides the main cause for the difference between Palearctic and Oriental regions, whilst at the same time providing the reason for the similarities between Ethiopian and Oriental. Oriental and Ethiopian represent the tropical fauna of the Old World.

### *Australian*

Australia differs from the other southern continents in having had no connexion with the north during the whole of the Cenozoic. As no early Cenozoic fossils are known from Australia it is difficult to tell when she acquired the ancestors of her modern fauna. Guesswork suggests that most of the land vertebrates were occasional immigrants at various times through the

Cenozoic from the Asiatic mainland along the islands of the Malay Archipelago.

Already by the cretaceous there were lungfish and crocodiles in the Australian region and probably also liopelmid and other frogs including hylids; but, curiously, no early remains have been found of the side-neck turtles in Australia, although they were otherwise widespread at the beginning of the Cenozoic. Ancestors of the egg-laying mammals may have been in Australia by the cretaceous although there is no evidence of this. Their remote ancestors are known from Palearctic triassic and jurassic days.

It is not known, either, when the marsupials arrived in Australia, but it is thought to have been in early Cenozoic or cretaceous days. How they got to Australia and why they, rather than their placental contemporaries, achieved this distinction is equally unknown. Earlier theories assumed both that

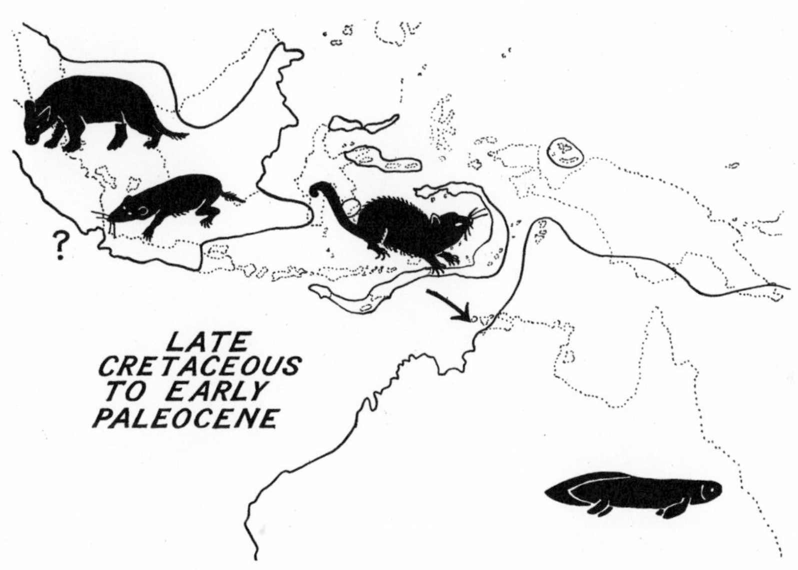


marsupials preceded placentals in time and that Australia had a land connexion with Asia in the early Cenozoic. Thus marsupials colonized Australia before the evolution of placentals. The land connexion with Asia broke down and the marsupials were isolated from later influxes of placentals. It is unlikely that this can be true. There is no evidence that marsupials were in existence before placentals and there is no evidence that Australia has had any land connexion with Asia since before the cretaceous.

How can the mammal fauna of Australia be explained? It could be supposed that although marsupials did not precede placentals, they increased in numbers and range at an earlier date. They might then have spread through southern Asia and along the island chain to Australia before the placentals had spread so far south. Once the marsupials were established in Australia it must be supposed that the stretches of sea between the islands increased in width and prevented the spread of the placentals along the islands. There is some evidence that this latter supposition is true but there is no evidence to support the first part of the proposition, that marsupials were more widespread than placentals. Neither marsupial nor insectivore fossils are known from the Oriental at this time.

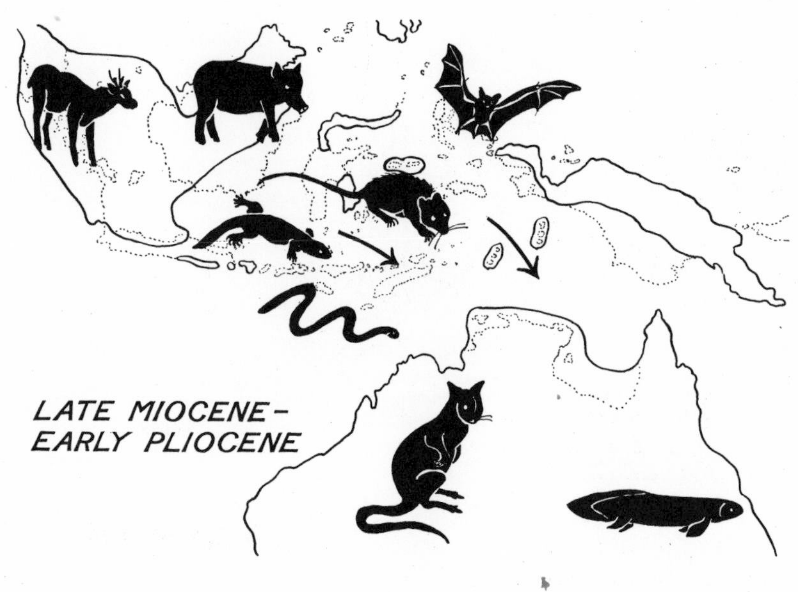


Simpson (1940) has suggested an alternative. He has supposed that there were both marsupials and insectivores in southern Asia in the cretaceous and that a string of islands lay between the Oriental mainland and Australia. He further supposes that because the marsupials were arboreal animals they would be more likely to make the journeys from island to island than the ground-living insectivores. Later the journeys became more difficult, and there is geological evidence to support this, so placental migrants arrived only on the rarest occasions. Established marsupials would have been able to prevent successful colonization by rare placental visitors.

However they got there or wherever they came from, the marsupials found the Australian region a suitable home. They were able to evolve into all sorts of different forms and parallel many of the placental types which occur in other parts of the world. Thus, today, Australia has marsupial carnivores, herbivores, rodents, insectivores and flying arboreal mammals.

The Australian region is not entirely free of native land placentals. There are murid rats and there are bats. The Australian murids probably arrived from Asia in the miocene. Pigs and dingo dogs were later arrivals.

Although a few placental mammals got into Australia, no marsupials spread back to Asia. The only westerly spread has been into a few islands of the Malay Archipelago as far as Celebes.

It is likely that most of the other native land vertebrates of Australia were also casual migrants. The occasional frogs, though rare, replaced the earliest liopelmids. An occasional turtle, agamid lizard and snake travelled from Asia from time to time. Birds arrived at different times, mainly from Asia.

The Cenozoic history of Australia differs greatly from that of other southern regions. Unlike any other region it has been isolated for the whole period. Australia and the Oriental regions are at opposite extremes: the one always isolated through the Cenozoic, the other not isolated until the end of the pliocene. In between are the Neotropical and Ethiopian regions with a comparatively long period of Cenozoic isolation and with northern connexions both before and after this isolation.

This interpretation of the arrival of the modern faunas of the six zoogeographical regions of the world is in accordance with the theory of the permanence of the continents, a theory that permits the making and breaking of only narrow necks of land between the six continents, in places where the sea is shallow today or where land connexions still exist. This theory has been shown to account satisfactorily for most of the Cenozoic patterns of distribution of land mammals, but some problems remain unexplained and little has been said of other land vertebrates.

# 9

# Land Bridges

## *Gondwanaland*

Although the theory of the permanence of the continents has provided a satisfactory basis for the interpretation of most Cenozoic distribution, there are other ways of explaining it. There are other ways of accounting in particular for the presence of marsupials in Australia and the New World and for the presence of lemur-like animals (true lemurs and lorises) in the Ethiopian region, Madagascar and the Oriental region, and for the even more difficult distributional irregularities shown by earlier vertebrates, fish, amphibia and reptiles.

The other ways are provided by the theories of land bridges and continental drift.

Ever since the early part of the last century, difficult problems of animal distribution have been explained by an appeal to land bridges. These land bridges are not the same as those narrow connexions of land demanded by the theory of the permanence of the continents and restricted to regions where the

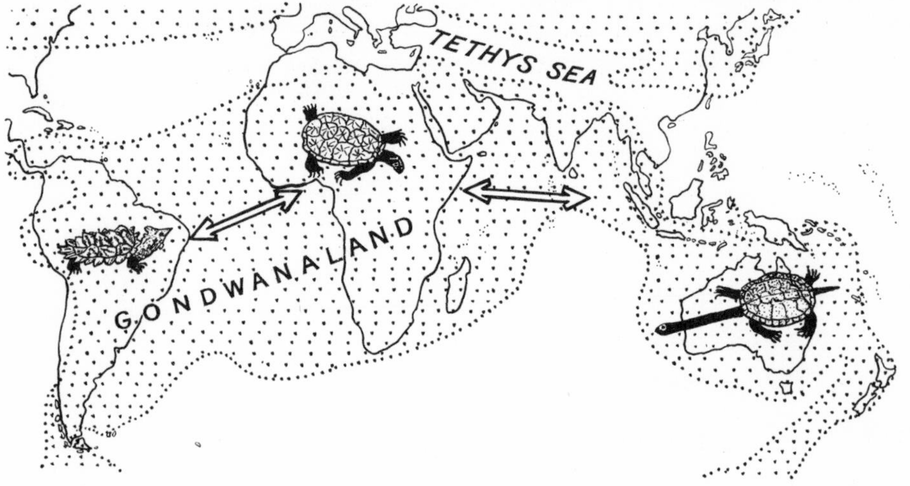


sea is shallow. The theory of land bridges demands bridges of continental size, stretching across what are now deep oceans, serving as a means of communication from one present-day continent to another. Some time during the Cenozoic, when they had served their purpose, these land bridges were supposed to have subsided beneath the oceans leaving no trace of their former existence.

For a long time it was thought that at the beginning of the Cenozoic and earlier, the land of the world was divided into two halves, a northern land mass taking in all of Eurasia, Greenland and North America, and a southern land mass, called Gondwanaland which included the three southern continents, New Zealand and Antarctica. The two land masses were separated by an extensive Tethys Sea. The continuity of the southern land was thought to account for the distribution of lungfish, side-neck turtles, flightless birds and even marsupials, all those animals in fact which are similar in the three southern continents today but which are not widespread through the rest of the world. However, the southern regions do not resemble one another enough to substantiate this theory. The Neotropical and Ethiopian regions are more like one another than either is like the Australian region. Modifications were made, therefore, in the continental bridge theory. Gondwanaland was abandoned, at any rate as an explanation of post-cretaceous distribution, and individual connexions were postulated. South America and Africa were joined by a huge South Atlantic land bridge leaving the other southern continents free, or alternatively, Africa, Madagascar and India were joined into the continent of Lemuria. South America and Australia were joined through a habitable continent of Antarctica. There were many other land bridges to account for local difficulties of animal and plant distribution, but these were the largest and the most widely used.

### *South Atlantic Bridge*

The South Atlantic continent at its greatest was supposed to have included besides Africa and South America, the South Atlantic islands of St. Helena, Tristan da Cunha and Ascension. Across this continent were supposed to have spread the lungfish, characin fish, pipid toads, side-neck turtles, ostriches, porcupines and monkeys; all those animals that Africa and South America have in common today but which are absent from most of the other regions. However, the monkeys and porcupines of the Old World and the New World are no longer thought to be closely related to one another, and it is likely that this is also true of the ostrich-like birds. Although not closely related, they are thought to have evolved to look like one another because they live under the same sort of conditions, just as many marsupials look like their placental counterparts. But even if they are related closely, belonging to the same families, to account for the distribution of mammals and birds by the South Atlantic land bridge would mean keeping the bridge until oligocene days (when monkeys and porcupines first appear in the rocks). By this time edentates and South American ungulates were well established and yet they do not seem ever to have been in Africa. A late land bridge across the South Atlantic raises as many awkward questions as it solves and must almost certainly be rejected. It is still possible however that a much narrower connexion in late Mesozoic days might have been responsible for the spread between the two continents of the turtles, toads and freshwater fish which they have in common. But fossils of side-neck turtles, lungfish and characin fish are known from cretaceous strata of the north and they could therefore have reached the southern continents by a southerly spread, making a direct east-west connexion between Africa and South America unnecessary. Moreover, the other land vertebrates of the late Mesozoic, the amphibia and reptiles, of Africa and South America are not more like one another than they are like those of North America of the same period. Striking similarities between the fossils of Africa and South America are not found until as far back as triassic and permian days and at this point in geological time it becomes difficult to deduce anything about the extent of the continents because of the rarity of fossils.

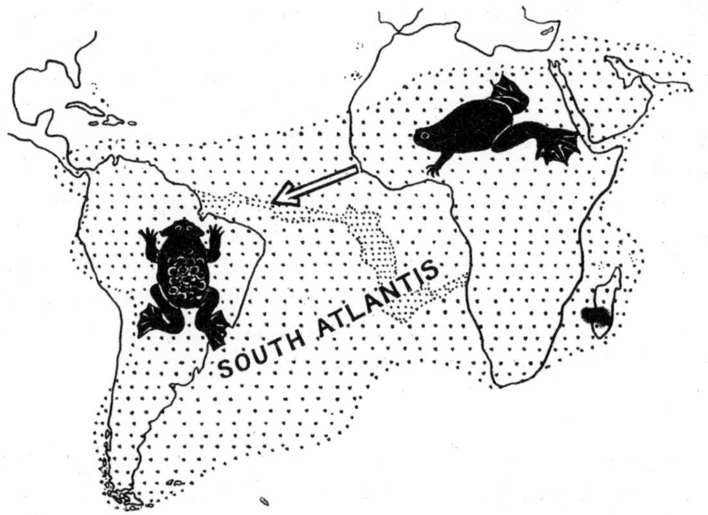


The zoological evidence then, suggests that the continental land bridge of the South Atlantic was unlikely to have existed later than Mesozoic days and that it is not essential for explaining any of the faunistic similarities between present-day Africa and South America. But the final decision for or against such a bridge should be based on geological evidence. Was there land in the South Atlantic or was it always ocean?

The ancient rocks of eastern South America and west Africa show resemblances to one another, though not more than they do to similar rocks in other parts of the world. Further, the South Atlantic is an unstable area, likely to throw up ridges and islands as a result of volcanic activity, which might seem to support a bridge theory, though it does not even suggest the position or the extent of such a bridge. In contrast, some geologists claim that there is evidence that the floor of the Atlantic has been an ocean floor since jurassic days. This would put the latest possible date for an extensive bridge back to the jurassic. This is as far as geological evidence goes. It does not provide a decisive answer. The decision after all has to be made on biological evidence and biology has an alternative explanation of northerly origin and southerly spread along narrow connexions to the permanent continents of

Africa and South America, which is at least as good, and some think better, than an Atlantic bridge. It does not preclude a narrow jurassic bridge nor other bridges in earlier epochs between Africa and South America. Judgment on these must be reserved for further evidence to become available, but the evidence already available makes a Cenozoic bridge of continental dimensions unlikely.

### *Lemuria*

The second big land bridge was the supposed continent of Lemuria. This was said to lie between Africa, the island of Madagascar and India. It was called Lemuria because it was invented in the first place to explain the curious distribution of 'lemurs'. The 'lemurs' were imagined as originating on Lemuria at the end of the Mesozoic and spreading to Africa and the Oriental region, where they are represented today by the lorises. The original lemurs were left on Madagascar when the rest of Lemuria sank below the seas sometime in the Cenozoic.

The reclassification of the primates in recent years has made this interpretation untenable. It is now supposed that although both lorises and lemurs derived from the early primate stock, which was widespread in the north in paleocene and eocene days, they are not otherwise very closely related to one another. Thus it is supposed that the ancestors of the modern lemurs, whose fossils are known in the north, spread south to Madagascar early in the Cenozoic. Only very much later did a second wave of similar primates spread

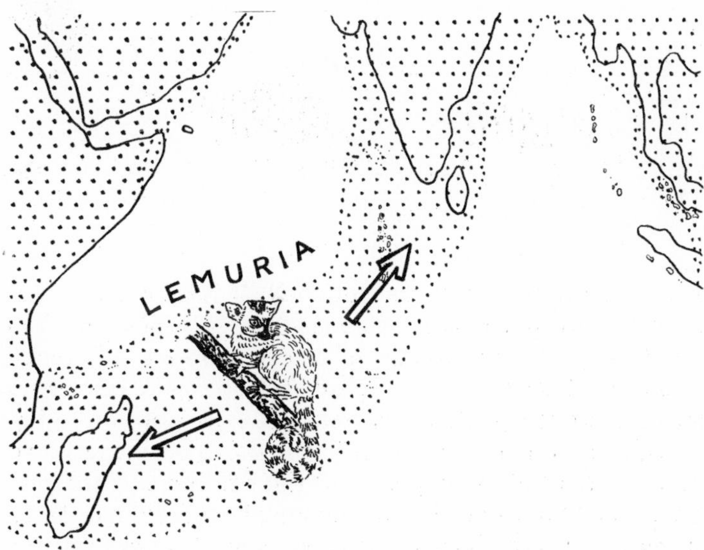


south as lorises to colonize the Ethiopian and Oriental regions becoming extinct in the north in much the same way as the rhinoceroses and monkeys. This would explain the close relationship between African and Asiatic lorises and their remote relationship with Madagascar lemurs much better than could a continent of Lemuria. Lemuria only complicates the zoogeographical problem as far as 'lemurs' are concerned for it implies that the most distantly related should be the two loris families, at opposite ends of the Lemurian continent. This is obviously unsatisfactory.

Other affinities that Madagascar has with the Oriental region can also be accounted for without Lemuria, and there is no conclusive geological evidence to decide the issue for or against the theory. Such as it is, the geological evidence suggests that Madagascar has been isolated from all continents during the whole of the Cenozoic and continental Lemuria should be rejected.

### *Antarctica*

The third of the big land bridges was supposed to have passed from South America through the Antarctic to Australia. It was supposed to account for the presence in South America and Australia of marsupials, hylid tree frogs,

flightless birds, side-neck turtles and lungfish. It is now almost certain that the flightless birds are not closely related to one another and are classified in separate orders, so their problems of distribution are different and need not be discussed in this context. Lungfish and side-neck turtles were widespread in the cretaceous and their discontinuous distribution today is therefore better accounted for by extinction in the north of formerly world-wide groups. There remain the marsupials and the amphibia of the two regions.

Neither marsupial fossils nor living marsupials or hylid tree frogs occur in the Oriental region, although marsupial fossils are known from many other parts of the world. How did marsupials and hylid frogs get into Australia? Is it bad luck that there are no fossils of these groups in the Oriental region, or did they get to Australia direct from South America? But the marsupials were contemporaneous with edentates and South American herbivores and yet there is no evidence for the occurrence of either of these orders in

Australia. They may simply not have spread, but even so the mammal populations of the two regions have more differences than similarities, a result which would hardly be expected if the regions had been connected by a bridge in the early Cenozoic. The same argument applies to the birds, reptiles, amphibia and fish. The likenesses are rare, side-necks and fish which are not even in the same family in the two regions, and hylids which are; the differences are frequent, Asiatic agamid lizards in Australia, iguanids in America, the only teleost freshwater fish family of Australia confined to the Old World. An Antarctic land bridge, like the other continental bridges, raises as many problems as it solves if applied to the distribution of Cenozoic and late Mesozoic animals only. It is possible, however, that the Antarctic was once less cold than it is today, and might have supplied at least stepping-stones from South America to Australia for some early animals, perhaps for invertebrates which show considerable resemblances between the two continents. Fossil beech leaves have been found in the Antarctic, but so far no animal fossils. Further paleontological work may throw light on the problem, but once again crucial evidence must come from non-biological sources, and once again it is not yet available.

Failing definite geological evidence one way or another the question of land bridges has to be decided on biological evidence, and yet it was for biological reasons that the bridges were first invented. This makes the decision difficult, but it is probably fair to conclude that as far as late Mesozoic and Cenozoic animals are concerned, the continental land bridge theory is unnecessary. What happened before this is an open question.

Cenozoic land bridges of continental size are not fashionable today, but in the nineteenth century they were considered essential to explain every small difficulty of animal and plant distribution. A bridge was invented to connect Portugal with Ireland, another from South America to the Galapagos Islands, and others from the continents to every island in the world. Today only those narrow corridors of land for which there is geological evidence, or which do not stretch the imagination too far, such as the Panama isthmus, Arabia and the Bering Straits bridge, and on a smaller scale the channel bridge between England and France, are generally believed in. The Cenozoic distribution of animals is usually explained today without vast continental land bridges.

# 10

# Continental Drift

At the beginning of this century Wegener (see du Toit 1937) put forward the theory of continental drift to account for the stranger facts of animal distribution. It did not require new land areas from under the sea like the land bridge theory. The total land mass remained the same as today, but the continents themselves changed their positions.

Wegener believed that the continents were made up of a comparatively light material, called sial because silica and aluminium formed a large proportion of it, and that the floors of the oceans were made up of the much

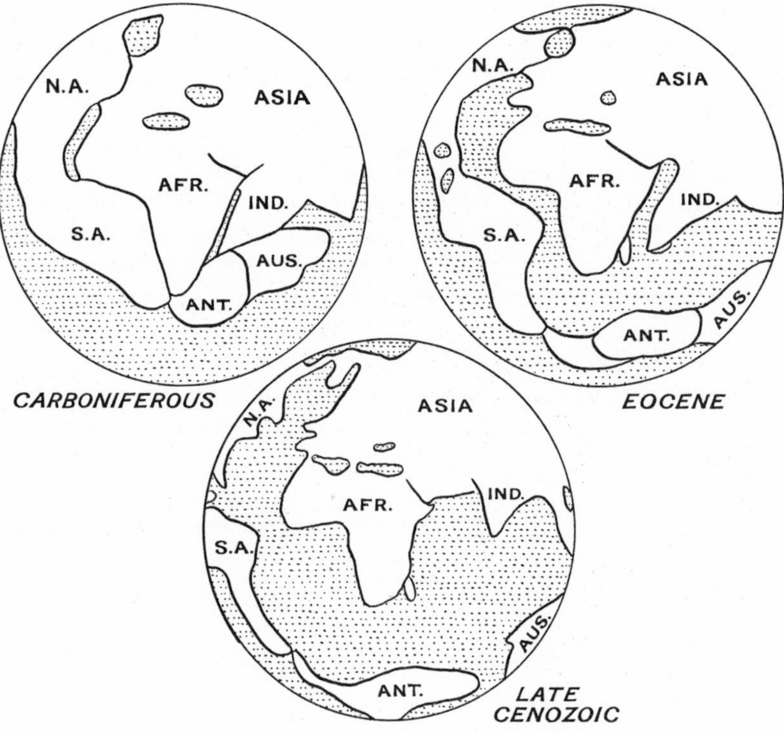


heavier sima, silica and magnesium. He believed that the light continents would float on the lower and heavier earth crust like icebergs. With this hypothesis in mind, and from a close study of the map of the world, he decided that it was possible that all the continents had once been joined together in one block and had then drifted apart to their present positions. This block of land would have existed in the carboniferous, but soon after would have started to break up and the continents would have floated away from one another. By the eocene the Atlantic Ocean was forming, and South America was losing touch with Africa. Australia and South America were still joined through the Antarctic, and not until comparatively recent times did Australia take up her present position. This was the theory of continental drift, and it had been put forward mainly to account for the biological similarities of the southern continents.

Wegener supposed that in the early days when all the continents were joined together they would have shared the same fauna and this was taken to account for the presence of flightless birds, side-neck turtles and lungfish in all three southern continents. A little later, once Australia and the Antarctic had become separated from the African part of the block, except by the long way round of South America, the fauna of the southern continents would have become differentiated into two main components. Australia and South America would share one of these, marsupials and hylid tree frogs being included, and South America and Africa would share the other, ostriches, pipid toads and characin fish for instance.

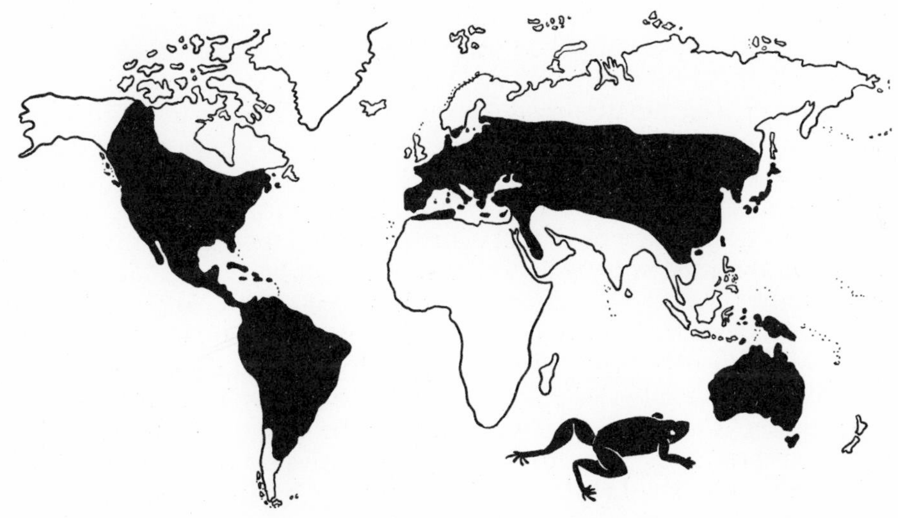

It is an attractive idea. South America and Africa would fit together very neatly, and there is no reason to reject the Antarctic connexion out of hand. But evidence for the drift theory is conflicting. The Atlantic and Indian Oceans may date from jurassic days at least, and this would make the drift theory necessarily a much earlier happening than Wegener estimated. Doubts have been cast on the sial-sima theory, since parts of the floors of the ocean are now known to be sial like the continents. On the other hand recent work on rock magnetism has brought up the whole problem of continental drift in a new light and further information must be awaited (see Irving and Green 1957).

If this modern work proves the drift theory to be correct, continental drift might be the answer to some of the difficult problems of discontinuous distribution. It might account for the distribution of some of the frogs and fish. But in its turn it will raise a host of new problems. Why if the continents were so close together at the end of the Mesozoic do the southern lands not show more similarities than they do? Although some of the South American fish, frogs, reptiles and birds are very much the same as the African ones, most of them are remarkably different. There are no mormyrid fish, polypedatid tree frogs, chameleons or agamid lizards in South America. There are no hylid tree frogs, electric eels or iguanid lizards in Africa. So, too, although Australia resembles South America in some ways, there are also some oustanding differences. Australia has no edentates or condylarth descendants, and yet their ancestors might have been expected to migrate as the marsupials are supposed to have done on the drift hypothesis, from South America to Australia in the paleocene. Australia has no South American lizards, but instead agamids and varanids which are typically Asiatic. The Australian vertebrate fauna is hardly consistent with a continental connexion of any kind. It is typical of a fauna acquired by chance island-hopping. An explanation of these problems will have to be found if Wegener's drift theory proves correct. It is likely that even if the continents were in a close compact mass and drifted apart, this happened considerably earlier than Wegener supposed. It could therefore explain the invertebrate distribution and even the freshwater fish, but the more conservative arguments involved in the theory of the permanence of the continents would still be needed to explain the dispersal of the mammals.

The argument is circular once again. A hypothesis is formulated (drift) based mainly on the facts of animal distribution and then the facts of animal distribution are fitted into the hypothesis, or cannot be fitted as the case may be, and all the time the physical evidence is not consulted. And yet physical evidence is necessary before a decision can be reached. So far, however, the modern work on rock magnetism has not been able to show whether the continents were actually closer to one another in an east-west direction than they are today. The general opinion seems to be that if the physical interpretation is correct, there has been rather a northward drift of Africa, India and Australia. This would make the Antarctic land bridge so much the more probable, but sheds little light on the rest of Wegener's hypothesis except to make drifting continents a possibility.

But it seems easier to make animals move round the world and fill permanent continents than to make the continents move round to collect them.

The theory of the permanence of the continents has been preferred as an explanation of late Mesozoic and Cenozoic vertebrate distribution because it is the simplest of the theories and because it raises fewer difficulties than the others. What happened in the early Mesozoic and the Paleozoic is much more difficult to guess, and at present there is so little evidence on which to base a theory that the question must be left open. It is hoped that increasing knowledge of the distribution of Mesozoic land reptiles may provide a basis for a theory of land distribution in triassic and permian days.

If geologists find that either drift or land bridges can be proved on physical evidence, then the zoological facts will have to be looked at again. But while the biological facts are the main evidence there is no conclusive reason why the theory of the permanence of the continents should be rejected.

# Part Four
# ISLANDS

# 11

# Island Patterns

## *Wallace's Line*

When the world was first divided into six zoogeographical regions, in the middle of the last century, it was found difficult to know where to draw the line between the Oriental and Australian regions. The main land masses of the two regions are separated from one another by several strings of islands, the Malay Archipelago. Which islands of this big group belong to which region?

It was obvious from the first that the large islands of Sumatra, Java and Borneo belonged to the Oriental region. They are separated from Malaya and from one another by only shallow sea, and their animals are very similar to those of Malaya. In the east, New Guinea and the Aru islands are close to Australia, within another shallow sea area, and have many animals in common with that continent, including some marsupials and cassowaries. They can therefore be assigned to the Australian region. This leaves the Philippines, Celebes, the Moluccas, Timor and several other groups of smaller islands to be fitted into the zoogeographical classification.

In the middle of the nineteenth century an English naturalist A. R. Wallace was working amongst the islands of the Malay Archipelago, collecting mammals and birds, insects and snails, to send home to England. At first he spent all his time in Malaya and Borneo, but one day in the summer of 1856, he travelled from the small island of Bali to the next island, twenty miles away, to Lombok. He was astonished at the difference in the fauna of the two islands. He had left behind on Bali green woodpeckers and barbets and had arrived on an island where the outstanding birds were white cockatoos and honeysuckers. In crossing twenty miles of sea he seemed to have sailed out of the Oriental region into the Australian. This passage from one region to the other had happened much further west than he had expected.

After this experience he visited Celebes, the Kei islands and the Aru islands, Timor, the Moluccas and New Guinea, and he studied the fauna of each new island in the light of his experience on the Bali-Lombok voyage. Island by island they were classified as being Oriental or Australian. When a number of these islands had been classified in this way he was able to decide where the Oriental region ended and where the Australian region began. In 1863 he drew on the map a line which he considered marked out the boundary between the two regions. This line became known, and still is known, as Wallace's Line, after its originator. The line runs between the Philippines and the Moluccas in the north, then south-west between Borneo and Celebes and finally south between the small islands of Bali and Lombok.

Some years after this another line was drawn between the Oriental and Australian regions, because it was thought to divide the two faunas better than Wallace's Line. This new line was called Weber's Line and was based mainly on observations of the mollusc and mammal faunas of the area. Weber's Line runs between the Moluccas and Celebes, and between the Kei Islands and Timor. It is further east than Wallace's Line.

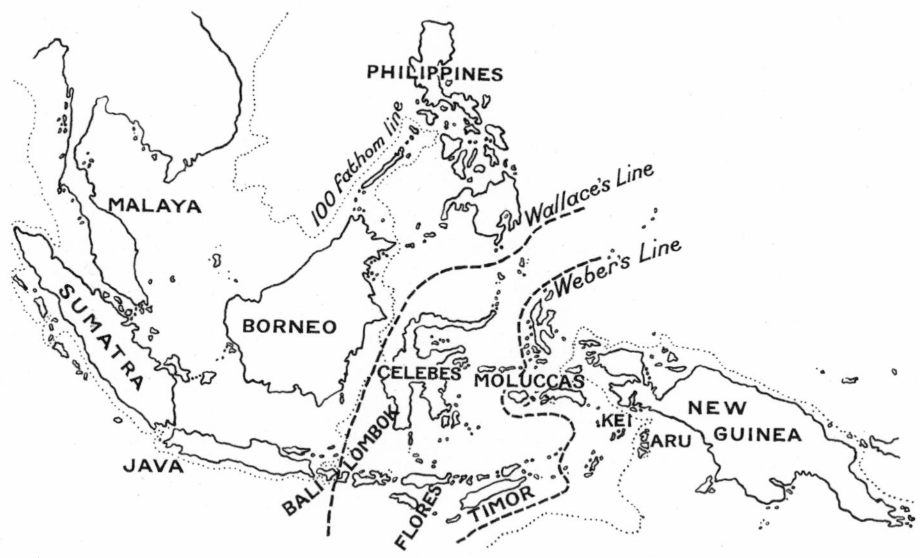


Some people prefer Wallace's Line as the boundary, others prefer Weber's Line. Why is it so difficult to draw a line?

Geologically, Wallace's Line marks off the easterly limit of what was once a land mass joined to Malaya, and Weber's Line more or less marks off the westerly limit of what was an Australian continent at one time. Thus there would seem to be geological evidence for both lines. Islands that once formed part of the mainland could be expected to have a considerable part of the fauna of that mainland. Thus the fauna of Borneo is mainly Oriental, that of New Guinea, Australian. But what is to be done with the islands that lie between the two lines, especially Celebes, Flores and Lombok? These middle islands of the Archipelago are not geologically part of the Oriental region nor part of the Australian region. Many of them were probably under the sea for most of the Cenozoic, thus losing all their earlier plant and animal inhabitants. When they re-emerged, towards the end of the Cenozoic, they were independent islands, never connected by land to either of the continents.

The middle islands have been colonized in a haphazard way by migrations across the sea from both the east and the west. Consequently they each have individual faunas, different from one another and different from either Malaya or Australia. Celebes for instance has very few mammals, hardly any amphibia, no freshwater fish and some peculiar birds. Most of the mammals come from Asia; the bats, shrews, tarsier, macaque monkey, squirrels, murid rats and mice, porcupine, civets, pigs and deer. Others, although belonging to Oriental families have differentiated into forms peculiar to Celebes. There is the dwarf buffalo, the babirussa pig and the black tailless baboon. In the pleistocene there was a small Celebesian elephant. Only the phalangers of Celebes are typically Australian. Presumably all the Celebesian mammals crossed the sea from one or other of the islands of the Archipelago with the result that the fauna is mixed, poor, and not exactly like that of any other island. The other middle islands show similar characteristics, although some have a larger proportion of Australian animals. They do not fall easily into either of the great regions on either side. Some zoogeographers have despaired of ever drawing any one line between the Orient and Australia which would satisfy all biologists and have suggested keeping the two lines, Wallace's and Weber's, and regarding all the middle islands as a separate region, Wallacea. Others insist that one line should separate the regions, and wish to draw it where the fauna is exactly half Oriental and half Australian. The difficulty of doing this is considerable because all groups of animals do not reach the 50:50 mark at the same place. But if one line were to be drawn on this basis it would certainly put Celebes, Lombok and Flores into the Oriental region.

Whichever view be accepted, the important thing to realize is that Wallacea is a transition area between two regions and that it is not unique in this. There

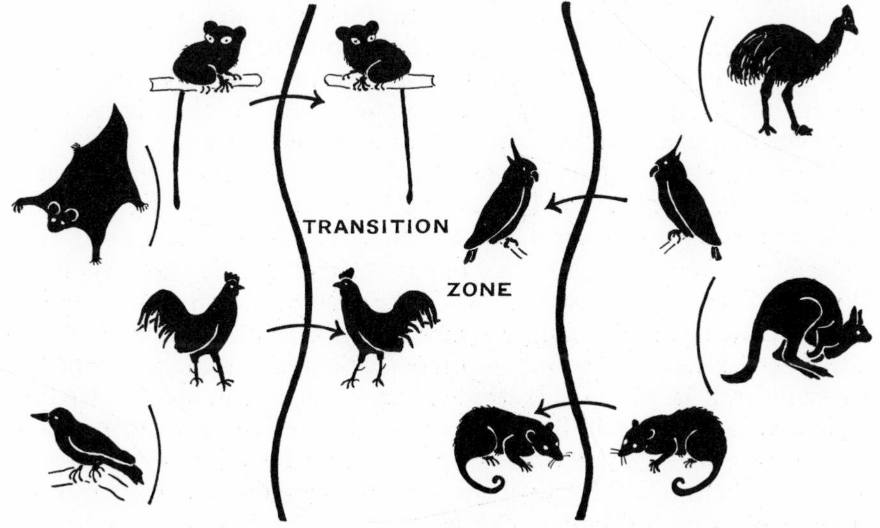


are transition areas in Central America where the faunas of the Nearctic and Neotropical overlap, and in north Africa where the Ethiopian and Palearctic overlap. The drawing of a precise boundary line across a transition area between two regions is impossible. Where faunas overlap the area of overlap may be large or small; not all groups of animals may extend to the boundary; the fractions of the main regional faunas involved may be large or small; there may be more overlapping in one direction than another. Therefore all

transition areas may vary greatly in extent and composition. Wallacea differs from these two other transition areas however in being an area of sea and islands and therefore its problems are even more complex. Wallacea is not simply a matter of Australian-Oriental crossmigration but of island cross-migration within the transition area itself, further complicated by the independent biological evolution of each island. Wallacea introduces some of the difficulties involved in the classification of islands.

### *Classification of Islands*

There are other islands besides those of the Malay Archipelago that are difficult to assign to a particular zoogeographical region. Islands are of two sorts: continental islands and oceanic islands. It is usually comparatively easy to put continental islands into their zoogeographical region, but oceanic islands are often more difficult.

Continental islands are those which at some time have been part of a large land mass, but which have lost their connexion with the parent land. Through the sinking of a neck of land or a rise in sea level, they have become separated from the continent by a stretch of sea. The sea may be narrow like the Straits of Dover which separate the continental island of Great Britain from the continent of Eurasia, or they may be 100 miles wide like the Formosa Strait which runs between Formosa and the east coast of China.

Continental islands differ from one another in the length of time for which they have been independent islands. Great Britain is a young continental island; Borneo, Formosa and Japan are older.

Most of the land fauna of a continental island can be expected to have reached the island across dry land when the island was still connected to the continent. The length of time for which a continental island has been independent determines the amount of difference between its fauna and the fauna of the mainland. If it is an old island it may be lacking in animals which are comparative newcomers to the mainland, and its own animals may have had time to evolve in different ways from their continental relatives. A young continental island is likely to differ little from the mainland, for it takes many thousands of years for animal species to change to fit a new environment. Continental islands, therefore, are likely to resemble their continents in a general way, and to have features peculiar to themselves only if they have been cut off from the continent for a long time.

In contrast, oceanic islands are islands which have never had a land connexion with a continent. They are of volcanic origin and often many hundreds of miles from the nearest land. The Azores, Bermuda, the Galapagos Islands, Sandwich Islands, Polynesian Islands, St Helena and

Tristan da Cunha are well-known oceanic islands.

The fauna of an oceanic island must be derived from across the sea. The direction from which the fauna comes will be determined to some extent by the prevailing winds and ocean currents, so that in many cases one zoogeographical region will have been the source of the fauna. But this is not always the case and the fauna may come from more than one region as that of Celebes has done. Sometimes, even, it is impossible to decide on the source of the fauna. In all cases, however, the fauna of an oceanic island is likely to be poor in basic groups, because few will have survived the sea-crossing. Those that have reached an oceanic island, however, may have evolved in ways different from those of their relatives left behind on some continent, and the fauna of an oceanic island is therefore likely to be very individual if the island is of some age.

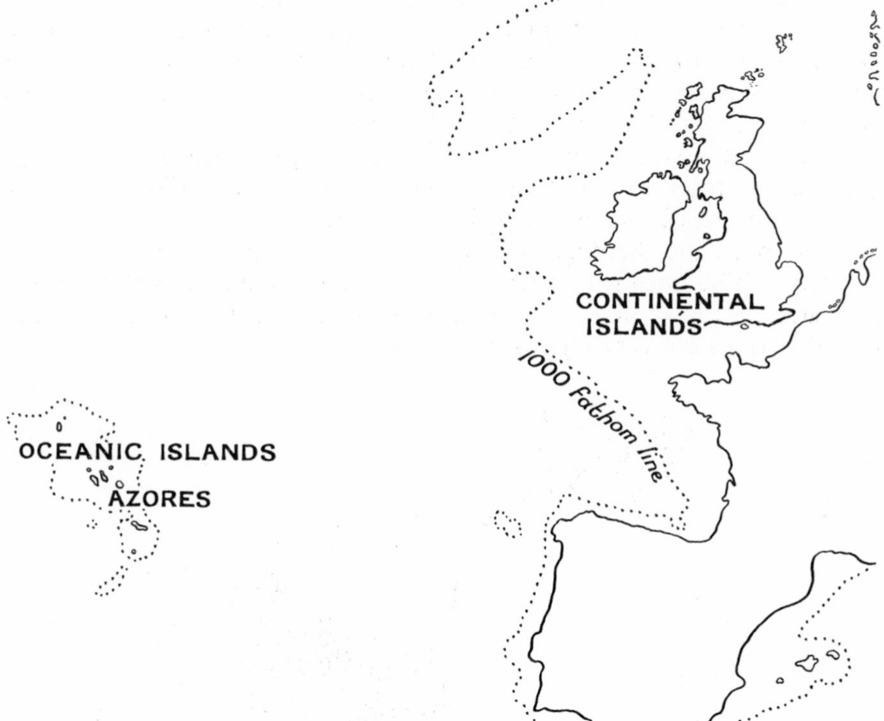


An oceanic island is likely to differ from the nearest continent in climate, vegetation and fauna. All these environmental differences will lead to the divergence of its inhabitants from their mainland relatives. The environment will also differ on different islands. But oceanic islands do have certain features in common. Both the vegetation and the fauna will tend to be sparse. Mammals, amphibia and strictly freshwater fish will be the rarest of all the inhabitants. And of the mammals, bats, rats, pigs and small arboreal animals are more likely to be present than others. This precludes the majority of carnivores.

Because of the lack of carnivores on oceanic islands, certain general trends

in the evolution of the other island inhabitants can be observed. Birds may gradually evolve into ground-living forms and become large and flightless, like the dodo which lived on the oceanic island of Mauritius where there were no native mammals. Other animals may also get very large, like the giant lizards of the Galapagos Islands and the giant tortoises which are found on several oceanic islands, including the Galapagos and the Seychelles.

Other general tendencies in the fauna of oceanic islands are the evolution of wingless insects, because those that had wings were constantly being blown off the island and were therefore progressively selected out of the population. Birds sometimes lose the bright colours of their mainland relatives, evolving into white or dark forms. And on islands that are very small, the larger inhabitants are liable to extinction because they cannot maintain an adequate population. This reduces the fauna still further.

It is generally agreed that islands can be classified into these two types, oceanic and continental, as Darwin had suggested in 1859. Within this broad classification, islands differ according to whether they are ancient or comparatively new, and their age affects the degree of endemic differentiation of their fauna. This means that a very ancient continental island has many of the characteristics of an oceanic island, because in fact it will have been an isolated island for a very long period.

# 12

# Oceanic Islands

## *St Helena*

St Helena is a volcanic oceanic island some ten miles long and eight wide, lying in deep water in the South Atlantic over 1,000 miles from Africa and considerably more from South America. The ocean currents and the prevailing winds reach the island from the south-west coast of Africa; a branch of the cold Benguela current sweeps up past the island, and the south-east trade winds blow over it.

The most outstanding feature of the fauna of St Helena is the extreme poverty of it. There are no native mammals, reptiles, amphibians nor freshwater fish and the only native land bird is a plover closely related to an African species. Besides the plover, the chief native inhabitants are insects and land molluscs.

There is no climatic reason for the poverty of the fauna as the successful introduction of mammals and insects by man has shown. In fact these introductions may be one of the causes of it. The Portuguese brought goats to the

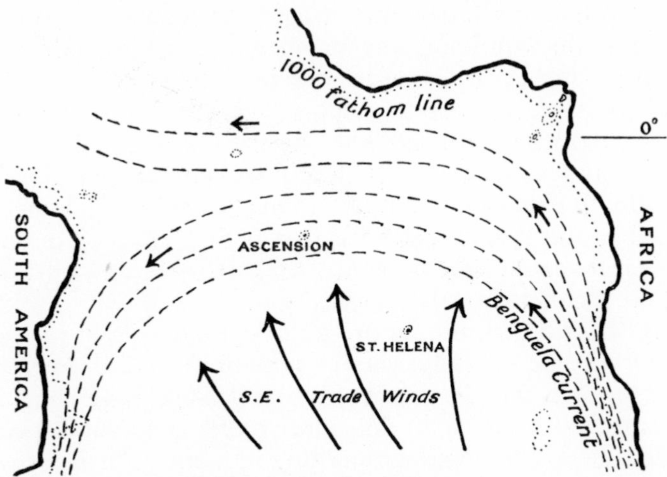


island in 1513 and the ravages of these animals together with the later stripping of the bark from the ebony and redwood trees for the tanning industry, robbed the island of much of its vegetation. As the vegetation was destroyed many animals that depended on it for food and shelter must have died out. This may have reduced the original native insect population in

particular and it is possible that others also suffered from the disappearance of the trees.

Even without this recent destruction the St Helena fauna was probably always sparse. Indeed its sparseness and its position in the middle of an ocean indicate that the whole flora and fauna has been acquired by chance immigration from across the sea. The direction of the currents and the prevailing winds suggest Africa as the main source.

The only vertebrate member of the population is the scarcely differentiated African plover. Some weevils are also related to African forms and so are many of the plants. That Africa has supplied some of the colonists is supported by the occasional arrival of driftwood from that continent. Weevils, being wood-boring insects, could have crossed the sea on many occasions buried in floating logs. This method of transport might also account for the St Helena molluscs. Some of the molluscs, however, are so specialized that it is impossible to know where their nearest relatives are to be found, and some weevils have European affinities. Whether molluscs and weevils came in wood by way of Africa and the Benguela current or whether they floated from a more northerly site is impossible to decide, but either of these explanations provides a reasonably acceptable hypothesis. More difficult to explain because the winds and currents cannot so obviously be utilized, is the presence on St Helena of plants that resemble those of South America.

Some biologists have therefore suggested that St Helena was once part of the South Atlantic continent and that it was then colonized from both Africa and South America. This might account for the South American element of the St Helena flora but the fauna has no such distinctly American characteristics, and it seems strange that if St Helena were once part of a lost continent it should have no land vertebrates except a bird whose arrival on the island is comparatively recent.

All things considered, the nature and the composition of the St Helena fauna support the view that the island is oceanic. The bird and the seeds could have come through the air, the invertebrates could have come by sea from Africa. The specialization of the fauna into native genera and species indicates a long residence on the island, amounting to many millions of years.

## *Galapagos Islands*

The Galapagos Islands lie in the Pacific, about 600 miles from the coast of Ecuador. They form a group of fifteen volcanic islands lying across the equator. The coastal areas of the islands are dry and bare, with low thorny bushes and prickly pears. Inland there are sometimes humid forests whose tall trees are covered with ferns and orchids, and sometimes open bare country. These islands have a sparse fauna, but even so it is richer than that of St Helena. It seems to have been easier for animals to cross the 600 miles of Pacific from America to the Galapagos than for them to cross the 1,000 miles of south Atlantic from Africa to St Helena.

Unlike St Helena, the Galapagos Islands have mammals, many land birds, and reptiles, but like St Helena they have no amphibians and no freshwater fish.

The two native mammal species are a bat and the cricetid rice rats. There are about twenty-six different land birds some of which are hardly different from Neotropical species. There is a penguin species, the only one to live in the tropics, and there are unique flightless cormorants. There are also those famous birds, Darwin's finches.

The finches are famous because Darwin studied them when he visited the islands, and as a result of his studies started to think about the reasons for the origin of new species, and eventually formulated his theory of evolution by natural selection. Darwin observed that there were finches of the same two genera spread over all the islands of the Galapagos group, but each island form was recognizably different from all others. In other words it was more or less true to say that each island had its own species. Thus one of the ground finches inhabiting some of the smaller outlying islands shows distinct differences in the proportions of the beak and in its feeding habits. On one island its beak is comparatively slim and it feeds on cactus, on another the beak is altogether broader and heavier and the finch feeds on the ground.

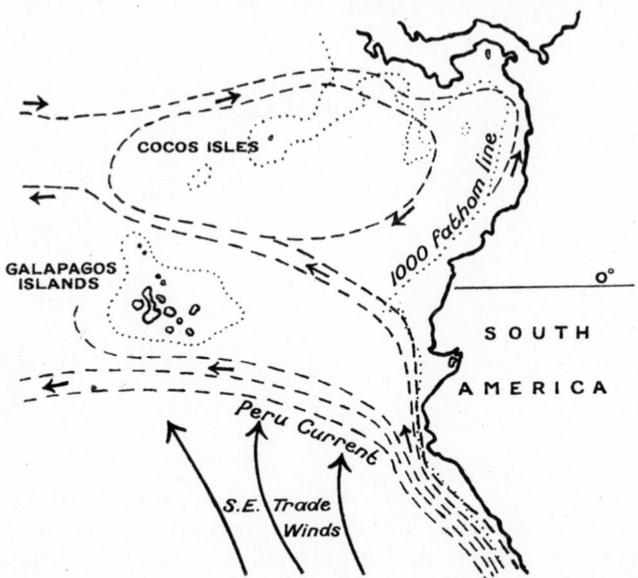


Darwin found it difficult to fit his observations into the then general belief in special creation, and came to the conclusion that the slight differences in the island forms had come about by natural means; that species could evolve into other species. He suggested that when finches colonized a new island, they would be in a slightly different environment from the one they had left, different perhaps in size of territory, in vegetation or in the composition of the other animal inhabitants. Gradually in succeeding generations the finches most fitted to the new surroundings, cactus-eating for instance, would survive and leave offspring whilst the others would die off. Separated from the parent population, the colony would finally evolve into a new species fitted to the new island and different from the original. A further interesting feature of the Galapagos finches is their evolution into forms with many different habits. Owing to the scarcity of other birds on the islands, the

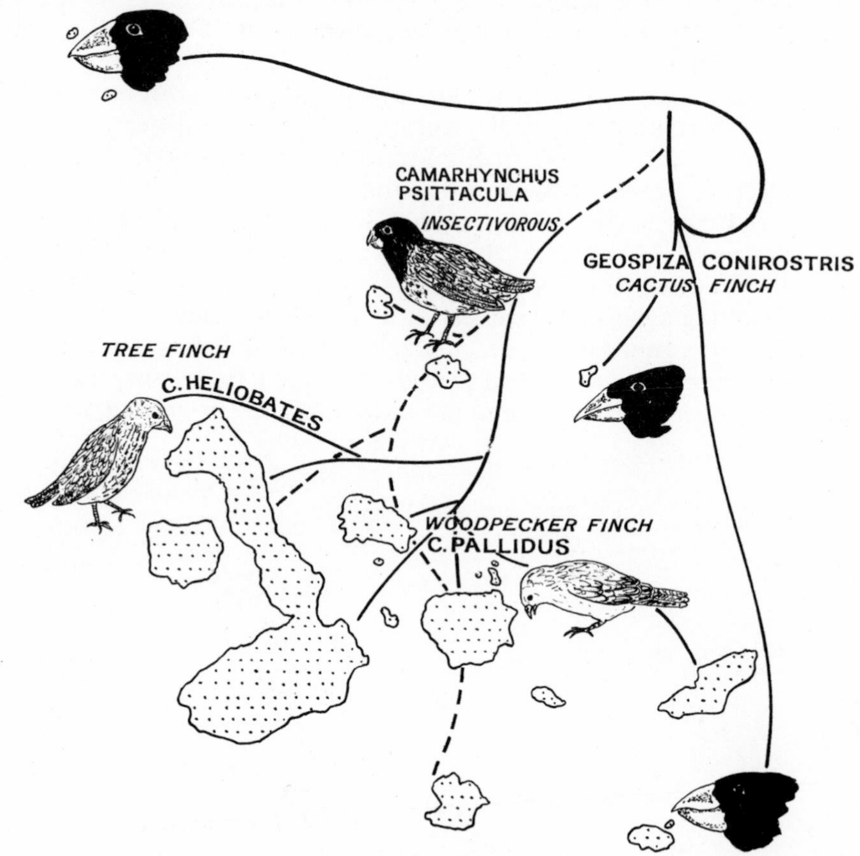


finches have evolved by natural selection from a seed-eating ancestor, not only into cactus-feeders, but also into woodpecker-finches, insectivorous tree finches, mangrove-finches and vegetarian tree finches, differing from one another in beak shape and size, and to a lesser degree in male plumage colour. None of the finches is brightly coloured, having island characteristics of dull plumage, varying in this case from black to light brown.

The giant tortoises, after which the islands are named, also vary from island to island. Unfortunately these lumbering reptiles are on the verge of

extinction. They provided excellent food and oil for the early buccaneers and whalers and for modern settlers. The same fate is overtaking the land iguanas, three foot long lizards that live in burrows and feed almost entirely on cactus. The marine iguanas, however, are still abundant. They live mainly on the shore, sunbathing and feeding on seaweed, while scarlet land crabs run over them eating their parasitic ticks. The other reptiles of the Galapagos, one species of snake, and two of lizards are less remarkable. The snakes and small iguanid lizards are unique species of tropical American genera while the geckos belong to a widely distributed genus.

Several attempts have been made to account for the fauna of the Galapagos by means of a land bridge from South America. True, America has provided most of the fauna, but the very rich South or Central American fauna is only scantily represented on the islands so that it seems more likely that chance sea-crossings can account for the fauna much better than a land bridge. There is no shallow sea area to provide good geological evidence of a land bridge, and the bridge builders are never united in deciding whether to bring the bridge from South America or from Central America.

The vertebrate fauna contains just those animals most likely to have crossed the sea successfully. There are no amphibians, no freshwater fish. Rats and bats are the most successful of mammalian voyagers. The penguin species almost certainly came from the south with the northward-flowing cold Humboldt (or Peruvian) current, but the cormorants probably flew to the islands, only evolving into a flightless species after their arrival. The reptiles, or their eggs, may have come on driftwood, but it also possible that the tortoises floated there in the sea.

There seems no reason to doubt Darwin's classification of the Galapagos Islands as oceanic.

### *Krakatau*

The tiny island group of Krakatau has very different characteristics from St Helena and the Galapagos Islands, for although the islands are volcanic, and genuine oceanic islands, they lie close to land and their fauna is of recent origin.

The three islands lie in the Sunda Straits between Sumatra and Java, twenty-five miles away from both these large continental islands. Early accounts of the Krakatau Islands describe one large island with three volcanoes on it and two small islands nearby. In 1883 the large island blew up, leaving only a small part of the original above water, and the islands completely covered in hot volcanic ash. Since then the islands have had an uneasy history, sinking and rising and changing their profiles. In spite of this always some part of each of them has remained above the sea during the years since 1883.

When the volcanoes erupted all the organic life of the islands was destroyed. The modern population has, therefore, arrived since then and has arrived from at least twenty-five miles away. It has been possible to observe the events in the repopulation of these oceanic islands over a period of about forty years.

The zoology of the islands was not known before the eruption, and indeed not until twenty-five years afterwards but since then the large island has been studied on three separate occasions. In 1908 the first brief investigation was made. The supposedly first vegetation, a covering of algal growth over the ground, followed by ferns, had already given way to the third stage in the floral population of volcanic islands, grass wilderness. Animals can only establish themselves in suit-

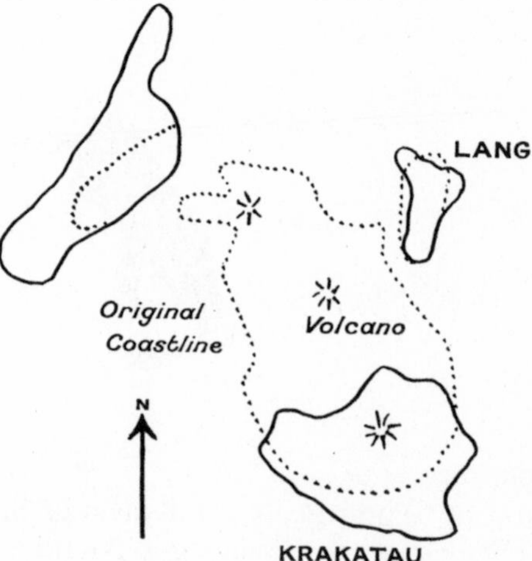

able conditions of vegetation, so that the sequence of their establishment on Krakatau depended on the conditions on the islands as well as the supply of colonists from the nearby islands of Sumatra and Java. Herbivorous animals must establish themselves on an island before carnivores can become part of the population.

By 1908, that is twenty-five years from the beginning of recolonization, there were already thirteen species of birds, including pigeons, kingfishers, orioles and a bulbul, on the large island. There was a species of monitor lizard and a house-gecko as well as 192 species of insects, in which ants and flies predominated. There were thirty-one species of beetle, six of butterflies and two of dragonflies. There were spiders and scorpions, a few woodlice, two species of snail, and very little else.

1908–1921

In 1921 when the next survey was made, there were three times as many species of animals as there had been thirteen years earlier. The grass wilderness was giving way to mixed forest and the first mammals had arrived. These were two species of bats and a species of house rat which had probably come over with a human visitor to the island. The birds had increased to twenty-nine species and included swifts and sunbirds. Another gecko, a skink and a python species had arrived, and the beetles, butterflies and dragonflies had increased enormously in number of species. Also two species of earthworm were now abundant.

Another twelve years later, in 1933, the mixed forest had become dominant, and with the disappearance of much of the grassland, the grass fauna, the gnats and flies for instance, had decreased both in total number and in number of species. But two more bat species had arrived, one an insect-eater. Another rat species, more birds, including flycatchers, another skink and a gecko, and a crocodile species were now on the island. Also almost all the other inhabitants had been joined by new species. Remarkably few forest forms, however, had come to live in the mixed forests of the island although there was now a total of 1,100 species. Only a few insects and a tree-snail represented the tropical forest fauna of the surrounding islands. No mammals, reptiles or leeches had migrated from the neighbouring forests.

Investigation showed that the majority of the colonists had come south from Sumatra, but a few were Javanese. The insects seemed to have been blown to the island, for they were found in the upper air currents. Probably a continuous wave of insects and spiders was being blown across the island and it is not surprising that the number of species increased rapidly once suitable vegetational conditions prevailed. The reptiles may have swum the twenty-five miles, but the earthworms must have come in driftwood or with the birds.

Krakatau is typical of oceanic islands in having no amphibians and no mammals other than bats and rats, in spite of its closeness to land. It has no endemic species for its fauna has not been on the island long enough to have differentiated from that of the nearby islands. It may not seem an ideal oceanic island, but it has been under continuing observation since soon after repopulation began and therefore provides one of the few experiments in oceanic island colonization.

13

# Continental Islands

*British Isles*

The geological history of the British Isles is complex. During the Paleozoic and Mesozoic the northern and western land may have been an outlying part of the large North America-Greenland continent, sharing its fauna. The more southerly parts were frequently below the sea or formed an archipelago of

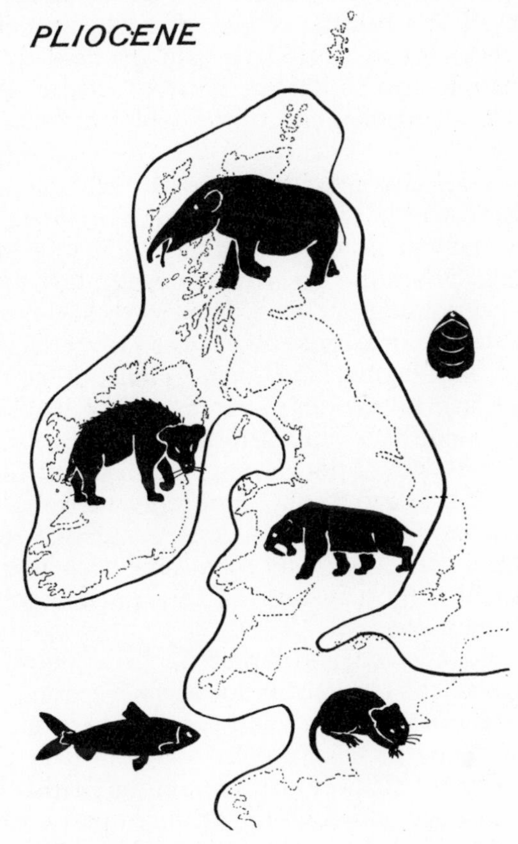


islands between the Nearctic and Palearctic continents of the northern hemisphere. Only at the end of the miocene did the British Isles become part of Europe with no land connexions across the North Atlantic (for details see Wills 1951).

The miocene-pliocene fauna was typical of the cooler zones of the northern hemisphere with sabre-tooth tigers, tapirs and mastodons, and Palearctic bears and hyenas. Crocodiles and turtles may have been found still in the rivers of the country and lizards and amphibia can be presumed to have been abundant.

None of this fauna exists in the British Isles today. There are no relicts of its early connexion to America with the dubious exception of a freshwater sponge, and there are no pliocene relicts of its European fauna. The whole of the British pliocene fauna was wiped out during the pleistocene and the modern fauna has been gained since then. But the pleistocene extinctions were not a simple event and the country was inhabited by several waves of European animals during that epoch.

At the beginning of the pleistocene the climate of the northern hemisphere had become cold, and ice covered the lands in the far north. This cold affected the fauna of the British Isles. Warmth-loving animals moved out or died out and the fauna became typical of a cold temperate region, with otters, red deer, rodents and mastodons. But the cold did not last and as warmer conditions returned so did the sabre-tooths, lions and Old World monkeys. The tapirs, crocodiles and turtles had vanished for ever from the fauna.

A few thousand years later ice covered the British Isles as far south as the Thames and the Severn estuary. This, the second pleistocene glaciation, was the most extensive and was responsible for the elimination of the whole of the earlier British fauna. When the ice retreated again, first reindeer and musk ox, and then monkeys, voles, hyenas, horses, rhinoceroses, pigs, hippos, deer and early Stone Age man, travelled across Doggerland, from Denmark and Germany, and the Channel land, from France, to the British Isles.

This fauna, too, had to give up its tenure of the British Isles when the third ice age made conditions difficult for life. The third ice age was not as rigorous as the second and, although many animals left the country others like the reindeer, musk ox and woolly rhinoceros were able to live on. Again the climate improved and wolves, bears, lions, mammoths, elephants, horses, rhinoceroses, hippos, deer, bison and man came back from Europe. There were also many small rodents in this last interglacial period hardly distinguishable from modern species.

The fourth ice age followed, and forced the fauna out of the British Isles yet again, and many of the pleistocene animals never returned.

Between the retreat of the last ice and the cutting of the Straits of Dover the modern fauna of the British Isles has come in over the Channel land and Doggerland. The last signs of glaciation in the British Isles disappeared only some 9,000 years ago, although the southern part of the land had been habitable before this. A little later the continental land links sank beneath the sea, the final severance from Europe coming when the Straits of Dover were completed between 7,000 and 8,000 years ago. There were therefore only two or three thousand years available for the post-glacial colonization of the British Isles.

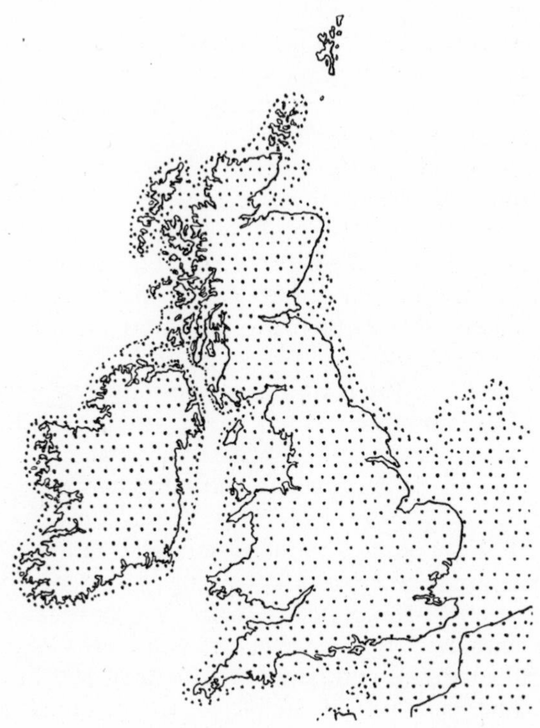

## *Great Britain*

A few thousand years to acquire a new fauna is a very short time in terms of animal evolution; seven thousand years of isolation is short in terms of speciation. It is not surprising therefore that the list of modern land vertebrates should be short, the list of endemic species even shorter.

Birds, and in particular sea birds which make up a large proportion of the avifauna, are an exception.

There are shrews, moles, hedgehogs; rabbits and hares; squirrels, cricetids (voles), murid rats and mice, dormice; mustelids (badgers, otters, martens, stoats and weasels), cats; a few cervids (roe deer and red deer), and a few bats. Many European mammals for which the climate seems suitable

are absent; there are no hamsters, lemmings, bears, ibexes, chamois or reindeer; and wolves, beavers and wild boar which were once typical of the land are no longer found.

Reptiles and amphibia are even more poorly represented. There are only three snakes, grass snake, adder and smooth snake and the last is restricted to a few southern counties. There are two species of lacertid lizards, the common brown lizard which is viviparous and the greener sand lizard which lays eggs and is restricted like the smooth snake to the south of the country. A legless lizard, the slow worm *Anguis* completes the reptile fauna.

There are only six species of amphibia, common toad, frog and natterjack amongst the anura, and three species of newt. The edible frog and the marsh frog are recent introductions and there are no midwife toads, no fire toads and no yellow-bellied toads which are common on the other side of the Channel.

There are perch, pike, loach and carp amongst the primary freshwater fish. The char and whitefish which have differentiated into numerous species in British lakes are capable of living in salt water and their problems of colonization are not, therefore, exactly the same as those of the more land-locked vertebrates.

Compared with Europe the modern fauna is sparse, rather less than half the western European species occurring and it has none of the large mammals and reptiles of the pliocene. There are only six species of amphibians compared with twelve in France and the Low Countries; only about 50 species of land mammal compared with nearly 100 in Germany and 70 in Scandinavia. The short time available for the colonization of the country must be the main cause of the omissions, but the climate may also be responsible for the absence of some European species such as the green lizard and European tree frog for example.

In seven thousand years the portion of the European fauna isolated in Great Britain has shown scarcely any evolutionary change. There is only one endemic species of land vertebrate, the red grouse, *Lagopus scoticus*, and the specific status of this is sometimes disputed. But although they may not have attained specific rank, several British land animals differ recognizably from their European relatives. The British red squirrel can be distinguished from the European red squirrel by the lighter colour of its tail. The British coal-tit has greenish upper parts, the European coal-tit, slate-blue. There has been some differentiation in seven thousand years and this is indicated in fauna lists by the addition of a sub-specific or varietal name to the usual binomial.

As far as is known the modern fauna of Great Britain was acquired mainly across land from its continental parent. It is typical of a recent island in the lack of differentiation of its fauna.

Whether any members of the fauna are even more recent immigrants from

across the sea is difficult to tell when the fauna is so little differentiated. Some birds are certainly recent, some having arrived and established themselves in historic times. Butterflies, too, are known to migrate to England; the Camberwell Beauty from Scandinavia; clouded yellows and several blues from France. There is no substantiated case of any other animals having crossed the sea and established breeding colonies in the country, but the possibility cannot be ruled out.

### *Ireland*

Ireland is a second-hand continental island. It acquired its fauna by way of Great Britain and became an independent island only recently, after it was isolated from the continent. Therefore the fauna is scanty, only about half the British species being represented, and the differentiation of the sparse fauna into Irish species has been slight. The Irish hare is sometimes differentiated from the British and European hares at the species level but most of the differences between Irish and British populations are so small as to merit subspecific rank at the most. Just as the British coal-tit differs from the European, so the Irish population can be distinguished from the British by slight colour differences of the cheeks. There is a subspecies of the red grouse and several invertebrates have distinctive characteristics.

Only eight families of mammals are represented in Ireland and with the exception of a deer they are all small and insignificant. There are shrews, hedgehogs, rabbits, squirrels, murids, foxes, mustelids and cervids. Only one of the four British shrews, the pygmy shrew, and one of the two British deer, the red deer, are found in Ireland. There are no moles, no cricetids, no dormice and no wild cats although all but the last of these families is abundant in Great Britain.

Of the twelve species of British reptiles and amphibians, itself a meagre number, only three are found in Ireland. These are the natterjack toad which is confined to a small area of Kerry, the common newt and the viviparous lizard. The frog which is a flourishing member of the fauna today was introduced in 1696. There are no snakes in Ireland but it is doubtful whether it was St Patrick who was responsible for banishing them.

Of the sixteen species of strictly freshwater British fish, only eight have reached Ireland.

Like the rest of the British Isles, Ireland was covered by ice during the second and third ice ages and it is unlikely that any of the pliocene fauna could have survived the severe climate. The animals of Ireland are therefore post-glacial arrivals. But unlike those of Great Britain, the Irish migrants had no direct land connexion from Europe to Ireland after the ice had left. As already indicated, their journey to Ireland passed through the greater part of Britain.

In the years immediately after the retreat of the ice, Ireland was connected to Scotland by a neck of land stretching from north-east Donegal to the islands of Islay and Jura in south-west Scotland. This was probably the only connexion that Ireland had and it lasted longer than the Channel land connecting Great Britain to the rest of Europe.

Ireland was therefore open to colonization by land for several thousand years and yet only about half the British animals reached Ireland. There was probably more than one reason for the sieving effect, but one of the most important must have been the situation of the land connexion. Being in the north of Great Britain, animals had to spread through almost the whole of the large island before they could gain access to Ireland. Some animals were too late arriving in Great Britain to travel as far north before the corridor was lost, others, even early arrivals, never spread far north for climatic or vegetational reasons and were therefore never eligible for the Irish journey.

The cricetid bank vole *Clethrionomys glareolus* and the dormouse were probably too late to reach Ireland. The dormouse is still confined to England and Wales but the bank vole is widespread over the whole of Great Britain, ranging as far west as some of the islands off the coast of Scotland.

The smooth snake and the sand lizard are confined, probably for climatic reasons, to the southern part of England where they are only found on dry

heaths and open woodland. The egg-laying habit of the sand lizard may be an important factor in its limitation, for the viviparous common lizard has spread over the whole of the British Isles. Whatever the precise reason, the range of the smooth snake and sand lizard has never extended northwards far enough to cover the Islay-Donegal land bridge.

It is more difficult to understand the absence of the mole, the adder, the toad and the newts. They are widespread over Great Britain today reaching to the north and west coasts of Scotland. It is possible, but seems unlikely, that all these vertebrates were too late arriving in Great Britain to extend their range northwards in time. However some of them may have been slow in spreading and others may have been prevented from crossing to Ireland by climatic factors. The adder may have extended its range far northwards only recently and the wide-ranging mole may have been stopped by the physical conditions of the land connexion itself. Moles usually burrow in well-drained soil and the soil of the land may have been too water-logged, frozen, or even too stoney.

There is yet another way of accounting for some of the gaps in the Irish fauna. Ireland is a comparatively small island, it has a uniform climate and little differentiation of vegetation. Some of the missing British vertebrates may have succeeded in colonizing Ireland but were unable to maintain them-

selves either because of the climate or because the populations were too small. It is possible that the climate was unsuitable for moles and perhaps also for grass snakes, so that they never established breeding colonies on the Irish side of the land corridor. The newts and toads on the other hand may have been successful initially but died out because they were unable to maintain big enough colonies. This last suggestion is supported to some extent by the present-day distribution of the natterjack in Ireland. Its small range in the far south-west is indicative of only small success, or approaching extinction.

The poverty of the Irish fauna can therefore be accounted for by its northerly connexion with another poorly populated island, its climate and its small area. Ireland has a selected portion of the British fauna. But there are four Irish animals which do not occur in Great Britain and although they are none of them vertebrates their unusual type of distribution is worth noticing. An earthworm, a woodlouse, a spotted slug and a moth have a small southerly range in Ireland and are otherwise only found in south-western Europe.

To explain this so-called Lusitanian element in the Irish fauna, Edward Forbes in 1846 suggested a land bridge from Portugal to Ireland. Forbes was one of the first scientific biogeographers but he was also a keen bridge builder. A pleistocene Lusitanian bridge is not acceptable on geological grounds and it seems likely that the Lusitanian species were once more widespread than they are today. They may even be survivals from the last interglacial period, becoming restricted in range as the climate of the fourth ice age deteriorated. The southerly part of Ireland was not ice-covered during the fourth, and last, glaciation and might have provided a refuge for these few survivors from a more temperate climate.

## 14

# Ancient Islands

### *New Zealand*

New Zealand lies about 1,000 miles east-south-east of Australia, in the south temperate zone. Within the 100,000 square miles of its two main islands there

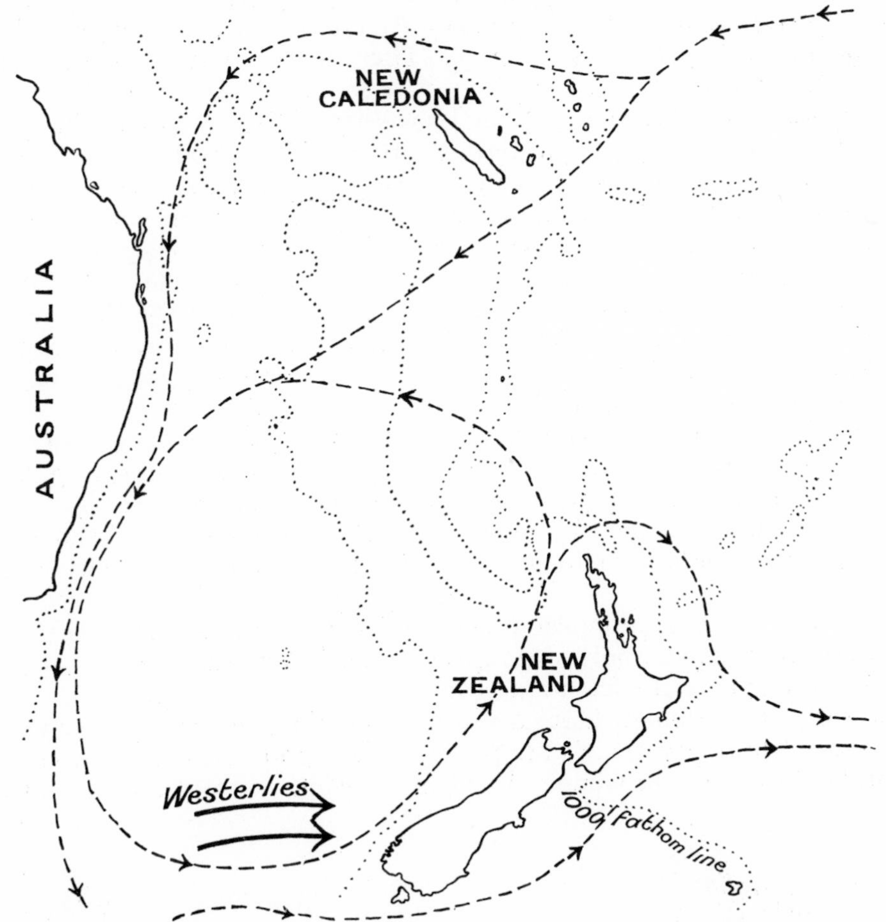


are both mountains and open country and a wide variety of temperate vegetation. Geologically it is complex, with extinct volcanoes as well as sedimentary rocks.

The fauna of New Zealand, like that of other islands, is characterized both by the absence of many animals and by the differentiation of those that are there. But typical of New Zealand itself are relicts of old vertebrate stocks and a high proportion of flightless birds, half of which are extinct.

There are no native mammals except two families of bats, one of which is endemic and one Australian. There are no climatic reasons for this deficiency of mammals because those recently introduced have been a great success. But correlated with the absence of mammals, and partially compensating for it in the fauna, is the unique array of flightless birds. There are several species of small kiwis, birds with soft, hair-like feathers and much reduced wings. Their sense of smell is highly developed which may be a primitive feature or connected with their nocturnal habits and diet of worms and insects. There are flightless rails and the kakapo, or owl parrot. The kakapo is hunted for food and although it lives in secluded places and only comes out at night, its numbers are becoming dangerously low. All the other flightless birds of New Zealand have already become extinct. There were twenty species of giant moas, some as large as ostriches. They lived in New Zealand from the end of the miocene until the coming of the Polynesians. There was also a flightless goose and a flightless wren, the only flightless perching bird known.

Of the flying birds, some belong to world-wide families, a few are Australian and there are two small endemic families; New Zealand wrens and the wattlebirds. A remarkable New Zealand bird is the kea, a genus of large parrot, whose habits have changed in an extraordinary way since the introduction into New Zealand of mammals, in this case, sheep. The kea sits on the sheep's back, tearing holes in its flesh to expose the kidney fat which it eats. Before there were any sheep the kea fed on insects, scratched out of crannies with its powerful beak.

New Zealand has geckos and skinks but no turtles or snakes except marine ones. But *Sphenodon*, the last surviving member of an order that disappeared from the fossil record a hundred million years ago, still lives in New Zealand. *Sphenodon*, the tuatara, looks like a large lizard with an overhanging beaked jaw. It is more or less amphibious and its eggs, laid in the sand, take over a year to hatch.

There is only one amphibian proper, the curious frog, *Liopelma*, with tail muscles, related today only to *Ascaphus* of North America.

There are no strictly freshwater fish.

Clearly, the vertebrate fauna is an ancient one containing as it does a relict reptile unknown elsewhere since the cretaceous, and a relict frog surviving only locally today. The fauna is also highly endemic, but at all levels, from an

endemic order (*Sphenodon*), through families (birds and bats), to many endemic genera (amphibian, reptiles and birds) and species (birds and bats).

Where did this fauna originate and how did it get to New Zealand? How long has New Zealand been an island?

New Zealand could have had a connexion with Australia in Mesozoic days. A narrow strip of shallow sea runs from the north-west corner of New Zealand to the north-east corner of Australia, a distance of some 1,000 miles, and this may indicate the site of a Mesozoic or Paleozoic land bridge. Alternatively, according to the drift theory, New Zealand may have been nearer to Australia and in a more southerly latitude, near the Antarctic, in those days.

If any of these land connexions existed, the archaic animals of New Zealand, which were once widespread through the northern continents in the Mesozoic, might have migrated to New Zealand at that time, across land. Invertebrates, *Liopelma* and *Sphenodon* might have used such a route. But any connexion would have been terminated by the jurassic at the latest, preventing the influx of other amphibia and reptiles, birds and mammals, which do not occur on New Zealand.

Thus although New Zealand may be an ancient continental island, the later part of its vertebrate fauna has been acquired like that of oceanic islands from across the sea.

There is no particular reason to suppose the flightless birds needed a land bridge, for there is no evidence that they were already flightless on arrival. No fossil flightless relatives are known from Australia, and it is therefore more likely that they arrived as flying forms at the beginning of the Cenozoic. In the absence of mammals and other predators they then evolved into the many ground-living forms.

The geckos and skinks are only generically different from Asiatic forms and are therefore obviously more recent casual arrivals from across the sea.

New Zealand then may be an ancient continental island with a relict fauna characteristic of an early phase of land connexion, but with a later fauna characteristic of an isolated island. Alternatively, because its relict fauna is so small, it may have been an island for the whole of the Mesozoic and Cenozoic, receiving all its vertebrate fauna, its tuatara and its *Liopelma*, its birds and its lizards at varying times from across the sea.

An island since the end of the Mesozoic, the earlier status of New Zealand is undecided.

### *Madagascar*

The problem is similar to that of New Zealand, but whereas most zoo-geographers believe that New Zealand has been independent for at least the whole of the Cenozoic, there are many who believe that Madagascar was part of Africa until paleocene or even eocene days, for Madagascar has native mammals.

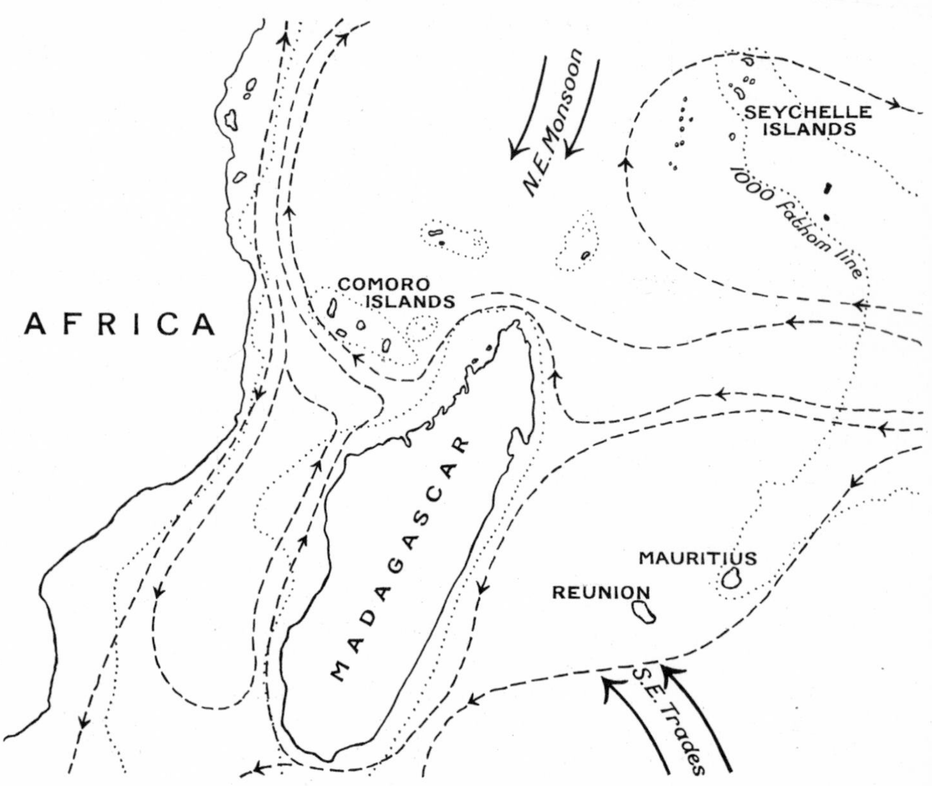


Madagascar is a large island, larger in area than the islands that make up New Zealand, and lies 260 miles from the east coast of Africa, in the Indian Ocean.

Geologically it is an old island, a granite plateau runs down the centre with scattered volcanic peaks. There are dense fern forests and bamboo thickets, tropical swamps, bare rock country and sand dunes. Many of the native mammals are forest-dwellers and it is probable that Madagascar was once more thickly forested than it is today.

Of modern Malagasy mammals, shrews, murid mice and an African bush pig are almost certainly recent human introductions. There are many bats, with both Ethiopian and Oriental affinities. The remaining seventy-five species of land mammal represent only four orders: Insectivora, Primates, Rodentia and Carnivora.

There is one family of insectivores, Tenrecidae, with thirty species. The family is unknown elsewhere, but in Madagascar it has paralleled more widely distributed insectivore forms. There are large spiny hedgehog tenrecs up to eighteen inches long, long-tailed mouse tenrecs, rice tenrecs with stout digging claws like moles, and water tenrecs with webbed feet and flattened tails.

The primates are represented by three families of lemurs. Two families contain mainly monkey-like animals, the well-known ring-tail lemurs, sportive lemurs, gentle lemurs, woolly lemurs and silky lemurs. The third is the aye-aye with chisel teeth specialized for a rodent life in the dense bamboo forests.

A subfamily of cricetid rats and several endemic genera of civets complete the modern mammal fauna. In addition a pygmy hippopotamus is known from pleistocene deposits.

There are plenty of birds on Madagascar. A large number are endemic, the majority of the rest African and a few are Oriental. Four families are confined to Madagascar, two of them flightless, the giant elephant birds which are extinct, and the rail-like mesoenatids. The other two families are philepittas and the black, white and chestnut vangas. Both forest families, the philepittas are fruit-eaters and the vangas feed mainly on chameleons and insects. But in contrast to diversity and mixed origin, there is a conspicuous lack in the avifauna of certain families. There are no ostriches, secretary-birds, touracos or mousebirds all of which are typical of Africa. There are no hornbills or woodpeckers, which are widely distributed through the Ethiopian and Oriental regions.

The reptile and amphibian component of the fauna follows the same pattern: absence of several African and Oriental families, a number of endemic genera, and the majority of the rest African. Thus agamid lizards (widespread through the Old World) and all poisonous snakes, pipid toads and common toads are absent. There are instead, pelomedusid side-neck turtles, land turtles, geckos, chameleons, skinks and spiny lizards which are mainly African and Old World families. But there are also land iguanids, a typically American family.

The polypedatid tree frogs, typical of Old World tropics, are well represented on Madagascar. Two genera are shared with Africa, one, *Polypedates*, with the Oriental region, and four are endemic.

There are no strictly freshwater fish in Madagascar.

The vertebrate fauna of Madagascar is a good deal more varied than that of New Zealand, but nevertheless it lacks the variety of its nearest neighbour, Africa. There are no large mammals or freshwater fish, and many families of Old World birds, reptiles and amphibia are lacking. In the main the fauna shows African affinities, but undoubtedly some of the birds and amphibia are more closely related to Oriental forms.

The many endemic families and genera on Madagascar indicate a long period of isolation, but as many of the endemic families are mammals and might need a land connexion, the isolation may date only from the paleocene or eocene. Madagascar may be, in fact, an ancient continental island and its continental connexions might be either with Africa or India, or both.

The continent of Lemuria, already discussed, would provide Madagascar with continental connexions in both an easterly and a westerly direction. Across Lemuria could have travelled lemurs, civets, some birds, chameleons and polypedatid frogs, to be shared by all. But Lemuria does not provide a satisfactory explanation of the animals it was particularly invented for, the lemurs, and has therefore already been dismissed.

It is more generally believed that Madagascar had a land connexion only with Africa during the Mesozoic. This would permit the African amphibia, reptiles, birds and earliest mammals to enter Madagascar by land. Thus some ancestral insectivores, lemurs, viverrids, cricetids, side-neck turtles and chameleons would have travelled to Madagascar between the cretaceous and the eocene. The difficulty with this theory is that there is no evidence that lemurs, viverrids and cricetids were in Africa all together or early enough. To put all the mammalian orders on the island by land, means waiting at least until eocene or even later days.

If this late date is correct, it is remarkable that, as far as is known, no condylarths populated Madagascar, nor any of the freshwater fish nor pipid toads which must have been in Africa then.

If land mammals require a land bridge to Madagascar it might be thought that amphibians needed one even more. But the polypedatid tree frogs are thought to have been late anuran derivatives, oligocene or miocene, and would need a late land bridge, presumably to both Africa and the Oriental region.

Bridges are rearing up in all directions at all times, and the geological evidence is against them.

The Mozambique channel between Africa and Madagascar is deep and the rock formations on either side suggest that the channel dates from at least triassic days. It may not always have been as wide as it is today but it seems to have been continuous. If this is confirmed, Madagascar must be considered to have been an island since the early Mesozoic.

The status of ancient island is supported by the composition of the Malagasy fauna. Many of the families are old, but neither are they all of the same age nor are they fully representative of an old African fauna. Some mammals and many amphibians are missing. Those that are found in Madagascar are mainly small and arboreal, just those that are most likely to sweep across the sea on 'rafts'. A short sea-crossing, selective by its very nature, can account for the endemic and African elements in the fauna, for

their apparent haphazard selection and for their varying ages. Tenrecs and the ancestors of the flightless elephant birds may have been early arrivals, followed by lemurs and cricetids, with civets, polypedatids and the pygmy hippo much later arrivals.

There is still the Oriental fraction of the fauna to be accounted for, and the American iguanids and the side-neck turtles.

The Oriental genera are comparatively few; four genera of birds, a few reptiles and frogs. It seems reasonable to suppose that the islands of the Indian Ocean that lie north of Madagascar may have been more numerous or more extensive at earlier dates and may have supplied stepping stones for these occasional migrants.

The iguanids and the side-neck turtles are a more difficult problem. Two genera of Malagasy side-necks are African but the third, *Podocnemis*, is South American. It is not easy to understand why American iguanids and a South American turtle should inhabit Madagascar. But fossil evidence suggests that the South American turtle was recently an inhabitant of Africa as well, and its presence in Madagascar is therefore no more surprising than that of any other African turtle. There is no such easy explanation of the iguanids. They are thought to have been a widespread family in the Mesozoic and the Malagasy genera may be relicts of an early African reptile fauna.

It is no easier to decide the status of Madagascar than it is to make a decision over New Zealand.

Madagascar has more mammals, reptiles and amphibia than New Zealand but they are not less highly differentiated, and, like New Zealand, is without primary freshwater fish. This might mean that Madagascar had a land connexion with Africa until the beginning of the Cenozoic to acquire its mammals and amphibia after which it became a discrete island, or it may mean, and the lack of freshwater fish and geological evidence supports this, that Madagascar has been an island since the early Mesozoic. If it has been an island for this length of time it should resemble New Zealand. In the specialization of its fauna it does resemble New Zealand but, in marked contrast to New Zealand, it has a flourishing fauna of mammals and amphibia. However, as the native mammals represent only four orders and the amphians only four families, it is likely that they derived from very few initial immigrants. One tenrec and one lemur colonization would have been enough to found the modern populations. The distance from Africa to Madagascar is only a quarter of that between Australia and New Zealand and may not have been as effective a sea barrier against amphibians and mammals.

Like New Zealand then, Madagascar has probably been isolated since the Mesozoic receiving its modern fauna from across the sea, but what happened before that cannot yet be decided.

# Conclusion

Animal populations evolve, spread and contract, limited by the geography, climate, flora, fauna and their own inherent propensities, and this complex and changing interaction of physical and living factors operates at all times. The study of present-day animal geography, the distribution of animals in space, is a cross-section taken at an arbitrary moment in time, of a process which has been going on steadily through the past. Only by understanding the changing scene, by combining and understanding the changes in time, the evolution, with changes in space, the distribution, can the apparent anomalies of animal geography be understood. The causes of distribution in the present are complex; they have been equally complex in the past.

# Book List

ALLEE, W. C., EMERSON, A. E., PARK, O., PARK, T. & SCHMIDT, K. P.: *Principles of Animal Ecology*: Philadelphia & London, 1949

BARTHOLOMEW, J. G., CLARKE, W. E. & GRIMSHAW, P. H.: *Atlas of Zoogeography*: Edinburgh, 1911

BEAUFORT, L. F. DE: *Zoogeography of the Land and Inland Waters*: London, 1951

BEIRNE, B. P.: *The Origin and History of the British Fauna*: London, 1952

COLBERT, E. H.: *Evolution of the Vertebrates*: New York, 1955

DARLINGTON, P. J.: *Zoogeography*: New York & London, 1957

DUNBAR, C. O.: *Historical Geology*: New York, 1949

EKMAN, S.: *Zoogeography of the Sea*: London, 1953

ELTON, C. S.: *The Ecology of Invasions by Animals and Plants*: London, 1958

HESSE, R., ALLEE, W. C. & SCHMIDT, K. P.: *Ecological Animal Geography*, 2nd edit: New York & London, 1951

HOLMES, A.: A revised geological time-scale: *Trans. Edin. Geol. Soc.* 17:183: 1960

IRVING, E. & GREEN, R.: Paleomagnetic evidence from the cretaceous and cainozoic: *Nature* 179:1064: 1957

JOLEAUD, L.: *Atlas de Paléogéographie*: Paris, 1939

LACK, D.: *Darwin's Finches*: Cambridge, 1947

MATTHEWS, L. HARRISON: *British Mammals:* London, 1952

MAYR, E.: Wallace's line in the light of recent zoogeographic studies: *Q.Rev.Biol.* 19:1: 1944

MAYR, E. (editor): The problem of land connections across the south atlantic with special reference to the mesozoic: *Bull.Amer.Mus.Nat.Hist.* 99:85: 1952

MAYR, E. & AMADON, D.: A classification of recent birds: *Amer.Mus. Novitates* 1496: 1951

MOREAU, R. E.: Africa since the mesozoic: *Proc.Zool.Soc.London* 121:869: 1952

NEAVERSON, E.: *Stratigraphical Paleontology*, 2nd edit: London, 1955

NOBLE, G. K.: *The Biology of the Amphibia*: New York, 1931

ROMER, A. S.: *Vertebrate Paleontology*, 2nd edit: Chicago, 1945

ROMER, A. S.: *Osteology of the Reptiles*: Chicago, 1956

SCOTT, W. B.: *A History of the Land Mammals in the Western Hemisphere*, Revised edit: New York, 1937

SIMPSON, G. G.: Antarctica as a faunal migration route: *Proc.6thPacific Sci.Congr.* 2:755: 1940

SIMPSON, G. G.: Mammals and the nature of continents: *Amer.J.Sci.* 241:1: 1943

SIMPSON, G. G.: The principles of classification and a classification of mammals: *Bull.Amer.Mus.Nat.Hist.* 85:1: 1945

SIMPSON, G. G.: Evolution, interchange, and resemblance of the North American and Eurasian cenozoic mammalian faunas: *Evolution* 1:218: 1947

SIMPSON, G. G.: History of the fauna of Latin America: *Amer.Scientist* 38: 361: 1950

SIMPSON, G. G.: *Life of the Past*: New Haven & Oxford, 1953
SIMPSON, G. G.: *Evolution and Geography*: Eugene, Oregon, 1953
TOIT, A. L. DU: *Our Wandering Continents*: Edinburgh, 1937
WALLACE, A. R.: *Geographical Distribution of Animals*: London, 1876
WALLACE, A. R.: *Island Life*: London, 1880
WILLS, L. J.: *Paleogeographical Atlas*: London & Glasgow, 1951
WOOD, A. E.: A revised classification of the rodents: *J. Mammal.* 36:165: 1955
YOUNG, J. Z.: *The Life of Vertebrates*: Oxford, 1950

# Index to Regional Illustrations

Read the animals on the illustrations from *left to right, from top to bottom*

GE 16. Carp *Cyprinus*, beaver *Castor*, Desman *Galemys*, wild horse *Equus*, pheasant *Phasianus*, *Hyaena*, giant salamander *Megalobatrachus*, mole rat *Spalax*, hedge sparrow *Prunella*, camel *Camelus*.

17. *Proteus*, spawn and tadpole *Rana*, salamander *Salamandra*, midwife toad *Alytes*, newt *Triturus*.

18. Mole *Talpa*, dormouse *Muscardinus*.

19. Beaver *Castor*, skunk *Mephitis*, *Ascaphus*, turkey *Meleagris*, rattlesnake *Crotalus*, pronghorn *Antilocapra*, pocket gopher *Geomys*, snapping turtle *Chelydra*, peccary *Tayassu*.

20. *Amphiuma*, axolotl *Ambystoma*, giant salamander *Cryptobranchus*, plethodont salamander *Eurycea*, *Siren*.

21. Garpike *Lepidosteus*, bowfin *Amia*.

22. Macaw *Ara*, two-toed sloth *Choloepus*, lungfish *Lepidosiren*, vampire bat *Desmodus*, tapir *Tapirus*, side-neck turtle *Chelys*, *Caiman*, *Lama*, peccary *Tayassu*, Surinam toad *Pipa*, hairy armadillo *Dasypus*, *Rhea*.

23. Squirrel monkey *Saimiri*, agouti *Dasyprocta*, paca *Cuniculus*, *Chinchilla*, marmoset *Oedipomidas*, capybara *Hydrochoerus*, woolly monkey *Lagothrix*, guinea pig *Cavia*.

24. Curassow *Crax*, umbrella bird *Cephalopterus*, humming bird *Chlorostillon*, toucan *Pteroglossus*, humming bird *Picaflor*, tanager *Thraupis*, cardinal *Cardenal*, trumpeter *Psaphia*.

25. Aardvark *Orycteropus*, hyena *Crocuta*, zebra *Equus*, chameleon *Chameleo*, okapi *Okapia*, rhinoceros *Diceros*, lungfish *Protopterus*, pangolin *Manis*, clawed toad *Xenopus*, side-neck turtle *Pelomedusa*, ostrich *Struthio*.

26. *Gorilla*, chimpanzee *Pan*, sacred baboon *Camopithecus*, mandrill *Mandrillus*, mangabey *Cercocebus*, macaque *Macaca*, Diana monkey *Cercopithecus*.

27. Gerenuk *Litocranius*, impala *Aepyceros*, klipspringer *Oreotragus*, gnu *Connochaetes*, kudu *Strepsiceros*.

28. *Hyaena*, gavial *Gavialis*, *Rhinoceros*, pangolin *Manis*, peacock *Pavo*, tapir *Tapirus*, Siamese fighting fish *Betta*, colugo *Cynocephalus*, cobra *Naia*, *Tarsius*.

29. Hornbill *Dichoceros*, drongo shrike *Dissemurus*, sunbird *Cinnyris*, Argus pheasant *Argusianus*, jungle fowl *Gallus*, tragopan *Ceriornis*, mynah *Eulabes*.

30. Tree shrew *Tupaia*, slow loris *Nycticebus*, langur *Presbytis*, gibbon *Hylobates*, orang utan *Pongo*.

30. Megapode *Talegallus*, *Moloch*, cassowary *Cassuaris*, kangaroo *Macropus*, lungfish *Neoceratodus*, cockatoo *Cacatua*, duckbilled platypus *Ornithorhynchus*, wombat *Phascolomis*, side-neck turtle *Chelodina*, lyre bird *Menura*.

31. Anteater *Myrmecobius*, marsupial mole *Notoryctes*, flying phalanger *Petaurus*, Tasmanian wolf *Thylacinus*, koala *Phascolarctos*.

32. Great bird of paradise *Paradisea*, long-tailed bird of paradise *Falcinellus*, magnificent bird of paradise *Diphyllodes*, six-shafted bird of paradise *Parotia*, twelve-wired bird of paradise *Seleucides*, red bird of paradise *Paradisea*.

PAGE 38. Jumping mouse *Zapus*, Gila monster *Heloderma*, prairie dog *Cynomys*, marmot *Marmota*, rattlesnake *Crotalus*, horned lizard *Phrynosoma*, kangaroo rat *Dipodomys*.

39. Jerboa *Jaculus*, gazelle *Addax*, ground squirrel *Xerus*, horned viper *Cerastes*, gerbil *Acomys*, spiny-tailed lizard *Cordylus*.

67. Side-neck turtle *Podocnemis*, side-neck turtle *Podocnemis*, lungfish *Ceratodus*, insectivore *Puercolestes*, insectivore *Deltatheridium*, condylarth *Oxyacodon*, lungfish *Ceratodus*, marsupial *Eodelphis*, creodont *Oxyclaenus*.

68. Primate *Adapis*, side-neck turtle *Podocnemis*, marsupial *Peratherium*, insectivore *Adapisorex*, creodont *Sinopa*, side-neck turtle *Taphrosphys*, camelid *Protylopus*, rhinocerotid *Prohyracodon*, condylarth *Hyopsodus*, insectivore *Phenacops*, sciuromorph rodent *Plesiarctomys*, sciuromorph rodent *Paramys*, insectivore *Adapisorex*, marsupial *Peratherium*, primate *Notharctus*, creodont *Sinopa*.

70. Rhinocerotid *Aceratherium*, side-neck turtle *Podocnemis*, marsupial *Peratherium*, insectivore *Talpa*, side-neck turtle *Taphrosphys*, pig *Paleochoerus*, beaver *Paleocastor*, camelid *Oxydactylus*, cat *Pseudaelurus*, insectivore *Proscalops*, marsupial *Peratherium*, proboscid *Gomphotherium*, deer *Blastomeryx*, peccary *Perchoerus*, deer *Amphitragulus*, beaver *Steneofiber*, cat *Archaelurus*, rhinocerotid *Diceratherium*.

71. Rhinocerotid *Dicerorhinus*, side-neck turtle *Paralichelys*, ape *Dryopithecus*, elephant *Stegolophodon*, insectivore *Talpa*, beaver *Castor*, pig *Sus*, beaver *Castor*, insectivore *Scalopus*, camelid *Procamelus*, hyena *Crocuta*, deer *Cervus*, deer *Cranioceras*, peccary *Prosthennops*, cat *Pseudaelurus*, murid *Parapodemus*, cat *Felis*, proboscid *Tetralophodon*, pronghorn *Sphenophalos*.

75. Side-neck turtle *Podocnemis*, lungfish *Ceratodus*, condylarth *Oxyacodon*, marsupial *Eodelphis*, lungfish *Ceratodus*, side-neck turtle *Podocnemis*.

76. Side-neck turtle *Taphrosphys*, sciuromorph, primate, condylarth *Didolodus*, armadillo *Utaetus*, notoungulate *Thomashuxleya*, marsupial *Ideodelphys*, side-neck turtle *Podocnemis*.

77. Camelid *Oxydactylus*, procyonid *Alectocyon*, side-neck turtle *Taphrosphys*, notoungulate *Adinotherium*, cebid *Homunculus*, marsupial *Prothylacinus*, chinchilla *Perimys*, litoptern *Thoatherium*, armadillo *Peltephilus*, side-neck turtle *Podocnemis*, marsupial *Microbiotherium*.

78. Peccary *Prosthennops*, camelid *Procamelus*, raccoon *Procyon*, notoungulate *Trigodon*, opossum *Didelphis*, carnivorous marsupial *Thylacosmilus*, litoptern *Promacrauchenia*, armadillo *Chaetophractus*, side-neck turtle *Podocnemis*, chinchilla *Euphilus*.

79. Side-neck turtle *Podocnemis*, lungfish *Ceratodus*, condylarth, lungfish *Ceratodus*, insectivore, side-neck turtle *Podocnemis*.

80. Primate *Adapis*, side-neck turtle *Podocnemis*, creodont *Sinopa*, proboscid *Moeritherium*, side-neck turtle *Podocnemis*, insectivore.

81. Side-neck turtle *Podocnemis*, rhinocerotid *Aceratherium*, *Arsinoitherium*, pig *Paleochoerus*, ape *Proconsul*, side-neck turtle *Podocnemis*, proboscid *Gomphotherium*, cat *Pseudaelurus*, creodont *Hyaenodon*, lungfish *Protopterus*.

82. Ancestral tree shrew, creodont *Propterodon*, side-neck turtle *Podocnemis*, primate *Pondaungia*, rhinocerotid *Fostercooperia*.

83. Proboscid *Gomphotherium*, deer *Amphitragulus*, side-neck turtle, cat *Hyaenaelurus*, pig *Paleochoerus*, rhinocerotid *Aceratherium*.

84. Hyena *Crocuta*, ape *Bramapithecus*, side-neck turtle *Shweboemys*, elephant *Stegodon*, murid *Parapodemus*, cat *Panthera*, rhinocerotid *Rhinoceros*, deer *Cervus*, pig *Sus*.

85. Condylarth *Phenacolophus*, insectivore, marsupial, lungfish *Ceratodus*.

86. Deer *Cervus*, pig *Sus*, bat, agamid lizard, murid, boid snake, phalangerid marsupial *Wynyardia*, lungfish *Neoceratodus*.

104. *Tarsius*, cockatoo *Cacatua*, dwarf buffalo *Anoa*, cuscus *Phalanger*, starling *Basilornis*, *Babirussa*, *Cynopithecus*, *Papilio*.

PAGE 108. Plover *Charadrius* (*Aegialitis*), goat *Capra*, snail *Helisiga*, carnivorous beetle *Haplothorax*, goat *Capra*.

111. Marine iguana *Amblyrhynchus*, giant tortoise *Testudo*, land iguana *Conolophus*.

111. Penguin *Spheniscus*, flightless cormorant *Nannopterum*.

115. Proboscid *Tetralophodon*, brachiopod *Terebratula*, *Hyaena*, sabre-tooth *Macairodus*, teleost *Clupea*, cricetid *Mimomys*.

117. Yellow-necked mouse *Apodemus*, mole *Talpa*, horseshoe bat *Rhinolophus*, red deer *Cervus*, stoat *Mustela*, hare *Lepus*.

118. Common frog *Rana*, palmate newt *Triturus palmatus*, common newt *T.vulgaris*, crested newt *T.cristatus*, natterjack *Bufo calamita*, common toad *B.bufo*.

124. Tuatara *Sphenodon*, rail *Notornis*, kiwi *Apteryx*, kakapo *Strigops*, *Liopelma*

125. Moa *Dinornis*, flightless goose *Cnemiornis*.

127. Black lemur *Lemur*, *Indri*, aye aye *Daubentonia*, hedgehog tenrec *Setifer*, cricetid *Neomys*, civet *Galidia*, civet *Viverricula*, bush pig *Potamochoerus*.

128. Helmet bird *Euryceros*, tree frog *Polypedates*, chameleon *Chameleo*, side-neck turtle *Pelomedusa*, *Vanga*.

# Index

AARDVARKS, 9, **25,** 26, 57, **58,** 72, 80
Africa, 5, 12, 14, 16, 17, 18, 22, 24-7, 28, 29, 30, 32, 33, 38, 39, 47, 48, 49, 66, 72, 74, 78-82, 83, 84, 87, 89, 90, 91, **94,** 95, 96, 103, 107, 108, 109, 126, 127, 128, 129
Agamids, 27, 29, **30,** 32, 55, **86,** 87, 93, 96, 127
Alamiqui, 7
Alaska, 48, 70
Aleutian Islands, 18, 49
Allee, W. C., 33, 131
Alligators, 17, 24
Alpacas, 21
Amazon River, 21, 24, 27, 35
Ambystomids, **20,** 24, **54,** 55, 66, 69, 70, 73
America, 8, 12, 17, 18-24, 27, 31, 32, 39, 48, 67, 72, 73, 77, 88, 89, 93, 94, 95, 103, 109, 111, 127, 129
  Central, 18, 20, 21, 24, 49, 103, 111
  North, 12, 13, **14,** 16, 17, 18-21, 23, 24, 26, 28, 33, 38, 39, 47, 48, 54, 65-73, 74, 75, 76, 77, 78, 80, 81, 89, 90, **94,** 103, 115, 116
  South, 12, 13, 14, 17, 18, 20, 21-24, 25, 26, 27, 28, 32, 33, 38, 47, 48, 49, 65, 74-8, 79, 81, 84, 87, 88-91, 92-3, **94,** 95, 96, 103, 107, 108, 109, 111, 129
Amphibia, classification, 5, **52,** 53, 54-5
  dispersal, 33, 34, 36, 37, 38
  distribution, 13, **17,** 18, 20, 24, 27, 29, 30, 32, 46, 66, 69, 71, 73, 74, 82, 85, 87, 88, 89, **90,** 92, 93, 95, 96
  evolution, 44, **52,** 53, 54-5
  on islands, 107, 109, 111, 114, 116, 118, 119, 121, 124, 125, 127, 128, 129
  tailed, 5, **16,** 17, 18, 20, 24, 27, 29, 32, 38, 54, 55, 66, 69, 70, 71, 73, 118, 119, 121
  tailless, 5, 13, **17,** 18, 20, **22,** 24, 27, 29, 30, 32, 33, 36, 38, 54, 55, 66, 74, 78, 82, 85, 87, 89, **90, 92,** 93, 95, 96, 118, 119, 121, 124, 125, 127, 128, 129
Amphiumidae, **20, 54**
Anaconda, 24
Andes, 21, 23, 48
*Anguis*, 118
Anomaluridae, 8, 26
*Anomalurus*, 26
Antarctic, 34, 89, 92-3, **94,** 95, 96, 125
Anteaters, 8, 22, 23, 61, 75
  Cape, **25,** 26
  marsupial, **31**
  scaly, 8, **25,** 26, 28, **58**
  spiny, 7, 32, 55
Antelopes, 10, 26, **27,** 39, **59,** 80
Antilocapridae, 10, 12, **19, 59, 61,** 66, 70, **71,** 73
Anura, 5, 13, **17,** 18, 20, **22,** 24, 27, 29, 30, 32, 33, 36, 38, 54, 55, 66, 74, 78, 82, 85, 87, 89, **90, 92,** 93, 95, 96, 118, 119, 121, 124, 125, 127, 128, 129
Apes, 8, **26,** 27, 29, **30,** 57, **71,** 80, **81, 84**
Aplodontidae, 8, 19, 20, 57
Apoda, 5, 54, 55
Arabia, 16, 24, 80, 93
Archipelagos, 5, 28, 30, 49, 85, 87, 101-4, 111-4, 115
Arctogea, 14
Armadillos, 8, 18, 21, **22,** 23, **58,** 75, **76,** 77, 78
*Arsinoitherium*, 79, **81**

Arthropods, **36,** 45, **50,** 51, 53, 101, **104, 106,** 107, 108, 113, 114, 122
Artiodactyla, 5, **6,** 10, 12, 13, **16,** 17, 18, 19, 20, 21, **22,** 23, 25, 26, **27,** 28, 31, 35, 37, 39, 56, 57, **58,** 59, 60, 61, 66, 68, 69, 70, 71, 72, 73, 77, **78,** 80, 81, 83, **84, 86,** 87, 103, **104,** 105, 107, **108,** 116, 117, 118, 119, 124, 126, 127, 129
Aru Islands, 101, **102**
*Ascaphus*, **19,** 20, **54,** 55, 124
Ascension Island, 89, **107**
Asia, 12, 16-8, 48, 66, 67, 80, 82-4, 85, 86, 87, 91, 93, **94,** 96, 101-4, 125
Atlantic Ocean, 47, 88, 89, 90, 94, 95, 107, 109, 116
Australian Region, 12, **14,** 17, 18, 23, 24, 28, 29, 30-2, 33, 35, 39, 49, 72, 74, 82, 84-7, 88, 89, 92, 93, **94,** 95, 96, 101-4, 123, 124, 125, 129
Axolotls, **20,** 24, **54,** 55, 66, 69, 70, 73
Aye aye, 8, 127
Azores, 33, 38, 104, **105**

BABIRUSSA, 103, **104**
Baboons, 26, 103, **104**
Badgers, 9, 117
Bali, 101, **102**
Bamboo rats, 8, 26, 28
Bandicoots, 7, 31
Barbets, 29, 32, 101, **103**
Barriers, to spread, 33, 35, 37, 46, 69, 81, 84, 86, 129
Bartholomew, J. G., 5, 131
Bass, 20
Bathyergidae, 9, 26
Bathyergomorpha, 9, 26
Bats, 7, 11, 16, 17, 18, 21, **22,** 23, 25, 28, 31, **36,** 37, 38, 56, **58,** 60, 68, 74, **86,** 87, 103, 105, 109, 111, 113, 114, 117, 124, 125, 126
Bears, 9, 17, 18, 21, 25, 29, 57, 61, 70, 71, 73, 77, 80, 116, 118
Beavers, 8, 12, **16,** 17, 18, **19,** 21, 25, 57, **60, 70, 71,** 72, 77, 83, 118
Beetles, **36, 50, 108,** 113
Bering Straits, 48, 70, 93
Bermuda, 104
Birds, 5, 11, 12, 13, 33, **34,** 35, **36,** 37, 38, 44, 46, **52,** 53, 55, 69, 74, 77, 78, 87, 89, 92, 93, 95, 96
  flightless, **22,** 23, 25, 27, **30,** 32, 33, 38, 69, 89, 92, 95, 101, **103,** 106, 109, 111, 124, 125, 127, 129
  of islands, 101, 103, **104,** 106, 107, 108, 109-110, 111, 113, 114, 117, 118, 119, 124, 125, 127, 128, 129
  of regions, **16,** 17, 19, 20, 23, 24, 26, 27, 28, 29, 30, 32
Birds of Paradise, 32
Bison, 116
Blackbirds, 17
Blackfish, 33
Blesmols, 9, 26
Boas, 24, **86**
Borneo, 28, 101, **102,** 104
Bovidae, 10, 17, 18, 19, 21, 23, 25, 26, **27,** 28, 39, 59, 61, 70, 71, 73, 77, 80, 103, **104,** 107, **108,** 116, 118, 124
Bowerbirds, 32
Bowfins, 20, **21,** 54
Bradypodidae, 8, 22, 23, 33, 60, 75
Brevicipitidae, **54**
British Isles, 35, **45, 47,** 48, **105,** 115-122
Buffalo, dwarf, 103, **104**
Bufonidae, 18, 20, 24, 30, 32, **54,** 55, 118, 119, 121, 127
Bulbuls, 113
Butterflies, 35, **104,** 113, 119

CAECILIANS, 5, 54, 55
Caenolestidae, 7, 23
Caimans, **22,** 24
Callithricidae, 8, 12, 23
Cambrian, 44, 47, 50, 51, 53
Camelidae, 10, 13, **16,** 17, 19, 21, **22,** 25, 35, 59, 60, **68,** 69, 70, 71, 72, 73, 77, **78**
Camels, 10, 13, **16,** 17, 19, 21, **22,** 25, 35, 59, 60, **68,** 69, 70, 71, 72, 73, 77, **78**
Cane rates, 9, 26
Canidae, 6, 9, 17, 18, 21, 25, 28, 31, 35, 57, 60, 69, 77, 80, 87, 116, 118, 119
Capuchins, **8,** 23, **58**
Capybaras, 9, **23**
Carboniferous, 44, 50, 52, 53, 94, 95
Cardinals, 20, **24**
Carnivora, 6, 9, **16,** 17, 18, **19,** 21, 25, 26, 28, 29, 31, 35, 37, 38, 56, 57, **58,** 59, 60, 61, 66, **67,** 69, 70, 71, 72, 73, 76, 77, **78,** 80, **81, 83, 84,** 87, 103, **115,** 116, 117, 118, 119, 127, 128, 129
Carp, 12, **16,** 18, 20, 24, 27, 30, 54, 69, 70, 73, 118
Cassowaries, **30,** 32, 101, **103**
Castoridae, 8, 12, **16,** 17, 18, **19,** 21, 25, 57, **60, 70, 71,** 72, 77, 83, 118
Castorimorpha, 8, **16,** 17, 18, **19,** 21, 25, 57, **60, 70, 71,** 72, 77, 83, 118
Catfish, 24, 27, 30
Cats, 6, 9, 17, 18, 21, 25, 26, 28, 57, 60, **70, 71,** 77, 80, **81, 83, 84,** 117, 119
  pouched, 31
Cattle, 10, 23
Caviomorpha, 9, 23, 57, 60, **77, 78**
Cavies, 57, 60
Cebidae, 8, 23, **58,** 60, **77**
Celebes, 87, 101, 102-4, 105
Cenozoic, 44, 48, 49, 50, 52, 53-61, 65-97, 102, 103, 115, 116, 118, 119, 122, 124, 125, 126, 127, 128, 129
Cercopithecidae, 8, 26, **30,** 103, **104**
Cervidae, 10, 17, 18, 19, 21, 28, 59, 60, 69, 70, **71,** 72, 77, 80, 83, **84, 86,** 103, 116, 117, 118, 119
Cetacea, 9, 31, **58**
Chameleons, **25,** 27, 55, 96, 127, 128
Chamois, 118
Channel, English, 93, 104, 116, 118, 119
Char, 118
Characins, 24, 27, 54, 66, 68, 74, 89, 95
Chelyidae, 24, **30,** 32, **88**
Chevrotains, 10, 26, 28, **59**
Chimpanzee, 26
China, 17, 28, 35, 104
Chinchillas, 9, 23, 57, 60, **77, 78**
Chiroptera, 7, 11, 16, 17, 18, 21, **22,** 23, 25, 28, 31, **36,** 37, 38, 56, **58,** 60, 68, 74, **86,** 87, 103, 105, 109, 111, 113, 114, 117, 124, 125, 126
Chordata, 5
Chrysochloridae, 7, 26, 79
Civets, 9, 17, 25, 28, 57, 60, 69, 103, 127, 128, 129
Clarke, W. E., 5, 131
Class, 5, 7, 10, 14, 24, 53
Classification, of animals, 7-10, 50, 52, 54, 55, 91, 92
  of continents, 14, 16-32
  of islands, 101-2, 104-6, 111

Climate, 14, 16, 18, 27, 28, 31, 33-5, 38, 39, 49, 53, 72, 81, 82, 84, 93, 105, 107, 116, 117, 118, 119, 120, 121, 122, 124, 130
Cockatoos, **30,** 32, 101, **103, 104**
Cock of the rock, 23
Cockroaches, 53
Coelenterates, **50,** 51
Colonization, of continents, 66-97
of islands, 101-129
Colugos, 7, **28,** 29, **58, 103**
Condylarths, 56, 57, **58,** 59, 60, 66, **67, 68,** 69, 75, 76, 79, **85,** 96, 128
Coneys, 9, 17, 25, 29, **58**
Continental drift, 46, 88, 94-7, 125
islands, 115-22
patterns, 16-32, 65-97
Continents, permanence of, 46-9, 66, 87, 88, 90, 96, 97
Cordylidae, 27, 39, 127
Cormorants, 109, 111
Cotingids, 23
Cracids, 23, **24**
Creation, 33, 109
Creodonts, 57, **58,** 59, 60, 66, 67, **68, 80, 81, 82**
Cretaceous, 44, 47, 48, 50, 52, 53, 54, 55, 56, 57, 60, 66, 67, 74, 75, 78-9, 81, 82, 85, 86, 90, 92, 124, 128
Cricetidae, 8, 17, 18, 21, 25, 28, 57, 60, 80, 109, **115,** 116, 117, 118, 119, 120, 127, 128, 129
Crocodiles, 17, **22,** 24, 27, **28,** 29, 32, 33, 55, 66, 74, 78, 82, 83, 85, 114, 116
Crows, 11
Cryptobranchidae, **20, 54**
Cryptodires, 17, **19,** 20, 24, 27, 29, 32, 33, **36,** 37, 55, 87, 106, 110, **111,** 116, 124
Ctenodactylidae, 8, 26
Cuckoos, 11, 27, 32
Curassows, 23, **24**
Current, Benguela, 107, 108
Humboldt, 109, 111
ocean, 34, 105, 107, 108, 109, 111, 123
Peru, 109, 111
Cynocephalidae, 7, **28,** 29, **58, 103**
*Cynocephalus*, **7, 28,** 29, **58**

DALLIIDAE, 33
Darlington, P. J., 5, 131
Darwin, C., 33, 106, 109-110, 111
Dasypodidae, 8, 18, 21, 22, 23, **58, 60,** 75, **76, 77,** 78
*Dasypus*, **8, 22,** 23, **58**
Dasyuridae, 7, 31, 35
Daubentonidae, 8, 127
Deer, 10, 17, 18, 19, 21, 28, 59, 60, 69, **70, 71,** 72, 77, 80, 83, **84, 86,** 103, 116, 117, 118, 119
Degus, 23
Dermoptera, 7, **28,** 29, **58, 103**
Deserts, 16, 21, 24, 34, 35, 38, 39
Devonian, 44, 50, 51, 52, 53
Didelphidae, 7, 18, 21, 23, **60, 67,** 75, **76,** 78
Dinosaurs, **52,** 53
Dipnoi, **22,** 24, **25,** 27, **30,** 32, 36, 54, 66, 67, 74, **75,** 78, **79, 81,** 85, **86,** 89, 92, 95
Dipodidae, 9, 17, 25, 29, 39
Discoglossidae, **17, 54**
Dispersal, 33-40
continental, 65-87, 96
island, 101-29
Distribution, 10, 11-32, 33, 34, 35, 36, 40, 46, 53, 65-130
discontinuous, 11, 13, 17, 21, 33, 38, 72, 73, 92, 96
maps, 11-15, **16, 19, 22, 25, 28, 30, 34, 65-97, 110, 115, 120, 121**
Dodo, 106
Dogs, 6, 9, 17, 18, 21, 25, 28, 31, 35, 57, 60, 69, 77, 80, 87
Doggerland, 116
Dormice, 9, 17, **18,** 25, 117, 119, 120
Douroucoulis, 23
Drills, 26
Dunbar, C. O., 47, 131

EARTH, age of, 43, 48
Echidnas, 7, 32, 55
Echinoderms, **50,** 51
Ecuador, 108, **109**
Edentata, 8, 18, 21, 22, 23, 56, 57, **58,** 60, 61, 67, 69, 72, 75, 76, 77, 78, 79, 89, 92, 96
Eels, 36,
electric, 24, 27, 96
Ekman, S., 5, 131
Elephant birds, 127, 129
Elephantidae, 9, 26, 28, 33, 55, **56, 58,** 59, 61, **71,** 72, 77, 79, 80, 81, 83, 84, 103, 116
Elephants, 9, 26, 28, 33, 55, **56, 58,** 59, 61, **71,** 72, 77, 79, 80, 81, 83, 84, 103, 116
Elephant shrews, 7, 26, 29, 79
Elk, Irish, 72
Elton, C. S., 33, 131
Emus, 32
Endemism, 17, 18, 19, 20, 21, 22, 23, 24, 26, 27, 28, 29, 31, 32, 69, 73, 103, 104, 105, 106, 108, 109, 110, 111, 114, 117, 118, 124, 125, 127, 128, 129
England, **45,** 93, 101
Eocene, 44, 48, 54, 55, 56, 57, 58, 59, 60, 67, 68, 69, 71, 76, 80, 82, 83, 91, 94, 95, 126, 128
Epochs, list, 44
Equidae, 5, 6, 10, **16,** 17, 20, 21, 23, 25, 26, 29, **58,** 59, **60,** 66, 68, 77, 116
*Equus*, 5, 6, **10, 16, 25,** 26, **58**
Erinaceidae, 7, 17, 18, 21, 25, 28, 57, 69, 117, 119
Ethiopian Region, 14, 16, 17, 18, 22, 24-7, 28, 29, 30, 32, 38, 39, 74, 78-82, 84, 87, 88, 89, 90, 96, 103, 126, 127, 128, 129
Eurasia, 16-8, 65-73, 80, 89, 104
Europe, 16-8, 45, 47, 48, 65, 66, 69, 108, 115-22
Eurypterids, **50,** 51, 53
Evolution of animals, 51-61, 66, 72, 74, 76, 78, 79, 81, 85, 87, 89, 104, 106, 109-10, 117, 118, 130
of continents, 43-9, 65-93, 130
Extinctions, 23, 51, 53, 66, 72, 73, 74, 78, 80, 81, 83, 84, 91, 92, 106, 107, 111, 116, 121-2, 124

FAIRY BLUEBIRDS, 29
Families, amphibian, 54-5
distribution of, 11-32, 65-97, 124-9
endemic, 17, 19-20, 21-4, 25, 26, 27, 29, 31, 32, 124, 127, 129
evolution of, 53-61
fish, 54
mammalian, 5-10, 55-61
on islands, 101-29
reptile, 55
Fauna, island, 101-29
regional, 13, 16-32, 38-9, 65-93
Faunal interchange, 69, 70, 72, 74, 83, 104
Felidae, 6, 9, 17, 18, 21, 25, 26, 28, 57, 60, 69, **70, 71,** 72, 77, 80, **81, 83, 84, 115,** 116, 117, 119

Finches, 17, 32, 109-10
Fish, 5, 12, **16,** 18, 20, **21, 22,** 24, **25,** 27, **28,** 30, 32, 33, 35, 36, 38, 51, **52,** 53, 54, 66, 67, 68, 69, 70, 73, 74, **75,** 78, **79,** 85, **86,** 88, 89, 92, 93, 95, 96, 103, 105, 107, 109, 111, **115,** 118, 119, 124, 127, 128, 129
Flores, 102, 103
Flowerpeckers, 32
Flycatchers, 114
Forbes, E., 122
Forests, 12, 16, 21, 23, 24, 26, 31, 34, 35, 45, 80, 108-9, 113, 114, 126, 127
Formosa, 104
Fossil distribution, 44-6, 65-97, 115-6, 124, 125, 127, 129
  evolution, 44-6, 50-61
Foxes, 31, 35, 119
France, 93, 116, 118, 119
Frogmouths, 32
Frogs, 5, 13, **17,** 18, 20, 24, 27, 30, 32, 33, 36, 38, **54,** 55, 66, 82, 85, 87, 96, 118, 119, 124, 125, 129

GALAGOS, 8, 26
Galapagos Islands, 93, 104, 106, 108-11
Garpikes, 20, **21,** 54
Gavials, **28,** 29, 83
Geckos, 20, 29, 32, 111, 113, 114, 124, 125, 127
Geese, 17, 124, **125**
Geladas, 26
Genus, 5, 6, 10
  endemic, 13, 20, 21, 24, 26, 31, 108, 109, 111, 125, 127, 129
Geomyidae, 8, 19, 20, 57, 60, 69, 70, 73
Gibbons, 26, **30**
Gila Monster, 20, **38,** 39
*Giraffa*, 5, **6, 59**
Giraffes, 5, **6,** 10, 12, 26, 59, 61, 70, 71, 77, 80, 83
Giraffidae, 5, **6,** 10, 12, **25,** 26, 59, 61, 70, 71, 77, 80, 83
Giraffinae, 5, **6**
Glaciation, 49, 73, 116, 122
Gliding-mice, 26
Gliridae, 9, 17, **18,** 25, 117, 119, 120
Glyptodons, 75, 78
Goats, 10, 107, **108**
Golden moles, 7, 26, 79
Gondwanaland, 88-9
Gorilla, 26
Grasslands, 12, 16, 19, 21, 24, 26, 80, 112-3
Great Britain, 104, **105,** 117-9, 120, 121, 122
Green, R., 96, 131
Greenland, 18, 47, 48, 89, 115
Grimshaw, P. H., 5, 131
Ground sloths, 72, 75, 78
Grouse, 20, 118, 119
Guanacos, 17, 21
Guenons, 26
Guinea pigs, 9, 23
Gundis, 8, 26
Gymnotids, 24, 27, 96

HAMMERHEADS, 27
Hamsters, 8, 118
Hares, 8, **58,** 117, 119
Hawks, 11, 32
Hedgehogs, 7, 17, 18, 21, 25, 28, 57, 69, 117, 119
Hedge sparrows, **16,** 17
Heilprin, A., 14
Helmet shrike, 27
Herbivores, South American, 75, 76, 77, **78,** 89, 92
Hesse, R., 33, 131
Heteromyidae, 9, 19, 20, **38,** 39
Himalayas, 16, 28, 48, 71, 83
Hippopotamidae, 10, 26, 37, 59, 116, 127, 129
Hippos, 10, 26, 37, 59, 116, 127, 129
Hoatzins, 23
Holarctic, 14
Holmes, A., 44, 131
Holostei, 20, **21,** 54, 66, 68, 70, 73
Hominidae, 8, 20, 31, 33, 44, 73, 80, 107, 113, 116, 126
Honeysuckers, 32, 101
Hornbills, 27, **29,** 127
Horses, 5, 6, 10, **16,** 17, 20, 21, 23, 25, 29, **58,** 59, 66, 68, 77, 116
House sparrows, 33
Humming birds, 20, **24,** 78
Hyaenidae, 9, **16,** 17, 18, 21, 25, 28, 57, **58,** 59, 61, 71, 72, 73, 77, 80, **84, 115,** 116
Hydromyinae, 31
Hyenas, 9, **16,** 17, 18, 21, 25, 28, 57, **58,** 59, 61, 71, 72, 73, 77, 80, **84, 115,** 116
Hylidae, 18, 20, 24, 27, 29, 32, **54,** 55, 85, 92, 93, 95, 96
Hynobidae, **54**
Hyracoidea, 9, 17, 25, 29, **58**
Hyraxes, 9, **58**
Hystricidae, 9, 17, 25, 26, 28, 60, 89, 103
Hystricomorpha, 9, 17, 25, 26, 28, 60, 89, 103

IBEX, 118
Ice Ages, 49, 72, 81, 116, 119, 122
Iguanidae, 20, 24, 27, **38,** 39, 55, 93, 96, 111, 127, 129
India, 14, 27, 28, 29, 33, 83, 89, 91, **94,** 96, 128
Indian Ocean, 28, 47, 88, 94, 95, 126, 129
Indridae, 8, **127**
Insectivora, 7, 12, **16,** 17, 18, 21, 25, 26, 28, 29, 31, 56, 57, **58,** 59, 60, 66, **67, 68,** 69, **70, 71,** 79, 80, 81, 82, **85,** 86, 103, 117, 119, **120,** 121, 127, 128, 129
Insects, 35, **36,** 45, **50,** 51, 53, 101, **104,** 106, 107, 108, 113, 114, 119, 122
Invertebrates, 5, 13, **36,** 45, **50,** 51, 53, 93, 96, 101, 102, 107, 108, 113, 114, **115,** 119, 122, 125
Ireland, 93, 119-22
Irving, E., 96, 131
Islands, 5, 10, 25, 28, 30, 33, 36, 37, 38, 74, 76, 85, 86, 87, 89, 90, 91, 93, 101-29
  ancient, 123-29
  continental, 104-5, 106, 112, 115-22, 125, 128
  hopping, 76, 86-7, 93, 96, 129
  oceanic, 104-14, 125
Isolation, 75-6, 77, 78, 79, 81, 84-7, 92, 104-14, 117, 119, 125, 127, 128

JAPAN, 49, 104
Java, 28, 101, **102,** 112, 113, 114
Jerboas, 9, 17, 25, 29, **39**
  pouched, 31
Jumping mice, 9, 17, 18, **38**
Jungle fowl, 29, **103**
Jurassic, 44, 45, 47, 50, 52, 53, 55, 85, 90, 91, 95, 125

KAKAPO, 124
Kangaroo rats, 9, **38,** 39
Kangaroos, 7, **30,** 31, **58,** 72, **103**
Kea, 124

Kei Islands, 101, 102
Kingfishers, 32, 113
Kiwis, 124
Koalas, **31,** 35
Komodo dragon, 32
Krakatau, 111-4

LACERTIDS, 27, 55, 118
Lagomorpha, 8, 17, 18, 21, 25, 28, 31, 33, 56, 57, **58,** 60, 67, 68, 69, 82, 117, 119
*Lama*, 21, **22**
Land bridges, 46, 88-93, 94, 96, 97, 111, 120, 122, 125, 128
connexions, 16, 20, 21, 24, 30, 47, 48, 49, 66, 69, 70, 71, 73, 74, 75, 76, 77, 79, 80, 81, 82, 84, 85, 86, 87, 88, 89, 90, 91, 93, 104, 115, 116, 119, 120, 121, 122, 125, 128, 129
Langurs, 26, **30**
Lemmings, 8, 118
Lemuria, 89, 91-2, 128
Lemuridae, 8, 66, 69, 79, 88, 91, 92, 127, 128, 129
Lemurs, 8, 66, 69, 79, 88, 91, 92, 127, 128, 129
*Lepidosiren*, **22,** 24, 27
Leporidae, 8, 17, 18, 21, 25, 28, 31, 33, 57, **58,** 69, 117, 119
Leptodactylidae, **54**
Limitation, 33-5, 36, 37, 38, 39, 40, 66, 68, 69, 71, 72, 73, 74, 77, 81, 86, 120, 130
Lions, 26, 116
*Liopelma*, 20, 55, 124, 125
Liopelmidae, 13, **19,** 20, **54,** 55, 66, 85, 87, 124, 125
Lizards, 17, 20, 24, 27, 29, **30,** 32, **38,** 39, 55, **86,** 87, 93, 96, 106, 110, 111, 113, 114, 116, 118, 119, 120, 124, 125, 127, 129
Llamas, 10, 21
Loach, 118
Lombok, 101, 102, 103
Lories, 32
Lorises, 8, 25, 26, 28, 29, **30,** 57, 88, 91, 92
Lorisidae, 8, 25, 26, 28, 29, **30,** 57, 88, 91, 92
*Loxodonta*, **9,** 26, **56, 58**
Lungfish, **22,** 24, **25,** 27, **30,** 32, 36, 54, 66, 67, 74, **75,** 78, **79, 81,** 85, **86,** 89, 92, 95
Lusitanian bridge, 122
Lyell, C., 47
Lyre birds, **30,** 32

MACAQUES, **26,** 103
Macaws, **22,** 24
Macropodidae, 7, **30,** 31, **58,** 72, **103**
Macroscelidae, 7, 26, 29, 79
Madagascar, 25, 79, 88, 89, 91, 92, 126-9
Malaya, 13, 28, 29, 38, 101, **102**
Malay Archipelago, 28, 30, 49, 85, 87, 101-4, 111-4
Mammals, classification, 5-10
dispersal, 33-8, 103, 105, 111, 113, 120, 121, 128-9
distribution, 11-3, 16-32, 38, 65-129
evolution, 52, 55-61
Mammoths, 55, 72, 116
Man, 8, 20, 31, 33, 44, 73, 80, 107, 113, 116, 126
Mangabeys, 26
Manidae, 8, **25,** 26, 28, **58**
Maps, 3-5, **45, 46, 47, 48, 49, 102, 105, 107, 109, 112, 117, 123, 126**
distribution, 11-5, **16, 19, 22, 25, 28, 30, 34, 43, 65,** 67-97, **110, 115, 120, 121**
Marmosets, 8, 12, **23**
Marsupials, classification, 7,
dispersal, 39
distribution, 18, 21, 23, 30, 31, 32, 35, 66, **67, 68,** 69, **70,** 71, 72, 74, 75, 76, 77, 78, 79, 82, 85, 86, 87, 88, 89, 92, 95, 96, 101, 103, **104**
evolution, 56, 57, **58,** 60
Martens, 117
Mastodons, 55, **56,** 59, 77, 79, 80, 116
Mauritius, 106, **126**
Mediterranean, 16, 49
Megapodes, **30,** 32
Mercator, 3, 4, 5
Mesoenatids, 127
Mesozoic, 44, 45, 47, 48, 50-3, 54, 55, 56, 57, 60, 66, 67, 74, 75, 78-9, 81, 82, 85, 86, 89, 90, 91, 92, 93, 95, 96, 97, 115, 124, 125, 128, 129
Mexico, 18, 21, 24
Mice, 8, 17, 18, 20, 21, 25, 28, 31, **39,** 57, 59, 60, 61, 80, **84, 86,** 103, 109, **115,** 116, 117, 119, 120, 126, 127, 128, 129
pouched, 31
Migrations, 65-97, 102, 108, 118, 119, 125, 129
Minnows, 36
Miocene, 44, 54, 55, 56, 57, 58, 59, 61, 65, 69-70, 80, 81, 83, 86, 87, 115, 116, 124, 128
Moas, 124, **125**
Mole rats, 8, **16,** 17, 57, 61, 72
Moles, 7, 17, **18,** 21, 25, 29, 31, 57, **58,** 69, **70, 71,** 117, 119, **120,** 121
marsupial, 7, **31**
Molluscs, 45, **50,** 51, 53, 101, 102, 107, 108, 113, 114, 122
Moluccas, 101, 102
Monkeys, New World, 8, 12, 23, 35, 57, **58,** 60, 76, **77,** 79, 89
Old World, 8, 23, **26,** 28, 29, 57, 60, 70, 72, 79, 81, 83, 84, 89, 91, 103, **104,** 116
Monotremata, 7, 31, 32, 55, 85
Mooneyes, 20
Moose, 72
Mormyrids, 27, 96
Mountains, 13, 16, 20, 21, 23, 24, 28, 34, 35, 43, 48, 71, 83, 123
Mousebirds, 27, 127
Muridae, 8, 11, 17, 20, 25, 28, 31, 33, 37, 38, **39,** 57, 59, 61, **71,** 74, 80, **84, 86,** 87, 103, 105, 111, 113, 114, 117, 119, 126
Musk ox, 116
Mustelidae, 9, 17, 18, **19,** 21, 25, 28, 37, 57, 60, 69, 77, 116, 117, 119
Myomorpha, 8, 9, 11, **16,** 17, 18, 19, 20, 21, 25, 28, 29, 31, 33, 37, 38, 39, 57, 59, 60, 61, 69, 70, **71,** 72, 73, 74, 80, **84, 86,** 87, 103, 105, 109, 111, 113, 114, **115,** 116, 117, 118, 119, 120, 126, 127, 128, 129
Myrmecophagidae, 8, 22, 23, 61, 75

NATTERJACKS, 118, 119, **121**
Nearctic Region, 14, 16, 17, 18-21, 23, 24, 26, 28, 33, 38, 39, 54, 65-73, 74, 75, 76, 77, 78, 80, 81, 90, 103, 115, 124
*Neoceratodus*, **30,** 32, 54, **86**
Neogea, 14
Neotropical Region, 14, 17, 18, 20, 21-4, 25, 26, 27, 28, 32, 74-8, 79, 81, 84, 87, 88-91, 92-3, 95, 96, 103, 109, 129
New Guinea, 30, 31, 101, **102**
Newts, 5, 17, 118, 119, 121
New World, 8, 12, 17, 18-24, 27, 31, 32, 67, 72, 73, 77, 88, 89, 93-5, 103, 109, 111, 127, 129
New Zealand, 11, 13, 20, 30, 38, 89, 123-5, 126, 127, 129

Notogea, 14
Notoryctidae, 7, 31
Nutrias, 23

Ochotonidae, 8, 17, 18, 57
Okapis, 5, **6,** 10, **25**
Old World, 12, 16-8, 21, 24-30, 31, 72, 78-84, 89, 93, 127
Oligocene, 44, 48, 54, 55, 56, 57, 58, 59, 60, 69, 70, 76, 79, 80, 81, 82, 83, 89, 128
Opossums, 7, 18, 21, 23, 31, 78
Orang utans, 26, **30**
Orders, 5, 6, 7, 8, 9, 10, 31, 33, 53, 54, 55, 56, 57, 60, 66, 69, 92, 124, 127, 128, 129
  endemic, 22-3, 26, 27, 29, 125
Ordovician, 44, 50, 52, 53
Oriental Region, 14, 16, 17, 21, 22, 24, 25, 26, 27, 28-30, 32, 48, 71, 80, 81, 82-4, 86, 87, 88, 91, 92, 101-4, 126, 127, 128, 129
Origin, centre of, 66, 68, 69, 73, 75-6, 79, 80, 90
Orioles, 12, 27, 113
Ornithorhynchidae, 7, **30,** 31, 55
Orycteropidae, 9, 25, 26, 57, **58,** 72, 80
Ostriches, **25,** 27, 69, 89, 95, 127
  American, **22,** 23, 89
Otters, 9, 37, 77, 116, 117
Otter shrews, 7, 12, 26, 79

Pacaranas, 23
Pacas, 23
Pacific Ocean, 13, 28, 30, 47, 108, 109
Paleanodonts, 67, 69, 75, 76, 79
Palearctic Region, 14, 16-8, 19, 20, 21, 25, 28, 29, 31, 32, 66-73, 74, 77, 79, 80, 81, 82, 83, 84, 85, 103, 115-22
Paleocene, 44, 48, 54, 57, 58, 60, 66-7, 74-5, 85, 91, 96, 126, 128
Paleodonts, **59, 60**
Paleogeography, 43-9
Paleontology, 44, 93
Paleotraginae, 5, **6**
Paleozoic, 44, 47, 48, 50-3, 90, 94, 95, 96, 97, 115, 125
Panama Isthmus, 48, 74, 76, 93
Pandas, 9, 17, 35, 38
Pangolins, 8, **25,** 26, 28, **58**
Parrots, 17, **22,** 24, 27, 29, **30,** 32, 34, 69, 70, 73, 101, **103, 104,** 124
Peacocks, **28,** 29
Peccaries, 10, 18, **19,** 21, **22, 58,** 59, 60, 69, **70, 71,** 73, 77, **78**
Pedetidae, 8, 26
Pelobatidae, **54**
Pelomedusidae, 24, **25,** 27, **88,** 127, **128**
Penguins, 33, 109, 111
Peramelidae, 7, 31
Perch, 18, 20, 36, 118
Perissodactyla, 5, 6, 10, 13, **16,** 17, 18, 20, 21, **22,** 23, 25, 26, 28, 29, 35, 38, 56, 57, **58,** 59, 60, 65, 66, 68, 69, **70, 71,** 72, 77, 81, **82,** 83, 84, 91, 116
Permian, 44, 48, 50, 51, 52, 90, 97
Petromuridae, 9
Phalangeridae, 7, 31, 35, **86,** 103, **104**
Phalangers, 7, 31, 103, **104**
Phascolomidae, 7, **30,** 31
Pheasants, **16,** 17, 24, 27, 29, 32
Philepittas, 127
Philippines, 28, 101, **102**
Pholidota, 8, **25,** 26, 28, **58**
Phylum, 5, 50
Pigeons, 27, 29, 32, **106,** 113
Pigs, 10, 17, 18, 20, 25, 28, 31, 37, 59, 60, 69, 70, **71,** 72, 73, **81,** 83, **84, 86,** 87, 103, **104,** 105, 116, 118, 126
Pikas, 8, 17, 18, 57
Pike, 18, 118
*Pipa*, **22,** 24, 55, **90**
Pipids, **22,** 24, 27, 30, **54,** 55, 66, 74, 78, 89, **90,** 95, 127, 128
Piranhas, 24
Plants, 34, 44, 45, 46, 49, 51, 53, 89, 102, 108
Platacanthomyidae, 9, 29
Platypuses, 7, **30,** 31, 55
Pleistocene, 44, 49, 54, 55, 56, 58, 59, 72-3, 75, 77, 78, 80-1, 84, 103, 116, 122, 127
Plethodontidae, **20, 54**
Pleurodires, **22,** 24, 27, **30,** 32, 55, 66, **67, 68, 70,** 71, 74, **75, 76, 77,** 78, **79, 80, 81,** 82, **83, 84,** 85, **88,** 89, 92, 93, 95, 127, 128, 129
Pliocene, 44, 48, 54, 56, 57, 58, 59, 61, 71-2, 76, 77, 78, 80, 81, 83, 84, 86, 87, 115, 116, 118, 119
Plovers, 107, **108**
Pocket gophers, 8, 19, 20, 57, 60, 69, 70, 73
Pocket mice, 9, 19, 20
*Podocnemis*, **67, 68, 70, 75, 76, 77, 78, 79, 80, 81, 82,** 129
Polynesia, 104, 124
*Polypedates*, **54,** 127, **128**
Polypedatidae, 18, 27, 29, **54,** 55, 96, 127, 128, 129
Pongidae, 8, 26, 27, 29, **30,** 57, **71,** 80, **81, 84**
Porcupines, 9, 17, 25, 26, 28, 60, 89, 103
Potamogalidae, 7, 12, 26, 79
Pottos, 26
Prairie dogs, 8, **38,** 39
Precambrian, **43,** 50
Primates, 8, 12, 20, 23, 25, 26, 27, 28, 29, **30,** 31, 33, 35, 44, 56, 57, **58,** 60, 66, **68,** 69, 70, **71,** 72, 76, **77,** 78, 79, 80, 81, 82, 83, 84, 88, 89, 91, 92, 103, **104,** 107, 113, 116, 126, 127, 128, 129
Proboscidea, 9, 26, 28, 33, 55, **56, 58,** 59, 60, 61, **70, 71,** 72, 77, 79, 80, 81, 83, 84, 103, **115,** 116
Procaviidae, 9, **58**
Procyonidae, 9, 17, 18, 21, 35, 38, 57, **61,** 76, **77, 78**
Projections, map, 3-5
Pronghorns, 10, 12, 19, 59, 61, 66, 70, **71,** 73
Proteidae, **17,** 18, **54**
*Proteus*, **17,** 18, **54**
*Protopipa*, 24
*Protopterus*, **25,** 27, **81**
Protozoa, **50,** 51
Python, 27, 29, 32, 113

Quail, 24

Rabbits, 8, 17, 18, 21, 25, 28, 31, 33, 57, 69, 117, 119
Raccoons, 9, 17, 57, 61, 76, **77, 78**
Rafts, 36, 37, 108, 111, 114, 128
Rails, 38, 124
Rainfall, 33, 34, 35, 37
*Rana*, **17,** 36, **54,** 118
Ranidae, **17,** 36, **54,** 118
Range, 11, 12, 13, 17, 18, 32, 33, 34, 35, 38, 65, 66, 72, 73, 77, 80, 82, 84, 86, 120, 121, 122
  northern, 18, 80
Rats, 8, 11, 31, 33, 37, 38, 57, 74, 87, 103, 105, 111, 113, 114, 117

Rattlesnakes, **19,** 20, **38,** 39
Recent, 44, 56, 76
Regions, zoogeographical, 13-32, 65-97
Reindeer, 116, 118
Replacement, 35
Reptiles, 5
dispersal, 33, **36,** 37
distribution, 17, **19,** 20, 22, 24, **25,** 27, **28,** 29, **30,** 32, **38,** 39, 46, 66, **67, 68, 70,** 71, 74, **75, 76, 77,** 78, **79, 80, 81,** 82, 83, 84, 85, **86,** 87, 88, 89, 90, 92, 93, 96, 97
evolution, 44, 52, 53, 54, 55
on islands, 106, 107, 109, 110-1, 113, 114, 116, 118, 119, 120, 121, 124, 125, 127, 128, 129
*Rhea*, **22,** 23
Rhinoceroses, 10, 21, **25,** 26, 28, 59, 68, **70, 71,** 72, 77, 80, 81, **82,** 83, 84, 91, 116
Rhinocerotidae, 10, 21, **25,** 26, 28, 59, 68, **70, 71,** 72, 81, **82,** 83, 84, 91, 116
*Rhynophrinus*, 24
Rhizomyidae, 8, 26, 28
Rice rats, 8, 109
Rivers, 5, 21, 24, 27, 35, 44, 69, 116
Rock magnetism, 96
Rock rats, 9, 26
Rocks, 43-6, 51, 54, 55, 56, 57, 65, 66, 69, 82, 89, 90, 95-6, 123, 128
Rodentia, 8, 9, 11, **16,** 17, 18, 19, 20, 21, 23, 25, 26, 28, 29, 31, 33, 35, 37, **38,** 39, 56, 57, **58,** 59, 60, 61, 67, **68,** 69, **70, 71,** 72, 73, 74, 76, 77, 78, 80, 82, 83, **84, 86,** 87, 89, 103, 105, 109, 111, 113, 114, **115,** 116, 117, 118, 119, 120, 126, 127, 128, 129
Romer, A. S., 10, 131

SAHARA, 16, 24, 39
St. Helena, 89, 104, 107-8, 109, 111
Salamanders, 5, **16,** 17, 18, 20, **54,** 55, 69, 71, 73
Salmon, 18, 36
Sandwich Islands, 104
Schmidt, K. P., 33, 131
Sciuridae, 8, 17, 18, 21, 25, 28, 33, 35, 38, 39, 57, **58, 60,** 61, 70, 103, 117, 118, 119
Sciuromorpha, 8, 17, 18, 21, 25, 26, 33, 35, 38, 39, 57, **58, 60,** 61, **68,** 70, **76,** 103, 117, 118, 119
Sclater, P. L., 13, 14
Scotland, **34,** 35, 119, 120, 121
Seals, 9, 31
Secretary birds, 27, 127
Selection, natural, 33, 109-10
*Selevinia*, 9, 17
Seleviniidae, 9, 17
Sewellels, 8, 19, 20, 57
Seychelle Islands, 106, **126**
Sheep, 10, 124
Shrews, 7, 17, 18, 21, 25, 28, 103, 117, 119, 126
Sial, 94, 95, 96
Silurian, 44, 48, 50, 52, 53
Sima, 94, 95
Simpson, G. G., 10, 86, 131, 132
Sirenidae, **20,** 54
Sirenia, 9, **58**
Skinks, 20, 29, 32, 113, 114, 124, 125, 127
Skunks, 9, **19**
Sloths, 8, 22, 23, 33, 60, 75
Slugs, 122
Snails, **50,** 51, 101, **108,** 113, 114
Snakes, 17, **19,** 20, 24, 27, **28,** 29, 32, **38,** 39, 55, **86,** 87, 111, 113, 118, 119, 120, 121, 124, 127
Solenodontidae, 7
Soricidae, 7, 17, 18, 21, 25, 28, 103, 117, 119, 126
South Atlantic Bridge, 89-91, 108
Spalacidae, 8, **16,** 17, 57, **61,** 72, 73
*Spalax*, **16,** 17
Species, 5, 6, 10, 21, 33, 113, 116, 119, 122, 127
endemic, 104, 108, 109, 110, 111, 114, 117, 118, 124, 125
origin of, 109-10, 117
*Sphenodon*, 55, 66, 124, 125
Spiders, **50,** 51, 113, 114
Spiny dormice, 9, 29
Spiny rats, 23
Sponges, **50,** 51, 116
Spread, 33, 34, 35-8, 40, 65, 66, 67, 68, 69, 70, 71, 72, 73, 74, 75, 76, 77, 80, 83, 86, 87, 89, 90, 91, 92, 93, 120, 121, 130
Spring haas, 8, 26
Squirrels, 8, 17, 18, 21, 25, 26, 28, 33, 35, 38, **39,** 57, **58,** 61, 70, 103, 117, 118, 119
marsupial, 31
Sticklebacks, 18, 36
Stoats, 117
Subclass, 31
Subfamily, 5, 6, 31, 32, 127
Suborder, 8, 9, 23, 24, 29
Subspecies, 118, 119
Suidae, 10, 17, 18, 20, 25, 28, 31, 37, 59, 60, 69, 70, **71,** 72, 73, **81,** 83, **84, 86,** 87, 103, **104,** 105, 116, 118, 126, **127**
Sumatra, 28, 101, **102,** 112, 113, 114
Sunbirds, 27, **29,** 113
Swifts, 113

TACHYGLOSSIDAE, 7, 32, 55
Talpidae, 7, **16, 18,** 21, 25, 29, 31, 57, **58,** 69, **70, 71,** 117, 119, **120,** 121
Tamarins, 23
Tanagers, 20, **24,** 78
Tapiridae, 10, 13, 18, 21, **22, 28,** 29, 35, 38, 59, 65, 66, 69, 72, 77, 83, 84, 116
Tapirs, 10, 13, 18, 21, **22, 28,** 29, 35, 38, 59, 65, 66, 69, 72, 77, 83, 84, 116
Tarsiers, 8, **28,** 29, 83, 103, **104**
Tarsiidae, 8, **28,** 29, 83, 103, **104**
Tasmanian wolf, 31, 35
Tayassuidae, 10, 18, **19,** 21, **22, 58,** 59, 60, 69, **70,** 71, 73, 77, **78**
Tegus, 24
Teiidae, 24, 55
Temperature, 31, 33-4, 35, 49, 53, 93, 123
Tenrecidae, 7, 127, 129
Tenrecs, 7, 127, 129
Terrapins, 20
Tethys Sea, 47, 49, 82, **88,** 89
Theridomyomorpha, 8, 26
Thryonomyidae, 9, 26
Tigers, 69
sabre tooth, 57, 69, 72, 77, **115,** 116
Time scale, 44
Timor, 101, 102
Tinamus, 23, 77
Tits, **34,** 35, 118, 119
Toads, 5, 18, 20, 24, 27, 30, 32, **54,** 55, 66, 74, 78, 82, 89, **90,** 95, 118, 119, 121, 127, 128
clawed, **25,** 27, **54,** 55, **90**
midwife, **17, 54,** 118
Surinam, **22,** 24, 55, **90**
Toit, A. L. du, 94, 132
Toucans, 23, **24**
Touracos, 27, 127

Tragulidae, 10, 26, 28, **59**
Transition area, 20, 101-4
Tree frogs, 18, 20, 24, 27, 29, 32, **54,** 55, 85, 92, 93, 95, 96, 118, 127, 128, 129
Tree porcupines, 9, 18, 21, 23, 57
Tree shrews, 8, 29, **30, 82,** 83
Triassic, 44, 50, 52, 55, 85, 90, 97, 128
Trilobites, **50,** 51, 53
Tristan da Cunha, 89, 105
Trogons, 32, 69
Tropics, 5, 21-32, 33, 49, 74-87, 107-114, 127
Trumpeters, 23, **24**
Tuatara, 124, 125
Tubulidentata, 9, 26, 57, **58,** 72, 80
Tucotucos, 23
Tupaiidae, 8, 29, **30**
Turkeys, **19,** 20
Turtles, 17, **19,** 20, 24, 27, 29, 32, 33, **36,** 37, 55, 87, 106, 110-1, 116, 124
side-neck, **22,** 24, 25, 27, **30,** 32, 55, 66, **67, 68, 70,** 71, 74, **75, 76, 77,** 78, **79, 80, 81,** 82, **83, 84,** 85, **88,** 89, 92, 93, 95, 127, 128, 129

UMBRELLA BIRDS, 23, **24**
Ungulates, South American, 75, 76, 77, **78,** 89, 92
Urodela, 5, **16,** 17, 18, 20, 24, 27, 29, 32, 38, 54, 55, 66, 69, 70, 71, 73, 118, 119, 121
Ursidae, 9, 17, 18, 21, 25, 29, 57, 61, 70, 71, 73, 77, 80, 116, 118

VANGAS, 127, **128**
Varanids, 29, 32, 55, 96, 113
Vegetation, 16, 18, 33, 34, 35, 38, 39, 53, 105, 107, 108, 109, 110, 112-4, 120, 121, 123
Vertebrate classification, 5
evolution, 51-61
Vicunas, 17, 21, 35
Vipers, 24, 27, 29, 39, 118
Viverridae, 9, 17, 25, 28, 57, 60, 69, 103, **127,** 128, 129
Volcanoes, 48, 49, 90, 104, 107, 108, 111, 112, 123, 126
Voles, 8, 116, 117, 120
Vultures, 17

WALLABIES, 7, 31
Wallace, A. R., 13, 14, 33, 101-4, 132
Wallacea, 103-4
Wallace's Line, 101-4
Warblers, 17, 20
Wattlebirds, 124
Weasels, 9, 57, 60, 69, 77, 117
Weber's Line, 102-3
Weevils, **36,** 108
Wegener, A., 94-6
Whales, 9, 31, **58**
Whitefish, 118
Wills, L. J., 47, 116, 132
Winds, 105, 106, 107, 108, 109, **123, 126**
Wolves, 116, 118
Wombats, 7, **30,** 31
Wood, A. E., 8, 132
Woodlouse, 122
Woodpeckers, 27, 29, 32, 101, 127
Woodswallows, 32
Woolly lemurs, 8, 127
World maps, 3-5, 11-15, **43,** 47-9, **65,** 88-97
Worms, **50,** 51, 113, 114, 122
Wrens, 17, 124

XENOPUS, **25,** 27, **54,** 55, **90**

ZAPODIDAE, 9, 17, 18, 38
Zebras, **25,** 26
Zoogeographical regions, 13, 14, 15, 16-32, 38, 39, 65-97, 101, 104, 105

Barch, A. M., Trumbo, D., & Nangle, J. Social Setting and Conformity to a Legal Requirement. From: *Journal of Abnormal and Social Psychology,* **55**, 1957: 396–398. Reprinted by permission of the senior author and the American Psychological Association. Copyright (1957) by the American Psychological Association.

Freedman, J. L., & Fraser, S. C. Compliance without Pressure: The Foot-in-the-door Technique. From: *Journal of Personality and Social Psychology,* **4**, 1966: 195–202. Reprinted by permission of the senior author and the American Psychological Association. Copyright (1966) by the American Psychological Association.

Helson, H., Blake, R. R., & Mouton, J. S. Petition-signing as Adjustment to Situational and Personal Factors. From: *Journal of Social Psychology,* **48**, 1958: 3–10. Reprinted by permission of the senior author and The Journal Press. Copyright (1958) by The Journal Press.

Lupfer, M., Kay, J., & Burnette, S. A. The influence of Picketing on the Purchase of Toy Guns. From: *Journal of Social Psychology,* **77**, 1969: 197–200. Reprinted by permission of the senior author and The Journal Press. Copyright (1969) by The Journal Press.

Hartmann, G. W. A Field Experiment on the Comparative Effectiveness of "Emotional" and "Rational" Political Leaflets in Determining Election Results. From: *Journal of Abnormal and Social Psychology*, **31**, 1936: 99-114. Reprinted by permission of the American Psychological Association.

## Chapter 4 THE EFFECTS OF SOCIAL STATUS

Doob, A. N., & Gross, A. E. Status of Frustrator as an Inhibitor of Horn-Honking Responses. From: *Journal of Social Psychology,* **76**, 1968: 213–218. Reprinted by permission of the senior author and The Journal Press. Copyright (1968) by The Journal Press.

Bickman, L. The Effect of Social Status on the Honesty of Others. From: *Journal of Social Psychology*, **85**, 1971: 87-92. Reprinted by permission of the author and the Journal Press. Copyright (1971) by The Journal Press.

Lefkowitz, M., Blake, R. R., & Mouton, J. S. Status Factors in Pedestrian Violation of Traffic Signals. From: *Journal of Abnormal and Social Psychology*, **51**, 1955: 704-706. Reprinted by permission of the senior author and the American Psychological Association. Copyright (1955) by the American Psychological Association.

Vidulich, R. N., & Wilson, D. J. The Environmental Setting as a Factor in Social Influence. From: *Journal of Social Psychology,* **71**, 1967: 247–255. Reprinted by permission of the senior author and The Journal Press. Copyright (1967) by The Journal Press.

Harari, H., & McDavid, J. W. Situational Influence on Moral Justice: A Study of "Finking." From: *Journal of Personality and Social Psychology,* **11**, 1969: 240–244. Reprinted by permission of the senior author and the American Psychological Association. Copyright (1969) by the American Psychological Association.

## Chapter 5 RACIAL PREJUDICE

LaPiere, R. T. Attitudes vs. Actions. From: *Social Forces,* **13**, 1934: 230–237. Reprinted by permission of the University of North Carolina Press. Copyright (1934) by The University of North Carolina Press.

McGrew, J. M. How "Open" Are Multiple-Dwelling Units? From: *Journal of Social Psychology,* **72**, 1967: 223–226. Reprinted by permission of the author and The Journal Press. Copyright (1967) by The Journal Press.

Selltiz, C. The Use of Survey Methods in a Citizens Campaign against Discrimination. From: *Human Organization*, **13**, 1955: 19–25. Reprinted by permission of the author and the Society for Applied Anthropology. Copyright (1955) by The Society for Applied Anthropology.

Parker, J. H. The Interaction of Negroes and Whites in an Integrated Church Setting. From: *Social Forces,* **46**, 1968: 359–366. Reprinted by permission of the author and The University of North Carolina Press. Copyright (1968) by The University of North Carolina Press.

Campbell, D. T., Kruskal, W. H., & Wallace, W. P. Seating Aggregation as an Index of Attitude. From: *Sociometry*, **29**, 1966: 1-15. Reprinted by permission of the senior author and the American Sociological Association. Copyright (1966) by the American Sociological Association.

Davis, M., Seibert, R., & Breed, W. Interracial Seating Patterns On New Orleans Public Transit. From: *Social Problems*, **13**, 1966: 298-306. Reprinted by permission of the senior author and The Society for the Study of Social Problems. Copyright (1966) by The Society for the Study of Social Problems.

Gaertner, S., & Bickman, L. A Nonreactive Indicator Measure of Racial Discrimination: The Wrong-Number Technique. A shorter version of this article is in press: *Journal of Personality and Social Psychology*.

## Chapter 6 COLLECTIVE BEHAVIOR

Sommer, R., & Becker, F. D. Territorial Defense and the Good Neighbor. From: *Journal of Personality and Social Psychology,* **11**, 1969: 85–92. Reprinted by permission of the senior author and the American Psychological Association. Copyright (1969) by the American Psychological Association.

Felipe, N. J., & Sommer, R. Invasions of Personal Space. From: *Social Problems,* **14**, 1966: 206–214. Reprinted by permission of the senior author and The Society for the Study of Social Problems. Copyright (1966) by The Society for the Study of Social Problems.

Mann, L., & Taylor, K. F. Queue Counting: The Effect of Motives upon Estimates of Numbers in Waiting Lines. From: *Journal of Personality and Social Psychology,* **12**, 1969: 95–103. Reprinted by permission of the senior author and the American Psychological Association. Copyright (1969) by the American Sociological Association.

Milgram, S., Bickman, L., & Berkowitz, L. Note on the Drawing Power of Crowds of Different Size. From: *Journal of Personality and Social Psychology,* **13,** 1969: 79-82. Reprinted by permission of the senior author and the American Psychological Association. Copyright (1969) by the American Psychological Association.

Sherif, M. Superordinate Goals in the Reduction of Intergroup Conflict. From: *American Journal of Sociology,* **63,** 1958: 349-356. Reprinted by permission of the author and the University of Chicago Press. Copyright (1958) by the University of Chicago Press.

**Chapter 7 ATTITUDES AND BEHAVIOR**

Abelson, R. P., & Miller, J. C. Negative Persuasion via Personal Insult. From: *Journal of Experimental Social Psychology,* **3,** 1967: 321-333. Reprinted by permission of the senior author and Academic Press, Incorporated. Copyright (1967) by the Academic Press, Inc.

Miller, N., & Levy, B. H. Defaming and Agreeing with the Communicator as a Function of Emotional Arousal, Communication Extremity, and Evaluative Set. From: *Sociometry,* **30,** 1967: 158-175. Reprinted by the permission of the senior author and the American Sociological Association. Copyright (1967) by the American Sociological Association.

Leventhal, H., & Niles, P. A Field Experiment on Fear Arousal with Data on the Validity of Questionnaire Measures. From: *Journal of Personality,* **32,** 1964: 459–479. Reprinted by permission of the senior author and the Duke University Press. Copyright (1964) by the Duke University Press.

Smith, E. E. The Power of Dissonance Techniques to Change Attitudes. From: *Public Opinion Quarterly,* **25,** 1961: 626-639. Reprinted by permission of the author and the Columbia University Press. Copyright (1961) by Columbia University Press.

Milgram, S. The Lost-Letter Technique. From: *Psychology Today,* June, 1969. Reprinted by permission of the author and Communications/Research/Machines/Inc. Copyright (1969) by Communications/Research/Machines/Inc. This article includes revisions by the author.

Wrightsman, L. S. Wallace Supporters and Adherence to "Law and Order." From: *Journal of Personality and Social Psychology,* **13,** 1969: 17-22. Reprinted by permission of the author and the American Psychological Association. Copyright (1969) by the American Psychological Association.

**Chapter 8 CONSUMER BEHAVIOR**

Doob, A. N., Carlsmith, J. M., Freedman, J. L., Landauer, T. K., & Tom, S., Jr. Effect of Initial Selling Price on Subsequent Sales. From: *Journal of Personality and Social Psychology,* **11,** 1969: 345–350. Reprinted by permission of J. Merrill Carlsmith and the American Psychological Association. Copyright (1969) by the American Psychological Association.

Brock, T. C. Communicator-Recipient Similarity and Decision Change. From: *Journal of Personality and Social Psychology,* **1,** 1965: 650–654. Reprinted by permission of the author and the American Psychological Association. Copyright (1965) by the American Psychological Association.

Regan, J. W., & Brehm, J. W. Compliance in Buying as a Function of Inducements That Threaten Freedom. Written especially for this volume.

Nisbett, R. E., & Kanouse, D. E. Obesity, Food Deprivation, and Supermarket Shopping Behavior. From: *Journal of Personality and Social Psychology,* **12,** 1969: 289–294. Reprinted by permission of the senior author and the American Psychological Association. Copyright (1969) by the American Psychological Association.

Goldman, R., Jaffa, M., & Schachter, S. Yom Kippur, Air France, Dormitory Food, and the Eating Behavior of Obese and Normal Persons. From: *Journal of Personality and Social Psychology,* **10,** 1968: 117–123. Reprinted by permission of Stanley Schachter and the American Psychological Association. Copyright (1968) by the American Psychological Association.

**Chapter 9 METHODS IN SEARCH OF MORE DATA**

Milgram, S. The Small-World Problem. The text is from: *Psychology Today,* May, 1967. Reprinted by permission of the author and Communications/Research/Machines/Inc. Copyright (1967) by Communications/Research/Machines/Inc. The illustrations are from: M. Sherif & C. W. Sherif (Eds.), *Interdisciplinary relationships in the social sciences.* Chicago: Aldine, 1969.

Landis, C. National Differences in Conversations. From: *Journal of Abnormal and Social Psychology,* **21,** 1927: 354–375. Reprinted by permission of the American Psychological Association.

McEvoy, J., Chesler, M. & Schmuck, R. Content Analysis of a Super Patriot Protest. From: *Social Problems,* **14,** 1967: 455–463. Reprinted by permission of Richard Schmuck and The Society for the Study of Social Problems. Copyright (1967) by The Society for the Study of Social Problems.

Kohn, M. L., & Williams, R. M., Jr. Situational Patterning in Intergroup Relations. From: *American Sociological Review,* **21,** 1956: 164–174. Reprinted by permission of the senior author and the American Sociological Association. Copyright (1956) by the American Sociological Association.

Shor, R. E. Shared Patterns of Nonverbal Normative Expectations in Automobile Driving. From: *Journal of Social Psychology,* **62,** 1964: 155–163. Reprinted by permission of the author and The Journal Press. Copyright (1964) by The Journal Press.

Davis, M., & Levine, S. Toward a Sociology of Public Transit. From: *Social Problems,* 15, 1967: 84-91. Reprinted by permission of the senior author and The Society for the Study of Social Problems. Copyright (1967) by The Society for the Study of Social Problems.

TO CORINNE AND ELEANOR

# CONTENTS

**FOREWORD** XI

Chapter 1
**INTRODUCTION** 1

Chapter 2
**HELPING BEHAVIOR** 7

*Introduction*

*James H. Bryan and Mary Ann Test* - Models and Helping: Naturalistic Studies in Aiding Behavior 11

*Harvey A. Hornstein, Elisha Fisch, and Michael Holmes* - Influence of a Model's Feeling about His Behavior and His Relevance as a Comparison Other on Observers' Helping Behavior 18

*Harvey Allen* - Bystander Intervention and Helping on the Subway 22

*Irving M. Piliavin, Judith Rodin, and Jane Allyn Piliavin* - Good Samaritanism: An Underground Phenomenon? 34

*Roy E. Feldman* - Response to Compatriot and Foreigner who Seek Assistance 44

Chapter 3
**SOCIAL INFLUENCE** 57

*Introduction*

*Charles K. Hofling, Eveline Brotzman, Sarah Dalrymple, Nancy Graves, and Chester M. Pierce* - An Experimental Study in Nurse-Physician Relationships 60

*Abram M. Barch, Don Trumbo, and John Nangle* - Social Setting and Conformity to a Legal Requirement 68

*Jonathan L. Freedman and Scott C. Fraser* - Compliance without Pressure: The Foot-in-the-Door Technique 71

*Harry Helson, Robert R. Blake, and Jane Srygley Mouton* - Petition-signing as Adjustment to Situational and Personal Factors 78

*Michael Lupfer, Jane Kay, and Sara Ann Burnette* - The Influence of Picketing on the Purchase of Toy Guns 82

*George W. Hartmann* - A Field Experiment on the Comparative Effectiveness of "Emotional" and "Rational" Political Leaflets in Determining Election Results 84

Chapter 4
**THE EFFECTS OF SOCIAL STATUS** 95

*Introduction*

*Anthony N. Doob and Alan E. Gross* - Status of Frustrator as an Inhibitor of Horn-honking Responses 98

*Leonard Bickman* - The Effect of Social Status on the Honesty of Others 102

*Monroe Lefkowitz, Robert R. Blake, and Jane Srygley Mouton* - Status Factors in Pedestrian Violation of Traffic Signals 105

*Robert N. Vidulich and Donna Jean Wilson* - The Environmental Setting as a Factor in Social Influence 108

*Herbert Harari and John W. McDavid* - Situational Influence on Moral Justice: A Study of "Finking" 113

**Chapter 5**
**RACIAL PREJUDICE 119**

*Introduction*

*Richard T. LaPiere* - Attitudes versus Actions 122

*John M. McGrew* - How "Open" Are Multiple Dwelling Units? 128

*Claire Selltiz* - The Use of Survey Methods in a Citizens Campaign against Discrimination 130

*James H. Parker* - The Interaction of Negroes and Whites in an Integrated Church Setting 139

*Donald T. Campbell, William H. Kruskal, and William P. Wallace* - Seating Aggregation as an Index of Attitude 146

*Morris Davis, Robert Seibert, and Warren Breed* - Interracial Seating Patterns on New Orleans Public Transit 155

*Samuel Gaertner and Leonard Bickman* - A Nonreactive Indicator of Racial Discrimination: The Wrong-Number Technique 162

**Chapter 6**
**COLLECTIVE BEHAVIOR 171**

*Introduction*

*Robert Sommer and Franklin D. Becker* - Territorial Defense and the Good Neighbor 173

*Nancy Jo Felipe and Robert Sommer* - Invasions of Personal Space 181

*Leon Mann and K. F. Taylor* - Queue Counting: The Effect of Motives upon Estimates of Numbers in Waiting Lines 187

*Stanley Milgram, Leonard Bickman, and Lawrence Berkowitz* - Note on the Drawing Power of Crowds of Different Size 196

*Muzafer Sherif* - Superordinate Goals in the Reduction of Intergroup Conflict 199

**Chapter 7**
**ATTITUDES AND BEHAVIOR 205**

*Introduction*

*Robert P. Abelson and James C. Miller* - Negative Persuasion via Personal Insult 208

*Norman Miller and Burton H. Levy* - Defaming and Agreeing with the Communicator as a Function of Emotional Arousal, Communication Extremity, and Evaluative Set 216

*Howard Leventhal and Patricia Niles* - A Field Experiment on Fear Arousal with Data on the Validity of Questionnaire Measures 226

*Ewart E. Smith* - The Power of Dissonance Techniques to Change Attitudes 237

*Stanley Milgram* - The Lost-Letter Technique 245

*Lawrence S. Wrightsman* - Wallace Supporters and Adherence to "Law and Order" 251

**Chapter 8**
**CONSUMER BEHAVIOR 257**

*Introduction*

*Anthony N. Doob, J. Merrill Carlsmith, Jonathan L. Freedman, Thomas K. Landauer, and Soleng Tom, Jr.* - Effect of Initial Selling Price on Subsequent Sales 259

*Timothy C. Brock* - Communicator-Recipient Similarity and Decision Change 264

*Judith Weiner Regan and Jack W. Brehm* - Compliance in Buying as a Function of Inducements That Threaten Freedom 269

*Richard E. Nisbett and David E. Kanouse* - Obesity, Food Deprivation, and Supermarket Shopping Behavior 275

*Ronald Goldman, Melvyn Jaffa, and Stanley Schachter* - Yom Kippur, Air France, Dormitory Food, and the Eating Behavior of Obese and Normal Persons 280

**Chapter 9**
**METHODS IN SEARCH OF MORE DATA** 287

*Introduction*

*Stanley Milgram* - The Small-World Problem 290

*Carney Landis* - National Differences in Conversations 300

*James McEvoy, Mark Chesler, and Richard Schmuck* - Content Analysis of a Super Patriot Protest 302

*Melvin L. Kohn and Robin M. Williams, Jr.* - Situational Patterning in Intergroup Relations 309

*Ronald E. Shor* - Shared Patterns of Nonverbal Normative Expectations in Automobile Driving 319

*Morris Davis and Sol Levine* - Toward a Sociology of Public Transit 324

**NAME INDEX** 329

**SUBJECT INDEX** 333

# FOREWORD

For more than a century, the laboratory experiment has been regarded by the psychologist as the prime source of data for behavioral science. Most social psychologists subscribe to this view, especially those whose parent discipline is psychology rather than sociology. Most of them see the behavioral scientist's primary task as the collection of "hard" data. Most have not engaged in field work, and when they have, they have often felt rather apologetic about their efforts.

In recent years, however, the limitations of laboratory experimentation as a research strategy have begun to emerge with some clarity. Laboratory situations are often as schematized as possible. Fragments of behavior, torn from their larger context in everyday life, are often the focus of study. The actions of participants are severely constrained, often restricted to pushing buttons, or saying "yes" or "no," "larger" or "smaller." There is a growing realization that removing such behavioral elements from their natural context in the field changes their very character, with the consequence that the investigator is studying elements very different from their counterparts in the field situation. It could thus be argued that contemporary social psychology pertains largely to esoteric behavior in a never-never land–artificial behavior in the culture of the laboratory–yielding knowledge that is difficult to generalize to the world outside the laboratory.

Laboratory experimentation quite naturally leads to a view of the participating persons as passive. They are objects to be "experimented upon." They are thought of as responding passively to the push and pull of forces exerted by the experimenter. This view of persons in experiments as objects subjected to various treatments and manipulations had the curious effect of blinding the psychologist to the fact that his subjects sometimes had ideas and feelings about the experimenter and what he was trying to accomplish, and that such notions sometimes affected their behavior and the results of the experiment. So in recent years we have had to rediscover the subject through social-psychological studies of the experiment.

An obvious alternative to laboratory investigation is observation and experimentation in field settings–naturally occurring, non-laboratory situations. In such settings behavior is more likely to be studied in its natural context, and to be minimally distorted. It is less likely to be fragmentary, and the behavior of the subject is apt to be freer and less constrained. The active contributions of the subject to his own behavior are more likely to be recognized and integrated into psychological knowledge.

Thus the editors of the present volume on field research have performed a great service for both students and social psychologists. One cannot help responding enthusiastically to this collection. When seen within the covers of a single volume, the range and variety of behaviors sampled and the ingenuity of many of the investigators in devising methods for studying them in the field are indeed impressive. In this book are to be found the seeds of a growing movement aimed at overcoming the limitations of a social psychology based upon too narrow a conception of science and depending too heavily on the psychological laboratory.

**Paul F. Secord**
Oxford University

CHAPTER **ONE**

# INTRODUCTION

The sequestering of social psychology to the confines of the laboratory is being questioned as never before by social psychologists (McGuire, 1967; Ring, 1967). Although the laboratory method is the technique with the greatest capability for reducing alternative explanations (Selltiz, Jahoda, Deutsch, & Cook, 1961), it is being confronted with two main problems: inadequate generalizability and the effects associated with the subject's awareness that he is in an experiment (Orne, 1962; Rosenthal, 1966; McGuire, 1967). Thus, in this sense, the time is short when the laboratory may still have hegemony over all social-psychological research efforts. We suggest that field research is the technique best answering the problems posed by an exclusive reliance on the laboratories. This idea is not new. For example, Lewin wrote in 1943:

> Although it appears possible to study certain problems of society in experimentally created, smaller, laboratory groups, we shall have also to develop research techniques that will permit us to do real experiments within existing "natural" social groups. In my opinion, the practical and theoretical importance of these types of experiments is of the first magnitude [p. 164].

Other authors have also stressed the need for field research. Recently, McGuire (1969) has called for an emphasis on basic research in natural settings. McGuire feels that testing of theoretically derived hypotheses in a field setting is "the best of both worlds for social psychology [p. 21]." Festinger and Katz (1953) have also shown their interest in field research by devoting separate chapters to field research and field experiments in their book on research methods. However, their interest lies in using field research where laboratory research is not possible, where social processes are too complex to reduce them to single variables for laboratory treatment, or where social action is being promulgated and experimental control allows more valid measurement of the efficacy of the changes. Thus, they see field research as an additional tool in the laboratory experimenter's armamentarium. We feel that field research, including field studies and field experiments, can stand by itself as a method of scientific investigation.

How seriously have the social sciences taken Lewin's advice in the past quarter of a century? Have there been efforts to create a research technique which uses and relates to the natural environment? Unfortunately, the answer is no. For example, only three percent of the articles published in the *Journal of Personality and Social Psychology* during 1968, 1969, and 1970 were concerned with field research.

This is not to say that field research is nonexistent in the literature. There are field studies, but finding them is usually a case of serendipity. We feel that this lack of a compilation prevents students and researchers from appreciating the numerous advantages of this type of research. The lack of exposure contributes to the perpetuation of the myth that the only real scientific research possible is that which takes place within a laboratory. It is also the impetus for the editing of this book.

It may be helpful at this point to review the reasoning behind our contention that social psychology would profit by increased attention to the world beyond the laboratory. Webb, Campbell, Schwartz, & Sechrest (1966) point out a number of factors that decrease the validity of research. We feel that the majority of these problems can be dealt with best by research in the field.

Most criticisms center on the concept of reactivity. This is the notion that certain measuring techniques may interfere or change the very event being measured. And although a great deal of field research is reactive (e.g., interviews and questionnaires), this problem can be very readily dealt with in well-designed field experiments.

Reactivity, however, is just one of the problems encountered as a result of the subject's awareness that he is in an experiment. Does the fact that an individual knows that his responses are being measured change those responses? There is ample evidence that this knowledge can alter or distort the subject's responses (Webb et al., 1966). One aspect of the problem of awareness has been investigated by Orne (1959, 1962). Orne has shown that the experiment can be conceived of as having its own unique form of social interaction. That is, the subject will seek to discover how he should behave in this novel situation. He will look for situational cues in order to play the proper role. Orne describes these cues as the "demand characteristics of the experiment." Thus, if the subject feels that he should play the role of the "good subject," which is often the case, he will try to conform to the perceived expectations of the experimenter. His resultant behavior may conflict with the way the subject would have responded had he been unaware of being in an experiment. Even some of the early, basic laboratory experiments in psychology, such as those on the influence of learning on perception, have been demonstrated to have been influenced by demand characteristics (Page, 1968).

In addition to this introduction of artifact by cooperativeness, there is also the possibility that the subject's evaluation of his own behavior can introduce systematic error. Rosenberg (1969) has demonstrated that a subject's response in a laboratory situation is affected by "evaluation apprehension." Rosenberg defines this as "an active, anxiety-toned concern that he [the subject] win a positive evaluation from the experimenter, or at least that he provide no grounds for a negative one" (p. 281). Sigall, Aronson, and Van Hoose (1970) have found that under conditions in which the subject could not simultaneously cooperate (by confirming the experimenter's stated hypothesis) and "look good," most subjects choose to disconfirm the experimenter's hypothesis in order to perform in a self-enhancing manner. Thus, the results of the typical laboratory experiment, where the subject is aware that some aspect of his behavior is being recorded, may be confounded by this artifact. This clearly would not be a problem in nonreactive field research.

To be sure, social psychology has attempted to deal with these problems. Unfortunately, the answer to these problems is to use deception to throw the subject off the track as to the purposes of the experiment. However, deceiving the college sophomore *qua* white rat is fast becoming a difficult undertaking (Kelman, 1967; Jourard & Kormann, 1968). In reviewing the research concerned with this problem, Schultz (1969) concluded that we cannot continue to conduct laboratory studies based on deception, "when we may be the only ones being deceived." We can no longer depend on the cooperative, unsuspicious, naive subject. And once deception is practiced, it becomes problematic to which population of situations we can generalize.

There is an awareness among college students, one is tempted to say an almost paranoid awareness, of the ways researchers gather information. The use of wiretapping devices, microphones, one-way mirrors, and stooges was bound to have an effect. In the authors' research in the laboratory, we have observed the result. It is almost common now for students who enter a laboratory to spot the microphones and one-way mirrors. They also say that they "don't trust psychologists," a phenomenon which has much more serious implications for psychology in general than it does for the finer points of research methodology.

One of the main reasons behind the difficulty of deceiving the subject is that college students are becoming very sophisticated about research technique. Since experiments are reported in newspapers and national magazines, it is not surprising that the "communication implosion" should affect our research tools (McLuhan, 1964). Goldstein, Heller, and Sechrest (1966) have spoken of the "reactivity of the environment." Once results have been widely disseminated, are the same results likely to be obtained again? For example, these authors believe that popular articles on "placebo" effects in psychotherapy and articles on the susceptibility of people to subliminal advertising are likely to lessen the impact of those phenomena, especially on those who read. They conclude: "It appears that any science operating in a reactive environment requires a continuous check on the status of its generalizations [p. 39]." How long will people, who are surfeited by evidence of the "devious" character of research, be deceived?

Recently, a number of experiments have been conducted to examine the effect of previous experimental experience of subjects on their performance in later experiments. Holmes and Appelbaum (1970) have concluded that attitudes and behavior developed by subjects in an earlier experiment affect subsequent independent experiments. In examining the effects of deception and debriefing on subsequent experiments, Silverman, Shulman, and Wiesenthal (1970) found that previously deceived subjects were not only more sensitized to the possible hidden purposes of the experiment, but they also tended to present themselves in a more favorable light. These authors strongly suggest that we should not rely only on college students as subjects.

Further complicating the deception problem are the findings that subjects who are illicitly informed by a confederate as to the true nature of the experiment may produce data which are similar to data produced by "naive" subjects (Golding & Lichtenstein, 1970). Thus, the same response may have a totally different meaning depending on whether the subject was actually deceived. This could possibly be dealt with if the effectiveness of the deception could be assessed. However, a survey of a number of social-psychological journals by Stricker (1967) showed that only 23.9 percent of all experiments using deception reported any information about the subjects' suspicions of the deception. In addition, there is evidence that subjects tend neither to confess suspiciousness of the procedure nor admit that they had any prior information about the experiment (Levy, 1967; Stricker, 1967; Golding & Lichtenstein, 1970).

The suspiciousness associated with deception in the laboratory experiment may eventually extend its sway to field experiments, too; but, for the present, the low level of awareness of the subjects that they are in an experiment is a good safeguard against that possibility.

Another major research problem is the generalizability of research findings. Campbell and Stanley (1963) speak of the *internal* as contrasted to the *external* validity of research. A similar distinction is made by Sidman (1960) with his notions of *reliability* and *generality*. Internal validity (reliability) refers to the confidence that the conclusions drawn are correct. External validity (generality) refers to the extent to which the conclusions drawn are applicable to populations or situations different from the experimental one; that is, how generalizable are the findings? So far our criticisms have been directed at the internal validity of laboratory research. Goldstein et al. note the novel notion that a certain amount of "sloppiness" or a "moderate degree of standardization" contributes positively to generalizability. "If an experiment is extremely well standardized, the results will have validity only for other similarly standard situations [1966, p. 37]." Campbell and Stanley refer to this as "heterogeneity of irrelevancies." By definition, field experiments tend to sample from a very heterogeneous population. However, to be sure, the latter population is of subjects; the situational character of the field may be quite specific.

Brunswick (1956) takes a similar approach. He feels that the experimental method (that is, the laboratory method) may combine variables in a way which is not representative of the way they exist in real life. Variables should be studied in their natural context. We should study the existing phenomenon, including all its concomitant interactions, rather than try artificially to control these interactions. Thus, we can avoid some of the faulty interpretations and overgeneralizations made from classical laboratory research.

Fillenbaum and Frey (1970) point out that the subject's behavior in an experiment may not generalize beyond the experimental situation, because of his "docility." They found that even "suspicious" subjects were "faithful" to the experimental situation. Fillenbaum and Frey doubt that persons outside the laboratory situation are so trusting. Thus, the trusting role may not only significantly affect the subjects' behavior in an experiment, but also may not be representative of everyday situations or peoples' behavior in them.

Schultz (1969) has pointed out another major weakness in our ability to generalize the results of our research. A review of current journals will convince anyone that psychologists are highly biased in the selection of subjects. Very few studies use the general adult as the subject. College students, especially male students, account for most of the subjects used in experiments. Schultz points out that 80 percent of our research is conducted on the 3 percent of the population now in college. In addition, the college student is not representative of the general population in age, intelligence, social class, or other variables. Another complicating factor is the manner in which we obtain these subjects. If we require students to participate, the resultant negative attitude generated probably affects the obtained results (Argyris, 1968). However, if we depend on volunteers, we encounter other problems. Volunteers have been shown to have significantly different attitudes and personalities than nonvolunteers. Rosenthal (1965) and Rosenthal and Rosnow (1969) have found volunteers to be younger and more intelligent, and to have greater interest and motivation and a greater need for social approval, than nonvolunteers. Whether we coerce students to participate or call for volunteers, we cannot say that the subjects were randomly chosen. These subjects are not representatives of the general population, the college population, or the class population, if they are not randomly selected. In contrast, most of the studies presented in this book make a stronger attempt to obtain a representative and randomly selected population of subjects.

A middle ground is maintained by Festinger (1953), who writes: "It should be stressed again, however, that the problem of application of the results of . . . laboratory experiments to the real-life situation is not solved by a simple extension of the result. Such application requires additional experimentation and study. It is undoubtedly important that the results of laboratory experiments be tested out in real life situations [p. 141]." Thus, a combination of laboratory and field research is needed in order to investigate thoroughly any phenomenon.

This book focuses on a certain area of field research. We are more concerned with field experiments than with field studies. The difference between the two is illustrated by French (1953): "The field experiment involves the actual manipulation of conditions by the experimenter in order to determine causal relations, whereas in the field study the researcher uses the selection of subjects and the measurement of existing conditions in the field setting as a method of determining correlations [p. 99]."

In addition, our interests lie in a special type of field experiment. The experiment should be nonreactive. That is, the subjects should be unaware that they are in an experiment, and the process of measurement should not alter the event being measured.

Weick (1968) very aptly describes the type of experiment in which the experimenter intervenes in the natural setting. However, instead of using the concept of nonreactivity, Weick states:

> It may seem that modification of a natural setting defeats the purpose of observational studies, namely, to study persons in habitats that are familiar to them. Clearly, massive interventions do render the familiar unfamiliar and make participants aware that they are being watched and that their actions are for the benefit of the investigators and not themselves. This is not the type of intervention we are advocating. *Subtle* modifications are the key. Perhaps the phrase that best captures what we have in mind is *tempered naturalness* [p. 367].

In addition, Weick points out how these modifications or interventions, because they occur in settings familiar to people, are not disruptive.

> Perhaps the most significant force that counteracts the disruptive effect of modifications is the fact that persons are operating in settings that are familiar. They are apt to be preoccupied with everyday events, and any slight changes in this routine are apt to be assimilated and to attract little attention. The modifications made by the observer may seem slightly out of the ordinary, but these discrepancies are likely to be swamped and forgotten because most of what the participants are doing is familiar. This state of affairs is quite in contrast to what occurs in the laboratory. Because of the unfamiliarity of the experimenter-subject relationship and the uniqueness of the demands that are made, the participant's attention is focused on the data-collection process. There are no routine or familiar activities to distract him or to make him less self-conscious. Even when deception is involved, the subject still is in a highly unfamiliar situation, and whatever happens tends to be organized around the fact that he is an object of study. In contrast, when the subject is in familiar surroundings doing familiar things, he is likely to organize his explanation of slightly unusual demands around the fact that they are part of his daily routine. When this occurs, the modifications made to clarify observation are minimally disruptive of natural events [p. 368].

Studying behavior in the natural environment, however, raises ethical questions concerning the deception of large numbers of people. Since one of the attractions of this research is that people are not aware that they are in an experiment, we cannot give forewarning to our subjects. Should people be used in a social-psychological experiment (or any experiment) without their permission or awareness? The question is difficult to answer. As pointed out earlier, if the field experiment is to retain its tempered naturalness, then it must not be a disruptive force in the subject's environment. The events staged by the experimenter should not have such a low probability of occurrence that the subject is suspicious about the naturalness of their origin. Thus, the well-designed field experiment can be interpreted as a simple acceleration of natural events. Instead of waiting for situations to occur naturally, the experimenter is staging them for both convenience and control. We feel that since most field experiments do not disrupt the normal behavior of the subjects, the permission of the subjects is not of crucial importance.

In sum, we have tried to choose studies for this book which meet certain criteria. The study should occur in a natural setting, be nonreactive, illustrate some scientific principle, and, in response to the ocean of yawns which most books of readings evince in our students, be interesting to read.

Unfortunately, not all the studies meet all these criteria. In some areas there are only studies, not experiments. In other areas there are not even studies. In this case we have presented proposals or techniques that can be used to study the area. However, most of the research studies presented in this volume meet one important criterion: in our opinion, they are interesting to read.

## REFERENCES

**ARGYRIS, C.** Some unintended consequences of rigorous research. *Psychological Bulletin,* 1968, **70,** 185-197.

**BRUNSWICK, E.** *Perception and the representative design of psychological experiments.* (2nd ed.) Berkeley: University of California Press, 1956.

**CAMPBELL, D. T., & STANLEY, J. C.** Experimental and quasi-experimental designs for research on teaching. In N. L. Gage (Ed.), *Handbook of research on teaching.* Chicago: Rand McNally, 1963, 171-246.

**FESTINGER, L.** Laboratory experiments. In L. Festinger & D. Katz (Eds.), *Research methods in the behavioral sciences.* New York: Holt, 1953, Pp. 136–172.

**FESTINGER, L., & KATZ, D.** (Eds.). *Research methods in the behavioral sciences.* New York: Holt, 1953.

**FILLENBAUM, S., & FREY, R.** More on the "faithful" behavior of suspicious subjects. *Journal of Personality,* 1970, 38, 43-51.

**FRENCH, J. R. P., JR.** Experiments in field settings. In L. Festinger and D. Katz (Eds.), *Research methods in the behavioral sciences.* New York: Holt, 1953, Pp. 98-135.

**GOLDING, S., & LICHTENSTEIN, E.** Confession of awareness and prior knowledge of deception as a function of interview set and approval motivation. *Journal of Personality and Social Psychology,* 1970, **14,** 213-223.

**GOLDSTEIN, A. P., HELLER, K., & SECHREST, L. B.** *Psychotherapy and the psychology of behavior change.* New York: Wiley, 1966.

**HOLMES, D. S., & APPELBAUM, A. S.** Nature of prior experimental experience as a determinant of performance in a subsequent experiment. *Journal of Personality and Social Psychology,* 1970, **14,** 195-202.

**JOURARD, S. M., & KORMANN, L. A.** Getting to know the experimenter, and its effect on psychological test performance. *Journal of Humanistic Psychology*, 1968, **8,** 155-159.

**KELMAN, H. C.** Human use of human subjects: the problem of deception in social psychological experiments. *Psychological Bulletin,* 1967, **67,** 1-11.

**LEVY, L.** Awareness, learning and the beneficent subject as expert witness. *Journal of Personality and Social Psychology,* 1967, 6, 365-370.

**LEWIN, K.** Problems of research in social psychology, 1943. In K. Lewin, *Field theory in social science: selected theoretical papers.* New York: Harper & Row, 1951.

**MCGUIRE, W. J.** Some impending reorientations in social psychology: Some thoughts provoked by Kenneth Ring. *Journal of Experimental Social Psychology,* 1967, **3,** 124-139.

**MCGUIRE, W. J.** Theory-oriented research in natural settings: the best of both worlds for social psychology. In M. Sherif & C. Sherif (Eds.), *Interdisciplinary relationships in the social sciences,* Chicago: Aldine, 1969, Pp. 21-51.

**MCLUHAN, H. M.** *Understanding media.* New York: McGraw-Hill, 1964.

**ORNE, M. T.** On the social psychology of the psychological experiment: with particular reference to demand characteristics and their implications. *American Psychologist,* 1962, **17,** 776-783.

**ORNE, M. T.** The nature of hypnosis: artifact and essence. *Journal of Abnormal and Social Psychology,* 1959, **58,** 277-299.

**PAGE, M. M.** Modification of figure-ground perception as a function of awareness of demand characteristics. *Journal of Personality and Social Psychology,* 1968, **9,** 59-66.

**RING, K.** Experimental social psychology: some sober questions about some frivolous values. *Journal of Experimental Social Psychology,* 1967, **3,** 113-123.

**ROSENBERG, M. J.** The conditions and consequences of evaluation apprehension. In R. Rosenthal and R. L. Rosnow (Eds.), *Artifact in behavioral research.* New York: Academic Press, 1969, Pp. 279-349.

**ROSENTHAL, R.** *Experimenter effects in behavioral research.* New York: Appleton-Century-Crofts, 1966.

**ROSENTHAL, R.** The volunteer subject. *Human Relations,* 1965, 18, 389-406.

**ROSENTHAL, R., & ROSNOW, R. L.** The volunteer subject. In R. Rosenthal and R. L. Rosnow (Eds.), *Artifact in behavioral research.* New York: Academic Press, 1969, Pp. 59-118.

**SCHULTZ, D. P.** The human subject in psychological research. *Psychological Bulletin,* 1969, **72,** 214-228.

**SELLTIZ, C., JAHODA, M., DEUTSCH, M., & COOK, S. W.** *Research methods in social relations.* New York: Holt, 1961.

**SIDMAN, M.** *Tactics of scientific research.* New York: Basic Books, 1960.

**SIGALL, H., ARONSON, E., & VAN HOOSE, T.** The cooperative subject: myth or reality? *Journal of Experimental Social Psychology,* 1970, **14,** 203-212.

**SILVERMAN, I., SHULMAN, A., & WIESENTHAL, D. L.** Effects of deceiving and debriefing psychological subjects on performance in later experiments. *Journal of Personality and Social Psychology,* 1970, **14,** 203-212.

**STRICKER, L.** The true deceiver. *Psychological Bulletin,* 1967, 68, 13-20.

**WEBB, E. J., CAMPBELL, D. T., SCHWARTZ, R. D., & SECHREST, L.** *Unobtrusive measures: nonreactive research in the social sciences.* Chicago: Rand McNally, 1966.

**WEICK, K.** Systematic observational methods. In G. Lindzey and E. Aronson (Eds.), *The handbook of social psychology,* Vol. 2. Reading, Mass.: Addison-Wesley, 1968, 357-451.

# CHAPTER TWO

# HELPING BEHAVIOR

The study of helping behavior is relatively new in social psychology. Although altruism has been a widely discussed concept in the social sciences, it has only recently been subjected to behavioral analyses which attempt to define conditions under which people do or do not help others. Krebs (1970), in an exhaustive review of the literature on altruism, points out that this concept is basic to religion, socialization, personality, psychoanalytic theory, and reinforcement theory. Thus, it is not surprising that interest in this area should experience a renaissance.

One reason for the increase in research being done on helping behavior may be the ability we now have to study this behavior in a scientific manner. Bringing altruism into the laboratory has had the advantage of stimulating more research. Moreover, the study of helping behavior in a field situation eliminates many of the problems of laboratory experiments, as pointed out in the introduction to this book. For example, because helping behavior is especially vulnerable to the effects of social desirability, it is important that the subject be unaware that his prosocial behavior is being measured. If he is aware of the experiment, he may help in order to present a positive appearance. Keeping the subject unaware of the real nature of the experiment is a difficult accomplishment in the laboratory, but relatively easy in a field situation. This may be one of the major reasons for the increasing number of experiments in this area which are being conducted in natural settings.

The first two experiments in this chapter explore the effect of models on helping behavior to determine whether the observation of another's helping behavior will affect our own. In the first experiment, Bryan and Test (page 11) studied helping behavior in department store parking lots and on a highway. These authors consistently found that the observation of another person helping significantly increased the frequency of helping behavior. The experiment by Hornstein, Fisch, and Holmes (page 18) examined characteristics of a model and the modeling situation. We have seen that modeling effects do occur, but is the effect dependent upon who the model is and how he feels about helping? In their experiment, these authors found that the feelings of a model who was dissimilar in nationality from the subject had no effect on the subject's helping behavior. However, if a model who was thought to be similar to the subject felt positive or neutral about helping, the subject helped more than he did when the model felt negative. This research is related to the last experiment in this chapter (Feldman), in which the dissimilar model was portrayed as being a foreigner.

In both of the above experiments, the models were portrayed as helping. Would we get an opposite effect if the model was seen as not helping? A recent laboratory experiment by Wagner and Wheeler (1969) and a field experiment by Bickman (1968) have both shown that models who do not help appear to reduce helping behavior in subjects. Thus, the behavior of a model can either increase or decrease the frequency of this behavior. Similarly, an experiment described in Chapter 3, by Helson, Blake, and Mouton shows that subjects will conform to either positive or negative behavior of a model.

Bryan and Test present a number of hypotheses which could account for the model's effect. One interesting possibility is that the model's behavior conveys to the subject what will happen if the subject chooses to follow the model's behavior. The Hornstein, Fisch, and Holms experiment can be used to support this interpretation.

The manner in which the recipient accepts help from the model may also affect the subject's perception of what will occur if he follows the model's behavior. In some pilot testing, Bickman has constructed a situation in which both the behavior of the model and the reaction of the person helped (or not helped) were experimentally manipulated. In this study, model, recipient and subject were in the New York City subway. Help consisted of giving money, while the recipient's behavior was either grateful or hostile. Preliminary data indicate that less help was given when the recipient acted with hostility toward the giving-model than was given when the recipient directed his hostility toward a nonhelping model. This result indicates that Bryan and Test's hypothesis about the effect of the model's behavior may also be extended to include behavior of the recipient. Thus, the subject's observation of model-recipient *interaction* is important in determining whether a subject will help.

Two other experiments in this chapter were conducted in the subway. Allen's research (page 22) uses a rather commonplace occurrence to study helping behavior in a novel way. New York City subways are famous for a number of things, one of which is the complexity of the system. People are frequently seen asking other people for directions. Allen uses this basic situation to answer a number of interesting questions about helping behavior. Will persons correct others who give misinformation to a person asking for directions? Allen found that people who apparently can hear the experimental confederate's misinformation tend not to correct the misinformation, unless the subject is the person asked directly and the confederate interrupts and gives the wrong answer. Again using this same basic paradigm, that is, willingness to correct the misinformation, Allen found interesting effects due to threat, modeling, and diffusion of responsibility.

Diffusion of responsibility is a concept (Darley & Latané, 1968) that is offered to explain the fact that persons do not help as often when there are others present as they do when they are alone. These authors reasoned that when there are other bystanders present, the responsibility for helping is shared by all the bystanders. Thus, in their research, they found that help is more likely to be given by a single bystander when he is alone than when there is a group of bystanders present. This finding has been replicated in other laboratory experiments (Bickman, 1971; Korte, 1969). However, the field experiments by Bryan and Test, by Allen, and by Piliavin, Rodin, and Piliavin have not confirmed that the amount of helping behavior is inversely related to the number of bystanders. Both Bryan and Test and Piliavin et al. offer some explanation for the discrepancy between field and laboratory results.

The research by Piliavin, Rodin, and Piliavin (page 34) investigates one aspect of helping behavior that is difficult to study in a field situation. Most of the field experiments have dealt with nonemergency situations, for example, donating money, asking for directions, or returning a wallet. However, the research of Piliavin et al. is concerned with helping an ill or drunk individual on a subway train. Since both the study by Allen and the study by Piliavin et al. use the subway as the location, it might be interesting to compare their results. One of the surprising findings of the research by Piliavin et al. was the large percentage of subjects who helped. Even in the situation where the victim was portraying a drunk, the victim was helped at least 67 percent of the time. (Within four of the seven experimental conditions, the victim received help 100 percent of the time.) By comparison, Allen found that only 27 percent of the subjects immediately corrected the misinformer about directions when the misinformer was the person directly asked. Part of the discrepancy between these two studies could result from the greater need of the victim. However, there could be another factor operating that is worthy of further investigation. While a large number of experiments on helping behavior refer to the murder of Kitty Genovese (this murder took place in New York while 28 persons watched and did nothing to help the victim) as the motivation for their research, few set up the experiment where two or more people who are directly involved with each other must be interrupted in order to help. That is, the subject is infrequently asked to interject himself into an established interaction. Allen's study, however, does contain this important factor. Thus, the responsibility of interjecting may be a significant inhibiting factor of helping behavior. Although Allen feels that the low level of helping may be due to the low cohesiveness of the group of bystanders found in the subway, the generality of this hypothesis is questioned by the findings of Piliavin et al. Interfering in the activities of two individuals, as in the Genovese case, may be a more difficult social action to perform than helping a drunk.

In addition to varying the emergency situation of the victim, Piliavin et al. also varied the victim's race. Although this latter manipulation is of questionable validity in this experiment, since only one black person was used, there was a slight tendency for people to help victims of the same race as themselves. Other studies have shown that the characteristics of the person in need of help are a strong determinant of whether help will be given. Bryan and Test found that a black Salvation Army officer was discriminated against in terms of donations. In Chapter 5, the study by Gaertner and Bickman uses helping behavior over the telephone as an indication of "racism." And finally, the study by Feldman, in this chapter, found that helping behavior is affected by whether one is perceived as being a foreigner or a compatriot.

In addition to studying the characteristics of the victim, the characteristics of the subject have been investigated. In most laboratory studies, this would be a difficult undertaking, but in field situations a wide variety of subjects can be tested simply by recording the subject's sex, race, apparent social class, and age. Feldman recorded the social class of his subjects and found generally that the higher the social class, the more help was given. Many studies have looked at the correlation of the subject's sex with help. Piliavin et al. report that men helped significantly more than women in emergencies. In the experiment by Gaertner and Bickman (Chapter 5), which was a nonemergency helping situation, the same result was obtained. Further work by Bickman confirmed this finding, using the same basic technique, but using victims of both sexes and a different population of subjects. The results of laboratory research have been equivocal, suggesting that the role of the subject's sex has still to be clarified.

The last experiment in this chapter, by Feldman, takes us across national boundaries to determine how compatriots and foreigners are treated in various cities. It is interesting to compare the results of this scientific study with the biases we have or even with the isolated experiences we might have had in traveling abroad.

This chapter focuses on the determinants of helping behavior. We have chosen to start the book with studies in this field, because we feel that it is one of the newest and most exciting areas in social psychology. Helping behavior is an important area of study for a number of reasons. It can be used to investigate such things as racism and international relations. Thus, a more complete understanding of the conditions under which people aid each other can generalize to many other aspects of social behavior.

## REFERENCES

**BICKMAN, L.** The effect of another bystander's ability to help on bystander intervention in an emergency. *Journal of Experimental Social Psychology,* 1971, **7**, 367-379.

**BICKMAN, L.** The effect of models on helping behavior in subways. Unpublished manuscript, 1968.

**DARLEY, J. D., & LATANÉ, B.** Bystander intervention in emergencies: diffusion of responsibility. *Journal of Personality and Social Psychology,* 1968, **8**, 377-383.

**KORTE, C.** Group effects on help-giving. Unpublished doctoral dissertation, Harvard University, 1969.

**KREBS, D. L.** Altruism–an examination of the concept and a review of the literature. *Psychological Bulletin,* 1970, **73**, 258-302.

**WAGNER, C., & WHEELER, L.** Model, need and cost effects in helping behavior. *Journal of Personality and Social Psychology,* 1969, **12**, 111-116.

# MODELS AND HELPING: NATURALISTIC STUDIES IN AIDING BEHAVIOR [1]

JAMES H. BRYAN AND MARY ANN TEST
*Northwestern University*

4 experiments concerned with helping behavior were conducted. 3 were addressed to the effects of altruistic models upon helping, while 1 was concerned with the impact of the solicitor's race upon donations. 3 investigations employed as a site parking lots of 2 large department stores in New Jersey, and indexed helping by contributions to the Salvation Army. A 4th experiment indexed helping by offers of aid by passing motorists to a woman with a disabled vehicle. Whether one employed motorists in California or shoppers in New Jersey, the results were quite consistent. The presence of a helping model significantly increased helping behavior. As race of the Salvation Army solicitor did affect the percentage of donors willing to contribute money, it was concluded that interpersonal attraction is a relevant variable affecting donations.

Recently, concern has been evidenced regarding the determinants and correlates of altruistic behavior, those acts wherein individuals share or sacrifice a presumed positive reinforcer for no apparent social or material gain. Studies addressed to these behaviors have explored both individual differences in the tendency to be altruistic and the situational determinants of such responses. Gore and Rotter (1963) found that students at a southern Negro college were more likely to volunteer for a social protest movement if they perceived sources of reinforcement as internally rather than externally guided. Subjects high on internal control were more likely to volunteer as freedom riders, marchers, or petition signers than subjects who perceived others as primary agents of reinforcement. Experimental evidence has been generated supporting the often-made assumption that guilt may serve as a stimulus to altruistic activity. Darlington and Macker (1966) found that subjects led to believe that they had harmed another through incompetent performances on the experimental tasks (three paper-and-pencil tests) were more willing than control subjects to donate blood to a local hospital. Aronfreed and Paskal[2] and Midlarsky and Bryan (1967) found that children exposed to treatment conditions designed to produce empathy were more willing to donate M&M candies than subjects given control conditions, while Handlon and Gross (1959), Ugurel-Semin (1952), Wright (1942), and Midlarsky and Bryan have found sharing to be positively correlated with age among school-age children. Lastly, Berkowitz and Friedman (1967) have demonstrated that adolescents of the working class and the bureaucratic middle class are less affected in their helping behaviors by interpersonal attraction than adolescents of the entrepreneur middle class.

Three hypotheses have emerged regarding the situational determinants of self-sacrificing behaviors. One suggests that individuals behave in an altruistic fashion because of compliance to a norm of reciprocity. That is, individuals are aware of the social debts and credits established between them, and expect that ultimately the mutual exchange of goods and services will balance (Gouldner, 1960). Berkowitz and Daniels (1964) have suggested that individuals might show a generalization of such obligatory feelings and thus aid others who had not previously assisted them.

A second hypothesis was put forth by Berkowitz and his colleagues (Berkowitz, 1966; Berkowitz &

[1] While Mary Ann Test collaborated with the senior author on Experiment I, the remaining work is the latter's sole responsibility.

Thanks are due to Cheryl Dellhoussay, Betty Umann, Joe McNair, and Frank Siri who served as the experimenters and stooges for Experiment I, and to Edward Nystrom, Alice Anderson, Katherine Moore, and Irene Paramoure who served as the models, observers, and solicitors in studies II, III, and IV. Studies II, III, and IV were carried out while the author was affiliated with Educational Testing Service and were supported by the National Institute of Child Health and Human Development, under Research Grant 1 PO1 HD1762-01. The authors are especially grateful to the Salvation Army of Trenton, New Jersey, and specifically to George H. Gibb, whose cooperation made these experiments possible. Thanks are also due to Perry London, David Rosenhan, Ladd Wheeler, Lawrence Stricker, and Bruce K. Eckland for the many helpful comments upon various portions of the manuscript.

[2] J. Aronfreed & V. Paskal. Altruism, empathy and the conditioning of positive affect. Unpublished manuscript, 1965.

Daniels, 1963; Berkowitz, Klanderman, & Harris, 1964; Daniels & Berkowitz, 1963) who have postulated the social responsibility norm. They have contended that dependency on others evokes helping responses even under conditions where the possibility of external rewards for the helper are remote. Using supervisor's ratings of an unknown and absent other to produce dependency, and a box-construction task as the dependent variable, considerable support has been generated for the suggestion that dependency increases helping.

A third major determinant of helping may be the presence of helping (or nonhelping) models. While attention to the effects of models has generally been directed toward antisocial behaviors (cf. Bandura & Walters, 1963; Freed, Chandler, Mouton, & Blake, 1955; Lefkowitz, Blake, & Mouton, 1955), some recent evidence suggests that observation of self-sacrificing models may lead to subsequent succorant behavior by children. For example, Rosenhan and White (1967) have demonstrated that children are more likely to donate highly valued gift certificates to residents of a fictitious orphanage if they have seen an adult do so. Hartup and Coates[3] found that nursery school children who have been exposed to a self-sacrificing peer were more likely to be altruistic than children not so exposed. Test and Bryan[4] found that female college students were more likely to render aid to another in computing arithmetic problems if they saw other people so doing.

The present series of experiments was designed to test the effects of models in natural settings on subject samples other than college or high school students, and in contexts other than a school room or university setting. The first three experiments reported are concerned with the impact of observing helping models upon subsequent helping behaviors, while the fourth is addressed to the influence of interpersonal attraction upon donation behavior.

## EXPERIMENT I: LADY IN DISTRESS: A FLAT TIRE STUDY

Few studies have been concerned with the effects of models upon *adults,* and fewer still with the impact of *prosocial* models upon them (Wheeler, 1966). Those that have been concerned with such behaviors have invariably employed college students as subjects. For example, Rosenbaum and Blake (1955) and Rosenbaum (1956) have found that college students exposed to a model who volunteered, upon the personal request of the experimenter, to participate in an experiment would be more likely to consent than subjects not exposed to such a model or than subjects who observed a model refuse to cooperate. Pressures toward conformity in these experiments were great, however, as the request was made directly by the experimenter and in the presence of a large number of other students.

Test and Bryan found that the observation of helping models significantly increased the subsequent offers of aid by observers. However, in that study, subjects were given the task of solving arithmetic problems and then rating their difficulty, a task ordinarily requiring autonomous efforts. Furthermore, the experiment was conducted within a university setting, a context where independence of thought is often stressed. The effects of the model may have been simply to increase the subjects' faith that assisting others was allowed. While questionnaire data of the study did not support this interpretation, such effects could not be ruled out entirely. Thus, it is possible that the model impact was simply a propriety-defining activity which reduced the inhibitions associated with such helping behavior.

In general, then, investigations of modeling that employ adults as subjects and that demand self-sacrifice on the part of subjects are limited in number, exploit strong pressures toward conformity, and rely upon college students as subjects. The present experiment was designed to assess the impact of models upon subsequent spontaneous offers of help in other than a university setting.

### Method

The standard condition consisted of an undergraduate female stationed by a 1964 Ford Mustang (control car) with a flat left-rear tire. An inflated tire was leaned upon the left side of the auto. The girl, the flat tire, and the inflated tire were conspicuous to the passing traffic.

In the model condition, a 1965 Oldsmobile was located approximately ¼ mile from the control car. The car was raised by jack under the left rear bumper, and a girl was watching a male changing the flat tire.

In the no-model condition, the model was absent; thus, only the control car was visible to the passing traffic.

The cars were located in a predominantly residential section in Los Angeles, California. They were placed in such a manner that no intersection separated the model from the control car. No turnoffs were thus available to the passing traffic. Further, opposite flows of traffic were divided by a separator such that the first U turn available to the traffic going in the opposite direction of the control car would be after exposure to the model condition.

The experiment was conducted on two successive Saturdays between the hours of 1:45 and 5:50 P.M. Each treatment condition lasted for the time required for 1000 vehicles to pass the control car. While private automobiles

[3] W. W. Hartup & B. Coates. Imitation of peers as a function of reinforcement from the peer group and rewardingness of the model. Unpublished manuscript, 1966.

[4] M. A. Test & J. H. Bryan. Dependency, models and reciprocity. Unpublished manuscript, 1966.

and trucks, motorscooters, and motorcycles were tallied as vehicles, commercial trucks, taxis, and buses were not. Vehicle count was made by a fourth member of the experiment who stood approximately 100 feet from the control car hidden from the passing motorists. On the first Saturday, the model condition was run first and lasted from 1:45 to 3:15 P.M. In order to exploit changing traffic patterns and to keep the time intervals equal across treatment conditions, the control car was moved several blocks and placed on the opposite side of the street for the no-model condition. The time of the no-model treatment was 4:00 to 5:00 P.M. On the following Saturday, counterbalancing the order and the location of treatment conditions was accomplished. That is, the no-model condition was run initially and the control car was placed in the same location that it had been placed on the previous Saturday during the model condition. The time of the no-model condition was 2:00 to 3:30 P.M. For the model condition, the control car was placed in that locale where it had been previously during the no-model condition. The time of the model condition was 4:30 to 5:30 P.M.

Individuals who had stopped to offer help were told by the young lady that she had already phoned an auto club and that help was imminent. Those who nonetheless insisted on helping her were told the nature of the experiment.

**Results** The dependent variable was the number of cars that stopped and from which at least one individual offered help to the stooge by the control car. Of the 4000 passing vehicles, 93 stopped. With the model car absent, 35 vehicles stopped; with the model present, 58 halted. The difference between the conditions was statistically significant ($\chi^2 = 5.53$, corrected for continuity, $df = 1$, $p < .02$, two-tailed). Virtually all offers of aid were from men rather than women drivers.

The time of day had little impact upon the offering of aid. Fifty vehicles stopped during the early part of the afternoon; 43 during the later hours. Likewise, differences in help offers were not great between successive Saturdays, as 45 offers of aid were made on the first Saturday, 48 on the second Saturday.

The results of the present study support the hypothesis that helping behaviors can be significantly increased through the observation of others' helpfulness. However, other plausible hypotheses exist which may account for the findings. It is possible to account for the differences in treatment effects by differences in sympathy arousal. That is, in the model condition, the motorist observed a woman who had had some difficulty. Such observations may have elicited sympathy and may have served as a reminder to the driver of his own social responsibilities.

Another explanation of the findings revolves around traffic slowdown. It is possible that the imposition of the model condition served to reduce traffic speed, thus making subsequent stopping to help a less hazardous undertaking. While the time taken for 1000 autos to pass the control car was virtually identical in the model and no-model condition and thus not supportive of such an explanation, the "slowdown" hypothesis cannot be eliminated. Assuming the model effect to be real, one might still argue that it was not a norm of helping that was facilitated by the model, but rather that inhibitions against picking up helpless young ladies were reduced. That is, within the model condition, the passing motorists may have observed a tempted other and thus felt less constrained themselves regarding similar efforts. Indeed, the insistence of some people to help in spite of the imminent arrival of other aiders suggested the operation of motives other than simply helping. Indeed, while the authors did not index the frequency of pick-up attempts, it was clear that a rather large number were evidenced.

Because of the number of alternative explanations, the evidence supporting the hypothesis that the observation of helpers per se will increase subsequent aiding is weak. Experiment II was designed to test further the prediction that the perception of another's altruistic activity would elicit similar behavior on the part of the observer.

## EXPERIMENT II: COINS IN THE KETTLE

The investigation was conducted on December 14th between the hours of 10:00 A.M. and 5:00 P.M. The subjects were shoppers at a large department store in Princeton, New Jersey. Observations made on the previous day indicated that the shoppers were overwhelmingly Caucasian females.

A Salvation Army kettle was placed on the sidewalk in front of the main entrance to the store. Two females, both in experimenter's employ, alternatively manned the kettle for periods of 25 minutes. One solicitor was a Negro, the other a Caucasian. Each wore a Salvation Army cape and hat. Although allowed to ring the Salvation Army bell, they were not permitted to make any verbal plea or to maintain eye contact with the passing shoppers, except to thank any contributor for his donation.

The model condition (M) was produced as follows: Once every minute on the minute, a male dressed as a white-collar worker would approach the kettle from within the store and contribute 5 cents. As the model donated, he started a stopwatch and walked from the kettle toward a parking lot as if searching for someone. He then returned to the store. The following 20-second period constituted the duration of the treatment condition.

Following a subsequent lapse of 20 seconds, the next 20-second period defined the no-model condition (NM).

Within any one minute, therefore, both M and NM treatments occurred. There were 365 occasions of each treatment.

It should be noted that it was possible that some subjects in the NM condition observed the contribution of the model or a donor affected by the model. If that hypothesis is correct, however, the effects of such incidents would be to reduce rather than enhance the differences between treatments.

**Results** The dependent variable was the number of people who independently donated to the Salvation Army. People obviously acquainted, as for example, man and wife, were construed as one potential donating unit. In such conditions, if both members of a couple contributed, they were counted as a single donor.

Since there were no differences in model effects for the Negro or Caucasian solicitor, data obtained from each were combined. The total number of contributors under the NM condition was 43; under the M condition, 69. Assuming that the chance distribution of donations would be equal across the two conditions, a chi-square analysis was performed. The chi-square equaled 6.01 ($p < .01$).[5]

In spite of precautions concerning the elimination of correlated observations within a treatment condition, it was possible for subjects in any one observational period to influence one another. Such influence may have been mediated through acquaintances not eliminated by our procedures or the observations of others as well as the model donating. A more conservative analysis of the data, insuring independent observation, was therefore made. Instead of comparing treatments by analyzing the number of donors, the analysis used, as the dependent variable, the number of observation periods in which there was a contribution, that is, those periods in which more than one donation occurred were scored identically to those in which only a single contribution was received. Occasions of donations equaled 60 in the M treatment, 43 in the NM condition. The chi-square equaled 2.89 ($p < .05$).

The results of Experiment II further support the hypothesis that observation of altruistic activity will increase such behavior among observers. But the matter is not yet entirely clear, for when the observer saw the model donate he saw two things: first, the actual donation, and second, the polite and potentially reinforcing interaction that occurred between the donor and solicitor. Conceivably, the observation of an altruistic model, per se, who was not socially reinforced for his behavior, would have little or no effect on an observer. The third experiment was designed to examine this possibility.

[5] All chi-square analyses were corrected for continuity and all tests of significance were one-tailed.

## EXPERIMENT III: COINS IN THE KETTLE II

The experiment was conducted at a Trenton, New Jersey, shopping center from the hours of 10:00 A.M. to 5:00 P.M. Again, the majority of the patrons were Caucasian females. It is likely, however, that these shoppers were of a lower socioeconomic status than those in the Princeton group.

Salvation Army kettles were placed before the main entrance of a large department store (Kettle 1) and a large food center (Kettle 2). The kettles were separated by more than 200 yards. During the first 120 observations (10:00 A.M. to 12:00 P.M.), two male college students, employed by the Salvation Army and wearing its uniform, manned the kettles. The site of the experiment was Kettle 1, except on those occasions where the worker took his "coffee break." At those times, data collection was centered at Kettle 2. An equal number of M and NM conditions were run at each site, although approximately two-thirds of the observational time was spent at Kettle 1. During the remaining 240 observational periods (1:00 P.M. to 5:00 P.M.) the same male worker and his spouse alternately manned Kettle 1. The wife was stationed by the kettle for 136 minutes, the male for 104 minutes. The experiment was conducted only at Kettle 1 during the afternoon period.

Solicitors were told to make no verbal appeals for donations or responses to the model upon his contribution. While they were not informed of the hypothesis underlying the experiment, they may well have deduced it. The model was the same as in Experiment II, and again was dressed as a white-collar worker.

The imposition of the treatment conditions were identical to those described in Experiment I with the following exceptions. Since the kettle was more visible at this site than at the previous one, 30-second rather than 20-second periods were used for each treatment. To simplify the procedures, no waiting periods between treatments occurred. Additionally, after donating, the model would return to the parking lot. There were a total of 360 occasions of each of the M and NM conditions.

**Results** The criteria defining a donor were identical to those outlined in Experiment I. Under the M condition, 84 donors were tallied; under the NM treatment, 56. The chi-square value was 4.86 ($p < .025$).

Since it was possible that one donor might have seen a donor other than the model receive social approval from the solicitor, the more conservative comparison of the treatments as outlined in Experiment II was made. That is, treatments were compared by noting the number of observational periods in which any donation occurred. Therefore, those donors who may have been influenced by a contributor receiving the solicitor's thanks were excluded. Of the 360 observational periods under the M condition, there were 75 in which some donation was made. Of the 360 periods, 51 were marked by contributions. Chi-square yielded a value of 5.09 ($p < .025$).

## EXPERIMENT IV: ETHNOCENTRISM AND DONATION BEHAVIOR

While Experiment III was conducted to eliminate the solicitor's explicit social approval as a mechanism underlying donation behavior, it is possible that the model's impact was due to the information communicated to the observer regarding the consequence of donations. Work by Bandura, Ross, and Ross (1963), for example, found that children observing a model rewarded for aggression would be more aggressive than children who had observed a model being punished for such behavior. Additionally, considerable data have been gathered within the university laboratory suggesting that interpersonal attraction may greatly influence the helping response. Berkowitz and Friedman (1967), Daniels and Berkowitz (1963), and Goranson and Berkowitz (1966) have suggested that positive affect increases the probability of low payoff helping behavior.

The present experiment was designed to assess the impact of the solicitor's race upon the donation behavior of shoppers. It was assumed that a Negro solicitor would be held in less esteem by Caucasian shoppers than a solicitor of their same race, and that such attitudes would affect contributions. While the applicability of the "consequence to the model" hypothesis in accounting for the model's effect was not tested directly, the study assesses the importance of interpersonal attraction in eliciting charitable behavior.

### Method

The experiment was conducted on December 2 and 3 between the hours of 10 A.M. and 6 P.M. at the Trenton area site. The subjects were Caucasian shoppers at a large department store.[6] Three thousand seven hundred and three shoppers were observed; 2,154 females and 1,549 males. In order to reduce the possibility of including the same subject in the experiment on more than one occasion, tallies were made only of exiting shoppers.

Two Salvation Army kettles were placed at two store exits, their location being separated by approximately 75 yards. Two female solicitors, a Negro and a Caucasian, manned the kettles. Both were in their early twenties, wore the uniform of the Salvation Army, and were in the employ of the experimenter. Each was instructed to make no verbal appeals for donations and to avoid eye contact with the shoppers. After a period of 25 minutes, the girls rotated kettle assignments, and during the last 10 minutes of the hour were allowed to take a coffee break. Hence, during a single hour, each solicitor manned both kettles. Each solicitor manned each kettle on seven occasions per day. Thus, each solicitor was observed for a total of 28 observational periods; 14 on each day (seven on each kettle) over a period of two days.

Two observers, each assigned to a particular kettle, tallied the number and sex of the existing shoppers and contributors during each of the 25-minute periods. In addition, records were kept of the amount of money donated within any period, although it was impossible on this measure to separate those donations made by incoming from outgoing customers.

[6]As there were very few Negro donors ($N = 7$), analysis was confined to the behavior of Caucasian shoppers.

**Results** The dependent variable was the percentage of donors contributing to the kettle within an observational period. That is, observational periods were assigned a percentage donor score. Shoppers within an observational period were treated as a single group, with differences between groups on percentage donor score forming the critical comparisons. The total $N$ of the study was then the 56 observational periods, rather than the 3,703 shoppers. Since the mean group size for the Negro solicitor was 70.32 and for the Caucasian 61.93 (standard deviations equal to 53.33 and 42.98, respectively), it was assumed that the percentage score was relatively stable.

The effects of race, kettle location, and day and their interactions were analyzed by analysis of variance.

As can be seen from [Table 2-1], both the main effect of race and of day were significant. As predicted, the Negro solicitor elicited a statistically significant lower percentage of donors than did the Caucasian. For the Negro solicitor, the average percentage donor score for observational periods was 2.22 ($SD$ = 2.36), while for the Caucasian solicitor the average

**[Table 2-1] Analysis of variance of percentage donor' scores**

| | *df* | *MS* | *F* |
|---|---|---|---|
| Race (A) | 1 | 38.778 | 4.84* |
| Day (B) | 1 | 98.315 | 12.28** |
| Kettle (C) | 1 | .018 | |
| A × B | 1 | 1.511 | |
| A × C | 1 | 11.340 | |
| B × C | 1 | 1.031 | |
| A × B × C | 1 | 3.206 | |
| Error | 48 | 8.009 | |

*$p < .05$ (2-tailed).
**$p < .01$ (2-tailed).

percentage donor score was 3.89 (*SD* = 3.60). Additionally, Saturday shoppers were by and large less generous than Friday customers. The average percentage donor score of the group was 1.73 (*SD* = 1.97) for the Saturday shopper, and 4.38 for the Friday shopper (*SD* = 3.52).

A second dependent variable was the amount of money donated during each time period. No significant differences were found for race, day, or kettle location.

The present investigation does support, albeit equivocally, the notion that interpersonal attraction may affect donations even when the solicitors are not the eventual recipients of such contributions. While it is possible that race differences simply fail to remind observers of their social responsibilities, it is also feasible that the subjects wanted to avoid interpersonal contact with a minority group member. If this is true, then it is interesting to note that interpersonal attraction may play an important role even in those situations where personal anonymity is high and escape from unpleasant situations easy.

## DISCUSSION

The results of the first three experiments clearly replicate those of Test and Bryan and extend the findings over a variety of subject populations, settings, and tasks. The results hold for college students, motorists, and shoppers; in the university laboratory, city streets, and shopping centers; and when helping is indexed by aiding others solve arithmetic problems, changing flat tires, or donating money to the Salvation Army. The findings then are quite consistent: the presence of helping models significantly increases subsequent altruistic behavior.

That generosity breeds generosity is interesting in light of the recent concern with helping behaviors in emergency contexts. Darley and Latané[7] and Latané and Darley[8] have found that subjects are less inclined to act quickly in emergency situations when in the presence of other potential helpers. Whether faced with a medical emergency (a simulated epileptic seizure) or a dangerous natural event (simulated fire), the rapidity with which students sought to aid was reduced by the presence of others. These findings have been interpreted in three ways: as reflecting the subjects' willingness to diffuse responsibility (others will aid); as reflecting their diffusion of blame (others didn't aid either); or as reflecting conformity to the nonpanicked stooges. It is clear that the results of the first three experiments in the present series do not follow that which might be predicted by the diffusion concepts. A giving model apparently does not lend credibility to the belief that others than the self will make the necessary sacrifices. The helping other did not strengthen the observer's willingness to diffuse his social obligations, but rather stimulated greater social responsibility. In light of these results, the delayed reaction exhibited by the subjects tested by Darley and Latané might be best attributable to conformity behavior. As they have suggested, subjects faced with a unique and stressful situation may have been either reassured by the presence of calm others or fearful of acting stupidly or cowardly. Additionally, it is possible that diffusion of responsibility is only associated with anxiety-inducing situations. The current data fail to indicate that such diffusion occurs in nonstressful situations which demand fulfillment of social obligations.

While it appears clear that the behavior of the motorists and shoppers was not dictated by a variety of situational and social pressures usually associated with the study of modeling in adults or experiment in academic settings (Orne, 1962), the mechanisms underlying the effects are not obvious. While the presence of the model in the flat-tire study may have reminded the motorists as to the social responsibility norm, a hypothesis does not appear reasonable in accounting for the results in the coins-in-the-kettle series. The bell-ringing Salvation Army worker, with kettle and self placed squarely in the pathway of the oncoming pedestrian, would seem to be reminder enough of one's obligation toward charity. A priori, it would not appear necessary to superimpose upon that scene the donating other for purposes of cognitive cueing (Wheeler, 1966).

One hypothesis to account for the model effect is that the observer is given more information regarding the consequences of such donation behavior. Experiment IV suggested that solicitor status or personal attraction might operate on donation behaviors even under conditions of personal anonymity and few social constraints. It is possible that the model serves to communicate to the potential donor relevant information concerning the consequences of his act. That is, the model may demonstrate that an approach to the solicitor does not involve an unwanted interpersonal interaction (e.g., lectures on religion).

A second hypothesis to account for the data pertains to the shame-provoking capacities of the model.

[7] J. Darley & B. Latané. Diffusion of responsibility in emergency situations. Unpublished manuscript, 1966.

[8] B. Latané & J. Darley. Group inhibition of bystander intervention in emergencies. Unpublished manuscript, 1966.

It is reasonable to assume that most people feel that they are, by and large, benevolent and charitable. Furthermore, it is likely that such a self-image is rarely challenged: first because charitable acts are not frequently required; second, at least in the street scenes employed in the current series of studies, solicitations are made in the context of many nongiving others. That is, a multitude of negative models—of noncharitable others—surround the solicitations in the current series of studies. Indeed, the contexts are such that most people are not helping; many more cars pass than stop to offer aid to the lady in distress; and there are many more people who refuse to put coins in the kettle than those who do. However, the witnessing of a donor, an individual who not only recognizes his social responsibility but in fact acts upon it, may produce a greater challenge to the good-self image of the observer. Acts rather than thoughts may be required of the observer in order to maintain the self-image of benevolence and charity. If such is the case, then the model characteristics most effective in producing prosocial behavior by socialized adults would be those directed toward shame or guilt production (e.g., donations from the poor), rather than those reflecting potential reinforcement power (e.g., donations from the high status).

Whatever the mechanism underlying the model effect, it does appear quite clear that prosocial behavior can be elicited through the observation of benign others.

## REFERENCES


**BANDURA, A., ROSS, D., & ROSS, S.** Vicarious reinforcement and imitative learning. *Journal of Abnormal and Social Psychology*, 1963, **66**, 601-607.

**BANDURA, A., & WALTERS, R. H.** *Social learning and personality development.* New York: Holt, Rinehart & Winston, 1963.

**BERKOWITZ, L.** A laboratory investigation of social class and national differences in helping behavior. *International Journal of Psychology*, 1966, **1**, 231-240.

**BERKOWITZ, L., & DANIELS, L.** Responsibility and dependency. *Journal of Abnormal and Social Psychology*, 1963, **66**, 429-436.

**BERKOWITZ, L., & DANIELS, L.** Affecting the salience of the social responsibility norm: Effects of past help on the response to dependency relationships. *Journal of Abnormal and Social Psychology*, 1964, **68**, 275-281.

**BERKOWITZ, L., & FRIEDMAN, P.** Some social class differences in helping behavior. *Journal of Personality and Social Psychology*, 1967, **5**, 217-225.

**BERKOWITZ, L., KLANDERMAN, S. B., & HARRIS, R.** Effects of experimenter awareness and sex of subject and experimenter on reactions to dependency relationships. *Sociometry*, 1964, **27**, 327-337.

**DANIELS, L., & BERKOWITZ, L.** Liking and response to dependency relationships, *Human Relations*, 1963, **16**, 141-148.

**DARLINGTON, R. B., & MACKER, C. E.** Displacement of guilt-produced altruistic behavior. *Journal of Personality and Social Psychology*, 1966, **4**, 442-443.

**FREED, A., CHANDLER, P., MOUTON, J., & BLAKE, R.** Stimulus and background factors in sign violation. *Journal of Personality*, 1955, **23**, 499.

**GORANSON, R., & BERKOWITZ, L.** Reciprocity and responsibility reactions to prior help. *Journal of Personality and Social Psychology*, 1966, **3**, 227-232.

**GORE, P. M., & ROTTER, J. B.** A personality correlate of social action. *Journal of Personality*, 1963, **31**, 58-64.

**GOULDNER, A.** The norm of reciprocity: A preliminary statement. *American Sociological Review*, 1960, **25**, 161-178.

**HANDLON, B. J., & GROSS, P.** The development of sharing behavior. *Journal of Abnormal and Social Psychology*, 1959, **59**, 425-428.

**LEFKOWITZ, M., BLAKE, R., & MOUTON, J.** Status factors in pedestrian violation of traffic signals. *Journal of Abnormal and Social Psychology*, 1955, **51**, 704-706.

**MIDLARSKY, E., & BRYAN, J. H.** Training charity in children. *Journal of Personality and Social Psychology*, 1967, **5**, 408-415.

**ORNE, M.** On the social psychology of the psychological experiment: With particular reference to demand characteristics and their implications. *American Psychologist*, 1962, **17**, 776-783.

**ROSENBAUM, M.** The effect of stimulus and background factors on the volunteering response. *Journal of Abnormal and Social Psychology*, 1956, **53**, 118-121.

**ROSENBAUM, M., & BLAKE, R.** Volunteering as a function of field structure. *Journal of Abnormal and Social Psychology*, 1955, **50**, 193-196.

**ROSENHAN, D., & WHITE, G. M.** Observation and rehearsal as determinants of prosocial behavior. *Journal of Personality and Social Psychology*, 1967, **5**, 424-431.

**UGUREL-SEMIN, R.** Moral behavior and moral judgment of children. *Journal of Abnormal and Social Psychology*, 1952, **47**, 463-474.

**WHEELER, L.** Toward a theory of behavioral contagion. *Psychological Review*, 1966, **73**, 179-192.

**WRIGHT, B. A.** Altruism in children and perceived conduct of others. *Journal of Abnormal and Social Psychology*, 1942, **37**, 218-233.

# INFLUENCE OF A MODEL'S FEELING ABOUT HIS BEHAVIOR AND HIS RELEVANCE AS A COMPARISON OTHER ON OBSERVERS' HELPING BEHAVIOR[1]

HARVEY A. HORNSTEIN, ELISHA FISCH, AND MICHAEL HOLMES
*Teachers College, Columbia University*

This study, which is part of a series of naturalistic field experiments, is concerned with the influence of social models on helping behavior. Data were collected unobtrusively from 105 pedestrians in midtown Manhattan. By chance, these people came upon an open envelope, from which was protruding a man's wallet obviously containing money. Wrapped around the wallet was a letter addressed to the wallet's owner, describing a previous finder's feelings about returning the wallet. When the previous finder (social model) was not characterized as being dissimilar from the subject, a letter reporting positive feelings on his part about returning the wallet produced a greater number of completely intact returns than a letter reporting negative feelings. If the model was dissimilar, the feelings of the previous finder produced no differences in the number of intact wallets returned.

The study presented in this paper is part of a series of naturalistic field experiments whose common objective is to investigate some social determinants of interpersonal helping behavior. The authors' particular concern in the present investigation is with the influence of social models on helping behavior. Past research (Bryan & Test, 1967; Rosenbaum & Blake, 1955; Rosenhan & White, 1967) dealing with this issue has concentrated on investigating the effects of the presence or absence of a helping model. The data collected by previous investigators support an intuitively plausible proposition: observation of a helping model increases the likelihood of helping behavior.

This study is concerned with identifying the conditions which qualify and refine this proposition. Hence, in all experimental conditions the model is performing the same helpful act. The authors reasoned, however, that an observer is influenced not only by what the model is doing but also by what consequences the model himself experiences as a result of his helpful act. If the observer anticipates having similar experiences for the same behavior, he will be less likely to emulate the model when the latter's experiences have been negative than when his experiences have been positive. Bandura (1965) has previously demonstrated that the observation of externally imposed reward and punishment to a film-mediated model will, respectively, increase and decrease imitative behavior. In contrast to the outcomes observed by subjects in Bandura's experiment, the subjects in this experiment observed the model's reported feelings about his helpful act. These feelings were either positive or negative, reflecting the extent to which he experienced helping another as pleasant or unpleasant.

In predicting that the observation of positive feelings increases the likelihood of helping acts (and the observation of negative feelings has the opposite effect), we are assuming that an observer uses the model's experiences as a valid predictor of his own future experiences. This assumption leads us to predict that in situations in which the potential helper perceives himself to be extremely dissimilar to the model, the model's experiences are not seen to be valid predictors of the observer's experiences. In such situations, the model is not a relevant comparison other and his outcomes, positive or negative, carry no information to the observer about the outcomes he should anticipate. Therefore, the model's experiences should not influence the likelihood of the observer's helping behavior.

To investigate these notions data were gathered unobtrusively from passers-by at two locations, 3 blocks apart, in a business area in midtown Manhattan. The basic procedure was to deposit an envelope on the ground at a pedestrian thoroughfare. Protruding from the envelope was a black, split-cowhide man's wallet, obviously containing money. Wrapped around the wallet was a typewritten letter which led the finder to believe that the wallet was lost not once, but twice. On the first occasion, it was found by the person who addressed the envelope to the wallet's owner and who wrote a letter describing his

[1]This study was supported by National Science Foundation Grant GS1715, "Experiments in the social psychology of prosocial behavior," whose principal investigator is Harvey A. Hornstein.

feelings about returning the wallet. This well-intentioned person then lost the wallet himself, along with the envelope and his letter. The subject had to decide: Should he emulate the previous finder's behavior by returning the wallet, or should he simply keep it for himself?

The authors predicted that when the previous finder was not perceived as dissimilar to the subject, a letter reporting the experience of positive feelings would produce a greater number of returns than a letter reporting the experience of negative feelings. When the previous finder was perceived to be dissimilar, however, no differences in the number of wallets returned were expected in these two conditions.

## METHOD

On Tuesday, January 30th, and Thursday, February 1, 1968, 30 pedestrians in midtown Manhattan found an addressed but unstamped envelope containing a wallet and a letter to the wallet's owner. These events were repeated, in detail, on Tuesday, February 13th, and Thursday, February 15th, when 30 additional persons found the same packet of objects. The wallet and the letters are both described below.

*The wallet.* The lost object was a black, split-cowhide man's wallet, which retailed for about $2. The wallet's contents were composed through the course of pilot work in which the goal was to construct an object which, in the absence of any experimental conditions, would produce a 50% return rate.

In a test of this, 35 wallets (of the type described below) were dropped without any envelope, letter, or accompanying material. Eighteen of the wallets were returned intact and the remaining 17 were not returned or were returned without any money.

The wallets' contents were as follows: $2 in cash, a $26.30 check to the "E.M.H. Co," a receipt for a rented tuxedo, a scrap of paper containing initials and a fictitious telephone number, and an identification card with the *name, address,* and *telephone number* of the wallet's owner. In addition, there were three 6-cent stamps, membership cards for a consumers' co-op and an athletic association (both fictitious), a blood donor's card, appointment and calling cards from a podiatrist, and a florist's calling card. The owner's name, Michael Erwin, was fictitious and was chosen to avoid any unequivocal ethnic or religious group identification.

**Similar model conditions** The stationery used for the letter was a 6 x 9-inch piece of white paper, with no identifying marks. Similarly, the envelope was plain, white, and unstamped. When found, it was properly addressed to the wallet's owner.

In all conditions the letter began in the same manner:

> Dear Mr. Erwin:
>
> I found your wallet which I am returning. Everything is here just as I found it.

In the *neutral* condition, the letter said no more than this. In the *positive* and *negative* conditions, however, the letter continued by discussing the previous finder's feelings about finding and returning the wallet.

In the positive conditions the letter added:

> I must say that it has been a pleasure to be able to help somebody in the small things that make life nicer. It's really been no problem at all and I'm glad to be able to help.

In the negative conditions it said:

> I must say that taking responsibility for the wallet and having to return it has been a great inconvenience. I was quite annoyed at having to bother with the whole problem of returning it. I hope you appreciate the efforts that I have gone through.

**Dissimilar model conditions** The procedure used in this phase of the experiment was similar to the one just described, except for the days of the data collection—March 12 (Tuesday), 14th (Thursday), and 19th (Tuesday)—and the character of the social model.

The authors fully recognized that collecting data on separate days allows one to interpret differences between the similar and dissimilar model condition as resulting from a "days" effect. Their experience with this form of helping behavior, however, made this interpretation seem extremely implausible. (Data is discussed below which support this contention.) Moreover, since this investigation involved a new experimental procedure, it seemed wiser and more efficient to be certain that similar model conditions produced differences (and to replicate these differences), before demonstrating that dissimilar model conditions produced no differences. An analysis of the overall return rates for the first 4 days (the similar model) and the last 3 days (the dissimilar model) is perfectly consistent with experimental findings gathered prior to and since this study was completed: there are no differences either within the two groups of days or between them. Although the sample is too small to analyze the data for a Days x Condition interaction, an examination of these data evidences absolutely no discernible trend. Barring major social events (e.g., a blackout, riot, or assassination), these data argue convincingly that we are dealing with a stationary stochastic process.

**The letter** For this phase of the investigation the authors had to simulate a model whose feelings about his helpful behavior would not be perceived by the subjects as valid predictors of their own feelings, should they perform in the same way. Moreover, since the population was heterogeneous, a model was needed who would be perceived as dissimilar by a wide variety of people. Finally, in order to avoid the possibility of having the model act as a negative referent, the authors did not wish the model to appear deviant or socially unacceptable.

The decision was to have the model characterize himself as dissimilar to members of this society and to provide him with justification for this characterization; it was decided, therefore, to make the model a visitor from an unspecified foreign nation.[2]

In all conditions the letter began by saying:

> Dear Mr. Erwin:
>
> I am visit your country finding your ways not familiar and strange. But I find your wallet which I here return. Everythings is here just as I find it.

The neutral letter said no more. Thus, the information in this letter and in the ones described below parallels the information provided in the letters from the previous part of the study.

In the positive conditions, the letter continued:

> It great pleasure to help somebody with tiny things which make life nicer. It is not problem at all and I glad to be able help.

In the negative conditions, the letter continued:

> To take responsibility for wallet and necessity to return it is great inconvenience. Is annoyance to bother with whole problem of return and hope you appreciate effort I went to.

In an effort to avoid any systematic biasing the dropping of letters was alternated in the different experimental conditions. Ordinarily one person surreptitiously dropped the envelope containing the wallet and the letter. At the same time, two unobtrusively located observers verified its recovery by a subject and recorded a number of the subject's characteristics on a standard observation form.[3]

[2]A group of independent judges was asked to identify the country of origin of the letter's author. A great number of countries were identified and no biases were evident. Moreover, there were no statistically significant differences in the judges' liking for the different authors.

[3]At the time of writing the authors have observed some 500 subjects in 10 different experimental conditions. They have recorded such things as race, sex, and apparent age, factors associated with socio-economic status, as well as a number of social conditions concurrent with subjects finding the wallet, for example, crowd size. The relationship between these factors and return-rate will be reported in a separate paper. Suffice it to say that in this study there was no disproportionate representation of any of these observational categories in the experimental conditions.

## RESULTS

Before describing the major results of this part of the investigation, the authors would like to provide a brief narrative description of how people react to finding the lost object.

Typically, the first person to see the object picks it up. Hence, there is little reason to believe that there is a serious self-selection problem. After finding the wallet people exhibit a variety of responses which range from nonchalantly placing the wallet in their pockets and walking off to hurriedly asking everyone in the area if the wallet belongs to them. Most frequently, the finder simply scanned the area in an apparent search for the loser and, while walking away, read the letter and examined the contents of the wallet.

**Population characteristics**[4] Males were disproportionately represented in the sample (for these descriptive data, $n = 95$); approximately 70% of the group was male, which is not surprising for a sample gathered in a business area. Each finder's age was estimated by two observers (interobserver estimates correlated .928). These estimates were then averaged together to form a final estimate of the finder's age. The distribution was as follows: 14%–under 25 years; 30%–26 to 35 years; 25%–36 to 45 years; 22%–46 to 55 years; 9%–over 55 years. Other data indicated that 70% of the group was white, while 19% and 11% were classified as black and Spanish-American, respectively.

**Return rate** Of the 105 wallets dropped, 40% were returned completely intact. A return was considered intact if neither the money nor the wallet and the money were missing (i.e., some people returned the cards but kept the money and the wallet). The data gathered in the first study (January 30th and February 1st) and the replication (February 13th and 15th) appear in [Table 2-2].

Chi-square analysis of these data indicates that the number of wallets returned in the positive and neutral conditions was significantly greater than the number returned in the negative conditions ($p < .05$). Quite obviously, there were no statistically significant differences between the two occasions on which data were collected. Hence, these data were combined and constitute our similar model condition.

For the reasons stated earlier, it was assumed that there was no "days" effect. Hence, the data from the six independent samples [Table 2-3] were analyzed

[4]These descriptive data are based on 90% of the entire sample of 105 subjects: $N = 95$. Inability to observe the wallet's recovery or clerical error account for the remaining 10%.

**[Table 2-2] Return rates by neutral, positive, and negative letter conditions: first study and replication**

| Condition | Returns | No returns | | |
|---|---|---|---|---|
| | | Total | Returned but not intact | Not returned |
| First study | | | | |
| Neutral | 7 | 3 | (0) | (3) |
| Positive | 7 | 3 | (1) | (2) |
| Negative | 1 | 9 | (3) | (6) |
| Replication | | | | |
| Neutral | 5 | 5 | (1) | (4) |
| Positive | 7 | 3 | (1) | (2) |
| Negative | 1 | 9 | (3) | (6) |

**[Table 2-3] Return rates for neutral, positive, and negative letter conditions for similar and dissimilar models**

| Condition | Total returns | No returns | | |
|---|---|---|---|---|
| | | Total no returns | Returned but not intact | No return |
| Similar model | | | | |
| Neutral | 12 | 8 | (1) | (7) |
| Positive | 14 | 6 | (2) | (4) |
| Negative | 2 | 18 | (6) | (12) |
| Dissimilar model | | | | |
| Neutral | 4 | 11 | (5) | (6) |
| Positive | 5 | 10 | (5) | (5) |
| Negative | 6 | 9 | (5) | (4) |

using a simultaneous interval technique analogous to Scheffé's (1953) procedure for use with the analysis of variance (Miller, 1966; also Goodman, 1964). This technique allowed testing of the hypothesis by examining a number of specific contrasts among these six populations, while maintaining the simultaneous (or joint) confidence interval for all contrasts at .95.

The findings are as follows: positive and neutral letters from a similar model produced more returns than negative letters ($p < .05$), but these two conditions were not significantly different from one another. Contrasts among the three dissimilar model conditions produced *no* statistically significant differences, nor were the return rates produced by these conditions different from the return rate obtained with a similar model sending a negative letter. Positive and neutral letters from similar models, however, produced more returns than positive and neutral letters from dissimilar models ($p < .05$). The overall return rates produced by similar and dissimilar models were not significantly different. To summarize: a letter from a similar model reporting positive or no experience produced more returns than a letter reporting negative experience; whereas, the experience (positive, negative, or neutral) reported by a dissimilar model had no effect on the return rate.

The contentions expressed earlier in this paper are clearly supported by the data reported here. Social models are not simply influential by virtue of what they are doing. When the model is observed to feel negatively about his behavior, there is evidence that observers are deterred from behaving in the same fashion, assuming that the model is perceived as similar and thus as a relevant comparison person. There is no evidence, however, that the observation of positive feelings about performing a helpful act produces more modeling than simply observing the act alone. It is not unlikely that in the neutral condition the finder assumed that the model had had a pleasant experience; that is, he believed that the model would not make an effort to help a stranger if he found that behavior unpleasant, rather than pleasant. If, however, the model openly expressed negative feelings about his behavior, the observer was deterred from performing the same act.

## REFERENCES

**BANDURA, A.** Influences of model's reinforcement contingencies on the acquisition of imitative responses. *Journal of Personality and Social Psychology,* 1965, **1,** 589-595.

**BRYAN, J. H., & TEST, M. A.** Models and helping: Naturalistic studies in aiding behavior. *Journal of Personality and Social Psychology,* 1967, **6,** 400-407.

**GOODMAN, L. A.** Simultaneous confidence intervals for contrasts among multinomial populations. *Annual Mathematical Statistics,* 1964, **35,** 716-725.

**MILLER, R. G., JR.** *Simultaneous statistical inference.* New York: McGraw-Hill, 1966.

**ROSENBAUM, M., & BLAKE, R.** Volunteering as a function of field structure. *Journal of Abnormal and Social Psychology,* 1955, **50,** 193-196.

**ROSENHAN, D., & WHITE, G. M.** Observation and rehearsal as determinants of prosocial behavior. *Journal of Personality and Social Psychology,* 1967, **5,** 424-431.

**SCHEFFE, H.** A method for judging all contrasts in the analysis of variance. *Biometrika,* 1953, **40,** 87-104.

# BYSTANDER INTERVENTION AND HELPING ON THE SUBWAY

HARVEY ALLEN
*New York University*

## INTRODUCTION

One night, while I was seated in a subway train waiting for it to leave the station, a young man entered the opposite end of the car, approached an older man, and asked him if the train went to a particular station. The older man proceeded to tell the younger one that he would have to go upstairs to take another train and later change to a second train in order to get to his desired destination. Even I, an infrequent traveler, knew that the present train would have taken him to his destination more directly and quickly. Because the train was quiet, it was apparent that a number of other passengers observed the transaction between the two men, but no one spoke up to correct or modify the incorrect directions.

This incident is similar to a number of other events reported by the mass media where bystanders have not intervened. Some of the reasons given by psychologists, sociologists, and commentators for such apparently apathetic and conscienceless behavior on the part of onlookers have been "alienation," "the impact of the megalopolitan society," "anomie," "demoralization," and so forth. While these terms may provide convenient labels and slogans, they offer little explanation for or analysis into what the onlooker is responding to in the situation. Interviews with bystanders in emergency situations suggest that factors other than apathy or indifference can affect the onlooker's decision to avoid intervening. Rosenthal (1964), while attempting to interview the observers of the Genovese murder, reported that the observers were reluctant to talk about the incident. Their underlying attitude or explanation for their behavior was a fear of involvement–any kind of involvement. In other situations, some onlookers were afraid to stick their necks out and risk trouble, while others reasoned that, since they were not the only ones watching, someone else was likely to take appropriate action.

An individual observing an incident in which his help is called for may be placed in a conflict situation; there are both rational and irrational fears about what might happen to a person who intervenes. The person who says "I didn't want to get involved" may be concerned not only about bodily injury, but also about public embarrassment and other unforeseeable, but imaginable, difficulties or dangers. These concerns may arise out of the dynamics of the situation in which the person finds himself.

Since there has been little research into these underlying dynamics, it is the aim of this study to explore some of the situational determinants of bystander action and inaction. It is not the intention of this study to provide an all-encompassing explanation or theory to account for all behavior of bystanders, but rather to provide some insight and understanding into what factors could account for a bystander's behavior or apparent lack of it. The approach in the study is to conduct theory-oriented research in a natural environment.

The experimental situation was prearranged: a subway passenger (a confederate) was given wrong directions by another passenger (a second confederate), in front of a naive bystander. The dependent measure was whether the naive bystander corrected the misinformer. The independent manipulations were varied within three separate situations. In general, in these situations where direct action was required by a naive bystander, we expected to find the following:

1. The way the situation develops can cause an individual to feel more or less responsible for intervening, even when the size of the group remains the same. That is, the less the bystander is directly involved in the action of the incident, the less likely he is to correct, and the more likely he is to diffuse the responsibility or blame.
2. The greater the probability of threat to the bystander for his intervention, the less likely he is to correct the misinformer.
3. The more deserving the bystander perceived the direction-asker to be, the more correction is expected from the bystander.

## GENERAL PROCEDURE

A young man in Manhattan enters a subway car which is traveling *uptown.* Appearing somewhat puzzled, he approaches two seated passengers and asks whether the train is going *downtown.* One of the passengers responds affirmatively that the train is going *downtown.* The young man thanks the passenger for the information and takes a seat nearby. A short while later, the passenger who had initially responded to the young man's inquiry stands up and leaves the car. The young man remains seated near the other passenger.

Let us take a closer look at the above incident. Both the young man who sought the directions and the passenger who gave the false directions were confederates acting out a given role. The former confederate will be referred to as the direction-asker (asker); the latter confederate will be referred to as the direction-giver (giver) or misinformer. The innocent passenger will be called the bystander or the subject.

In general, the asker always asked if the train was traveling in a direction that was opposite to the one in which the train actually was going. If the train was headed uptown, the asker inquired if the train was going downtown; on the downtown train, he asked if it was going uptown. In each of the incidents the giver misinformed the asker. In all cases the giver misinformed the asker before the bystander had an opportunity to respond, and in a voice loud enough for the bystander to hear; however, he did not speak so loudly as to involve other passengers seated nearby.

A short time after the incident, the giver left the subway car by walking into the next car through the connecting doorways. If the bystander had not immediately corrected the giver during the misinforming incident, the asker stood or seated himself near the bystander and pretended to read a book or newspaper. The asker positioned himself a very short distance from the bystander (within sight and earshot). He did not stare at the bystander, but neither did he pretend to look out the windows of the subway car. If the bystander had not corrected the misinformation by the next station, the asker then left the subway car.

## LOCATION OF THE STUDY

The study was conducted on four subway lines traveling within the borough of Manhattan in New York City. The experimental conditions of the study were randomized by days of the week (Monday through Friday), by hours of the day (between 10:30 A.M. and 3:30 P.M.), by the direction the train was going (uptown and downtown), and by the four subway lines.

## SUBJECTS

The subjects used were the subway riders of New York City. In general, the giver's prudence concerning whom he sat next to was an important consideration. The giver was instructed to seat himself next to a bystander in an area of the car which was not too crowded with passengers. However, he was told not to make himself too obvious by seating himself next to an isolated individual. He was instructed to try not to make distinctions in the age, sex, or race of the bystander. In many of the incidents, however, the seating choice of the giver was not determined so much by his own wishes or choice as by the dictates of the situation and the characteristics of the passengers on a particular subway car at a particular time. Frequently, it was impossible to perform an incident because the subway car was too empty or too crowded. In the former situation, it was not advisable to create an incident, since it would look suspicious if the giver sat next to an isolated passenger while the rest of the car remained relatively empty. A crowded car also created problems, such as the possible influences on the bystander of the presence of many other bystanders.

## THE DEPENDENT VARIABLE

The dependent variable in the study was whether or not the bystander corrected the misinformation given by the giver to the asker.

The "total" number of corrections is broken down into two types of corrections: immediate and "post" corrections. Immediate corrections are those made by the bystander immediately after he heard the giver misinform the asker. "Post" corrections are those made by the bystander after the giver left the subway car. The sum of immediate corrections plus post corrections yields the total corrections. The major concern of this study is immediate corrections.

Certain procedures were used to discard certain incidents. The total number of subjects eliminated by these procedures was 39 (7.37 percent of the total population), 7 because of language problems and 32 because the bystander showed no sign of noticing what had taken place. The elimination of these cases poses no real problem in explaining the final results.

## INDEPENDENT VARIABLES

**1. Diffusion of Responsibility** A frequent explanation given by onlookers for not intervening in emergency and nonemergency situations calling for helping behavior is that the situation was none of their business. It would seem that among the factors affecting the behavior of an observer in such a situation are the degree to which he sees himself included in the situational field and how he perceives his position in that field—that is, whether he sees himself as a central or peripheral figure in the action. Another determining factor would be whether there were other central or peripheral figures present. For example, when there are several bystanders present, the pressure to intervene does not focus on any one bystander specifically but is shared by all. Thus, in a situation where a communication for help is directed to a group of bystanders, an individual bystander may avoid intervention in the belief (or rationalization) that others share in his responsibility. In those instances when the bystander is not addressed and remains an onlooker, he may choose to ignore the situation in order to avoid any further involvement.

This notion of "diffusion of responsibility" was introduced by Wallach, Kogan, and Bem (1964) in a study dealing with real risks and payoffs. As an explanation for their finding of a group-induced shift in risk-taking, they suggested a process of diffusion or spreading of responsibility which occurs as a result of knowing that one's decisions are being arrived at jointly with others, rather than alone. Diffusion of responsibility was also investigated by Latané and Darley (1966) and Darley and Latané (1968), who dealt with socially responsible behavior in emergency situations. The major independent variable in their first study was the size of the group the subject believed himself to be a member of. One of their conclusions is that there "was conclusive evidence that the perceived presence of other onlookers can markedly reduce the likelihood that a bystander will intervene in an emergency situation." Their second study indicated that subjects will less often report an emergency situation when there are other people in the room with them. Thus, a single or isolated individual should feel greater pressure to show responsible behavior than an individual in a similar situation in which there are other bystanders present whom he sees as sharing his responsibility to act.

The objects of investigation in this study are the consequences of changing the bystander's relationship and involvement with a person seeking help and the effects of this change on the bystander's feelings of responsibility. The two methods that were considered which could be effective in altering the bystander's degree of involvement with the person seeking help were varying the number of other involved bystanders present during the misinforming incident and varying the source or direction of the asker's request for help.

It is expected that, by varying the direction of communication, the forces which influence the bystander's decision to intervene should also vary. In the situation where a bystander is directly addressed and no other bystanders are present, the force to intervene should be at its strongest. Any increase in the number of bystanders present and addressed by the direction-asker should result in a sharing of responsibility, thereby decreasing the forces that act on the individual to intervene. When another passenger is addressed, the bystander may not perceive the scene as his responsibility and perceive that it is not his business to intervene.

**Procedure** The general procedure used was outlined earlier. In these conditions, however, the number of the recipients of the asker's inquiry was varied. The asker would direct his question to the giver alone, to the giver and bystander(s) (the "group"), or to the bystander alone (excluding the giver). In all the conditions, the giver misinformed the asker before the bystander had a chance to reply.

The number of bystanders present was also varied. Thus, the giver, upon entering the subway car, would seat himself next to either "one" bystander or "two or more" bystanders (never exceeding three bystanders).

In the diffusion conditions, the giver left the subway car 30 seconds after the misinforming incident.

**Results** Inasmuch as the tests of immediate, post, and total corrections between "one bystander" groups and "two or more bystanders" groups indicated no significant difference in the number of corrections given by both bystander groups, the correlations for both groups were combined into a total-corrections figure.

An examination of the total-immediate-corrections column in [Table 2-4] clearly shows that when the bystander alone is asked for information by the asker and the giver intercedes with the wrong information, the bystander almost always immediately corrects the giver (93 percent immediate corrections). The next greatest number of immediate corrections occurs in the condition where the bystander and giver are the source of the asker's question (47 percent immediate corrections). The least number of immediate corrections (27 percent) occurs in the condition when the giver alone is addressed by the asker. The $U'_0$ of 37.61 for the total immediate corrections in the diffusion condition was significant at beyond the .001 level. Multiple comparisons between diffusion conditions indicate that all but the group and giver conditions are significantly different from each other in the number of immediate corrections ($p < .05$). The point-biserial $r$ of .55 for total immediate corrections is also highly significant indicating a significant linear trend ($p < .01$). The above results appear to confirm the expectation that varying the direction of the asker's question produces an initial diffusion of responsibility.

The influence of post corrections on the total number of corrections is clearly shown. Although the

**[Table 2-4] Number of immediate, post, and total corrections made, with one or two or more bystanders present, by direction of the asker's question**

| Direction of asker's question | Immediate corrections | | Post corrections | | Total corrections | | Total |
|---|---|---|---|---|---|---|---|
| | No. | % | No. | %+ | No. | % | N |
| To the giver | 8 | 26.67 | 8 | 36.36 | 16 | 53.33 | 30 |
| To the group | 14 | 46.67 | 2 | 12.50 | 16 | 53.33 | 30 |
| To the bystander | 28 | 93.33 | 1 | 50.00 | 29 | 96.67 | 30 |
| Total | 50 | 55.56 | 11 | 36.67 | 61 | 67.78 | 90 |
| | $U'_0{}^{++} = 37.61$ $p < .001$ | | $U'_0 =$ n.s. | | $U'_0 = 25.96$ $p < .001$ | | |

+This percentage is computed by using as a base the number of remaining bystanders who did not immediately correct.
++$U'_0$ is $\chi^2$ distributed with $(K - 1)$ degrees of freedom (see Cohen, 1967).

$U'_0$ of 25.96 for the combined total corrections by diffusion condition is highly significant ($p < .001$), the significance appears to be accounted for by the difference between the giver and group conditions and the bystander condition. Nevertheless, the demonstration of post corrections suggests that the presence or absence of the misinformer can have an effect on the elicitation or inhibition of subsequent bystander helping behavior. The significance of the misinformer's presence will become clearer in the following sections.

After reviewing the data from the "diffusion" study, it was decided to eliminate the number of bystanders as a variable to be manipulated, and to continue working with only one bystander. The elimination of the number of bystanders as a variable was done for three reasons: (1) Results with the single-bystander condition were simpler and less difficult to interpret. In incidents where two or more bystanders were present, a correction by only one released the others from taking any action; it was no longer necessary for them to correct. Since little could be said about the other bystanders' behavior, little would be added to the results. (2) The diffusion data indicated no significant differences between the results from the one-bystander condition and the two-or-more-bystanders condition. (3) It was difficult to establish distinct categories of number of bystanders and their influence on group or individual behavior. That is, how many bystanders make a difference? Do we talk of groups of two, three, or four bystanders? In general, the variation in the number of bystanders should be the focus of further studies. This study, however, will focus on the use of only one naive bystander.

**2. Threat** Threat can elicit feelings of uneasiness, uncertainty, or insecurity. A person's feeling that he lacks safety may be accompanied by a feeling of danger or impending disaster. The threat may be sensed as one to the body, the psychological self, or both. A great many threat stimuli are symbolic in nature, involving a word, a gesture, or a social configuration (status or a power ranking of individuals). Ambiguity in a situation will enhance threat; if the tone of the situation is ominous, even though the nature of the threat is unclear, threat is likely to increase in intensity.

One frequent explanation given by an onlooker for not intervening in situations calling for help is the threat to his physical or psychological self which could accompany his involvement. The bystander who becomes involved in helping a person becomes responsible for his actions and must account for his behavior not only to the person seeking help but also to the other persons in the situation. Thus, the bystander opens himself to any possible danger which may be present within the situation and which may result from his confrontation with the misinformer. More specifically, the danger in the correcting situation is the possible reprisal or retaliation from the person who has done the misinforming. If the bystander is to correct the giver's misinformation, he must "confront" the misinformer with the fact that he is wrong and that the bystander is right. On the other hand, the bystander, by intervening and correctly directing the direction-asker, stands to gain self-satisfaction and enhanced self-esteem.

The purpose of this portion of the study is to investigate the effects of varying levels of threat on the bystander's decision to correct or not to correct the misinformer. One way to increase the misinformer's threat potential is to vary his physical characteristics. Thus, the bigger and tougher-looking the misinformer, the less intervention (correction) would be expected from bystanders. However, since physical characteristics are not always a totally reliable indicator of a person's potential threat, a more reliable procedure was devised. It was decided that manipulating the misinformer's actual behavior would best arouse several levels of potential threat to the bystander. Four different levels of threat were varied, with the anticipation that the greater the probability of threat to the bystander for intervening, the less likely he would be to correct the misinformer.

**Procedure**

*High probability of physical threat* In order to arouse high threat, it was felt that the bystander must anticipate the severest reprisal for his intervention: the probability of physical assault by the misinformer.

In this condition, the giver was made to appear to be a highly impulsive person, likely to retaliate physically against anyone who meddled with him. The giver would, as usual, seat himself next to the bystander and pretend to read a muscle-building magazine. A third confederate, who entered the same car from a different subway car door, would walk toward the area where the giver was seated. Shortly before the third confederate passed in front of him, the giver would stretch his legs into the aisle of the car. The third confederate would accidentally trip over the giver's outstretched legs. The giver would jump up from his seat, tense his arms, and make a fist as if he were about to hit the confederate. However, he would hold back and say in a moderately loud voice, "Watch out, buddy, you want to get hurt?" The threatened confederate would turn slightly towards the misinformer and respond with "I'm sorry, just take it easy," and then continue to walk away from the misinformer to a different area of the car. The misinformer would reseat himself next to the bystander and continue to read his magazine. Approximately 60 seconds later, the asker, who had up to this time remained out of sight during the entire tripping incident, would approach the misinformer and the bystander and direct his question to both of them.[1]

[1]Inspection of the diffusion data resulted in the decision to restrict the focus (direction) of the asker's inquiry to the giver and the bystander, and to exclude the two other conditions. This was done because the giver-and-bystander condition was the only condition of the three which came closest to a 50:50 split in the number of immediate corrections (53.33 percent immediate corrections in the one-bystander condition, and 46.6 percent immediate corrections of the total immediate corrections). The number of immediate corrections in the other two diffusion conditions were more extreme in the direction and number of corrections, and seemed less susceptible to change as a consequence of any manipulations.

*High probability of embarrassment threat* The object of this condition was to decrease the bystander's expectation of physical threat and to increase his expectation of a less serious form of possible retaliation from the misinformer–verbal assault or embarrassment.

The situation employed was similar to the one used in the high-physical-threat condition. However, after the third confederate tripped over the giver's outstretched legs, the giver would not jump up from his seat or feign a possible physical attack on the confederate. Instead, the giver would laugh sarcastically and say to the confederate, "What's the matter, baldy, can't you see without your toupee?" (The third confederate used was clearly balding.) The giver would continue to chuckle and look at the confederate as he walked away. Once again, after 60 seconds, the asker would approach and request directions of the giver and bystander.

*Low probability of physical or embarrassment threat (control)* This condition was considered a low potential threat, since there were no overt signs of possible physical or embarrassment threat from the misinformer. Of course, potential retaliation from the misinformer is always a possibility, however minimal. The procedure used in this condition was the same as the general procedure outlined earlier.

*Minimal probability of physical or embarrassment threat* It was expected that if the misinformer were uncertain of his own information, a more open and less threatening situation would be created. The misinformer's uncertainty, then, would act as an invitation to the bystander to intervene, and would keep any potential threat to a minimum.

Once again, the general misinforming procedure was used. However, during these incidents, when the giver would respond to the asker's request for directions, he would reply with uncertainty, "I think so," rather than with his usual emphatic "Yes."

In all four of the potential-threat conditions, the time interval that elapsed between the misinforming incident and the time that the misinformer left the subway car was 15 seconds.

**Results** The data shown in [Table 2-5] support the expectation that as the probability of threat increases, the number of immediate corrections decreases ($U'_O = 59.78$, $p < .001$). The least number of immediate corrections (16 percent) occurs in the high-physical-threat condition, and the greatest number of immediate corrections (82 percent) is exhibited in the minimal-threat condition, the number of immediate corrections in the two other conditions falling in

[Table 2-5] **Number of immediate, post, and total corrections made by bystanders, with only one bystander present, by degree of probable threat**

| Threat condition | Immediate corrections No. | Immediate corrections % | Post corrections No. | Post corrections %+ | Total corrections No. | Total corrections % | Total *N* |
|---|---|---|---|---|---|---|---|
| High probability of physical threat | 8 | 16.00 | 7 | 16.67 | 15 | 30.00 | 50 |
| High probability of embarrassment threat | 14 | 28.00 | 5 | 13.89 | 19 | 38.00 | 50 |
| Low probability of physical or embarrassment threat | 26 | 52.00 | 14 | 58.33 | 40 | 80.00 | 50 |
| Minimal probability of physical or embarrassment threat | 41 | 82.00 | 1 | 11.11 | 42 | 84.00 | 50 |
| Total | 89 | 44.50 | 27 | 24.32 | 116 | 58.00 | 200 |
| | $U'_0 = 59.78$ $p < .001$ | | $U'_0 = 17.01$ $p < .001$ | | $U'_0 = 53.26$ $p < .001$ | | |

+This percentage is computed by using as a base the number of remaining bystanders who did not immediately correct.

between. Multiple comparison indicates significant differences among all the threat conditions except between the high-physical-threat and high-embarrassment-threat conditions and between the high-embarrassment-threat and low-threat conditions ($p < .05$). The point-biserial *r* of .59 for immediate corrections by level of threat is significant at beyond the .01 level, pointing to a significant linear trend. The results confirm the expectation that a bystander will be more reluctant to intervene and correct the misinformer as the degree of probable threat increases.

It might be useful to view the different levels of probable threat as two different levels of arousal, whereby the high-physical and high-embarrassment-threat conditions would be the "high-arousal" group. When the number of immediate corrections for the two arousal groups are compared, the resulting $U'_0$ of 45.15 is highly significant ($p < .001$). The phi coefficient between the two arousal groups is .48, indicating a significant association between level of arousal and immediate corrections. Thus, high arousal appears to have an inhibiting effect on the probability of the bystander's intervening and correcting the misinformer.

The $U'_0$ of 17.01 for post corrections is significant at better than the .01 level, which indicates a difference among the threat conditions in the number of corrections elicited after the misinformer leaves. The least amount of post corrections (15 percent) occurred in the high-physical-threat and high-embarrassment-threat conditions, while in the low- and minimal-probability physical- or embarrassment-threat conditions, 45 percent of the bystanders who had not initially corrected did so when the misinformer left the car. Multiple comparisons of post corrections among the threat conditions indicate significant differences in three of the six comparisons ($p < .05$). There are no significant differences between the high-physical-threat condition and each of the high-embarrassment-threat and no-threat conditions and between the high-embarrassment-threat and minimal-threat conditions. The point-biserial *r* for post corrections by level of threat is not significant.

When we group post corrections into the high-arousal and low-arousal groups, the difference between them is highly significant ($U'_0 = 10.64, p < .01$). The phi coefficient between the two arousal conditions is .31. Thus, in terms of arousal, it appears that high arousal has an inhibitory or perseverative effect on subsequent bystander correction behavior, as demonstrated by the small number of post corrections in the high-arousal conditions. However, low arousal has little inhibitory effect on bystander correction behavior occurring shortly after the misinforming incident.

It is surprising that the least amount of post corrections occurred in the high-arousal conditions, inasmuch as there were more bystanders available in these conditions to post correct than in the low-arousal conditions. If there were such a person as a "helpful person," who was previously inhibited from correcting because of any potential threat, one would expect him to offer his help eagerly as soon as the threat was eliminated or had passed. However, this did not occur.

These results support the contention that high

levels of probable threat have negative influences on eliciting bystander helping behavior and suggest that high levels of probable threat can inhibit helping behavior, which may occur after the threat has passed.

**3. Deservingness** The question arises whether the elicitation of socially responsible behavior is independent of the type of person who is in need of help. The way we respond to other people is strongly influenced by our perceptions of others' status, attractiveness, and role, and these perceptions are especially significant when a situation specifically calls upon us to offer help. Daniels and Berkowitz (1963) have demonstrated that the interpersonal attraction of the needy was an important factor in determining the degree of aid eventually received.

Still another factor that might considerably influence a bystander's helping behavior is his perceptions of how helpless the person seeking help is.

A blind person, for one example, is particularly likely to elicit helping behavior from onlookers, because he is perceived as helpless. Bryan (1966) investigated the relationship between dependency and helping in a naturalistic setting and concluded that "dependency elicits helping behavior where the likelihood of material reward is remote."

The ability of a person to help himself may be substantially changed by his "familiarity" with his immediate environment. The individual who is perceived by observers as within his "home" territory is also considered to be able to take care of himself. The stranger, on the other hand, is seen as more helpless and less self-sufficient.

Test and Bryan (1967), in a series of studies that were conducted in the laboratory, in city streets, and in shopping centers, have shown that the observation of helping models significantly increased subsequent offers of aid by observers. Their studies involved students aiding other students to solve arithmetic problems, motorists helping disabled motorists to change flat tires, and shoppers donating money to the Salvation Army. Their findings in all these situations were consistent; the presence of helping models significantly increased subsequent helping behavior.

Of the innumerable avenues for investigation, it was decided that the present study should concentrate on the effects of deservingness and modeling behavior upon helping behavior. Two types of deservingness were employed. The first type presented the asker as unfamiliar with his environment; this unfamiliarity was intended to suggest his increased dependence upon others for help. The second condition employed a manipulation in which the asker was not only seen as more deserving of help than other passengers would be in a similar asking situation, but also served as his own model for bystander helping behavior. It was expected that each deservingness condition would elicit greater correction from bystanders than the control condition.

**Procedure**

*Helplessness (tourist) condition* In this condition, the asker's appearance was that of a tourist. He wore a loud sport shirt, and in each hand he held a valise with tourist stickers and airline luggage claim tags attached. He carried a camera around his neck. The general direction-asking procedure was used.

*Increased deservingness (model) condition* This condition called for an additional confederate, a young woman, who appeared to have just come from shopping. She carried two shopping bags filled with boxes and packages and had several additional boxes under her arm.

The young woman would sit nearby the bystander, in a position which would permit the giver to sit directly next to the bystander (the giver would sit between the female confederate and the bystander). After the giver was seated, the asker would approach the area where the young woman, the giver, and the bystander were seated. Just before the asker was about to pass in front of the young woman, she would get up and accidentally drop the packages that were on her lap. The asker would help her retrieve the dropped packages. The young woman would thank the asker for his help and would promptly walk away and exit from the car at the next station. After 15 seconds, the asker, standing in front of the giver and bystander, would look about in a confused manner and ask his directions of the two parties.

In both deservingness conditions, the time interval between which the misinforming occurred and the misinformer left the situation was divided into two intervals: 15 and 30 seconds. That is, in half of the incidents (in each of the conditions), the misinformer waited 30 seconds after misinforming before he left the car, while in the other half of the incidents he waited only 15 seconds before exiting.

**Results** [Table 2-6] presents the number of immediate corrections for each of the deservingness conditions and the control condition. The $U'_O$ of 4.37 for the three conditions is insignificant and indicates that the deservingness of the asker is not sufficient to appreciably affect aiding behavior. Multiple comparisons among deservingness conditions revealed no significant differences.

**[Table 2-6] Number of immediate, post, and total corrections made by bystanders, with only one bystander present, in two deservingness conditions**

| Deservingness condition | Immediate corrections | | Post corrections | | Total corrections | | Total |
|---|---|---|---|---|---|---|---|
| | No. | % | No. | %⁺ | No. | % | N |
| Helplessness (tourist) | 31 | 62.00 | 4 | 21.05 | 35 | 70.00 | 50 |
| Increased deservingness (model) | 34 | 68.00 | 5 | 31.25 | 39 | 78.00 | 50 |
| Total deservingness | 65 | 65.00 | 9 | 25.71 | 74 | 74.00 | 100 |
| Control | 24 | 48.00 | 7 | 26.92 | 31 | 62.00 | 50 |
| Total | 89 | 59.33 | 16 | 26.23 | 105 | 70.00 | 150 |
| | $U'_0$ = n.s. | | $U'_0$ = n.s. | | $U'_0$ = n.s. | | |

⁺The percentage is computed by using as a base the number of remaining bystanders who did not immediately correct.

Because the two deservingness conditions are not significantly different from each other, the number of corrections in each were combined into a "total deservingness" group and compared with the control group. Even after combining the two deservingness groups, however, there still is no significant difference between the total deservingness group and the control group. The resulting $U'_0$ of 3.54, however, proves to be significant at the .07 level (interpolating in the table), indicating a marginally significant difference between the total deservingness group and the control group. Thus, although there is marginal support for the view that deservingness manipulated both ways influences helping behavior, there is no support for the view that either deservingness manipulation alone has a marked influence on helping behavior.

It was pointed out in the procedure that in half of each of these conditions, the time interval between the misinforming incident and the exit of the misinformer was set at 30 seconds, whereas in the other half the time interval was set at 15 seconds. However, there are no significant differences in the number of post corrections for the two time intervals or among the post corrections for the three experimental conditions. Thus, neither helplessness nor modeling has any significant effect on bystander behavior, not even when the misinformer is no longer present.

The combination of immediate and post corrections into total corrections demonstrates little effect on altering the preceding findings. There are no significant differences in total corrections for the three experimental conditions, nor between the total deservingness condition and the control condition. Although the results are in the expected direction, the differences are not nearly great enough to produce statistically significant findings.

**4. Replicability of Findings** It is possible that the results were a function of the particular question asked by the asker (whether the train was going uptown or downtown). It was decided to test the reliability of the results by attempting to replicate an earlier finding: having the asker request directions to a specific station. It was generally assumed that the bystander would know which direction the train was traveling in, especially since the distinction between uptown and downtown appeared to be such a simple one. Again, it was decided to make a test of this assumption.

The specific direction-asking incidents were tried, using the diffusion-of-responsibility paradigm. The asker would direct his question to the giver alone, the bystander alone, or the giver and the bystander together. The incidents were conducted with only one bystander present. No attempt was made to measure the effects of the misinformer's absence on later (post) corrections.

The results obtained here are comparable to the results previously obtained in the diffusion study. Once again, the results are highly significant ($U'_0 = 28.21$, $p < .01$) and in the same direction as the results obtained earlier. Thus, the generality of the specific direction-asking procedure used in this study is highly generalizable and valid in another direction-asking situation.

**Discussion of Results**

*1. Diffusion of responsibility* The results of varying the target of the direction-asker's request for information on the variation on bystander's responsibility are quite strong. When the misinformer cut in to give information in response to a question that was directed to the naive bystander, the naive bystander almost always corrected him and did so immediately, often exhibiting impatience and indignance. When, however, the original question was addressed not to the naive bystander, but simply toward the group of which he was a member, he corrected considerably less frequently. Finally, when the question was directed toward the misinformer, the bystander corrected least frequently of all. From these results it can be concluded that in a situation where direct intervention is required, the way the situation evolves can influence the degree of responsibility the individual feels toward intervening.

Although there were no significant differences in accounting for diffusion between the one-bystander and two-or-more-bystander conditions, those incidents where two or more bystanders were present appeared to show a stronger diffusion effect, especially in the condition where the misinformer alone was addressed. This may be explained by the bystander's attempt to diffuse responsibility, and may also reflect the bystander's diffusion of blame or his conformity to the behavior of others present in the situation.

It appeared that the bystander's behavior was influenced by the presence of other passengers who he believed overheard the misinforming incident. Even in those situations where the asker directed his question to the misinformer and the bystander, other bystanders seated nearby could have overheard the misinforming incident. This was true because there were no physical or conventional closures or barriers to cut off the nonparticipants from the participants in the incident. Thus, the bystander might have believed he was conforming to and maintaining the group norm of silence or nonintervention. In addition to using the behavior of the nonparticipating bystanders as a guide to his own behavior, the bystander could have been considerably influenced by his belief that the others who overheard, although not directly addressed by the asker, still shared in his responsibility.

The size of the group, however, does not operate in isolation to impede socially responsible actions. No matter what size the group is, an important element is the cohesiveness and the morale of the group. It is possible for a group to exhibit either extreme helping behavior (as in disasters) or extreme self-centeredness (as in mob behavior), depending upon the individuals' identification with the group. When the subject is a member of a larger, cohesive group, he may exhibit more willingness to be helpful than he would if he were alone (Grinker & Spiegel, 1945). The individual may feel the support of the group in addition to an increased self-confidence and competence. On the other hand, when there is little group cohesion or identification with the group, as on the subway, he may feel unwilling or unable to act.

*2. Threat* According to the economic theories of behavior (Homans, 1961, and Thibaut & Kelley, 1959) and the norm of social responsibility (Berkowitz & Daniels, 1964), the individual anticipates the costs and consequences of his behavior before he takes action. The costs that the bystander anticipates may be not only physical harm but also threats to the psychological self, such as embarrassment, humiliation, or loss of self-esteem.

As was expected, the amount of immediate corrections given by bystanders varied according to the level of threat they anticipated if they intervened and confronted the misinformer. Approximately one out of every six bystanders in the high-physical-threat condition corrected the misinformation, and approximately one out of four bystanders corrected in the high-embarrassment-threat condition. The low-threat condition produced a greater probability of correction, since one out of every two bystanders corrected immediately. The minimal-threat condition, however, displayed the greatest amount of immediate corrections; approximately four out of every five bystanders in this condition corrected. The importance of threat is, then, obvious, especially since bystanders in the low- and minimal-threat conditions corrected more than three times as often as bystanders in the high- and moderate-threat conditions. As indicated in the section on results, high arousal appears to have had an inhibitory influence on bystanders' intervention.

*3. Deservingness* The third section of the study dealt with two aspects of deservingness. In the first condition, the help-seeker was made to appear more helpless and deserving (and thus more dependent on the bystander) by displaying his unfamiliarity with the situation (the subway system). In the second condition, the help-seeker was made to appear more deserving by suggesting that he was a commendable person. In the latter condition, the help-seeker not only appeared to be more deserving, but acted as a "helping model" for the other bystanders. Previous research had indicated that the presence of a helping model increased subsequent helping behavior.

The results were not as expected. Neither manipulation produced significantly greater immediate corrections than the control condition, although when combined they approached significance. The deservingness-model condition produced a slightly higher percentage of corrections than the helplessness condition (68 percent and 62 percent immediate corrections, respectively).

It is quite possible that the youth of the confederate who acted as the tourist, and his generally good physical condition, offset any feelings of sympathy for his plight.

Rosenhan and White (1967) have reported that although the observation of a model is a powerful determinant of helping behavior, in itself it is not sufficient. They suggest that rehearsal in the presence of the model may assist in establishing the habit of helping behavior, because the subject assumes that the model approves of his behavior. In the subway situation, although the bystander may approve of the asker's (model) behavior, he may also anticipate the misinformer's disapproval. In addition, the observation of a model does not necessarily teach a particular behavior to the observer, but rather cues previously learned behavior. Thus, if helping behavior is not a part of the bystander's habit hierarchy, his observation of a model might have little or no effect on his subsequent behavior.

It is also likely that the deservingness manipulations used in this study were not strong enough. Deservingness is a complex dimension, and comparisons between the many ways it might manifest itself are difficult. It would be foolish to compare the deservingness and helplessness of a tourist with those of a person who is physically unable to take care of himself—for example, a blind man. Future investigations might focus on clarifying the concept of deservingness. If it can be ordered along a dimension of intensity, at what point along this dimension will the bystander's reluctance to intervene and offer help be overcome?

*4. Post and total corrections* Onlookers of both threatening and nonthreatening situations have frequently excused their behavior, or lack of it, by claiming that they were afraid of getting involved. The direct intervention of an onlooker opens him to possible retaliation by any of the members of the group involved. The fear of retaliation which could ensue from a confrontation with the threatening agent might be substantially reduced, however, if the onlooker were able to act either anonymously (indirectly) or after the threatening agent had left or was removed.

In the subway situation, if the bystander was to correct immediately, he had to confront the misinformer directly under fear of retaliation. To see if the bystander would correct after the misinformer was no longer present (when the fear of retaliation should be no longer active), the misinformer would leave the subway car when one of several preset time intervals had elapsed after the occurrence of the misinforming incident. The asker would remain near the bystander so that he could receive any post corrections the bystander might make.

In the diffusion study there were no significant differences between any of the diffusion conditions in the number of post corrections made by bystanders. However, the inclusion of post corrections eliminated any differences (although nonsignificant) that initially existed between the misinformer and group conditions.

As expected, the presence of the misinformer was especially important in yielding the results arrived at in the threat conditions. Not only did increasing threat decrease the number of immediate corrections, but both the high-physical-threat and high-embarrassment-threat conditions inhibited post corrections, whereas the low-physical-threat and low-embarrassment-threat conditions increased post corrections. There are several possible explanations for there being fewer post corrections in the higher-threat conditions. One is that the effects of stress or fear persevered for a short time after the threatening incident and produced rigid and confused thinking in the bystander. Stress might have also resulted in "freezing" behavior on the part of the bystander because of his fright or inability to arrive at an acceptable set of decisions. Another possibility is that the bystander was reluctant to correct afterwards because he might fear that the asker would think he was a coward for not initially correcting the misinformer. The bystander might thus incur a possible reprisal from the asker. Still another possibility is that the bystander might have rationalized his behavior during this time interval.

As was indicated in the sections on results in the threat conditions, the inclusion of the post corrections had some influence on the pattern of total corrections. Both the high-physical-threat and high-embarrassment-threat conditions demonstrate a comparable percentage of total corrections; both the low-threat and the minimal-threat conditions similarly showed a comparable percentage of total corrections.

The latter combined group showed almost 2½ times the number of total corrections (82 corrections) than the former combined group (34 corrections).

As was suggested in the section on results, the data generally seem to point to an arousal interpretation. High levels of arousal are seen as having an inhibitory influence on bystander helping behavior at the time of the stressful event and for at least a short time period thereafter.

## SUMMARY AND CONCLUSIONS

Socially responsible behavior is based on the cultural norm which prescribes that a person should help those who are dependent upon him for help. However, what are the prerequisites for dependency when there are a number of other people present who have observed the event and the plight of the help-seeker? In some situations the expectations for bystander action are clear; in other situations they are uncertain or questionable because of the ambiguity of the situation or because there are alternative explanations for the event. There appear to be no guidelines for behavior when the individual's physical well-being is at stake. In times of danger the instinct of self-preservation dominates. And yet, does one remain idle while another person's life is threatened? The answer to this is not simple. What is the individual's relationship to the victim? What are the characteristics of the victim? What barriers, physical or psychological, are present in the situation? The anticipation of harm or violence is known to produce not only "freezing" behavior, but also cognitive confusion and rigidity.

Although many of our cultural norms, such as aiding others in need of help, are held up as ideals toward which all should strive, many of these moral precepts are couched in general terms. Consequently, in stating a norm one must specify the kind of behavior required, the kind of situation in which the behavior occurs, and the kind of person who is behaving. Expectations may vary according to age, sex, socioeconomic class, and so on. Empathy may be activated in the observer as a result of his identification with the help-seeker. The observer's familiarity with the environment may increase the possibilities for appropriate action. Individual and personality differences may account for different interpretation, as well as for responsivity to the event. Such unaccounted-for and uncontrolled factors as the mood of the situation, the presence of communication opportunities, and the possibilities for cohesive action, may be operating in a specific incident. It is improbable that one of these factors alone could be chosen as the single factor that explains the phenomenon; rather, many of these factors interact to produce a given result. It is possible, however, to isolate a number of these factors and determine their relative importance in describing the phenomena. Such was the purpose of this exploratory study.

In the subway situation, when the bystander was faced with the decision to correct or not correct obviously wrong directions, he corrected in approximately half of the situations. This figure was significantly influenced by the presence of other bystanders who were addressed by the direction-asker. The presence of the other bystanders permitted the bystander to diffuse the responsibility or blame. Similarly, when the bystander was not a direct target of the asker's request for information, he appeared to absolve himself of any responsibility to intervene and correct. The presence of various levels of probable threat significantly influenced the basic percentage of corrections made by bystanders. Increased probable threat decreased the percentage of helping responses. However, bystanders were not moved to extend help to the asker who was presented as more helpless and more deserving of their aid. Many of the bystanders refrained from correcting until after the misinformer left the situation. Whether or not the bystander corrected after the misinformer left was often determined by the length of time that elapsed between the misinforming incident and the misinformer's exit. The results were applicable to another type of direction-asking incident, and were not specific to the type of directions asked by the asker.

Observations made of bystanders' behavior underline the difficulty in concluding that failure to intervene was a result of apathy or indifference. There is a difference between not caring (apathy) and the feeling of being unable to act because of questionable or ominous overtones in the situation. The behavior of the bystanders in incidents where correction did not occur, or where correction occurred after the misinformer departed, suggests that bystanders avoided any confrontation or extended self-involvement, possibly because of threats to their physical or psychological self-system. Such threats have resulted in fear and indecisiveness. The bystander who did not correct, immediately or later, appeared to behave in a way that reduced his sense of guilt or diminished social esteem or self-esteem. Bystanders attempted to minimize their felt presence by avoiding the glances of the involved and uninvolved parties, and by using "shields" against involvement, such as newspapers. It is likely that these overt behavioral tendencies were accompanied by the covert operation of such behavior mechanisms as rationalization (whereby the bystander may have claimed that he did what everyone else did or would have done), projection (whereby his responsibility may have been projected onto the misinformer, since it was the misinformer's fault), or denial that the situation was serious or that he had overheard what had taken place.

There appears to be little doubt that the urban environment plays an important role in influencing bystanders' reaction to calls for help. The city dweller's contacts and interactions with others often take the form of an economic exchange, where reciprocity and other similar reward-cost considerations are prevalent. In addition, increased crime in the city, coupled with feelings of isolation, can result in increased feelings of apprehension and anxiety about one's own well-being and safety. Many of the urbanite's interpersonal encounters with strangers are overshadowed with suspicions of their intentions and expectations. As Milgram and Hollander (1964) pointed out, the middle-class person is totally unequipped to deal with the occurrence of violence. "He is unable to use personal violence, either singly or collectively, even when it is required for productive and socially valued ends." In addition, the urban dweller seeks to preserve his anonymity, whereas the rural person's anonymity may be all but eliminated. The city person's desensitization and conditioning to aspects of his environment cause him to unintentionally ignore events that might attract the attention of a rural person.

Are the results reported in this study specific to the subway only? It can be argued that the subway environment does add a somewhat different dimension to the problem of investigating helping behavior. The subway car not only limits the possibilities for escape in case of danger, but possesses an aura of threat and fear for some people.

One may raise not only the question whether these results are specific to the subway, but also the question whether they are specific to the subways of New York City. Subways are in operation not only in other cities in the United States, but also in many foreign countries. It is difficult to speculate about how different the findings would be in the subways of Paris, Tokyo, London, or Moscow, because of the operation of other factors, such as cultural differences.

In general, although the base rates reported in the subway situation may not be generalizable to other similar situations, the relationships found should tend to be generalizable to other similar situations. This study was an exploratory one, in the judgment of the experimenter, and it would be profitable to continue exploring. Among other things, there is a need for better and more controlled manipulations and situations, and for more refined methods of recording bystander behavior and characteristics. There is a need to determine the possible interactions of several variables operating at any one time and in any one particular situation. In other words, there is a need for further analysis and understanding of bystander behavior rather than an acceptance of pat labels—"apathy," "indifference"—or of pat answers by onlookers—"It was none of my business," "I didn't want to get involved."

## REFERENCES

**BERKOWITZ, L., & DANIELS, LOUISE.** Affecting the salience of the social responsibility norm: effects of past help on the response to dependency relationships. *Journal of Abnormal and Social Psychology,* 1964, **68,** 275-281.

**BRYAN, J. H.** Helping and hitch-hiking. Unpublished manuscript, Educational Testing Service, 1966.

**COHEN, J.** An alternative to Marascuilo's "large-sample multiple comparisons" for proportions. *Psychological Bulletin,* 1967, 67, 199-201.

**DANIELS, LOUISE, & BERKOWITZ, L.** Liking and response to dependency relationships. *Human Relations,* 1963, **16,** 141-148.

**DARLEY, J., & LATANÉ, B.** Bystander intervention in emergencies: diffusion of responsibility. *Journal of Personality and Social Psychology,* 1968, 8, 377-383.

**GRINKER, R. R., & SPIEGEL, J. P.** *Men under stress.* Philadelphia: Blakiston, 1945.

**HOMANS, G.** *Social behavior: its elementary forms.* New York: Harcourt, Brace, 1961.

**LATANÉ, H., & DARLEY, J.** Group inhibition of bystander intervention in emergencies. Paper read at American Psychological Association, New York, Sept., 1966.

**MILGRAM, S., & HOLLANDER, P.** The murder they heard. *Nation,* 1964, **198,** 602-604.

**ROSENHAN, D., & WHITE, G.** Observation and rehearsal as a determinant of pro-social behavior. *Journal of Personality and Social Psychology,* 1967, 5, 424-431.

**ROSENTHAL, A. M.** Study of the sickness called apathy. *New York Times Magazine,* May 3, 1964, p. 24.

**TEST, M. A., & BRYAN, J. H.** Dependency, models, and reciprocity. Unpublished manuscript.

**THIBAUT, J., & KELLEY, H.** *The social psychology of groups.* New York: Wiley, 1959.

**WALLACH, M. A., KOGAN, N., & BEM, D. J.** Diffusion of responsibility and level of risk taking in groups. *Journal of Abnormal and Social Psychology,* 1964, **68,** 263-274.

# GOOD SAMARITANISM: AN UNDERGROUND PHENOMENON?[1]

IRVING M. PILIAVIN
*University of Pennsylvania*

JUDITH RODIN
*Columbia University*

JANE ALLYN PILIAVIN
*University of Pennsylvania*

A field experiment was performed to investigate the effect of several variables on helping behavior, using the express trains of the New York 8th Avenue IND as a laboratory on wheels. Four teams of students, each one made up of a victim, model, and two observers, staged standard collapses in which type of victim (drunk or ill), race of victim (black or white), and presence or absence of a model were varied. Data recorded by observers included number and race of observers, latency of the helping response and race of helper, number of helpers, movement out of the "critical area," and spontaneous comments.

Major findings of the study were that (1) an apparently ill person is more likely to receive aid than is one who appears to be drunk, (2) race of victim has little effect on race of helper except when the victim is drunk, (3) the longer the emergency continues without help being offered, the more likely it is that someone will leave the area of the emergency, and (4) the expected decrease in speed of responding as group size increases–the "diffusion of responsibility effect" found by Darley & Latané (1968)–does not occur in this situation. Implications of this difference between laboratory and field results are discussed, and a brief model for the prediction of behavior in emergency situations is presented.

Since the murder of Kitty Genovese in Queens, a rapidly increasing number of social scientists have turned their attentions to the study of the Good Samaritan's act and an associated phenomenon, the evaluation of victims by bystanders and agents. Some of the findings of this research have been provocative and non-obvious. For example, there is evidence that agents, and even bystanders, will sometimes derogate the character of the victims of misfortune, instead of feeling compassion (Lerner & Simmons, 1966; Berscheid & Walster, 1967). Furthermore, recent findings indicate that under certain circumstances there is not "safety in numbers," but rather "diffusion of responsibility." Darley and Latané (1968) have reported that among bystanders hearing an epileptic seizure over earphones, those who believed other witnesses were present were less likely to seek assistance for the victim than were bystanders who believed they were alone. Subsequent research by Latané and Rodin (1969) on response to the victim of a fall confirmed this finding and suggested further that assistance from a group of bystanders was less likely to come if the group members were strangers than if they were prior acquaintances. The field experiments of Bryan and Test (1967), on the other hand, provide interesting findings that fit common-sense expectations; namely, one is more likely to be a Good Samaritan if one has just observed another individual performing a helpful act.

Much of the work on victimization to date has been performed in the laboratory. It is commonly argued that the ideal research strategy over the long haul is to move back and forth between the laboratory, with its advantage of greater control, and the field, with its advantage of greater "reality." The present study was designed to provide more information from the latter setting.

[1]This research was conducted while the first author was at Columbia University as a Special NIMH Research Fellow under Grant Number 1-F3-MH-36, 328-01. The study was partially supported by funds supplied by this grant and partially by funds from NSF Grant GS-1901 to the third author. The authors thank Virginia Joy for allowing the experimental teams to be recruited from her class, and Percy Tannenbaum for his reading of the manuscript and his helpful comments.

The primary focus of the study was on the effect of type of victim (drunk or ill) and race of victim (black or white) on speed of responding, frequency of responding, and the race of the helper. On the basis of the large body of research on similarity and liking as well as that on race and social distance, it was assumed that an individual would be more inclined to help someone of his race than a person of another race. The expectation regarding type of victim was that help would be accorded more frequently and rapidly to the apparently ill victim. This expectation was derived from two considerations. First, it was assumed that people who are regarded as partly responsible for their plight would receive less sympathy and consequently less help than people seen as not responsible for their circumstances (Schopler & Matthews, 1965). Secondly, it was assumed that whatever sympathy individuals may experience when they observe a drunk collapse, their inclination to help him will be dampened by the realization that the victim may become disgusting, embarrassing and/or violent. This realization may, in fact, not only constrain helping but also lead observers to turn away from the victim—that is, to leave the scene of the emergency.

Aside from examining the effects of race and type of victim, the present research sought to investigate the impact of modeling in emergency situations. Several investigators have found that an individual's actions in a given situation lead others in that situation to engage in similar actions. This modeling phenomenon has been observed in a variety of contexts including those involving Good Samaritanism (Bryan & Test, 1967). It was expected that the phenomenon would be observed as well in the present study. A final concern of the study was to examine the relationship between size of group and frequency and latency of the helping response, with a victim who was both seen and heard. In previous laboratory studies (Darley & Latané, 1968; Latané & Rodin, 1969), increases in group size led to decreases in frequency and increases in latency of responding. In these studies, however, the emergency was only heard, not seen. Since visual cues are likely to make an emergency much more arousing for the observer, it is not clear that, given these cues, such considerations as crowd size will be relevant determinants of the observer's response to the emergency. Visual cues also provide clear information as to whether anyone has yet helped the victim or if he has been able to help himself. Thus, in the laboratory studies, observers lacking visual cues could rationalize not helping by assuming assistance was no longer needed when the victim ceased calling for help. Staging emergencies in full view of observers eliminates the possibility of such rationalization.

To conduct a field investigation of the above questions under the desired conditions required a setting which would allow the repeated staging of emergencies in the midst of reasonably large groups which remained fairly similar in composition from incident to incident. It was also desirable that each group retain the same composition over the course of the incident and that a reasonable amount of time be available after the emergency occurred for Good Samaritans to act. To meet these requirements, the emergencies were staged during the approximately 7½-minute express run between the 59th Street and 125th Street stations of the 8th Avenue IND branch of the New York subways.

## METHOD

**Subjects** About 4,450 men and women who travelled on the 8th Avenue IND in New York City, weekdays between the hours of 11:00 A.M. and 3:00 P.M., during the period from April 15 to June 26, 1968, were the unsolicited participants in this study. The racial composition of a typical train, which travels through Harlem to the Bronx, was about 45 percent black and 55 percent white. The mean number of people per car during these hours was 43; the mean number of people in the "critical area," in which the staged incident took place, was 8.5.

*Field situation* The A and D trains of the 8th Avenue IND were selected because they make no stops between 59th Street and 125th Street. Thus, for about 7½ minutes there was a captive audience who, after the first 70 seconds of their ride, became bystanders to an emergency situation. A single trial was a nonstop ride between 59th and 125th Streets, going in either direction. All trials were run only on the old New York subway cars which serviced the 8th Avenue line, since they had two-person seats in group arrangements rather than extended seats. The designed experimental or "critical" area was that end section of any car whose doors led to the next car. There are 13 seats and some standing room in this area on all trains (see [Figure 2-1]).

**Procedure** On each trial, a team of four Columbia General Studies students, two males and two females, boarded the train using different doors. Four different teams, whose members always worked together, were used to collect data for 103 trials. Each team varied the location of the experimental car from trial to

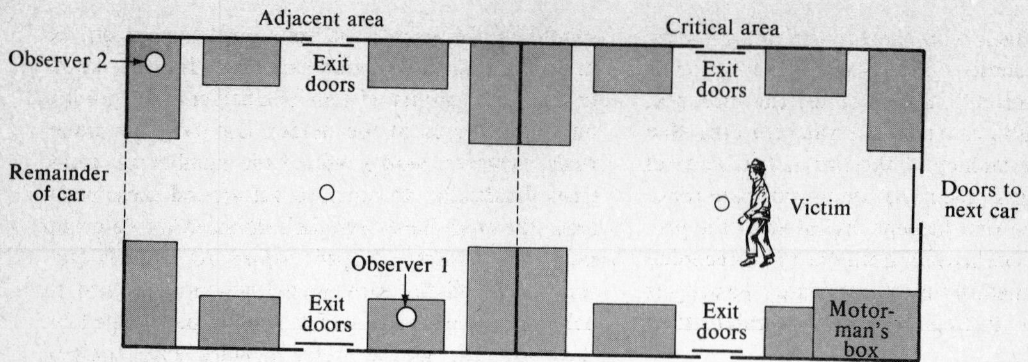


[FIGURE 2-1] Layout of adjacent and critical areas of subway car.

trial. The female confederates took seats outside the critical area and recorded data as unobtrusively as possible for the duration of the ride, while the male model and victim remained standing. The victim always stood next to a pole in the center of the critical area (see [Figure 2-1]). As the train passed the first station (approximately 70 seconds after departing), the victim staggered forward and collapsed. Until receiving help, the victim remained supine on the floor looking at the ceiling. If the victim received no assistance by the time the train slowed to a stop, the model helped him to his feet. At the stop, the team disembarked and waited separately until other riders had left the station. They then proceeded to another platform to board a train going in the opposite direction for the next trial. From 6 to 8 trials were run on a given day. All trials on a given day were in the same "victim condition."

*The victim* The four victims (one from each team) were males between the ages of 26 and 35. Three were white and one was black. All were identically dressed in Eisenhower jackets, old slacks, and no tie. On 38 trials the victims smelled of liquor and carried a liquor bottle wrapped tightly in a brown bag (drunk condition), while on the remaining 65 trials they appeared sober and carried a black cane (cane condition). In all other aspects, victims dressed and behaved identically in the two conditions. Each victim participated in drunk and cane trials.[2]

*The model* Four white males between the ages of 24 and 29 assumed the roles of model in each team. All models wore informal clothes although they were not identically attired. There were four different model conditions used across both victim conditions (drunk or cane).

1. *Critical area–early:* Model stood in critical area and waited until passing 4th station to assist victim (approximately 70 seconds after collapse).
2. *Critical area–late:* Model stood in critical area and waited until passing 6th station to assist victim (approximately 150 seconds after collapse).
3. *Adjacent area–early:* Model stood in middle of car in area adjacent to critical area and waited until passing 4th station.
4. *Adjacent area–late:* Model stood in adjacent area and waited until passing 6th station.

When the model provided assistance, he raised the victim to a sitting position and stayed with him for the remainder of the trial. An equal number of trials in the no-model condition and in each of the four model conditions were preprogrammed by a random number table and assigned to each team.

*Measures* On each trial, one observer noted the race, sex, and location of every rider seated or standing in the critical area. In addition, she counted the total number of individuals in the car and the total

[2]It will be noted later that not only were there more cane trials than drunk trials, they were also distributed unevenly across black and white victims. The reason for this is easier to explain than to correct. Teams 1 and 2 (both white victims) started the first day in the cane condition. Teams 3 (black) and 4 (white) began in the drunk condition. Teams were told to alternate the conditions across days. They arranged their running days to fit their schedules. On their fourth day, Team 2 violated our instruction and ran cane trials, when they should have run drunk trials; the victim "didn't like" playing the drunk! Then the Columbia student strike occurred, the teams disbanded, and the study of necessity was over. At this point, Teams 1 and 3 had run on only 3 days each, while 2 and 4 had run on 4 days each.

number of individuals who came to the victim's assistance. She also recorded the race, sex, and location of every helper. A second observer coded the race, sex, and location of all persons in the adjacent area. She also recorded the latency of the first helper's arrival after the victim had fallen and, on appropriate trials, the latency of the first helper's arrival after the programmed model had arrived. Both observers recorded comments spontaneously made by nearby passengers and attempted to elicit comments from a rider sitting next to them.

## RESULTS AND DISCUSSION

As can be seen in [Table 2-7], the frequency of help received by our victims was impressive, at least as compared to earlier laboratory results. The victim with the cane received spontaneous help, i.e., before the model acted, on 62 of the 65 trials. Even the drunk received spontaneous help on 19 of 38 trials. The difference is not explicable on the basis of gross differences in the numbers of potential helpers in the cars. (Mean number of passengers in the car on cane trials was 45; on drunk trials, 40. Total range was 15 to 120.)

On the basis of past research, relatively long latencies of spontaneous helping were expected; thus it was assumed that models would have time to help, and their effects could be assessed. However, in all but three of the cane trials planned to be model trials, the victim received help before the model was scheduled to offer assistance. This was less likely to happen with the drunk victim. In many cases, the early model was able to intervene and in a few, even the delayed model could act (see [Table 2-7] for frequencies).

A direct comparison between the latency of response in the drunk and cane conditions might be misleading, since on model trials one does not know how long it might have taken for a helper to arrive without the stimulus of the model. Omitting the model trials, however, would reduce the number of drunk trials drastically. In order to get around these problems, the trials have been dichotomized into a group in which someone helped *before* 70 seconds (the time at which the early model was programmed to help) and a group in which no one had helped by this time. The second group includes some trials in which people helped the model and a very few in which no one helped at all.[3] It is quite clear from the first section of [Table 2-8] that there is more immediate, spontaneous helping of the victim with the cane than of the drunk. The effect seems to be essentially the same for the black victim and for the white victims.[4]

What of the total number of people who help? On 60% of the 81 trials on which the victim receives help, he receives it not from one Good Samaritan but from two, three, or even more.[5] There are no significant differences between black and white victims, or between cane and drunk victims in the number of helpers subsequent to the first who come to his aid. Seemingly, then, the presence of the first helper has important implications which override whatever cognitive and emotional differences were initially engendered among observers by the characteristics of

**[Table 2-7] Percentage of trials on which help was given, by race and condition of victim, and total number of trials run in each condition (in parentheses)[a]**

| Percentage of trials on which help was received | White victims | | Black victim | |
|---|---|---|---|---|
| | Cane | Drunk | Cane | Drunk |
| No-model trials | 100% | 100% | 100% | 73% |
| (No. of trials run) | (54) | (11) | (8) | (11) |
| Model trials | 100% | 77% | — | 67% |
| (No. of trials run) | (3) | (13) | (0) | (3) |
| Total no. of trials | (57) | (24) | (8) | (14) |

[a]Distribution of model trials for the drunk was as follows:
Critical area: early, 4; late, 4
Adjacent area: early, 5; late, 3
The three model trials completed for the cane victim were all early, with 2 from the critical area and 1 from the adjacent area.

[3]If a comparison of latencies is made between cane and drunk non-model trials only, the median latency for cane trials is 5 seconds, and the median for drunk trials is 109 seconds (assigning 400 seconds as the latency for non-respondents). The Mann-Whitney $U$ for this comparison is significant at $p < .0001$.

[4]Among the white victim teams, the data from Team 2 differ to some extent from those for Teams 1 and 4. All the "cane-after 70 seconds" trials are accounted for by Team 2, as are 4 of the 5 "drunk-before 70" trials. Median latency for cane trials is longer for Team 2 than for the other teams; for drunk trials, shorter. This is the same team that violated our "alternate days" instruction. It would appear that this team is being rather less careful—that the victim may be getting out of his role. The data from this team have been included in the analysis, although they tend to reduce the relationships that were found.

[5]The data from the model trials are not included in this analysis because the model was programmed to behave rather differently from the way in which most real helpers behaved. That is, his role was to raise the victim to a sitting position and then appear to need assistance. Most real helpers managed to drag the victim to a seat or to a standing position on their own. Thus the programmed model received somewhat *more* help than did real first helpers.

[Table 2-8] **Time and responses to the incident**[a]

| Trials on which help was offered | (1) Total number of trials | | (2) % of trials on[c] which 1+ people left critical area | | (3) % of trials on[c] which 1+ comments were recorded | | (4) Mean number of comments | |
|---|---|---|---|---|---|---|---|---|
| | White victims | Black victim | White victims | Black victim | White victims | Black victim | White victims | Black victim |
| Before 70 seconds | | | | | | | | |
| Cane | 52 | 7 | 4% | 14% | 21% | 0% | .27 | 0.00 |
| Drunk | 5 | 4 | 20% | 0% | 80% | 50% | 1.00 | .50 |
| Total | 57 | 11 | 5% | 9% | 26% | 18% | .33 | .18 |
| After 70 seconds | | | | | | | | |
| Cane | 5 | 1 | 40% | – | 60% | – | .80 | – |
| Drunk | 19 | 10 | 42% | 60% | 100% | 70% | 2.00 | .90 |
| Total | 24 | 11 | 42% | 64% | 96% | 64% | 1.75 | .82 |
| | $\chi^2 = 36.83$ $p < .001$ | b $p < .03$ | $\chi^2_{time} = 23.19$ $p < .001$ $\chi^2_{cane\text{-}drunk} = 11.71$ $p < .001$ | | $\chi^2_{time} = 31.45$ $p < .001$ $\chi^2_{cane\text{-}drunk} = 37.95$ $p < .001$ | | | |

[a]Percentage and means not calculated for $n$'s less than 4.
[b]Fisher's exact test, estimate of two-tailed probability.
[c]Black and white victims are combined for the analyses of these data.

the victim. It may be that the victim's uniformly passive response to the individual trying to assist him reduces observers' fears about possible unpleasantness in the drunk conditions. Another possibility is that the key factor in the decisions of second and third helpers to offer assistance is the first helper. That is, perhaps assistance is being offered primarily to him rather than to the victim. Unfortunately, our data do not permit adequate assessment of these or other possible explanations.

**Characteristics of Spontaneous First Helpers** Having discovered that people do, in fact, help with rather high frequency, the next question is "who helps?" The effect of two variables, sex and race, can be examined. On the average, 60% of the people in the critical area were males. Yet, of the 81 spontaneous first helpers, 90% were males. In this situation, then, men are considerably more likely to help than are women ($\chi^2 = 30.63$; $p < .001$).

Turning now to the race variable, of the 81 first helpers, 64% were white. This percentage does not differ significantly from the expected percentage of 55% based on racial distribution in the cars. Since both black and white victims were used, it is also possible to see whether blacks and whites are more likely to help a member of their own race. On the 65 trials on which spontaneous help was offered to the white victims, 68% of the helpers were white. This proportion differs from the expected 55% at $p < .05$ ($\chi^2 = 4.23$). On the 16 trials on which spontaneous help was offered to the black victim, half of the first helpers were white. While this proportion does not differ from chance expectation, we again see a slight tendency toward "same-race" helping.

When race of helpers is examined separately for cane and drunk victims, an interesting although non-significant trend emerges (see [Table 2-9]). With both the black and white cane victims, the proportion of helpers of each race was in accord with the expected 55-45% split. With the drunk, on the other hand, it is mainly members of his own race who come to his aid.[6]

This interesting tendency toward same-race helping only in the case of the drunk victim may reflect more empathy, sympathy, and trust toward victims of one's own racial group. In the case of an innocent victim (e.g., the cane victim), when sympathy, though

[6]It is unfortunate from a design standpoint that there was only one black victim. He was the only black student in the class from which our crews were recruited. While it is tenuous to generalize from a sample of one, the problems attendant upon attributing results to his race rather than to his individual personality characteristics are vitiated somewhat by the fact that response latencies and frequencies of help to him in the cane condition fall between responses to Teams 1 and 4 on the one hand and Team 2 on the other.

[Table 2-9] **Spontaneous helping of cane and drunk by race of helper and race of victim**[a]

| Race of helper | White victims | | | Black victim | | | All victims | | |
|---|---|---|---|---|---|---|---|---|---|
| | Cane | Drunk | Total | Cane | Drunk | Total | Cane | Drunk | Total |
| Same as victim | 34 | 10 | 44 | 2 | 6 | 8 | 36 | 16 | 52 |
| Different from victim | 20 | 1 | 21 | 6 | 2 | 8 | 26 | 3 | 29 |
| Total | 54 | 11 | 65 | 8 | 8 | 16 | 62 | 19 | 81 |
| | $\chi^2 = 2.11, p = .16$ | | | $p = .16$ (two-tailed estimate from Fisher's exact probabilities test) | | | $\chi^2 = 3.26, p = .08$ | | |

[a]$\chi^2$, are corrected for continuity.

differentially experienced, is relatively uncomplicated by other emotions, assistance can readily cut across group lines. In the case of the drunk (and potentially dangerous) victim, complications are present, probably blame, fear, and disgust. When the victim is a member of one's own group—when the conditions for empathy and trust are more favorable—assistance is more likely to be offered. As we have seen, however, this does not happen without the passing of time to think things over.

Recent findings of Black and Reiss (1967) in a study of the behavior of white police officers towards apprehended persons offer an interesting parallel. Observers in this study recorded very little evidence of prejudice toward sober individuals, whether white or black. There was a large increase in prejudice expressed towards drunks of both races, but the increase in prejudice towards blacks was more than twice that towards whites.

**Modeling Effects** No extensive analysis of the response to the programmed model could be made, since there were too few cases for analysis. Two analyses were, however, performed on the effects of adjacent area vs. critical area models and of early vs. late models within the drunk condition. The data are presented in [Table 2-10]. While the area variable has no effect, the early model elicits help significantly more frequently than does the late model.

**Other Responses to the Incident** What other responses do observers make to the incident? Do the passengers leave the car, move out of the area, make comments about the incident? No one left the car on any of the trials. However, on 21 of the 103 trials, a total of 34 people did leave the critical area. The second section of [Table 2-8] presents the percentage of trials on which someone left the critical area as a function of three variables: type of victim, race of victim, and time to receipt of help (before or after 70 seconds). People leave the area on a higher proportion of trials with the drunk than with the cane victim. They also are far more likely to leave on trials on which help is not offered by 70 seconds, as compared to trials on which help is received before that time.[7] The frequencies are too small to make comparisons with each of the variables held constant.

Each observer spoke to the person seated next to her after the incident took place. She also noted spontaneous comments and actions by those around her. A content analysis of these data was performed, with little in the way of interesting findings. The distribution of number of comments over different sorts of

[7]Individuals are also somewhat more likely to leave the area with the black victim than with the white victims ($\chi^2 = 3.24, p < .08$). This race effect is most probably an artifact, since the black victim ran more drunk trials than cane trials, the white victims vice versa.

[Table 2-10] **Frequency of help as a function of early (70 seconds) versus late (150 seconds) and adjacent versus critical area programmed models (drunk trials only)**[a]

| | Critical area | | | Adjacent area | | | Both areas | | |
|---|---|---|---|---|---|---|---|---|---|
| | Early | Late | Both | Early | Late | Both | Early | Late | Total |
| Help received | 4 | 2 | 6 | 5 | 1 | 6 | 9 | 3 | 12 |
| No help | 0 | 2 | 2 | 0 | 2 | 2 | 0 | 4 | 4 |
| Total | 4 | 4 | 8 | 5 | 3 | 8 | 9 | 7 | 16 |

Early versus late: $p < .04$ (two-tailed estimate from Fisher's exact test).

[a]All three cane-model trials were early model trials; 2 critical area, one adjacent. Help was received on all.

**[Table 2-11] Mean and median latencies (in seconds) as a function of number of males in the critical area (Model trials omitted; no response assigned 400 seconds)**

| Number of males in critical area | Cane | | | Drunk | | |
|---|---|---|---|---|---|---|
| | White victims | Black victim | Total | White victims | Black victim | Total |
| 1–3 | | | | | | |
| Mean | 16 | 12 | 15 | – | 309 | 309 |
| Median | 7 | 12 | 7 | – | 312 | 312 |
| *N* | (17) | (2) | (19) | | (4) | (4) |
| 4–6 | | | | | | |
| Mean | 20 | 6 | 18 | 155 | 143 | 149 |
| Median | 5 | 4 | 5 | 105 | 70 | 73 |
| *N* | (23) | (4) | (27) | (4) | (4) | (8) |
| 7 and up | | | | | | |
| Mean | 3 | 52 | 9 | 107 | 74 | 97 |
| Median | 1 | 52 | 1.5 | 102 | 65 | 84 |
| *N* | (14) | (2) | (16) | (7) | (3) | (10) |
| Kruskal-Wallis Test (*H*) | | | 5.08 | | | 6.01 |
| *p* value | | | .08 | | | .05 |

trials, however, did prove interesting (see Section 3 of [Table 2-8]). Far more comments were obtained on drunk trials than on cane trials. Similarly, most of the comments were obtained on trials on which no one helped until after 70 seconds. The discomfort observers felt in sitting inactive in the presence of the victim has led them to talk about the incident, perhaps hoping others would confirm the fact that inaction was appropriate. Many women, for example, make comments such as "It's for men to help him" or "I wish I could help him–I'm not strong enough." "I never saw this kind of thing before–I don't know where to look." "You feel so bad that you don't know what to do."

**A Test of the Diffusion of Responsibility Hypothesis:** In the Darley and Latané experiment, it was predicted and found that as the number of bystanders increased, the likelihood that any individual would help decreased and the latency of response increased. Their study involved bystanders who could not see each other or the victim. In the Latané and Rodin study, the effect was again found, with bystanders who were face to face, but with the victim still only heard. In the present study, bystanders can see both the victim and each other. Will the diffusion of responsibility finding still occur in this situation?

In order to check this hypothesis, two analyses were performed. First, all non-model trials were separated into three groups, according to the number of males in the critical area (the assumed reference group for spontaneous first helpers). Mean and median latencies of response were then calculated for each group, separately by type and race of victim. The results are presented in [Table 2-11]. There is no evidence in these data for diffusion of responsibility; in fact, response times, using either measure, are consistently faster for the "7 or more" groups compared to the "1 to 3" groups.[8]

As Darley and Latané point out, however, different-size real groups cannot be meaningfully compared to one another, since as group size increases the likelihood that one or more persons will help also increases. A second analysis as similar as possible to that used by the above authors was therefore performed, comparing latencies actually obtained for each size group with a baseline of hypothetical groups of the same size made up by combining smaller groups. In order to have as much control as possible, the analysis was confined to cane trials, with white victims and male first helpers coming from the critical area. Within this set of trials the most frequently occurring natural groups (of males in the critical area) were those of size three ($n$ = 6) and seven ($n$ = 5). Hypothetical groups of three ($n$ = 4) and seven ($n$ = 25) were composed of all combinations of smaller sized groups. For example, to obtain the hypothetical latencies for groups of seven, combinations were made of (1) all real size six groups with all real size one groups, plus (2) all real size five groups with all real size two groups, etc. The latency assigned to each of

[8]The total number of people in the car was strongly related to the number of males in the critical area. Similar results are obtained if latencies are examined as a function of the total number of people in the car.

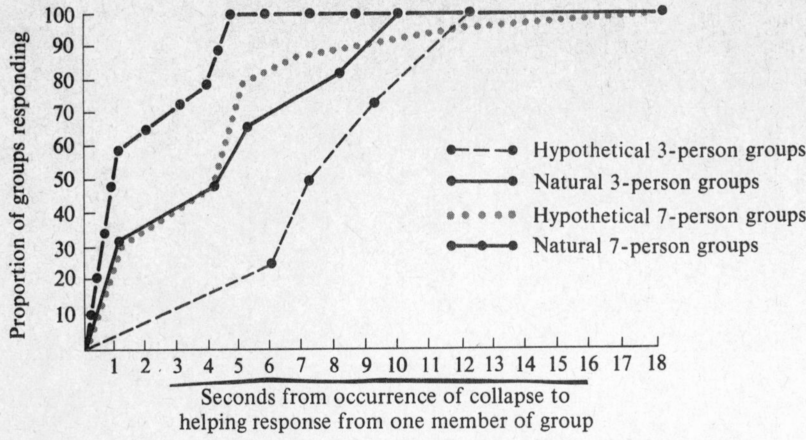


[FIGURE 2-2] Cumulative proportion of groups producing a helper over time (cane trials, white victims, male helpers from inside critical area).

these hypothetical groups was that recorded for the faster of the two real groups of which it was composed. Cumulative response curves for real and hypothetical groups of three and seven are presented in [Figure 2-2].

As can be seen in [Figure 2-2], the cumulative helping response curves for the hypothetical groups of both sizes are lower than those for the corresponding real groups. That is, members of real groups respond more rapidly than would be expected on the basis of the faster of the two scores obtained from the combined smaller groups. While these results together with those summarized in [Table 2-11] do not necessarily contradict the diffusion of responsibility hypothesis, they do not follow the pattern of findings obtained by Darley and Latané and are clearly at variance with the tentative conclusion of these investigators that "a victim may be more likely to receive help . . . the fewer people there are to take action (Latané & Darley, 1968)."

Two explanations can be suggested to account for the disparity between the findings of [Table 2-11] and [Figure 2-2] and those of Darley and Latané and Latané and Rodin. As indicated earlier in this paper, the conditions of the present study were quite different from those in previous investigations. First, the fact that observers in the present study could see the victim may not only have constrained observers' abilities to conclude there was no emergency, but may also have overwhelmed with other considerations any tendency to diffuse responsibility. Second, the present findings may indicate that even if diffusion of responsibility *is* experienced by people who can actually see an emergency, when groups are larger than two the increment in deterrence to action resulting from increasing the number of observers may be less than the increase in probability that within a given time interval at least one of the observers will take action to assist the victim. Clearly more work is needed in both natural and laboratory settings before an understanding is reached of the conditions under which diffusion of responsibility will or will not occur.

## CONCLUSIONS AND DISCUSSION

In this field study, a personal emergency occurs in which escape for the bystander is virtually impossible. It is a public, face-to-face situation, and in this respect differs from previous laboratory studies. Moreover, since generalizations from field studies to laboratory research must be made with caution, few comparisons will be drawn. However, several conclusions may be put forth:

1. An individual who appears to be ill is more likely to receive aid than is one who appears to be drunk, even when the immediate help needed is of the same kind.
2. Given mixed groups of men and women and a male victim, men are more likely to help than are women.
3. Given mixed racial groups, there is some tendency for same-race helping to be more frequent. This tendency is increased when the victim is drunk, as compared to when he is apparently ill.
4. There is no strong relationship between number of bystanders and speed of helping; the expected increased "diffusion of responsibility" with a greater number of bystanders was not obtained for groups of these sizes. That is, help is not less frequent or slower in coming from larger as compared to smaller groups of bystanders; what effect there is is in the opposite direction.
5. The longer the emergency continues without help being offered: (a) the less impact a model has on the helping behavior of observers, (b) the more likely it is that individuals will leave the immediate area (that is,

they appear to purposively move to another area in order to avoid the situation), and (c) the more likely it is that observers will discuss the incident and its implications for their behavior.

A model of response to emergency situations consistent with the above findings is currently being developed by the authors. It is briefly presented here as a possible heuristic device. The model includes the following assumptions: Observation of an emergency creates an emotional arousal state in the bystander. This state will be differently interpreted in different situations (Schachter, 1964) as fear, disgust, sympathy, etc., and possibly a combination of these. This state of arousal is higher (1) the more one can empathize with the victim (i.e., the more one can see oneself in his situation) (Stotland, 1966), (2) the closer one is to the emergency, and (3) the longer the state of emergency continues without the intervention of a helper. It can be reduced by one of a number of possible responses: (1) helping directly, (2) going to get help, (3) leaving the scene of the emergency, and (4) rejecting the victim as undeserving of help (Lerner & Simmons, 1966). The response that will be chosen is a function of a cost-reward matrix that includes costs associated with helping (e.g., effort, embarrassment, possible disgusting or distasteful experiences, possible physical harm, etc.), costs associated with not helping (mainly self-blame and perceived censure from others), rewards associated with helping (mainly praise from self, victim, and others), and rewards associated with not helping (mainly those stemming from continuation of other activities). Note that the major motivation implied in the model is not a positive "altruistic" one, but rather a selfish desire to rid oneself of an unpleasant emotional state.

In terms of this model, the following after-the-fact interpretations can be made of the findings obtained:

1. The drunk is helped less because costs for helping are higher (greater disgust) and costs for not helping are lower (less self-blame and censure because he is in part responsible for his own victimization).
2. Women help less because costs for helping are higher in this situation (effort, mainly) and costs for not helping are lower (less censure from others; it is not her role).
3. Same-race helping, particularly of drunk, can be explained by differential costs for not helping (less censure if one is of opposite race) and, with the drunk, differential costs for helping (more fear if of different race).
4. Diffusion of responsibility was not found on cane trials because costs for helping in general are low and costs for not helping are high (more self-blame because of possible severity of problem). That is, the suggestion is made that the diffusion of responsibility effect will increase as costs for helping increase and costs for not helping decrease. This interpretation is consistent with the well-known public incidents in which possible bodily harm to a helper is almost always involved, and thus costs for helping are very high, and also with previous research done with non-visible victims in which either (a) it was easy to assume someone had already helped and thus costs for not helping were reduced (Darley & Latané) or (b) it was possible to think that the emergency was minor, which also reduces the costs for not helping (Latané & Rodin).
5. All of the effects of time are also consistent with the model. The longer the emergency continues, the more likely it is that observers will be aroused and therefore will have chosen among the possible responses. Thus (a) a late model will elicit less helping, since people have already reduced their arousal by one of the other methods, (b) unless arousal is reduced by other methods, people will leave more as time goes on, because arousal is still increasing, and (c) observers will discuss the incident in an attempt to reduce self-blame and arrive at the fourth resolution, namely, a justification for not helping based on rejection of the victim.

Quite obviously, the model was derived from these data, along with data of other studies in the area. Needless to say, further work is being planned by the authors to systematically test the implications of the model.

## REFERENCES

**BERSCHEID, E., & WALSTER, E.** When does a harm-doer compensate a victim? *Journal of Personality and Social Psychology,* 1967, **6**, 435-441.

**BLACK, D. J., & REISS, A. J.** Studies in crime and law enforcement in major metropolitan areas. (Report submitted to the President's Commission on Law Enforcement and Administration of Justice.) Washington, D. C.: United States Government Printing Office, 1967.

**BRYAN, J. H., & TEST, M. A.** Models and helping: naturalistic studies in aiding behavior. *Journal of Personality and Social Psychology,* 1967, **6**, 400-407.

**DARLEY, J., & LATANÉ, B.** Bystander intervention in emergencies: diffusion of responsibility. *Journal of Personality and Social Psychology,* 1968, **8**, 377-383.

**LATANÉ, B., & DARLEY, J.** Group inhibition of bystander intervention in emergencies. *Journal of Personality and Social Psychology,* 1968, **10**, 215-221.

**LATANÉ, B., & RODIN, J.** A lady in distress: inhibiting effects of friends and strangers on bystander intervention. *Journal of Experimental Social Psychology,* 1969, 5, 189-202.

**LERNER, M. J., & SIMMONS, C. H.** Observer's reaction to the "innocent victim": compassion or rejection? *Journal of Personality and Social Psychology,* 1966, 4, 203-210.

**SCHACHTER, S.** The interaction of cognitive and physiological determinants of emotional state. In L. Berkowitz (Ed.), *Advances in Experimental Social Psychology,* Vol. 1, New York: Academic Press, 1964.

**SCHOPLER, J., & MATTHEWS, M. W.** The influence of the perceived causal locus of partner's dependence on the use of interpersonal power. *Journal of Personality and Social Psychology,* 1965, 4, 609-612.

**STOTLAND, E.** A theory and experiments in empathy. Paper presented at the American Psychological Association Meetings, 1966.

# RESPONSE TO COMPATRIOT AND FOREIGNER WHO SEEK ASSISTANCE[1]

ROY E. FELDMAN
*Massachusetts Institute of Technology*

5 experiments examined the differential treatment of foreign and compatriot strangers by Parisians, Athenians, and Bostonians in different social contexts. In each case Ss could have been helpful or antisocial toward the compatriot or foreign stranger. Generally, a social classification of the Ss was positively related to their helpfulness. The foreigner's use of the language of the city was positively related to the helpfulness received in Paris and Athens, but not in Boston. When differences occurred in the treatment of compatriots and foreigners, the compatriots were treated better in Paris and Boston, but the foreigners were treated better in Athens. Some results in Athens support ingroup-outgroup and role differential findings of Triandis, Vassiliou, and Nassiakou.

This is a report of five field experiments designed to explore the dimensions of cooperation toward foreigners and compatriots in three different sociocultural settings. The objectives of the experiment were, first, to discover the general nature of the response to foreigners and compatriots who asked for help in different sociocultural contexts. Triandis, Vassiliou, and Nassiakou (1967) have demonstrated the utility of the constructs ingroup and outgroup in interpreting cultural differences in the perception of a variety of Greek and American roles, among them the native-tourist role. They suggest that different cognitive definitions of the ingroup and the outgroup help account for differential behaviors toward members of respective ingroups and outgroups. The experiments described here add overt behavioral data to the empirical role differential method of Triandis et al. (1967). Inkeles and Levinson (1954) have noted that significant behavioral differences have not yet been established for large populations using relatively large samples. These experiments do this and take us beyond earlier conjectural approaches, permitting objective descriptions of some behavioral characteristics of Parisians, Athenians, and Bostonians along with social correlates of these behaviors. Since impressionistic observations are at least partially responsible for national stereotypes, the collection of data sheds some light on their validity.

The second objective was to examine the general concept of "cooperation" as a way of describing the interactions of foreigners with compatriots of different populations. The initial hypothesis was that "cooperation" could be operationally defined by a series of typical social encounters which could be intercorrelated. The third aim was to establish a logical base line for discussing the treatment of the foreigner in different sociocultural settings. This was done by examining the treatment of the compatriot under identical circumstances in each city. Since we only used three cities, it made more sense to emphasize the differential treatment of compatriots and foreigners *within* each city rather than across three cities. The fourth object was to determine the relationship between social class differences and the treatment of the foreigner within cities. The fifth aim was to determine the importance of situational factors such as whether the encounter was casual or structured, whether the foreigner spoke the language of the city or a foreign language, and how opportunity to cheat the foreigner influenced the encounter. Finally, the experiments permitted direct examination of the relevant behavior under standardized conditions to reduce the effects of personal bias and make measurement more precise. The basic paradigm consisted of controlled standard-

[1]In 1965 the investigation was supported by a Ford Foundation Grant in International Studies under the auspices of the Department of Social Relations, Harvard University. In 1966 the research was supported, in part, by a grant from the Comparative International Studies Program of the Harvard Department of Social Relations and by a grant from the Milton Fund of Harvard University. During 1965, the author was appointed a Travelling Fellow in Social Relations by the President and Fellows of Harvard College. The investigator acknowledges research assistance from the following: Noel Buffet, Marie-Agnèse Caillot, Jean Plas, Marie Ruffat, Pierre Bennoun, François Haymann, Alain Mocellin, M. et Mme. Gerard Courtieux, Panayiotis Skordakis, Maria Katsika, John Williamson, P. B. Doeringer, and Lucretia Petros Richardson. Special thanks for advice and criticism are due to Stanley Milgram, Jean-Pierre Gruère, Penny Hollander Feldman, Demetrius Bubas, Cornelius Passani, Robert Pages, George Vassiliou, Harry C. Triandis, David Armor, Alex Inkeles, and Victor Ernoult. Of course, none of these are responsible for any errors or faults in this investigation.

ized observations of behavioral episodes that were initiated via the intervention of a member of the experimental team.

## RESEARCH DESIGN

In carrying out experimental research on population characteristics, it was not possible to work with all-embracing characterizations. The study focused upon specific themes which have general social significance and can be approached by experimental means. Five experiments were devised in which subjects could show cooperative or uncooperative behavior in natural ongoing field situations. Paris and Athens were selected as the sample populations because data on stereotypes regarding treatment of the foreigner were available and contrasting, and Boston was added as a third population because it provided a convenient testing ground for developing the research design.

In varying the social context for each of the experiments, four structural factors can be used to differentiate the experimental encounters: whether the encounter was (*a*) casual or (*b*) occupational, and (*c*) whether there was the opportunity to cheat the stranger or (*d*) whether the stranger asked for a nonmonetary favor.

*Casual encounter.* In the first three experiments subjects were stopped under a reasonable pretext and confronted by a person under apparently chance and casual circumstances. The subject's behavior was free from any formal supervision and he was free to respond without the possibility of reproach or reprimand from anyone outside of the encounter. Subjects remained anonymous and might have anticipated thanks from the stranger for any obvious assistance rendered, but were unlikely to foresee any difficulty following unfriendly behavior on their part.

*Occupational encounter.* In the final two experiments all subjects were approached while performing their occupational duties. Moreover, that commercial service was performed on the premises occupied by the subject. Some of the subjects in Experiment IV were under formal supervision and all were subject to obvious legal sanctions if it were proved that they had violated the law. Freedom to respond was constrained by the institutional structure of the encounters with subjects. The probability of the subject's affective evaluation of a stranger influencing the interaction seemed less likely as the amount of formal structure surrounding the encounter increased.

Sampling considerations were (*a*) assuring the absence of experimenter bias in the selection of subjects, and (*b*) obtaining a representative sample within the city. The first three experiments drew the sample from people walking in the main shopping district of the city, with a relatively high density of people on the street. This prevented outside interference with the experimental paradigm. Socioeconomic classification was used as an independent variable in these experiments in order to ascertain the differential behavior of these classes. In Experiments IV and V the sample was randomly selected from specific occupational groups.

## EXPERIMENT I: ASKING FOR DIRECTIONS

The general objective was to find out how Parisians, Athenians, and Bostonians treated foreigners (compared with fellow citizens) who stopped them on the street and asked for information in both their native language and in the major language of the citizens being questioned.

**Experimenters** A native and a foreign couple were employed as experimenters in each city. The American experimenter couple in Boston also acted as the foreign experimenter couple in both Paris and Athens. The foreigners in Boston were French.

**Subjects** Excluded as subjects were all women, males judged to be under the age of 18 years, and foreign tourists who could be identified because they were carrying a camera or tourist guide book. All other people were permissible subjects.

**Apparatus** The FI-Cord 101 pocket tape recorder was used to tape episodes in Experiment I.

**Location** The three locations used in this study were Paris, Athens, and Boston. In each city the location chosen was a main shopping district: Boulevard Haussmann in Paris, Venizelou Street and Stadiou Street in Athens, and Washington Street in Boston. The locations were matched in terms of the heavy crowd of shoppers that was found in all three places. The target location was chosen to be about 1½ miles from the original location. In all three cities it was possible to go from the original location to the target location via underground public transportation.

**Procedure** A compatriot couple and a foreign couple operated at each location on different days. The primary objective of the subject selection procedure was to avoid letting the experimenters bias the outcome by selecting subjects on the basis of some systematic, idiosyncratic bias. Experimenters began each experimental "episode" by counting subjects coming toward them. Each subject about to walk past the experimenters was counted and the fourth one was the automatic and compulsory choice as the subject for the experiment. Because of both the density of people on the street and the fact that people walk at different speeds, it was not possible to determine

**[Table 2-12] Treatment of subjects in each city: Experiment I**

| Couple | Language used | |
|---|---|---|
| | *S*s asked in native language | *S*s asked in foreign language |
| Native *E*s | ½ *N* | 0 |
| Foreign *E*s | ¼ *N* | ¼ *N* |

NOTE.—For each location *N* = total sample of subjects.

who the fourth man would be before beginning the counting procedure. The fourth man was approached just as he was about to pass the experimenters, and the male experimenter asked: "Excuse me, sir, how do I get to Copley Square?" (In Paris, the target location was La Place des Ternes; in Athens, Plateia Kyriakou). Before asking for directions, the male experimenter activated a concealed tape recorder which continued for the duration of the episode.

In order to see if the socioeconomic variable was an important factor relative to the dependent variable (but without the possibility of obtaining relevant information from the subjects) each subject was classified into one of three categories according to the clothes he wore at the time of the experimental episode. For each city a determination was made of what constituted well-dressed, upper socioeconomic status (Class 1), poorly-dressed, "working clothes" (Class 3), or medium-dressed, between Class 1 and Class 3 (i.e., Class 2). For each city native social scientists helped in formulating the categories. Experimenters practiced classifying men on the street until there was almost no disagreement in classification. During the experimental episode, it was the female experimenter who was primarily responsible for this classification. When rare disagreements occurred, they were resolved by placing the subject in Class 2. Subjects who attempted to give directions by underground transportation were asked to give directions by foot. After the subject had finished directing the experimenters, a brief summary of the episode was dictated into the tape recorder. The summary included: (*a*) socioeconomic classification, (*b*) whether or not the subject gave directions, (*c*) whether or not directions, if given, were accurate, (*d*) any accent discernable to the native experimenters, (*e*) any other miscellaneous information of interest. After this was done, the subject-selection procedure began again.

[Table 2-12] illustrates the treatment of subjects for each city.

## EXPERIMENT II: DOING A FAVOR FOR A STRANGER

At major underground Metro stops, under a plausible pretext, male subjects were stopped and asked to mail a letter for a stranger who said that he was "waiting for a friend." Half of the letters were unstamped. The main measure was the proportion of people who agreed to do the favor. The letter was addressed to the experimenter's headquarters (cf., Milgram, Mann, & Harter, 1965).

**Experimenters** Two male experimenters were used in each city—a compatriot and a foreigner.

**Subjects** Criteria for subjects were the same as in Experiment I.

**Location** The sites of the experiments were the Washington Street Metropolitan Transit Association station in Boston, Chausee D'Antin and Havre Caumartin Metro stops in Paris, and the Omonia Square Metro stop in Athens.

**Procedure** Subject selection was the same as in Experiment I. Each time the experiment was begun, the fourth man to approach the experimenter was the automatic and compulsory choice of the experimenter as the next subject. Only on rare occasions was a man who appeared as a subject not selected. These instances occurred when the man was a severe cripple, or when he was carrying so much "baggage" that it was clear that he could not possibly take the letter in hand. Compatriot and foreign experimenters both addressed the subjects in the native language of the city involved.

As in Experiment I, each subject was classified into one of three categories according to the clothes he wore at the time of the experimental episode. Experimenters operated at each location at matched times of the day. After subject selection the subject was stopped and the experimenter said, "Excuse me, sir. I'm waiting for someone here. Could you please mail this letter for me?" If subjects said, "What?" or "Huh?" the question was repeated, or it was further explained that the experimenter was waiting for a friend, and wanted the letter to be mailed as soon as possible as it was an important letter. If the subject said, "Why don't you mail it yourself?" the experimenter repeated that he was waiting for someone where he was standing, and that he could not leave as he might miss his rendezvous.

Each letter was coded and the letters were addressed to the experimenter's headquarters, so that the ultimate disposition of each letter by each subject could finally be ascertained. For the half of the letters which were stamped at the foreign air mail rate on air mail envelopes, this was the full procedure. For the other half of the envelopes which were unstamped, the procedure was modified slightly: (*a*) If the subject did not notice that there was no stamp on the envelope, nothing was said; (*b*) for half of the subjects given unstamped envelopes (¼ of the total *N*) the experimenter looked for a stamp if the subject pointed out that there was no stamp on the envelope. The experimenter "failed" to find a stamp, and offered the subject cash for the amount of postage; (*c*) for the other half of the subjects given unstamped envelopes (¼ of the total *N*), the experimenters never spontaneously offered the cash amount of the postage. Cash was only given if the subject himself asked for it or suggested that possibility.

## EXPERIMENT III: FALSELY CLAIMING MONEY

In the first experiment (Asking for Directions), cooperativeness was exhibited by accurately telling a stranger how to get to his destination. In Experiment I, behavior was labeled "antisocial" only when it seemed quite clear that the strangers were *mis*-directed *with intent.* (See Results.) There was no material profit for the subject. We can only speculate as to the "satisfaction" attained by directing a strange compatriot or foreigner into a cul-de-sac. In Experiment III, the subject had the opportunity to materially profit by falsely claiming money from the stranger. The experimenter approached the subject and asked if he had just dropped a 5 franc note (or an appropriate Greek or United States currency). Actually, the subject had not dropped the money.

**Experimenters** Two male experimenters were used in each city, a compatriot and a foreigner (see [Table 2-13]).

The compatriot and the foreigner both addressed the subjects in the native language of the city involved. As in Experiment II, the accent of the foreigner was extremely obvious and the citizens of each country had no difficulty in establishing that the foreigner was indeed foreign, although his true identity was not always accurately perceived. This was determined through a number of interviews with the subjects after the termination of the experiment.

**Selection of Subjects** Subject selection was the same as in Experiments I and II. The fourth man coming toward the experimenter *and passing him* was the automatic and compulsory choice of the experimenter as the next subject. When the experimenter completed the experimental procedure with the subject, he recorded the outcome on tape or on a data sheet and began the same procedure to select a new subject.

**Location** The site of the experimental procedure was the same as in Experiment I.

**Procedure** As in Experiments I and II, each subject was classified into one of three categories according to the clothes he wore at the time of the experimental episode.

Two sets of experimenters operated at each location at matched times of the day. After subject selection, the experimenter came up from behind the subject and said, "Excuse me, sir. Did you just drop this dollar bill?" The subject's behavior and his positive or negative response were noted on the data sheet along with notation of his dress classification.

**[Table 2-13] Experimenters used in each city–Experiments II, III, and IV**

| City | *E*s | |
|---|---|---|
| | Compatriot | Foreigner |
| Paris | Frenchman | American |
| Athens | Greek | American |
| Boston | American | Frenchman |

**[Table 2-14] Amount of money used in each city: Experiment III**

| City | Money used | |
|---|---|---|
| | Lower amount | Higher amount |
| Paris | 5 F[a] | 10 F |
| Athens | 20 DR[b] | 50 DR |
| Boston | $1 | $5 |

[a]5 francs = $1 (1966).
[b]20 drachmas = $.66 (1966).

For half of the subjects in each city (total $N = 160$ in each city) the approximate equivalent at the current exchange rate of $1 was offered. For the other half of the subjects, the note of the next highest denomination was used (see [Table 2-14]).

A set of interviews was obtained with some "typical" subjects *following* the experimental procedure. No subjects knew that they were involved in an experimental episode, and none of the interviewed subjects knew that they had been interviewed. The interview procedure was conducted so as to obtain the subject's perceptions of the experimental episode which had just transpired about a quarter minute before. The interviewer walked along the crowded street, and positioned himself to be walking beside the subject just as the experimental episode terminated. When a subject took the money from an experimenter and walked on, the interviewer, who was then walking next to the subject, turned to the subject and said, "Hey, is that guy giving money away?" Almost all subjects approached in this manner then proceeded to give their version of the experimental episode. The interviewer, after listening to the subject's story and asking a few probe questions, walked away and recorded the conversation to the best of his recollection.

## EXPERIMENT IV: CASHIER EXPERIMENT

In making a variety of small purchases, a few "pennies" over the actual cost were added to the payment by the experimenter, who then slowly left the store. The amount of overpayment actually was from one-fourth to one-third of the total purchase. The behavior of the cashier in keeping or returning the overpayment to the experimenter was recorded. In Experiment III (Falsely Claiming Money) above, the subject had to overtly *take* the money which did not belong to him. In this situation, he only had to tacitly accept the overpayment.

**Experimenters** Two male experimenters were used in each city, a compatriot and a foreigner. The compatriot and foreigner both addressed the sales person and cashier in the native language of the city involved.

**Selection of Shops and Subjects** One necessity in this experiment was to make a relatively large number of purchases on a relatively small budget. Pastry shops were prevalent in large numbers in all three cities and in all sections of each city, and relatively good guides were available to compile complete lists of *all* the pastry shops in each city from which random samples were drawn. Details of sampling are given in Feldman (1967). Thirty-nine percent of all shops were sampled in Paris, 31% in Athens, and 18% in Boston.

**Procedure** The experimenter entered the shops selected in the random sample and requested an item or items which cost approximately $.20. Where the price was not known, an item (or items) was chosen which the experimenter estimated to cost about $.20. After being told the total cost of his purchase, the experimenter paid that amount *plus* about 25% above the total cost of the purchase. For the total cost of $.20, for example, the experimenter paid the cashier 5 nickles ($.25). He then gave the cashier a chance to count the money and slowly began to walk out of the pastry shop. The behavior of the cashier was observed and recorded as soon as the experimenter had left the premises. The main measure was whether or not the cashier returned the overpayment.

## EXPERIMENT V: TAXICAB CHARGES

Some taxicab drivers have a reputation for taking passengers to the destination via indirect and longer routes, and for overcharging people who appear to be unfamiliar with the vicinity. This study investigated whether or not compatriots and foreigners were charged the same fare over identical routes.

**Experimenters** Two male experimenters were used in each city, a compatriot and a foreigner (see [Table 2-14]).

**Subjects** Cabs were "hailed" in different parts of the city. A number of identical cab drivers were used as subjects for both the compatriot and the foreigner. Sixty rides were taken in Paris, 42 in Athens, and 44 in Boston; one-half by compatriot and one-half by foreigner.

**Location** Most of the taxi rides in each of the three cities were taken from one public place to another. Many locations were matched in each city, for example, railroad stations, the stock exchange, a post office, an observatory, a hospital, and a sports stadium. A few addresses of private residences were also used. A complete listing for each city is presented in Feldman (1967). The beginning points for each of the individual rides taken by compatriot and foreigner were always identical, but there were occasions when the foreigner was not taken to the destination requested.

**Procedure** Compatriot and foreigner did the experiment at the same time of day, and within minutes of each other in each of the three cities. The compatriot addressed the taxicab driver in his native language. The foreigner did not *directly* ask for the location to which he was going. Rather, he handed the taxi driver a slip of paper with his destination written on it in script by a compatriot and read the destination location from the slip of paper. First, one of the two experimenters would hail a cab, and after he had left the starting location, the other experimenter would hail another cab to the same location. At times it was possible for the first of the experimenters to hail the cab which had just deposited the second experimenter. Thus it was possible for the compatriot experimenter to hear a taxicab driver's remarks about the foreign experimenter who was the previous rider in that taxi. The main dependent variable was the cost of the ride to the compatriot as compared to the foreigner.

## EXPERIMENTAL FINDINGS

### Results of Experiment I: Asking for Directions

*Behavior toward foreigners versus compatriots* Both the Parisian and Athenian samples gave help more often at the request of fellow citizens than at the request of foreigners. Use of native versus a foreign language was a contributing factor (see [Table 2-15]). In Boston there was no large difference between the treatment of the American compatriots and the French foreigners. Asking for directions in French made little difference in the way Bostonians treated Frenchmen.

Forty-five percent of the Parisian sample either did not give directions at the request of the foreigners, or directed them the wrong way if they did stop, compared with 24% who refused to stop at the request of fellow citizens. Thirty-six percent of the Athenian sample either did not give directions at the request of the foreigners, or gave them false directions, compared with 32% toward fellow citizens. Twenty percent of the Bostonian sample did not give directions at the request of the foreigners or sent them the wrong way. This was about the same as the treatment of the American compatriots (21%). The Bostonians were more helpful in terms of giving directions and accuracy toward foreigners (80%) than either the Athenian (64%; $p < .001$) or the Parisian samples (55%; $p < .001$). The Parisian and Athenian samples differed by 9% ($.10 < p < .20$).

*Accuracy of directions* In Paris, the compatriots were never given inaccurate directions, but the foreigners were directed the wrong way 10% of the time ($p < .001$). The misunderstanding of the foreigner was ruled out for the case of the foreigner using the native language of the city because all responses were tape-recorded and the subjects clearly *repeated* the name of the target location. Bostonians gave equally accurate directions to compatriots versus foreigners (96% versus 95%). The Athenians gave more accurate directions to foreigners than compatriots but the null hypothesis is not rejected ($.10 < p < .20$).

*Socioeconomic classification* Giving help in the Parisian sample was positively related to higher socioeconomic classification ($p < .001$). This was also true

**[Table 2-15] Information given to foreigner in each city**

| Group | Information given | | | |
|---|---|---|---|---|
| | Did not give directions to compatriots | Did not give directions to foreigners | Gave false directions to compatriots | Gave false directions to foreigners |
| Paris[a] | 24 | 35 | 0 | 10 |
| In French | | 31 | | |
| In English | | 40 | | |
| Athens[b] | 26 | 33 | 6 | 3 |
| In Greek | | 29 | | |
| In English | | 37 | | |
| Boston[c] | 17 | 15 | 4 | 5 |
| In English | | 13 | | |
| In French | | 17 | | |

NOTE.—The foreigners asked for directions in the language of the city and in a foreign language. Figures given are in percentages.
[a] $N = 401$.
[b] $N = 551$.
[c] $N = 422$.

for the Athenian sample ($p < .01$). The null hypothesis could not be rejected for the Boston sample ($.05 < p < .10$).

*Observations* The experiment received considerably more attention in Athens than in either Paris or Boston. In Paris and Boston the experiment proceeded with relative anonymity. In Athens, sales personnel in the stores observed experimenters asking for directions and on one occasion, a saleslady came out to the street and told a subject not to respond because the experimenters had already asked someone else. The subject responded, but the experimenters had to move from Stadiou Street to Venizelou Street. In all three cities, the foreigners were sometimes asked where they were from, but only in Athens was the compatriot asked this. One subject maintained that he was a countryman of the Greek compatriot experimenter (it was not true) and offered the experimenter five drachmas to go where he wanted by bus.

**Results of Experiment II: Doing a Favor for a Stranger** The main measure here was whether or not people would take the letter from the foreigner or compatriot stranger. Except for the socioeconomic dress classification of the subjects, other measures did not prove especially interesting. Virtually all of the letters accepted by the men in the subway were mailed. In general, more people took the stamped envelopes than the envelopes without stamps. The only exception to this was the treatment of the foreigner in Athens where there was no difference [Table 2-16]

*Base line: treatment of the compatriot* The treatment of the compatriot in Boston and Paris did not differ significantly, varying between 32% and 35%, but the treatment of the compatriot for both cities differed significantly from the treatment in Athens ($p < .001$), where 93% of the Athenian sample refused to mail a letter for a fellow-Greek.

*Treatment of the foreigner* Although compatriots were treated about the same in Boston and Paris, this was clearly not so for the foreigners we have studied. The Parisians treated the American foreigner significantly better than the total sample of Bostonians treated the French foreigner, helping 69% versus 51%

**[Table 2-16] Percentage refusing to mail a letter for a compatriot versus a foreigner**

| City | Refusals to compatriot | | Refusals to foreigner | |
|---|---|---|---|---|
| | With stamped letter | With unstamped letter | With stamped letter | With unstamped letter |
| Paris | 32[a] | 38[b] | 12[a] | 44[b] |
| | (73) | (81) | (57) | (89) |
| Athens | 88[c] | 97[d] | 52[c] | 51[d] |
| | (33) | (36) | (35) | (33) |
| Boston | 15[e] | 44[f] | 25[e] | 60[f] |
| | (59) | (90) | (55) | (125) |

NOTE.—Total $N = 765$ (*n's* in parentheses).
[a] $\chi^2 = 5.82, p < .05$. These cells differ from the findings in the other experiments.
[b] $\chi^2 = .33$, *ns.*
[c] $\chi^2 = 7.21, p < .01$.
[d] $\chi^2 = 14.30, p < .001$.
[e] $\chi^2 = .84$, *ns.*
[f] $\chi^2 = 4.84, p < .05$.

($p < .01$). This is clearly at odds with part of the American stereotype of the Parisian's behavior toward the American. In fact, the American received exactly the same level of cooperation in Boston and in Paris. The Frenchman, on the other hand, was refused help by 36% of his compatriots, but by 49% of the Bostonians. Bostonians and Athenians did not treat the foreigner significantly differently, not helping him 49% and 52% of the time. The treatment of the foreigner in Paris was significantly better than the treatment of the foreigner in Athens ($p < .01$).

*Paris* Summing across all 300 subjects studied in Paris during Experiment II, there was no significant difference in the treatment of compatriot and foreigner, but for subclasses of these subjects in Paris, and for subparts of the experiment, differences did appear. In the experimental paradigm in which Parisians were asked to mail a letter *which was stamped,* the American foreigner actually received better treatment than the French compatriot ($p < .05$; see [Table 2-16]). As the amount of cooperation requested was increased, however, from just mailing a letter to providing a stamp or buying one, the amount of cooperation exhibited toward the American decreased considerably, and at this level there was no significant difference between the treatment of the American foreigner and the French compatriot (see [Table 2-16]). The proportion of those who refused to help the American foreigner increased from 12% when aid was to mail a stamped letter to 44% when asked to mail an unstamped letter. This 44% refusal rate is exactly the same as the American is accorded under the same circumstances in Boston (see [Table 2-16]). Although no difference was reported between the treatment of the compatriot and the American foreigner who asked Parisians to mail letters without stamps, there was an important difference which suggests that the Frenchman was better received than the American when the demand of the stranger was increased. Only 12% (6/50) took money from their compatriot to mail the unstamped letter, but 44% (22/50) took money from the foreigner. In the condition in which the subject himself had to ask for money in order to receive it 36% of the Parisians (9/25) asked the American foreigner for the money, but none of the Parisians asked his compatriot for the money.

*Socioeconomic classification* As in Experiment I, prosocial behavior declined with lower socioeconomic dress classification ($p < .01$; see [Table 2-17]). Parisians in the highest socioeconomic classification treated the American foreigner better than any other

**[Table 2-17] Treatment of foreigner and compatriot by socioeconomic dress class of subjects: Paris**

| Give help | Class | | |
|---|---|---|---|
| | 1 | 2 | 3 |
| **Foreigner with stamped letters[a]** | | | |
| Yes | 94 | 88 | 50 |
| **Foreigner with unstamped letters[b]** | | | |
| Yes | 66 | 29 | 30 |
| **Compatriot with stamped letters[c]** | | | |
| Yes | 76 | 61 | 65 |
| **Compatriot with unstamped letters[d]** | | | |
| Yes | 52 | 76 | 53 |

NOTE.—In percentages.
[a] $n = 56$.
[b] $n = 89$.
[c] $n = 74$.
[d] $n = 81$.

subsample in this entire experiment, with only 6% of these subjects refusing to help the foreigner when asked to mail a stamped letter. When we look at the lowest class, however, we find that the refusal rate has gone up to 50%. In the experiment without stamps the rate of refusal rose from 34% for Class 1 to 71% and 70% for Classes 2 and 3, respectively. These class differences relative to the treatment of the foreigner are not duplicated with regard to the treatment of the compatriot. Here the relationship appears more complex, particularly in the condition without stamps, where a curvilinear relationship appears. The middle-class subjects treat their compatriot considerably better than the upper or lower classification (see [Table 2-17]). The question of money rarely arose in the case of the French compatriot without stamped letters.

*Athens* The compatriot is treated overwhelmingly worse in Athens than in either Paris or Boston. The foreigner, on the other hand, was treated about the same as the foreigner in Boston, but significantly worse than the foreigner in Paris. In spite of the fact that the foreigner is treated worse here than in Paris or Boston, the Athenians treated a foreigner better than a compatriot. Across all subjects in this experiment in Athens ($N = 137$), 52% of the Athenian subjects refused to help the foreigner, but 93% of the Athenian subjects refused to help a compatriot ($p < .001$). This finding remained in the paradigm with stamps ($p < .01$) and without stamps ($p < .001$; see [Table 2-16]). Since nearly all the Athenians refused

**[Table 2-18] Treatment of foreigner by socioeconomic dress class of subjects: Athens**

| Give help | Class 1 | Class 2 | Class 3 |
|---|---|---|---|
| With stamped letters[a] | | | |
| Yes | 40 | 57 | 25 |
| With unstamped letters[b] | | | |
| Yes | 20 | 48 | 71 |

NOTE.–In percentages.
[a] $n = 35$.
[b] $n = 33$.

to help their compatriot in this experiment, it is not possible to discriminate their behavior as a function of class. [Table 2-18] suggests that under the condition of highest demand the lowest class may be the most helpful toward the foreigner, but the very small number of subjects who fell into cells of Class 1 and Class 3 in this condition prevent us from meaningfully resorting to tests of significance. In this condition, the Greek compatriot was never able to get to the point of offering money to the subjects for the unstamped letter. Refusals were quite blunt and adamant. Fifty-six percent took money from the American foreigner when asked to mail the letter.

*Boston* As noted above, the Bostonians ($N = 328$) treated the French foreigner significantly worse than the American compatriot ($p < .01$), helping 51% and 68% of the time, respectively. This was true for the condition without stamps ($p < .05$; see [Table 2-16]). For the condition with stamps the foreigner is treated worse by 10% of the Bostonians, but the difference was not statistically significant.

The association between behavior and dress classification of the Bostonians was not statistically significant, but it is clear that the Bostonians in the lowest class accorded the French foreigner the worst treatment. In the paradigm with stamps, 18% of the subjects in Class 1 refused to help. Twenty-two percent of the subjects in Class 2 refused and 45% of the subjects in Class 3 refused. In the condition without stamps, 59% of the Class 1 subjects refused, 56% of the Class 2 subjects refused, and 70% of the Class 3 subjects refused. For all paradigms and five of the six class comparisons the Bostonians treated the French foreigner worse than the American compatriot (see [Table 2-19]).

**[Table 2-19] Treatment of foreigner and compatriot by socioeconomic dress class of subjects: Boston**

| Give help | Class 1 | Class 2 | Class 3 |
|---|---|---|---|
| Foreigner with stamped letters[a] | | | |
| Yes | 82 | 78 | 55 |
| Foreigner with unstamped letters[b] | | | |
| Yes | 41 | 44 | 30 |
| Compatriot with stamped letters[c] | | | |
| Yes | 81 | 92 | 86 |
| Compatriot with unstamped letters[d] | | | |
| Yes | 60 | 56 | 52 |

NOTE.–In percentages.
[a] $n = 55$.
[b] $n = 125$.
[c] $n = 59$.
[d] $n = 90$.

**Results of Experiment III: Falsely Claiming Money** The main dependent variable in Experiment III was whether the subject would falsely claim money from a stranger. Interviews following the experimental procedure indicated that the desired social context was established. This experiment did not establish differences between the treatment of the compatriot and foreigner within cities, but did show differences between cities and between socioeconomic classifications within cities. Since there were only 160 subjects in each city sample for this experiment, and since the actual number of subjects who falsely claimed money never exceeded 16% in any city, the actual number of subjects who falsely claimed money was quite low, too low to meaningfully compare the treatment of compatriot versus foreigner within cities.

The best treatment accorded a stranger was in Paris where 6% of the Parisians falsely took money from their compatriot or the American foreigner. The next best treatment accorded the stranger was in Athens where 13% took money falsely, and the worst treatment was shown the stranger in Boston, where 17% of the people kept the money. Such differences should not be expected to occur by chance ($p < .05$).

Over all subjects, conditions, and cities there was a trend for the proportion of takers to decrease as the amount of money increased. However, the trend is only large enough to amount to a suggestion that needs further testing (see [Table 2-20]). An alternative hypothesis still compatible with the data is that people are less likely to falsely claim larger amounts of money from foreigners than from compatriots. A larger quota of subjects who falsely claim the money must be obtained before this can be determined. A comparison of the lower of the two amounts of money offered to the men in each city is interesting. Five percent of the Parisian sample took 5 francs from the American foreigner. Fifteen percent of the Athenian sample took 20 drachmas from the American foreigner. Twenty-seven percent of the Bostonian sample took $1 from the French foreigner.

As in Experiment II, the American stereotype of the Parisian treating the American foreigner unfairly was not confirmed in comparison with how the Bostonian treated a fellow-citizen under the same circumstances (see [Table 2-20]). The Bostonians falsely took the money from 14% of their American compatriots, but the Parisians falsely took the money 2.5% of the time from the American foreigner. Although differences were not large, the Parisian population was the only one which treated the foreigner better than the compatriot.

*Socioeconomic classification* The lower the class, the higher the proportion of "takers." For the treatment of foreigners in each city, in spite of the *very small* absolute number of takers in the experiment, this relationship is clear (see [Table 2-21]). This tendency of the lower-class people to take the money which did not belong to them also appeared in the treatment of the compatriot (see [Table 2-21]).

**Results of Experiment IV: Cashier Study** No differences were found between the treatment of compatriot and foreigner in Paris, Athens, or Boston. In Paris, 54% kept the money from both. In Athens, the overpayment was not returned to the compatriot 50% and the foreigner 51% of the time. In Boston, the money was kept 38% from the compatriot and 27% from the foreigner.

**[Table 2-20] Proportion of people falsely claiming money: summary**

| *E* | Lower amount[a] | Higher amount[b] |
|---|---|---|
| Paris (6% kept money) | | |
| American foreigner | 5 (40) | 0 (40) |
| French compatriot | 8 (40) | 10 (40) |
| Athens (13% kept money) | | |
| American foreigner | 15 (40) | 12 (40) |
| Greek compatriot | 12 (40) | 10 (39) |
| Boston (17% kept money) | | |
| French foreigner | 27 (41) | 11 (36) |
| American compatriot | 10 (40) | 18 (40) |

NOTE.–The observed frequencies of people keeping the money in the three cities differed from the expected frequencies: $\chi^2 = 7.15$, $p < .05$ ($n$'s in parentheses). Figures in percentages.

[a]Paris: 5 francs; Athens: 20 drachmas; Boston: 1 dollar.

[b]Paris: 10 francs; Athens: 50 drachmas; Boston: 5 dollars.

**[Table 2-21] Percentage falsely claiming money: socioeconomic dress classification of subjects**

| City | Class 1 | Class 2 | Class 3 |
|---|---|---|---|
| Falsely claiming money from foreigners | | | |
| Paris | 2 (44) | 0 (29) | 14 (7) |
| Athens | 12 (42) | 13 (30) | 25 (8) |
| Boston | 7 (29) | 21 (38) | 50 (10) |
| Falsely claiming money from compatriots | | | |
| Paris | 3 (36) | 10 (29) | 20 (15) |
| Athens | 0 (14) | 11 (54) | 28 (11) |
| Boston | 13 (23) | 16 (31) | 12 (26) |

NOTE.–$n$'s in parentheses.

**Results of Experiment V: Taxi Charges** In neither Boston nor Athens was the foreigner overcharged significantly more often than the compatriot, and the compatriot never believed that he was ever taken by any other than the most direct route known to the driver. In Paris, however, the American foreigner *was* overcharged significantly more often than the French compatriot, in a variety of ingenious ways ($p < .02$; see [Table 2-22]). The cases of equal fares were divided equally between "more" and "less" categories.

The compatriot in Paris was generally taken by the most direct route to his destination. The foreigners in both Athens and Boston believed that they were always taken by a direct route, and that the driver did not attempt to take advantage of them. This was confirmed by a number of discussions with the drivers. The taxi drivers in Paris had a wide variety of techniques for increasing the fare to the American foreigner. Some drivers gave the wrong change and suggested the amount the tip ought to be (eliminating the possibility that they were including the tip in the total fare). Some drivers began the ride with the meter reading continuing from their previous fare. Occasionally drivers hung a rag over the meter after the foreigner entered the taxi and said that the meter was

**[Table 2-22] Taxi charges across cities: charges to the foreigner compared with the compatriot**

| City | Payment of the foreigner | | |
|---|---|---|---|
| | More | Equal | Less |
| Paris | 18* | 7 | 5 |
| Athens | 10 | 2 | 9 |
| Boston | 9 | 10 | 3 |

NOTE.–No significant differences were found between the treatment of the compatriot and the foreigner in Boston or Athens.
*$p < .02$.

not working. Some drivers misread meters which were outside of the cab out of the direct view of the passenger. One driver drove the foreigner kilometers out of the way and abandoned the passenger a number of kilometers away from the destination written on the slip of paper handed to him. The driver incorrectly insisted that this was the correct location, pointing to a nonexistent sign for confirmation.

A number of drivers in Boston expressed verbal hostility toward Frenchmen in conversation with the American compatriot; one even said that he would "take" (cheat) any Frenchman riding in his cab. As a matter of fact, however, this Boston driver was entirely honest with the French rider, took him by the most direct route and charged him the correct fare.

## DISCUSSION AND CONCLUSIONS

Data on over 3,000 subjects in the five field experiments revealed consistent differences in the treatment of compatriots and foreigners in different sociocultural environments. In general, when a difference was observed, the Athenians treated the foreigner better than the compatriot, but Parisians and Bostonians treated compatriots better than foreigners. We could, however, also differentiate socioeconomic correlates within the cities studied. This means that we can do considerably better than speak of Parisians, Athenians, and Bostonians in sweeping terms. We can make meaningful statements about subgroups of these populations.

**Dimensions of Cooperation** We can also elaborate on the concept of cooperation, which the five experiments were intended to operationally define. It would appear that cooperation is a multidimensional concept. One dimension is related to the role of the subject from whom cooperative behavior is solicited. Is the subject approached in a casual situation or in an occupational context? The first three experiments were designed to measure cooperation in casual encounters and the last two to measure it in occupational encounters, where, presumably, modes of response were more narrowly circumscribed by role. A second dimension is related to the nature of the cooperative act required of the subject. Did the experimenter seek a favor from the subject or simply a discrimination between right and wrong? The first two experiments involved "doing a favor" for a stranger, while the last three involved a choice between honesty and "cheating." The first two were personal nonfinancial transactions, while the last three involved money and were, therefore, to some extent less personal.

Thus far, the nature of the cooperative act is a better indicator of the conditions under which populations discriminate between compatriot and foreigner than is the fact that the encounter is casual or occupational. Across the five experiments in each of the three cities, the casual encounter condition discriminated between compatriot and foreigner 33% of the time; and occupational encounter, 17%. The difference in discrimination related to whether the subject was asked to perform a personal favor or to choose between right and wrong was larger. The "doing a favor for a stranger" experiments discriminated 50% of the time, while the honesty experiments discriminated in only 11% of the cases. Subjects were more likely to treat compatriots different from foreigners when they were asked to provide a personal service than when they were required to enter into a monetary transaction.

**Ingroup-Outgroup Conceptualization** We have indicated above that situational factors seem to affect the differential treatment of foreigners and compatriots in different sociocultural environments. Attitudinal factors prior to and operating within the experimental encounter also seem important. Our data provide some behavioral confirmation for the role differential method of Triandis et al. (1967) and an extension of their ingroup-outgroup conceptualization from role perception to overt social behavior.

*Athens* Triandis et al. (1967) defined the ingroup in Greece to include: family, friends, friends of friends, and tourists, "who are treated as members of the ingroup because of an age-long hospitality norm which is an important aspect of the culture." Our data tend to substantiate this definition and to confirm a second hypothesis that members of the upper class have a more inclusive definition of the ingroup than members of the middle and lower social classes.

In our experiments, when Athenians discriminated between strange compatriot and foreigner, the Greek compatriot received worse treatment than the foreigner. Data on the role differential (Triandis, et al.,

1967) indicated that suspicion and hostility characterize behavior toward outgroup members, while cooperation and concern over welfare characterize behavior toward ingroup members. The hostility expressed by Athenians toward Greek compatriots thus suggests that native strangers were defined as outgroup members while foreign tourists, in line with the hypothesis of Triandis et al., were defined as (temporary) members of the ingroup.

Field reports provide supporting observations regarding outgroup discrimination in Greece. Lee (1953) noted that Greek cooperation is obtained by personal loyalty and that Greeks do not respond to an impersonal plea from another Greek. Sanders (1962) has asserted "that the Greeks cooperate only in a crisis." Among the historical events likely to leave behind suspicion and fratricidal hostility was the mass removal of over 23,000 Greek children from the country during the Greek Civil War of 1944-1949 (cf. Report of United Nations Balkan Commission, Dec., 1948, in O'Ballance, 1966). Arnhoff, Leon, and Lorge (1964) found that 78% of a Greek student sample believed that "old people are suspicious of others," but only 38% of United States college students believed this ($p < .01$). Triandis (1965) also found that Greeks claimed to trust Americans even more than Americans see themselves as being trusted by Greeks.

In Experiment I, upper-class Greeks were more often helpful to the foreigner than were lower-class Greeks. There was also a tendency in this direction in Experiment III. In Experiment II (mailing a letter for an American foreigner), however, there was a tendency for the lower-class subjects to give better treatment than the upper-class subjects. The strong rural tradition of hospitality to the foreigner may help explain this finding. If it is true that lower-class subjects in Experiment II were closer to rural origins than middle- or upper-class subjects, we might have a plausible explanation of the preferential treatment by the lower-class Athenian subjects. Subjects in this experiment were specifically asked to go out of their way to assist the foreigner. This was not true in Experiment I, where saying a few words accommodated the foreigner, and was not true of Experiments III, IV, or V, where the subjects were presented with the opportunity for material gain if they took advantage of the American foreigner.

*Paris* Role differential data are not available for a Parisian sample. Pitts (1957) has suggested that the Frenchman is likely to snub an outgroup member whenever possible to demonstrate his superiority over that person, but Pitts' suggested definition of the ingroup is generally restricted to the family circle, and data reported here imply that there is a broader definition of the ingroup, at least for the Parisian upper class. The restricted definition of the ingroup may hold, however, for some subgroups of the Parisian population. Examples would include taxi drivers and lower-class men.

Antisocial behavior toward Americans is not an all-pervasive phenomenon in Paris. It is more manifest under some types of situations than others. In Experiments II (Doing a Favor for a Stranger) and III (Falsely Claiming Money) the Parisians treated the American foreigner better than the Americans in Boston treated a Frenchman. On the other hand, when Americans in Paris have occasion to ask for directions and to use taxis, they are likely to encounter uncooperative behavior and to be cheated by the taxi drivers of Paris. Although these two social contexts are typical of encounters which some American foreigners are likely to have with Frenchmen, interactions in other social contexts and comparisons with how the American is treated in Boston warn us against sweeping generalizations about "the Frenchman."

*Boston* Defining the ingroup for Bostonians as "people like me" (Triandis et al., 1967) helps explain some of the discrimination against the French foreigner. The experimenters were upper-middle-class in appearance and were treated better by subjects in the upper class than in Class 2 or 3. Varying the appearance of the experimenters would help determine the effects of status disparity between the subjects and the stranger who approached them upon the treatment of the stranger. By doing this we could specify the range of the "people like me" category for different social classes, and determine how status disparity has contributed to our finding and the suggestion of Triandis et al. (1967) that upper classes in general have a more inclusive definition of the ingroup. The fact that a language other than English was the mother tongue of many Bostonians may have helped label the French-speaking foreigner as someone "like me." Throughout Experiment I it was observed that many of the Bostonians had foreign accents. This may account for the special consideration showed to the Frenchman who asked for directions in French.

**Other Considerations** Although the correlation of the subjects' behavior with socioeconomic classification was an important finding in this series of experiments, the socioeconomic classification is still a mask for more specific antecedent variables. By identifying populations grossly by the city they live in and by socioeconomic classification or occupational group, we are delimiting some antecedent contingencies presumably encountered by our subjects earlier in their lives. In future research we wish to identify the occasions on which learning of ingroup-outgroup discriminations take place, and then to isolate specific learning patterns which are correlated with differential treatment of compatriot versus foreign strangers. One way to make this easier would be to observe the behavior of people who had a more homogeneous background than the subjects we observed.

## REFERENCES

**ARNHOFF, F. N., LEON, H. F., & LORGE, I.** Cross cultural acceptance of stereotypes toward the aging. *Journal of Social Psychology,* 1964, **63**, 41-58.

**FELDMAN, R. E.** The response to compatriot and foreigner who seek assistance: Field experiments in Paris, Athens, and Boston. Unpublished doctoral dissertation, Harvard University, 1967.

**INKELES, A., & LEVINSON, D. J.** National character: The study of modal personality and sociocultural system. In G. Lindzey (Ed.), *Handbook of social psychology.* Vol. 2. Cambridge: Addison-Wesley, 1954.

**LEE, D.** Greece. In M. Mead (Ed.), *Cultural pattern and technical change.* Paris: UNESCO, 1953. (Republished: New York, New American Library, 1958.)

**MILGRAM, S., MANN, L., & HARTER, S.** The lost letter technique: A tool of social research. *Public Opinion Quarterly,* 1965, **29**, 437-438.

**O'BALLANCE, E.** *The Greek civil war, 1944-1949.* New York: Prager, 1966.

**PITTS, J. R.** The bourgeois family and French economic retardation. Unpublished doctoral dissertation, Harvard University, 1957.

**SANDERS, I. T.** *Rainbow in the rock: The people of rural Greece.* Cambridge: Harvard University Press, 1962.

**TRIANDIS, H. C.** An exploratory study of barriers to cooperation between persons belonging to different cultures. University of Illinois, August, 1965. (Mimeo)

**TRIANDIS, H. C., VASSILIOU, V., & NASSIAKOU, M.** Some cross-cultural studies of subjective culture. Technical Report No. 45, 1967, Group Effectiveness Research Laboratory, University of Illinois, Office of Naval Research.

# CHAPTER THREE

# SOCIAL INFLUENCE

Social influence is a broad and somewhat vaguely defined area of social psychological research concerned with how one can change others' behavior or attitudes. The studies presented in this chapter are concerned with behavior changes in the face of social influence. The studies cover a wide range of behavior: from relationships between nurses and physicians to behavior while driving, and from picketing to signing petitions. All these experiments have at least one thing in common. They isolate circumstances in which one person can get others to behave as he wants.

The study by Hofling, Brotzman, Dalrymple, Graves, and Pierce (page 60) shows how persons may be influenced by the roles they play in society. In this experiment, the relationship between doctor and nurse, with respect to obeying essentially illicit orders, is examined. The findings of this research show the power certain persons have over others' behavior. Milgram (1965) has examined this type of influence over punitive behavior in a series of laboratory experiments. The results of his experiments show that persons will comply with the orders of an experimenter, even though such compliance could harm another individual. Thus, both field and laboratory experiments confirm each other's findings. It appears to be fairly easy to order an individual to harm another person. Conceivably, he perceives (or rationalizes) the responsibility as being that of the authority figure and *not* his own.

Clearly, the concern about the type of obedience that occurred in Nazi Germany motivated Milgram in his research. His research and that of Hofling et al. examine behavior which is excused by saying, "I was only following orders." There is strong evidence that Nazis are not the only ones who can succumb to this type of logic. Soldiers in all wars have been accused of committing atrocities and have justified their behavior with this reasoning. The understanding of obedience is obviously important. However, the experiment by Hofling et al. is the only field study of this nature to date. The place of obedience in society is certainly worthy of more study.

Turning to acts which are not as deleterious to the health of others, it has been found that higher-status persons can influence others to perform harmless but unpleasant tasks. For example, Pepitone and Wallace (1955) asked subjects to sort garbage for a variety of reasons. Regardless of the implausibility of the reasons given, the subjects performed the task without hostility towards the experimenter. The authors point out that the subjects felt that the experimenter had a justifiable reason for asking them to perform this unpleasant task, regardless of what they were told. From our teaching experience, the authors feel that the same relationship may exist between teacher and student.

One variable that has been neglected in the area of social influence is the role of the uniform in eliciting obedience. Bickman (1971) has evidence from a field experiment which indicates that a person in a private guard's uniform can persuade passersby to pick up papers in the street or to give money to a stranger. Even in our relatively nonmilitaristic tradition, the uniform has power to influence. This point is also discussed in the chapter on status.

Two other points raised by the research of Hofling et al. relate to other studies in this book. Compliance is not always a matter of conscious conflict followed by choice. We are sometimes influenced by others *without* our awareness. The study by Barch, Trumbo and Nangle (page 68) shows that others can influence us in small ways in our everyday behavior. People should become more sensitive to things that affect their behavior. In that way, they may be able to have more control over their own behavior.

A second point that Hofling et al. raised is our inability to predict our own behavior. As pointed out in the introduction to this book, this is a theme that runs through most of the research in this book. The discrepancy between attitudes or beliefs and the way we actually behave is usually large. In a number of experiments dealing with helping behavior, social status, and prejudice, we find this discrepancy. Some of the reasons for this finding are presented in a chapter that specifically deals with this problem: attitudes and behavior.

The study by Freedman and Fraser (page 71) examines compliance in a unique way. Can we induce people to perform certain acts through a series of small requests rather than one large request? Thus getting our "foot in the door," will we be able to get the whole door open? In contrast to the studies already presented, Freedman and Fraser attempted to get their subjects to perform some socially useful task. The authors contended that their research may produce a change in the self image of the subject; i.e., he now sees himself as a person who will do things for others. If so, this certainly seems a way to increase the helping behavior of others.

Research by Helson, Blake, and Mouton (page 78) uses the petition as a means of investigating conformity. Other research dealing with petitions has found that the number of signatures, the manner in which the subject is asked (Blake, Mouton, & Hain, 1965), and who is doing the asking are all important in determining whether a person will sign the petition. In addition, Bickman has found that the willingness of people to sign a petition is affected by the status of those who have previously signed it. Thus, the petition can be used as a nonreactive method to measure people's attitudes toward certain groups. The study by Helson et al. indicates that modeling may be a potent force affecting petition-signing.

From a practical point of view, for demonstrating conformity for classroom use, the study of petition-signing itself is important. The petition in our society is a highly valued political device for expressing public sentiment. Knowledge about how easily this sentiment can be manipulated is relevant in a society which uses petitions as a means of demonstrating protest.

The two other studies presented in this chapter also deal, in a broad sense, with political behavior. The experiment by Lupfer, Kay, and Burnette (page 82) examines the effect of picketing on the sale of toy guns. Although picketing is a widespread form of social influence via protest, scientists have not experimentally explored this form of social behavior. Thus, we present the experiment by Lupfer et al. as having merit, because it is the first experiment we have been able to find in this area. What is interesting about their research is that they found that picketing was successful (reducing the number of buyers of toy guns by one-half), even though the picketing was rather weakly carried out; that is, there was no explicit statement urging people not to buy guns. On the basis of this experiment, it appears that picketing as a form of social influence and protest may be a more effective way to influence behavior than most think. In this age of escalating means of confrontation, it is crucial to be able to measure the effectiveness of these techniques.

The next experiment, by Hartmann (page 84), examines the question of whether an emotional versus a rational political leaflet would be more effective in influencing voters. Although Hartmann found that the emotional leaflet was more effective, there should be qualifications of this finding. The type of communication has differential effects depending upon to whom the message is directed and who is doing the directing (Berschied & Walster, 1969). Although Hartmann's research was done in 1935, reports of this type of research are almost nonexistent in later psychology journals. Recent elections have shown that emotion is still an important consideration in running a political campaign. The Goldwater-Johnson presidential contest in 1964 was based rather heavily on emotional campaigns.

## REFERENCES

**BERSCHIED, E., & WALSTER, E.** Attitude change. In J. Mills (Ed.), *Experimental Social Psychology.* New York: Macmillan, 1969, Pp. 123-231.

**BICKMAN, L.** Effect of different uniforms on obedience in field situations. *Proceedings of the 79th Annual Convention of the American Psychological Association,* 1971, **5**, 359-360.

**BLAKE, R. R., MOUTON, J. S., & HAIN, J. D.** Social forces in petition-signing. *Southwestern Social Scientific Quarterly*, 1956, **36**, 385-390.

**MILGRAM, S.** Some conditions of obedience and disobedience to authority. *Human Relations*, 1965, **18**, 57-76.

# AN EXPERIMENTAL STUDY IN NURSE-PHYSICIAN RELATIONSHIPS

CHARLES K. HOFLING, M.D.[1], EVELINE BROTZMAN, R.N., M.S.[2], SARAH DALRYMPLE, R.N., M.A.[3], NANCY GRAVES, R.N., M.S.[4] AND CHESTER M. PIERCE, M.D.[5]

As physicians move increasingly out of their traditional channels of functioning and into broader areas of the community, their relationships with members of the other health disciplines assume increasing significance. Similarly the intradisciplinary conflicts which beset these other professionals become of greater concern to the physician, since his own effectiveness comes to depend more and more upon others. This paper is an account of the way in which a group of psychiatrists and nurses have attempted to obtain a picture in depth of the effect of certain aspects of the nurse-physician relationship.

There is no doubt that the professional status and standards of nurses are at times challenged by the behavior of doctors (1, 3, 8). From a consideration of naturally occurring situations in which such challenges occur, two particularly significant categories appear to be: 1) the situation in which the doctor violates an accepted procedure of which the nurse is customarily in charge (*e.g.*, entering an isolation unit without taking the proper precautions); and 2) the situation in which the doctor directs the nurse to carry out a procedure which is in some fashion against her professional standards (*e.g.*, ordering the nurse to administer intravenous medication in a hospital where nurse-administrative policy opposes such action). Since the former situation can take place without the nurse's attention necessarily being directed to the problem, we selected the latter as the type of incident to create experimentally and to study.

## METHOD

It was decided to construct the incident around an irregular order from a doctor to a nurse for her to administer a dose of medication.

**Ingredients of the Experimental Conflict** 1) The nurse would be asked to give an obviously excessive dose of medicine. For reasons of safety it was decided to use a placebo. 2) The medication order was to be transmitted by telephone, a procedure in violation of hospital policy. 3) The medication would be "unauthorized," *i.e.*, a drug which had not been placed on the ward stock-list and cleared for use. 4) The order would be given to the nurse by an unfamiliar voice.

**Overall Approach** The conflict situation was contrived at a public and a private hospital on 12 and ten wards, respectively. A questionnaire was administered to a group of nurses at a third hospital as a matched control. The control subjects were asked what they would do if confronted with the circumstances of the experimental conflict. A group of student nurses was also given the questionnaire, in order to see how less experienced nurses thought they would react.

## EXPERIMENTAL DESIGN

**Ward Incident** Pill boxes bearing hospital labels were marked as follows:

ASTROTEN
5 mg. capsules
Usual dose: 5 mg.
Maximum daily dose: 10 mg.

These were placed on the wards. Each box contained pink placebo capsules filled with glucose. To standardize the telephone order, a written script was prepared for the caller. In order to standardize the stimulus call as much as possible, a set of standardized replies to the likeliest responses of the nurse was composed and closely adhered to.

It was decided that the emotional tone conveyed by the caller would be one of courteous but self-confident firmness. As a precaution against unintentional departures from this tone, it was arranged to have the calls monitored by another member of the research team, whose function it would be to signal to the caller if he started to vary from the prescribed tone.

[1] Department of Psychiatry, University of Cincinnati, College of Medicine, Cincinnati, Ohio.

[2] 1490 Morris Drive, Peninsula, Ohio.

[3] Nursing Service, Cincinnati General Hospital, Cincinnati, Ohio.

[4] 94 Faren Drive, Highland Heights, Kentucky.

[5] Department of Psychiatry, University of Oklahoma School of Medicine; Veterans Administration Hospital, Oklahoma City, Oklahoma.

All telephone calls were tape-recorded. It was arranged to have a colleague, an expert in verbal behavior, listen to the tape after the experiment and mark as invalid any calls in which he perceived an appreciable variation from the prescribed tone or any cues suggesting that the call was not genuine.

Termination points for the telephone conversation were as follows: 1) compliance upon the part of the subject; 2) a clear-cut, sustained refusal; 3) insistence upon calling or talking to any third party of equal or superior rank in the hospital hierarchy; 4) the subject's becoming emotionally upset; 5) inability to find the medication in two attempts; and 6) prolongation of the telephone call—by any means—to ten minutes.

To study the subjects' environment and their nonverbal behavior as well as to halt the experiment before the involvement of any patient, an observer—a staff psychiatrist—was placed on each unit selected. It was his function to terminate the situation by disclosing its true nature when: 1) the nurse had "poured" the medication and started for the patient's bed; 2) she had ended the telephone conversation with a refusal to accept the order; 3) she began to telephone or otherwise contact another professional person; or 4) at the expiration of ten minutes following the end of the call if none of the foregoing alternatives had been adopted.

It was anticipated that a post-incident conversation between observer and subject would allow the observer to assume two additional functions. He could obtain some further material from the subject (as to her inner responses to the experience), and he could offer psychiatric "first-aid" if indicated, to allay any disquieting feelings which might be mobilized by the experiment.

The experiment was conducted during the period from shortly before to shortly after evening visiting hours (7:00-9:00 P.M.) and was performed on medical, surgical, pediatric and psychiatric wards. This period was selected because it is a time when the administration of therapeutic measures is at a minimum. It is also (regrettably) a time when interns and residents tend to absent themselves from the wards; thus the nurse would have to make her own immediate decision regarding the telephone calls.

It was arranged that, as soon as the doctor-observer decided that the ward conditions safely permitted the experiment, he would give a signal by calling in from the ward telephone to the office being used by the investigators, using a code sentence.

One of the nurse investigators visited all of the experimental sites in succession within a half-hour of the incident. She explained the value of further information and requested an appointment for follow-up interview (for which the subject would be offered payment at extra-duty rates). To avoid undue retrospective distortion, the appointments were all made for interviews within 48 hours of the critical incident.

These follow-up interviews, of about 45 minutes each, were relatively unstructured. However, the nurse-investigator had, in the meantime, reviewed the telephone recordings and the reports of the psychiatrist-observers, and she endeavored to cover the following points in her interviews, as opportunity was afforded.

1. Unguided narrative: ("Please tell me what happened last night, starting with whatever you were doing just before the phone call about Astroten.")
2. Emotions: ("What were your feelings at the point where . . . .")
3. Discrepancies, if any: ("Are you sure it happened just that way?")
4. Comparable naturally occurring experiences: ("Try to leave out, for the moment, your present knowledge that the incident was experimental. Suppose it to have been 'real.' Can you think of similar situations which you have experienced? Tell me about them.")
5. Retrospective view: ("What are your feelings about the incident now? What are they about the experience as such?")
6. Eliciting biographical data not otherwise mentioned: age, religion, marital status, children, place(s) of birth and of growing up, nursing experience, other work experience, professional ambitions.
7. Offering support and reassurance if indicated: renewing assurance of subject's anonymity if indicated.

**Graduate Nurse Questionnaire** The hospital chosen for the questionnaire phase was a general hospital, as were the first two. Like the others, it had over 500 beds and was located in the Midwest. The subjects given the hypothetical situation were closely matched with the experimental subjects at the public hospital as to: age, sex, race, marital status, length of work week (part-time or full-time), amount of professional experience, type of nursing education (three-year or four-year program), and geographical area of origin. There were 12 graduate nurses in the control group.

The questionnaire was administered in a large conference room with the subjects being provided with writing materials and seated at widely spaced intervals from one another.

The investigator, a physician, spoke to the subjects as follows:

> I should like you to imagine yourself, as vividly as possible, in this situation. You are a staff nurse, working

3:00 P.M. to 11:00 P.M. on a ward of a general hospital, and in charge of the ward during that period.

It is the official policy of this hospital that medication orders are to be written by the physician before being carried out by the nurse. This policy fairly often is not adhered to.

You are the only nurse on the ward, the head nurse and the departmental supervisor having left the hospital. None of the house doctors are on ward, which is moderately busy.

Dr. Smith is known to be on the staff of the hospital, but you have not met him. Mr. Jones is one of the patients on your ward.

At about 8:00 P.M. you receive the following telephone message:

"This is Dr. Smith, from Psychiatry, calling. I was asked to see Mr. Jones this morning, and I'm going to have to see him again tonight–I don't have a lot of time, and I'd like him to have had some medication by the time I get to the ward. Will you please check your medicine cabinet and see if you have some Astroten? That's ASTROTEN."

Your medicine cupboard contains a pillbox, bearing the label of the hospital pharmacy, and reading as follows:

ASTROTEN
5 mg. capsules
Usual dose: 5 mg.
Maximum daily dose: 10 mg.

You return to the telephone, and the message continues as follows:

"You have it? Fine. Now will you please give Mr. Jones a stat dose of 20 milligrams–that's four capsules–of Astroten. I'll be up within ten minutes, and I'll sign the order then, but I'd like the drug to have started taking effect."

The nurses were then handed sheets of paper upon which was printed everything which had just been read to them. They were invited to read these sheets, being told that this was merely to help them keep the details in mind.

The investigator then said to the subjects: "Please write down exactly what you would say and do."

After this answer was completed, the investigator said to the subjects, "Please write down the rationale for what you said and did in this episode, that is to say, the considerations influencing your decision."

The next question presented to the subjects was, "What do you think a majority of nurses would have done in this situation?"

The last question offered the subjects was, "What do you think a majority of this group will have written?"

**Nursing Student Questionnaire** To compare and contrast with what graduate nurses did in the stress situation and with what they thought they would do in it, the hypothetical case was presented to a group of 21 degree-program nursing students. The method of presentation of the hypothetical situation and of presenting the questionnaire was the same as has been described for the graduate nurses.

## RESULTS

**Ward Incident** In all, a total of 22 subjects can be reported: 12 from the municipal hospital and ten from the private hospital.

1. Twenty-one subjects would have given the medication as ordered.

2. Telephone calls were invariably brief. Exclusive of time spent in looking for the medication the calls averaged only two minutes in duration. Essentially no resistance to the order was expressed to the caller.

The transcript of a typical telephone call runs as follows:[6]

*Nurse:* Ward 18; Miss Rolfe.
*Caller:* Is this the nurse in charge?
*Nurse:* Yes, it is.
*Caller:* This is Dr. Hanford, from Psychiatry, calling. I was asked to see Mr. Carson today, and I'm going to have to see him again this evening.
*Nurse:* Yes.
*Caller:* I haven't much time and I'd like him to have received some medication by the time I get to the ward. Will you please check the medicine cabinet and see if you have some Astroten.
*Nurse:* Some what?
*Caller:* Astroten. That's ASTROTEN.
*Nurse:* I'm pretty sure we don't.
*Caller:* Would you take a look, please?
*Nurse:* Yes, I'll take a look, but I'm pretty sure we don't.

(45 seconds' pause)

*Nurse:* Hello.
*Caller:* Well?
*Nurse:* Yes.
*Caller:* You have Astroten?
*Nurse:* Yes.
*Caller:* O.K. Now, will you give Mr. Carson a stat dose of twenty milligrams–that's four capsules–of Astroten. I'll be up in about ten minutes, and I'll sign the order then, but I'd like the medicine to have started taking effect.

---

[6] All proper names and the designation of the ward have been changed.

*Nurse:* Twenty cap . . . Oh, I mean, twenty milligrams.
*Caller:* Yes, that's right.
*Nurse:* Four capsules. O.K.
*Caller:* Thank you.
*Nurse:* Surely.

3. There was little or no conscious attempt at delay. Twenty-one of the subjects offered no delay after conclusion of the call.

4. On interview, 11 of the subjects expressed their having had an awareness of the dosage discrepancy. The remainder professed lack of awareness of it.

5. During the telephone conversation none of the subjects insisted that the order be given in written form before implementation, although several sought reassurance that the "doctor" would appear promptly. On interview, 18 of the subjects indicated a general awareness of the impropriety of nonemergency telephone orders. Most of the subjects agreed, however, that it was not an uncommon impropriety.

6. In 17 cases phenomena falling into the category of "psychopathology of everyday life" were noted in the course of the observations. That is to say, the subjects exhibited such behavior as mishearing, misplacing of familiar objects, temporary forgetting, and the like, during the time beginning with the stress telephone call and ending when the on-the-spot observer terminated his conversation with the subject and left the ward.

An example of "psychopathology" of this type is afforded by the transcript of a telephone call given above. When the nurse, in response to the caller's last long statement, begins to say, "twenty capsules," this is undoubtedly an unconsciously determined slip and not a simple misunderstanding.

A very frequent example is the one referred to in paragraph 4, namely the repression of awareness of the dosage discrepancy.

A third example—also frequent—has to do with the subjects' not being able to see the Astroten boxes when they first looked for them. In all cases, the boxes had been placed in prominent locations in the medicine cabinets shortly before the experiment. Yet several times the nurses were unable to locate the boxes at the first trial. When a second trial was insisted upon, the boxes were found rather rapidly.

7. None of the subjects became overtly hostile to the telephone caller or to the observer. Only one of the subjects, the one who refused to accept the order, indicated to the observer that she felt some hostility to the caller during the call.

8. The overt emotional tones of the subjects' responses upon disclosure of the experiment as such varied considerably. The range was from mild scientific interest, through chagrin and mild confusion, to anxiety and some sense of guilt, and, in a few instances, irritation or veiled anger. The modal response could be said to involve chagrin, mild anxiety, and a hint of guilt.

9. Opinions differed as to the details of a "correct" response, but 16 of the subjects felt that the response should have involved greater resistance to the telephone order.

10. Sixteen subjects felt quite unsure that their responses had been typical.

11. On interview, 15 of the subjects spontaneously recalled similar naturally occurring experiences. The remainder could recall such experiences when asked if they had occurred. A majority of the subjects referred to the displeasure of doctors on occasions when nursing resistance had been offered to instructions which had been considered improper.

12. Only one of the subjects seriously questioned the identity of the observer or the propriety of his presence on the ward (before his having identified himself).

**Graduate Nurse Questionnaire** The results obtained from the subjects in the hypothetical situation may be summarized as follows:

1. Ten of the 12 subjects reported that they would not have given the medication; two of the subjects said that they would have given the medication.

2. In discussing the rationale for what they would have done, seven subjects referred to the dosage discrepancy in one way or another. Four of the ten subjects who said that they would have refused to give the drug mentioned the dosage discrepancy as the principal reason; the others gave greater emphasis to "hospital policy" or the "necessity for a written order."

3. Seven subjects said they thought that a majority of nurses would handle the situation in the way that they would do. Two subjects said that they thought a majority of nurses would not have handled the situation in their ways. Three responses were equivocal.

4. Ten nurses said that they thought a majority of the nurses present would have responded in the same way that they did.

Examples of the subjects' reports as to what they would say and do in the situation presented are as follows:

> I'm sorry, but I cannot give the medication until the order is written. If you can't come down, perhaps you could have another doctor come and write the order. I

would then be very happy to carry it out. I'm wondering, too, if your order refers to the same Mr. Jones here on my ward, as the label on this box of Astroten states that ten milligrams is the maximum daily dose, and you have stated that you would like for the patient to receive twenty milligrams.

I'm sorry, Dr. Smith, but I cannot give this medication without a written order. This is the policy of the hospital.

**Student Nurse Questionnaire**

1. Of the 21 nursing students, all believed that they would not have given the medication as ordered.

2. Eight students gave as the principal reason for refusing to accept the order their concern lest the patient suffer ill effects from the apparently excessive dosage.

3. Nineteen of the subjects—either in the fantasied telephone conversations or in giving the rationale for their behavior—specifically referred to the apparently excessive dosage, although in 11 of these instances this concern was not given as the chief objection.

4. In most instances, the conversation which the nursing student fantasied herself holding with the caller was more extended and more illuminating than were any of the actual conversations recorded in the experiment. Even the brief refusals typically included a statement recognizing some of the principal features of the situation.

5. Nearly all replies were distinctly courteous; none were discourteous.

Examples follow of the students' reports as to what they imagined themselves saying and doing in the situation.

Upon finding the medication in the cupboard, I would question the dosage of the medication being twenty milligrams when the maximum dose was ten milligrams. I would not administer the medication unless the supervisor was present to o.k. the order, because I did not know the doctor who phoned in the order and am not accustomed to give any medication unless it is written order; also, because the medication is one that I am not familiar with, I would be also unfamiliar with the toxic effects.

I'm sorry, sir, but I am not authorized to give any medication without a written order, especially one so large over the usual dose and one that I'm unfamiliar with. If it were possible, I would be glad to do it, but this is against hospital policy and my own ethical standards. If you would come to the ward and write the order, I would be glad to administer the drug. In addition to the above, I would include something about the actual dosage.

## DISCUSSION

Perhaps the first point to be stressed is that the primary, overt response of the subjects was unexpected and, in particular, unexpectedly uniform. None of the investigators and but one of the highly experienced nurse consultants with whom the project had been discussed in advance predicted the outcome correctly.

It has long been recognized that when there is friction between doctors and nurses, it is the patients who chiefly suffer (7). However, the present study underscores the danger to patients in unresolved difficulties of the nurse-doctor relationship even when there is little or no friction in the usual sense of the word. In a real-life situation corresponding to the experimental one, there would, in theory, be two professional intelligences, the doctor's and the nurse's, working to ensure that a given procedure be undertaken in a manner beneficial to the patient or, at the very least, not detrimental to him. The experiment strongly suggests, however, that in the real-life situation one of these intelligences is, for all practical purposes, nonfunctioning.

The experiment indicates quite clearly that, insofar as the nurse is concerned, the psychological problems involved in a situation such as the one under discussion are operating to a considerable extent below the threshold of consciousness. Perhaps the most striking evidence of this is the fact that, whereas nearly all of the subjects quite correctly either repeated the dosage ordered or asked that it be repeated, none of them gave any evidence of conscious concern at the discrepancy between the dose ordered and the alleged maximum safe dose.

Since there is so little evidence of *conscious* conflict in the situation, one may perhaps be inclined to question the existence of appreciable conflict at any level. For a small minority of the subjects, it may indeed be true that their adaptation to situations like the experimental one had reached the point that they experienced no significant conflict, at any level, but, for a majority, the evidence of preconscious or unconscious conflict is persuasive.

It is clear that the subjects, when interviewed, were reacting to at least a double stimulus to the realization that 1) their behavior, irrespective of what it had been, had been professionally observed without their prior knowledge; and 2) their *specific* behavior had been noted. It was believed, on careful questioning, that the embarrassment, irritation, and such anger as was present were in response to the first portion of the stimulus, namely, the disclosure of observation *per se.*

On the other hand, in the face of an attitude on the part of the interviewers which was sympathetic rather than purely neutral, *a majority of the subjects were clearly defensive of their specific handling of the situation*. Moreover, all of those slips of behavior which we have called "psychopathology of everyday life" and of which one or more examples were offered by 17 of the 21 subjects, are indicative of preconscious or unconscious conflict. With the disclosure of the experiment as having been such, elements of the conflict moved into consciousness, as was attested by those reactions which included anxiety, chagrin, and a sense of guilt.

Even in the hypothetical presentation of the critical incident, a considerable amount of subsurface tension was induced. One example of the effects of this tension was the *non sequitur* uttered by the nurse who said, "I'm wondering, too, if your order refers to the same Mr. Jones here on my ward, as the label on this box of Astroten states that ten milligrams is the maximum daily dose, and you have stated that you would like for the patient to receive twenty milligrams." This statement is not far removed from the phenomena referred to in the actual test situation as "psychopathology of everyday life."

There is evidence that a considerable amount of self-deception goes on in the average staff nurse. In nonstressful moments, when thinking about her performance, the average nurse tends to believe that considerations of her patient's welfare and of her own professional honor will outweigh considerations leading to an automatic obedience to the doctor's orders at times when these two sets of factors come into conflict.

Insofar as these matters are concerned, there is in some respects a close correspondence between the way in which nursing students have been taught to think of themselves and their professional functions (*i.e.*, the "official" faculty position),[7] the way in which they actually do think of these things as upperclassmen, and the way in which they will think of them—in moments free of stress—several years later as staff nurses. Concern has been expressed as to the degree to which this view corresponds to reality (4). This investigation tends to show that the view involves an illusion, which, although perhaps shallow, is widespread and enduring. This illusion is, of course, that the nurse will habitually defend the well-being of her patients as she sees it and strive to maintain the standards of her profession.

The present investigation surely has among its implications the idea that all is not well in the professional relationships of nurses and physicians and that these difficulties, whatever they may be, exert a limiting effect upon the nurse's resourcefulness and, in some situations, increase the hazard to which the patients undergoing treatment are exposed. Just because these implications are very strong, it is correct to point out that there is another side to the professional relationship of nurses and physicians, as disclosed in this investigation, and another set of comments to be made about the nurses' effectiveness in crisis situations.

There is no question but that the physician, whether he deserves it or not, is still the recipient of certain quite positive attitudes on the part of the nurse (2, 8). During the data-gathering phase of the present investigation, transcripts were made of 27 nurse-physician telephone conversations, and written records were obtained of 35 fantasied nurse-physician (or nursing student-physician) conversations. In a very great majority of these conversations, a note of courtesy and respect on the part of the nurse toward the physician was unmistakable.

Then there is the matter of trust. The inference is very strong that the nurses' almost invariable acceptance, in the actual stress situation, of the caller as being what he said he was and of doing what he said he was going to do involved a definite (generalized) element of trust.

There is also the matter of efficiency. It has been mentioned that, in the actual test situation, there was a strong, almost uniform tendency for the nurses to implement what they took to be the doctor's wishes promptly and with minimum wasted effort.

It is necessary to recognize that all of these characteristics can, in their place, be of inestimable value to physicians and to their patients. It is easy to recall crisis situations in which the nurse's loyalty to the physician, her appreciation of the value of his judgment, and her willingness and ability to act promptly and efficiently without wasting precious time in discussion have made the difference between life and death for the patient.

The present investigation does not imply that these values should be sacrificed. Rather, it implies that it would be worth an extensive effort on the part of the nursing and medical professions to find ways in which these traditional values can be reconciled with the

---

[7] A point not demonstrated experimentally, but brought out in individual discussions with faculty members.

nurse's fuller exercise of her intellectual and ethical potentialities.

We believe that the typical nurse of today has certain conscious motivations—aspirations and ideals—with respect to her position and functions which may be summarized as the wish both to be and to be considered a professional person in her own right (5). This wish involves several component desires and strivings: mastery of a body of scientific knowledge, application of intelligence, exercise of judgment, assumption of responsibility for patients while offering services to them, gaining the respect of colleagues in related disciplines. All these motivations were expressed by our nurse-subjects collectively, and many of them were expressed by each subject individually.

On the other hand, the nurse retains another group of (largely conscious) motivations with respect to her relationship with the doctor. These include the wish to be liked by him, to receive his gratitude, praise and approval, and to avoid blame and recriminations. These strivings are indicated in various portions of the experimental material: in the courtesy of the telephone conversations (usually ending with a "thank you"), in the unquestioning attitudes; in the promptness of execution of the order; and in the fear of disapproval upon disclosure.

It is to be noted that the first set of motivations is currently being strongly reinforced by nursing education, particularly in its more formal aspects (5, 6). The second set receives reinforcement in the expectations and responses of a majority of physicians. The first set is best served by an intellectual and emotional orientation which is, in many ways, quite active. The second set requires an orientation which is, in some ways, distinctly passive.

The duties and responsibilities of a nurse are, of course, sufficiently extensive and varied to afford opportunity for the gratification of each set of motivations at one time or another. The present study indicates, however, that the two sets can be—or can appear to the nurse to be—mutually incompatible and thus that a state of conflict can be produced on certain occasions when they are stimulated simultaneously. The study indicates further that, in such situations, the second set of motivations will win out in a very great majority of instances. Crucial to this conflict is the fact that in hospital psychodynamics most doctors are male and most nurses are female. Thus the nurse has biocultural as well as politico-legal reasons to be passive to the doctor's wishes.

Since this investigation does not shed light upon the motivational states of physicians in their relationships to nurses, it would be premature to offer much comment on the degree to which the conflict in the nurse is reality-based, rather than based upon inferences of questionable accuracy. However, one can assert with confidence the general truth that inner conflict is productive of anxiety and that, beyond a certain low intensity, anxiety tends to reduce the versatility and inventiveness of a personality. Thus, one can feel reasonably certain that, in situations such as the experimental one, solutions affording gratifications to both sets of the nurses' strivings are found far less often than is theoretically possible.

Perhaps the last statement can be clarified by returning to specifics. Any attempt to submit an "ideal solution," a formula of conduct, for the handling of situations like the experimental one would, of course, be unduly rigid and arbitrary. Yet, one has the distinct impression that the observance of professional courtesy and loyalty need not have precluded the making of relevant inquiries. It need not have precluded the nurses' making some sort of *appraisal* of the situation and then arriving at a *conscious decision* instead of an automatic response. Whether such a decision would lead to eventual compliance, to refusal, or to some temporizing measure is not pertinent to the present question. The point is that there appears to be room for greater intellectual activity—the pursuit of which need not be aggressive, destructive, or (to speak of the majority of nurses) unfeminine. One can feel quite sure that, whatever its precise, overt nature, a response based upon a sense of appraisal and decision would be far less likely to produce inner tension than one reached quasi-automatically on the basis of barely perceived inner forces.

This last statement reverts once again to the recognition that the conflict state, in both its interpersonal (nurse versus doctor) and intrapersonal (nurse versus herself) aspects, appears to involve components which do not reach the level of full awareness.

At this point the current presentation reaches something of a dilemma: to conclude without further reference to the nature of these unconscious components may give the false impression that they seem of little significance; to attempt a further discussion of these elements—a discussion based very largely upon inference—may give a false sense of assurance that they have been fully and correctly identified. What follows, therefore, is offered tentatively and merely as the line of speculation which appears best to fit the limited data.

If one accepts the view that the subjects' emotions of shame, embarrassment, and guilt following the experimental incident were derived, at least in part, from the nature of their activities and fantasies during the incident, one has a clue to these less obvious forces. It must be remembered that: 1) the subjects had not behaved in an unusual manner during the incident, but, rather, in their customary fashion; 2) very few of the subjects had any reason to suppose they had behaved differently from the great majority of subjects; 3) neither the psychiatrist-observer nor the nurse-interviewer expressed thoughts or feelings other than those of friendly curiosity, and, of course; 4) in no instance was there the faintest possibility that patient-care had suffered.

Yet the emotions were unmistakable. The question thus becomes, "What subsurface motivations led the nurse to feel ashamed, embarrassed and guilty?" One can dismiss out of hand the speculation that hostile feelings toward the patient (leading to a sense of guilt and thus to a need for punishment or abuse) were of great significance: the life-patterns, the personal and professional adjustments of the subjects make this clear. If a further argument were needed, one is readily at hand: the individual patients in the experimental situation varied from nurse to nurse and varied widely, yet some elements of the emotional response remained qualitatively almost constant.

Although it rests upon inference and only indirectly upon the data, the likeliest answer to the above question appears to be that the nurse is responding, in situations like the experimental one, on the basis of transference to the doctor. The transference seems typically to involve both an erotic and an aggressive component. On this view, the preconscious or unconscious wish to win the doctor's love and the utilization of reaction-formation against aggressive impulses toward him, born of frustration, lead the nurse at times to compromise her conscious professional standards.

## REFERENCES


1. **BULLOCK, R. P.** Position, function and job satisfaction of nurses in the social system of a modern hospital. Nurs. Res., *11:*4-14, 1953.
2. **JOHNSON, M. AND MARTIN, H.** A sociological analysis of the nurse role. Amer. J. Nurs., *58:*373-377, 1958.
3. **LOEB, M. B.** Role definition in the social world of a psychiatric hospital. In Greenblatt, M. *et al.*, eds. *The Patient and the Mental Hospital*, pp. 14-19. Free Press, Glencoe, Illinois, 1957.
4. **MAUKSCH, H.** Becoming a nurse: A selective view. Ann. Amer. Acad. Polit. Soc. Sci., *346:*88-98, 1963.
5. **NEWTON, M. E.** Nurses' caps and bachelors' gowns. Amer. J. Nurs., *64:*73-77, 1964.
6. **PETERSON, F. K.** The new diploma schools. Amer. J. Nurs., *64:*68-72, 1964.
7. **RUESCH, J., BRODSKY, C. AND FISCHER, A.** *Psychiatric Care*, pp. 135-136. Grune & Stratton, New York, 1964.
8. **RUSHING, W. A.** Social influence and the social-psychological function of deference: A study of psychiatric nursing. Soc. Forces, *41:*142-148, 1963.

# SOCIAL SETTING AND CONFORMITY TO A LEGAL REQUIREMENT[1,2]

ABRAM M. BARCH, DON TRUMBO, AND JOHN NANGLE
*Michigan State University*

The purpose of the study was to note the effect on a subject's behavior of observing others conform or fail to conform to a legal requirement. The specific hypothesis under test was that the signalling behavior of the driver of a motor vehicle preparing to turn at an intersection would be related positively to the signalling behavior of the driver of an immediately preceding motor vehicle.

The research was stimulated by the work of Blake and his associates concerned with the influence of social background or social setting on conformity behavior (1, 2, 3, 4), but the data are also relevant to other formulations of imitation and social conformity. In the situation studied, there is a minimum of interaction between the subject and the model, and the subjects can be assumed to have had considerable opportunity to learn what the typical behavior of other individuals in situations similar to the test situation would be. Unlike the settings investigated by Blake *et al.*, conformity or nonconformity in the present situation is to a legal requirement.

## METHOD

**The Observations** Preliminary observations indicated that the variation in turn-signalling present in the naturalistic situation was sufficient for the purpose of the study.

Four different intersections in the Greater Lansing area were observed for a total of 61 hours over a four-week period in the summer of 1956. The particular hours during which the intersections were observed depended on considerations involved in a broader study of turn-signalling behavior; all data were collected during daylight hours and in good weather (no fog or rain). Intersections studied included two instances of two two-lane roads meeting at a two-way stop, one four-lane highway intersecting a two-lane road at a stop signal, and one six-lane divided highway intersecting a three-lane road at a stop signal.

During any period of observation, the observer noted all cars moving from a given direction on a given leg of the intersection and recorded the following information for all turning cars: (*a*) presence or absence of a signal to turn; (*b*) direction of turn; (*c*) presence of another car 100 feet or less behind the turning car when it began its turn; (*d*) sex of the driver. (At two of the seven legs observed, only cars turning in a given direction were recorded because of the low occurrence of turns in one direction and/or the difficulty of accurately noting turns in both directions.)

The observer stationed himself near the intersection where he could best make the observations required. In most cases he was diagonally across the intersection from the observed traffic movement. At other times he stood about 100 feet ahead of the intersection along the lane(s) being observed. Data collected under control conditions designed to eliminate the possibility that drivers might note the presence of observers indicated that the visible presence of observers did not affect the percentage of cars signalling for a turn. In a reliability check, agreement between two observers for the same cars was 99 per cent or better for all categories except "the presence of a following car" (94 per cent).

During the periods of observation, 4,229 male drivers and 1,004 female drivers of passenger cars turned at the locations under study.

**Criteria for Scoring Conformity** Michigan state law requires that intention to turn be signalled by either hand signal or electric signal but does not specify the distance this signal must be given prior to turning or make a distinction between a signal for a left and one for a right turn. Therefore, a driver was designated as signalling if he blinked his left or right turn signal light or gave any hand signal, except a hand signal for stopping, regardless of the direction of turn.

## RESULTS

The first step in the analysis consisted of extracting the appropriate pairs from the field observation data. The criteria for selection were: (*a*) both cars turned at the intersection under study; (*b*) the following car was 100 feet or less behind the lead car when the lead car began its turn; and (*c*) no cars were in the same lane between the two turning cars. A given car

[1]The study was supported by the Highway Traffic Safety Center of Michigan State University.

[2]The authors are indebted to Dr. Charles Hanley for statistical advice and assistance.

could appear in only one pair of cars; i.e., it could not be a following car for one pair and the lead car for the next pair. The total number of such pairs was 1,195. Of these, 723 pairs had a conforming model and 472 pairs had a nonconforming model.

The signalling behavior of the follower was significantly related at the .01 level to the signalling behavior of the lead car ($\chi^2$ = 15.78, 1 *df*). This positive relationship, although highly significant, was found to be a weak one. The strength of the association as estimated by tetrachoric *r* was .19.

A future analysis of the data was felt desirable since the general level of conformity (percentage of all turning cars signalling without regard to presence of a model car) varied with the direction of turn and the leg of the intersection. Women also tended to signal more frequently than men. However, the difference was small and the pattern of relationships within the data for women was quite similar to that for men. Therefore, men and women drivers were combined in all comparisons.

[Table 3-1] presents the number and percentage of subjects signalling or failing to signal in relation to the signalling behavior of the model under various conditions of direction of turn of the subject and the general conformity level characteristic of the intersection leg at which the turn was observed. General conformity level for an intersection leg was taken as the percentage of turn-signalling for all cars turning in a given direction without regard to the presence of a model car. Intersection legs were classified as high conformity if the percentage of turning-signalling for left turns was between 62.5 and 88 and the percentage of signalling for right turns was between 37.5 and 62.5. Low conformity legs had a signalling percentage between 37.5 and 62.5 for left turns and one between 20 and 37.5 for right turns.

[Table 3-2] presents the results of the $\chi^2$ analyses

**[Table 3-1] Reactions of subjects to signalling (S) and nonsignalling (NS) models**

| Behavior of model | | Behavior of subjects | | | | | | | |
|---|---|---|---|---|---|---|---|---|---|
| | | High conformity legs | | | | Low conformity legs | | | |
| | | Right turn | | Left turn | | Right turn | | Left turn | |
| | | S | NS | S | NS | S | NS | S | NS |
| S | *n* | 140 | 74 | 167 | 62 | 48 | 100 | 77 | 55 |
| | % | 65 | 35 | 73 | 27 | 32 | 68 | 58 | 42 |
| NS | *n* | 84 | 64 | 36 | 21 | 42 | 103 | 64 | 58 |
| | % | 57 | 43 | 63 | 37 | 29 | 71 | 52 | 48 |

**[Table 3-2] Statistical analyses of the influence of the model**

| Respondent categories | $\chi^{2a}$ | *p* | $r_{tet}$ |
|---|---|---|---|
| All cases | 15.78 | .01 | .19 |
| All left turns | 6.62 | .05 | .20 |
| All right turns | 4.82 | .05 | .14 |
| All cases at high conformity legs | 6.75 | .05 | .18 |
| All cases at low conformity legs | 1.17 | — | .09 |
| Left turns at high conformity legs | 1.67 | — | .18 |
| Right turns at high conformity legs | 2.43 | — | .14 |
| Left turns at low conformity legs | 0.66 | — | .09 |
| Right turns at low conformity legs | 0.27 | — | .07 |

[a] All analyses have 1 *df*.

of the influence of the signalling behavior of the model on the subject's signalling for various combinations of conditions. Tetrachoric *r* is provided for each combination to show the strength of the association. In all comparisons the relationship was positive to the hypothesis of influence. The strength of the relationship was low for all analyses, ranging from .07 to .20.

An attempt was made to increase the possible identification of the subject with the model by considering only those pairs in which both members of the pair were of the same sex and turned in the same direction. There were 691 such pairs. The $\chi^2$ for this analysis, as would be expected, was significant at the .01 level ($\chi^2$ = 7.33, 1 *df*). However, the tetrachoric *r* was found to be .17, essentially the same as that obtained for the other comparisons.

The results supported the hypothesis that the behavior exhibited by others in a situation involving a legal norm influences a subject's behavior. The weakness of the demonstrated influence should be considered in light of the lack of formal relationships or of interaction, except in a minimal sense, between the model and the subject and the subject's ample opportunity to observe the behavior of others in the same or similar situation prior to the test observation.

## SUMMARY

Observations made under normal traffic conditions were analyzed to determine the influence on the signalling behavior of automobile drivers of the signalling behavior of other drivers. A weak but significant positive relationship was found between observation of conformity of others to a legal requirement and self conformity.

## REFERENCES

1. **BLAKE, R. R., & MOUTON, JANE S.** Present and future implications of social psychology for law and lawyers. *Symposium Issue, Emory Univer. J. Public Law*, 1955, 3, 352-369.

2. **FREED, A. M., CHANDLER, P. J., MOUTON, JANE S., & BLAKE, R. R.** Stimulus and background factors in sign violation. *J. Pers.*, 1955, **23**, 499.

3. **LEFKOWITZ, M., BLAKE, R. R., & MOUTON, JANE S.,** Status factors in pedestrian violations of traffic signals. *J. abnorm. soc. Psychol.*, 1955, **51**, 704-706.

4. **ROSENBAUM, M., & BLAKE, R. R.** Volunteering as a function of field structure. *J. abnorm. soc. Psychol.*, 1955, **50**, 193-196.

# COMPLIANCE WITHOUT PRESSURE: THE FOOT-IN-THE-DOOR TECHNIQUE[1]

JONATHAN L. FREEDMAN AND SCOTT C. FRASER[2]
*Stanford University*

2 experiments were conducted to test the proposition that once someone has agreed to a small request he is more likely to comply with a larger request. The 1st study demonstrated this effect when the same person made both requests. The 2nd study extended this to the situation in which different people made the 2 requests. Several experimental groups were run in an effort to explain these results, and possible explanations are discussed.

How can a person be induced to do something he would rather not do? This question is relevant to practically every phase of social life, from stopping at a traffic light to stopping smoking, from buying Brand X to buying savings bonds, from supporting the March of Dimes to supporting the Civil Rights Act.

One common way of attacking the problem is to exert as much pressure as possible on the reluctant individual in an effort to force him to comply. This technique has been the focus of a considerable amount of experimental research. Work on attitude change, conformity, imitation, and obedience has all tended to stress the importance of the degree of external pressure. The prestige of the communicator (Kelman & Hovland, 1953), degree of discrepancy of the communication (Hovland & Pritzker, 1957), size of the group disagreeing with the subject (Asch, 1951), perceived power of the model (Bandura, Ross, & Ross, 1963) etc., are the kinds of variables that have been studied. This impressive body of work, added to the research on rewards and punishments in learning, has produced convincing evidence that greater external pressure generally leads to greater compliance with the wishes of the experimenter. The one exception appears to be situations involving the arousal of cognitive dissonance in which, once discrepant behavior has been elicited from the subject, the greater the pressure that was used to elicit the behavior, the less subsequent change occurs (Festinger & Carlsmith, 1959). But even in this situation one critical element is the amount of external pressure exerted.

Clearly, then, under most circumstances the more pressure that can be applied, the more likely it is that the individual will comply. There are, however, many times when for ethical, moral, or practical reasons it is difficult to apply much pressure when the goal is to produce compliance with a minimum of apparent pressure, as in the forced-compliance studies involving dissonance arousal. And even when a great deal of pressure is possible, it is still important to maximize the compliance it produces. Thus, factors other than external pressure are often quite critical in determining degree of compliance. What are these factors?

Although rigorous research on the problem is rather sparse, the fields of advertising, propaganda, politics, etc., are by no means devoid of techniques designed to produce compliance in the absence of external pressure (or to maximize the effectiveness of the pressure that is used, which is really the same problem). One assumption about compliance that has often been made either explicitly or implicitly is that once a person has been induced to comply with a small request he is more likely to comply with a larger demand. This is the principle that is commonly referred to as the foot-in-the-door or gradation technique and is reflected in the saying that if you "give them an inch, they'll take a mile." It was, for example, supposed to be one of the basic techniques upon which the Korean brainwashing tactics were based (Schein, Schneier, & Barker, 1961), and, in a somewhat different sense, one basis for Nazi propaganda during 1940 (Bruner, 1941). It also appears to be implicit in many advertising campaigns which attempt to induce the consumer to do anything relating to the product involved, even sending back a card saying he does not want the product.

The most relevant piece of experimental evidence comes from a study of conformity done by Deutsch and Gerard (1955). Some subjects were faced with incorrect group judgments first in a series in which the stimuli were not present during the actual judging and then in a series in which they were present, while the order of the memory and visual series was reversed for other subjects. For both groups the memory

[1]The authors are grateful to Evelyn Bless for assisting in the running of the second experiment reported here. These studies were supported in part by Grant GS-196 from the National Science Foundation. The first study was conducted while the junior author was supported by an NSF undergraduate summer fellowship.

[2]Now at New York University.

series produced more conformity, and when the memory series came first there was more total conformity to the group judgments. It seems likely that this order effect occurred because, as the authors suggest, once conformity is elicited at all it is more likely to occur in the future. Although this kind of conformity is probably somewhat different from compliance as described above, this finding certainly lends some support to the foot-in-the-door idea. The present research attempted to provide a rigorous, more direct test of this notion as it applies to compliance and to provide data relevant to several alternative ways of explaining the effect.

## EXPERIMENT I

The basic paradigm was to ask some subjects (Performance condition) to comply first with a small request and then 3 days later with a larger, related request. Other subjects (One-Contact condition) were asked to comply only with the large request. The hypothesis was that more subjects in the Performance condition than in the One-Contact condition would comply with the larger request.

Two additional conditions were included in an attempt to specify the essential difference between these two major conditions. The Performance subjects were asked to perform a small favor, and, if they agreed, they did it. The question arises whether the act of agreeing itself is critical or whether actually carrying it out was necessary. To assess this a third group of subjects (Agree-Only) was asked the first request, but, even if they agreed, they did not carry it out. Thus, they were identical to the Performance group except that they were not given the opportunity of performing the request.

Another difference between the two main conditions was that at the time of the larger request the subjects in the Performance condition were more familiar with the experimenter than were the other subjects. The Performance subjects had been contacted twice, heard his voice more, discovered that the questions were not dangerous, and so on. It is possible that this increased familiarity would serve to decrease the fear and suspicion of a strange voice on the phone and might accordingly increase the likelihood of the subjects agreeing to the larger request. To control for this a fourth condition was run (Familiarization) which attempted to give the subjects as much familiarity with the experimenter as in the Performance and Agree-Only conditions with the only difference being that no request was made.

The major prediction was that more subjects in the Performance condition would agree to the large request than in any of the other conditions, and that the One-Contact condition would produce the least compliance. Since the importance of agreement and familiarity was essentially unknown, the expectation was that the Agree-Only and Familiarization conditions would produce intermediate amounts of compliance.

## METHOD

The prediction stated above was tested in a field experiment in which housewives were asked to allow a survey team of five or six men to come into their homes for 2 hours to classify the household products they used. This large request was made under four different conditions: after an initial contact in which the subject had been asked to answer a few questions about the kinds of soaps she used, and the questions were actually asked (Performance condition); after an identical contact in which the questions were not actually asked (Agree-Only condition); after an initial contact in which no request was made (Familiarization condition); or after no initial contact (One-Contact condition). The dependent measure was simply whether or not the subject agreed to the large request.

### Procedure

The subjects were 156 Palo Alto, California, housewives, 36 in each condition, who were selected at random from the telephone directory. An additional 12 subjects distributed about equally among the three two-contact conditions could not be reached for the second contact and are not included in the data analysis. Subjects were assigned randomly to the various conditions, except that the Familiarization condition was added to the design after the other three conditions had been completed. All contacts were by telephone by the same experimenter who identified himself as the same person each time. Calls were made only in the morning. For the three groups that were contacted twice, the first call was made on either Monday or Tuesday and the second always 3 days later. All large requests were made on either Thursday or Friday.

At the first contact, the experimenter introduced himself by name and said that he was from the California Consumers' Group. In the Performance condition he then proceeded:

> We are calling you this morning to ask if you would answer a number of questions about what household products you use so that we could have this information for our public service publication, "The Guide." Would you be willing to give us this information for our survey?

If the subject agreed, she was asked a series of eight innocuous questions dealing with household soaps (e.g.,

"What brand of soap do you use in your kitchen sink?") She was then thanked for her cooperation, and the contact terminated.

Another condition (Agree-Only) was run to assess the importance of actually carrying out the request as opposed to merely agreeing to it. The only difference between this and the Performance condition was that, if the subject agreed to answer the questions, the experimenter thanked her, but said that he was just lining up respondents for the survey and would contact her if needed.

A third condition was included to check on the importance of the subject's greater familiarity with the experimenter in the two-contact conditions. In this condition the experimenter introduced himself, described the organization he worked for and the survey it was conducting, listed the questions he was asking, and then said that he was calling merely to acquaint the subject with the existence of his organization. In other words, these subjects were contacted, spent as much time on the phone with the experimenter as the Performance subjects did, heard all the questions, but neither agreed to answer them nor answered them.

In all of these two-contact conditions some subjects did not agree to the requests or even hung up before the requests were made. Every subject who answered the phone was included in the analysis of the results and was contacted for the second request regardless of her extent of cooperativeness during the first contact. In other words, no subject who could be contacted the appropriate number of times was discarded from any of the four conditions.

The large request was essentially identical for all subjects. The experimenter called, identified himself, and said either that his group was expanding its survey (in the case of the two-contact conditions) or that it was conducting a survey (in the One-Contact condition). In all four conditions he then continued:

> The survey will involve five or six men from our staff coming into your home some morning for about 2 hours to enumerate and classify all the household products that you have. They will have to have full freedom in your house to go through the cupboards and storage places. Then all this information will be used in the writing of the reports for our public service publication, "The Guide."

If the subject agreed to the request, she was thanked and told that at the present time the experimenter was merely collecting names of people who were willing to take part and that she would be contacted if it were decided to use her in the survey. If she did not agree, she was thanked for her time. This terminated the experiment.

## RESULTS

Apparently even the small request was not considered trivial by some of the subjects. Only about two thirds of the subjects in the Performance and Agree-Only conditions agreed to answer the questions about household soaps. It might be noted that none of those who refused the first request later agreed to the large request, although as stated previously all subjects who were contacted for the small request are included in the data for those groups.

**[Table 3-3] Percentage of subjects complying with large request in experiment I**

| Condition | % |
|---|---|
| Performance | 52.8 |
| Agree-Only | 33.3 |
| Familiarization | 27.8* |
| One-Contact | 22.2** |

NOTE—$N$ = 36 for each group. Significance levels represent differences from the Performance condition.
*$p < .07$.
**$p < .02$.

Our major prediction was that subjects who had agreed to and carried out a small request (Performance condition) would subsequently be more likely to comply with a larger request than would subjects who were asked only the larger request (One-Contact condition). As may be seen in [Table 3-3], the results support the prediction. Over 50% of the subjects in the Performance condition agreed to the larger request, while less than 25% of the One-Contact condition agreed to it. Thus it appears that obtaining compliance with a small request does tend to increase subsequent compliance. The question is what aspect of the initial contact produces this effect.

One possibility is that the effect was produced merely by increased familiarity with the experimenter. The Familiarization control was included to assess the effect on compliance of two contacts with the same person. The group had as much contact with the experimenter as the Performance group, but no request was made during the first contact. As the table indicates, the Familiarization group did not differ appreciably in amount of compliance from the One-Contact group, but was different from the Performance group ($\chi^2 = 3.70$, $p < .07$). Thus, although increased familiarity may well lead to increased compliance, in the present situation the differences in amount of familiarity apparently were not great enough to produce any such increase; the effect that was obtained seems not to be due to this factor.

Another possibility is that the critical factor producing increased compliance is simply agreeing to the small request (i.e., carrying it out may not be necessary). The Agree-Only condition was identical to the Performance condition except that in the former the subjects were not asked the questions. The amount of compliance in this Agree-Only condition fell between the Performance and One-Contact conditions and was not significantly different from either of them. This leaves the effect of merely agreeing somewhat ambiguous, but it suggests that the agreement alone may produce part of the effect.

Unfortunately, it must be admitted that neither of these control conditions is an entirely adequate test of the possibility it was designed to assess. Both conditions are in some way quite peculiar and may have made a very different and extraneous impression on the subject than did the Performance condition. In one case, a housewife is asked to answer some questions and then is not asked them; in the other, some man calls to tell her about some organization she has never heard of. Now, by themselves neither of these events might produce very much suspicion. But, several days later, the same man calls and asks a very large favor. At this point it is not at all unlikely that many subjects think they are being manipulated, or in any case that something strange is going on. Any such reaction on the part of the subjects would naturally tend to reduce the amount of compliance in these conditions.

Thus, although this first study demonstrates that an initial contact in which a request is made and carried out increases compliance with a second request, the question of why and how the initial request produces this effect remains unanswered. In an attempt to begin answering this question and to extend the results of the first study, a second experiment was conducted.

There seemed to be several quite plausible ways in which the increase in compliance might have been produced. The first was simply some kind of commitment to or involvement with the particular person making the request. This might work, for example, as follows: The subject has agreed to the first request and perceives that the experimenter therefore expects him also to agree to the second request. The subject thus feels obligated and does not want to disappoint the experimenter; he also feels that he needs a good reason for saying "no"–a better reason than he would need if he had never said "yes." This is just one line of causality–the particular process by which involvement with the experimenter operates might be quite different, but the basic idea would be similar. The commitment is to the particular person. This implies that the increase in compliance due to the first contact should occur primarily when both requests are made by the same person.

Another explanation in terms of involvement centers around the particular issue with which the requests are concerned. Once the subject has taken some action in connection with an area of concern, be it surveys, political activity, or highway safety, there is probably a tendency to become somewhat more concerned with the area. The subject begins thinking about it, considering its importance and relevance to him, and so on. This tends to make him more likely to agree to take further action in the same area when he is later asked to. To the extent that this is the critical factor, the initial contact should increase compliance only when both requests are related to the same issue or area of concern.

Another way of looking at the situation is that the subject needs a reason to say "no." In our society it is somewhat difficult to refuse a reasonable request, particularly when it is made by an organization that is not trying to make money. In order to refuse, many people feel that they need a reason–simply not wanting to do it is often not in itself sufficient. The person can say to the requester or simply to himself that he does not believe in giving to charities or tipping or working for political parties or answering questions or posting signs, or whatever he is asked to do. Once he has performed a particular task, however, this excuse is no longer valid for not agreeing to perform a similar task. Even if the first thing he did was trivial compared to the present request, he cannot say he never does this sort of thing, and thus one good reason for refusing is removed. This line of reasoning suggests that the similarity of the first and second requests in terms of the type of action required is an important factor. The more similar they are, the more the "matter of principle" argument is eliminated by agreeing to the first request, and the greater should be the increase in compliance.

There are probably many other mechanisms by which the initial request might produce an increase in compliance. The second experiment was designed in part to test the notions described above, but its major purpose was to demonstrate the effect unequivocally. To this latter end it eliminated one of the important problems with the first study which was that when the experimenter made the second request he was not blind as to which condition the subjects were in. In this study the second request was always made by someone other than the person who made the first request, and the second experimenter was blind as to what condition the subject was in. This eliminates the possibility that the experimenter exerted systematically different amounts of pressure in different experimental conditions. If the effect of the first study were replicated, it would also rule out the relatively uninteresting possibility that the effect is due primarily to greater familiarity or involvement with the particular person making the first request.

## EXPERIMENT II

The basic paradigm was quite similar to that of the first study. Experimental subjects were asked to comply with a small request and were later asked a considerably larger request, while controls were asked only the larger request. The first request varied along two dimensions. Subjects were asked either to put up a small sign or to sign a petition, and the issue was either safe driving or keeping California beautiful. Thus, there were four first requests: a small sign for safe driving or for beauty, and a petition for the two issues. The second request for all subjects was to install in their front lawn a very large sign which said "Drive Carefully." The four experimental conditions may be defined in terms of the similarity of the small and large requests along the dimensions of issue and task. The two requests were similar in both issue and task for the small-sign, safe-driving group, similar only in issue for the safe-driving-petition group, similar only in task for the small "Keep California Beautiful" sign group, and similar in neither issue nor task for the "Keep California Beautiful" petition group.

The major expectation was that the three groups for which either the task or the issue were similar would show more compliance than the controls, and it was also felt that when both were similar there would probably be the most compliance. The fourth condition (Different Issue-Different Task) was included primarily to assess the effect simply of the initial contact which, although it was not identical to the second one on either issue or task, was in many ways quite similar (e.g., a young student asking for cooperation on a noncontroversial issue). There were no clear expectations as to how this condition would compare to the controls.

[Table 3-4] **Percentage of subjects complying with large request in experiment II**

| Issue[a] | Task[a] | | | |
|---|---|---|---|---|
| | Similar | *N* | Different | *N* |
| Similar | 76.0** | 25 | 47.8* | 23 |
| Different | 47.6* | 21 | 47.4* | 19 |

One-Contact 16.7 ($N = 24$)

NOTE–Significance levels represent differences from the One-Contact condition.
[a]Denotes relationship between first and second requests.
$*p < .08$.
$**p < .01$.

## METHOD

The subjects were 114 women and 13 men living in Palo Alto, California. Of these, 9 women and 6 men could not be contacted for the second request and are not included in the data analysis. The remaining 112 subjects were divided about equally among the five conditions (see [Table 3-4]). All subjects were contacted between 1:30 and 4:30 on weekday afternoons.

Two experimenters, one male and one female, were employed, and a different one always made the second contact. Unlike the first study, the experimenters actually went to the homes of the subjects and interviewed them on a face-to-face basis. An effort was made to select subjects from blocks and neighborhoods that were as homogenous as possible. On each block every third or fourth house was approached, and all subjects on that block were in one experimental condition. This was necessary because of the likelihood that neighbors would talk to each other about the contact. In addition, for every four subjects contacted, a fifth house was chosen as a control but was, of course, not contacted. Throughout this phase of the experiment, and in fact throughout the whole experiment, the two experimenters did not communicate to each other what conditions had been run on a given block nor what condition a particular house was in.

The small-sign, safe-driving group was told that the experimenter was from the Community Committee for Traffic Safety, that he was visiting a number of homes in an attempt to make the citizens more aware of the need to drive carefully all the time, and that he would like the subject to take a small sign and put it in a window or in the car so that it would serve as a reminder of the need to drive carefully. The sign was 3 inches square, said "Be a safe driver," was on thin paper without a gummed backing, and in general looked rather amateurish and unattractive. If the subject agreed, he was given the sign and thanked; if he disagreed, he was simply thanked for his time.

The three other experimental conditions were quite similar with appropriate changes. The other organization was identified as the Keep California Beautiful Committee and its sign said, appropriately enough, "Keep California Beautiful." Both signs were simply black block letters on a white background. The two petition groups were asked to sign a petition which was being sent to California's United States Senators. The petition advocated support for any legislation which would promote either safer driving or keeping California beautiful. The subject was shown a petition, typed on heavy bond paper, with at least 20 signatures already affixed. If she agreed, she signed and was thanked. If she did not agree, she was merely thanked.

The second contact was made about 2 weeks after the initial one. Each experimenter was armed with a list of of houses which had been compiled by the other experimenter. This list contained all four experimental conditions and the controls, and, of course, there was no way for the second experimenter to know which condition the subject had been in. At this second contract, all subjects were asked the same thing: Would they put a large sign concerning safe driving in their front yard? The experimenter identified himself as being from the Citizens for Safe Driving, a different group from the original safe-driving group (although it is likely that most subjects who had been in the safe-driving conditions did not notice the difference). The subject was shown a picture of a very large sign reading "Drive Carefully" placed in front of an attractive house. The picture was taken so that the sign obscured much of the front of the house and completely concealed the doorway. It was rather poorly lettered. The subject was told that: "Our men will come out and install it and later come and remove it. It makes just a small hole in your lawn, but if this is unacceptable to you we have a special mount which will make no hole." She was asked to put the sign up for a week or a week and a half. If the subject agreed, she was told that more names than necessary were being gathered and if her home were to be used she would be contacted in a few weeks. The experimenter recorded the subject's response and this ended the experiment.

## RESULTS

First, it should be noted that there were no large differences among the experimental conditions in the percentages of subjects agreeing to the first request. Although somewhat more subjects agreed to post the "Keep California Beautiful" sign and somewhat fewer to sign the beauty petition, none of these differences approach significance.

The important figures are the number of subjects in each group who agreed to the large request. These are presented in [Table 3-4]. The figures for the four experimental groups include all subjects who were approached the first time, regardless of whether or not they agreed to the small request. As noted above, a few subjects were lost because they could not be reached for the second request, and, of course, these are not included in the table.

It is immediately apparent that the first request tended to increase the degree of compliance with the second request. Whereas fewer than 20% of the controls agreed to put the large sign on their lawn, over 55% of the experimental subjects agreed, with over 45% being the lowest degree of compliance for any experimental condition. As expected, those conditions in which the two requests were similar in terms of either issue or task produced significantly more compliance than did the controls ($\chi^2$'s range from 3.67, $p < .07$ to 15.01, $p < .001$). A somewhat unexpected result is that the fourth condition, in which the first request had relatively little in common with the second request, also produced more compliance than the controls ($\chi^2 = 3.40, p < .08$). In other words, regardless of whether or not the two requests are similar in either issue or task, simply having the first request tends to increase the likelihood that the subject will comply with a subsequent, larger request. And this holds even when the two requests are made by different people several weeks apart.

A second point of interest is a comparison among the four experimental conditions. As expected, the Same Issue-Same Task condition produced more compliance than any of the other two-contact conditions, but the difference is not significant ($\chi^2$'s range from 2.7 to 2.9). If only those subjects who agreed to the first request are considered, the same pattern holds.

## DISCUSSION

To summarize the results, the first study indicated that carrying out a small request increased the likelihood that the subject would agree to a similar larger request made by the same person. The second study showed that this effect was quite strong even when a different person made the larger request, and the two requests were quite dissimilar. How may these results be explained?

Two possibilities were outlined previously. The matter-of-principle idea which centered on the particular type of action was not supported by the data, since the similarity of the tasks did not make an appreciable difference in degree of compliance. The notion of involvement, as described previously, also has difficulty accounting for some of the findings. The basic idea was that once someone has agreed to any action, no matter how small, he tends to feel more involved than he did before. This involvement may center around the particular person making the first request or the particular issue. This is quite consistent with the results of the first study (with the exception of the two control groups which as discussed previously were rather ambiguous) and with the Similar-Issue groups in the second experiment. This idea of involvement does not, however, explain the increase in compliance found in the two groups in which the first and second request did not deal with the same issue.

It is possible that in addition to or instead of this process a more general and diffuse mechanism underlies the increase in compliance. What may occur is a change in the person's feelings about getting involved or about taking action. Once he has agreed to a request, his attitude may change. He may become, in his own eyes, the kind of person who does this sort of thing, who agrees to requests made by strangers, who takes action on things he believes in, who cooperates with good causes. The change in attitude could be toward any aspect of the situation or toward the whole business of saying "yes." The basic idea is that the change in attitude need not be toward any particular issue or person or activity, but may be toward activity or compliance in general. This would imply that an increase in compliance would not depend upon the two contacts being made by the same person, or concerning the same issue or involving the same kind of action. The similarity could be much more general, such as both concerning good causes, or requiring a similar kind of action, or being made by pleasant, attractive individuals.

It is not being suggested that this is the only mechanism operating here. The idea of involvement continues to be extremely plausible, and there are probably a number of other possibilities. Unfortunately, the present studies offer no additional data with which to support or refute any of the possible explanations of the effect. These explanations thus remain simply descriptions of mechanisms which might produce an increase in compliance after agreement with a first request. Hopefully, additional research will test these ideas more fully and perhaps also specify other manipulations which produce an increase in compliance without an increase in external pressure.

It should be pointed out that the present studies employed what is perhaps a very special type of situation. In all cases the requests were made by presumably nonprofit service organizations. The issues in the second study were deliberately noncontroversial, and it may be assumed that virtually all subjects initially sympathized with the objectives of safe driving and a beautiful California. This is in strong contrast to campaigns which are designed to sell a particular product, political candidate, or dogma. Whether the technique employed in this study would be successful in these other situations remains to be shown.

## REFERENCES

**ASCH, S. E.** Effects of groups pressure upon the modification and distortion of judgments. In H. Guetzkow (Ed.), *Groups, leadership and men; research in human relations.* Pittsburgh: Carnegie Press, 1951. Pp. 177-190.

**BANDURA, A., ROSS, D., & ROSS, S. A.** A comparative test of the status envy, social power, and secondary reinforcement theories of identificatory learning. *Journal of Abnormal and Social Psychology*, 1963, **67**, 527-534.

**BRUNER, J.** The dimensions of propaganda: German shortwave broadcasts to America. *Journal of Abnormal and Social Psychology*, 1941, **36**, 311-337.

**DEUTSCH, M., & GERARD, H. B.** A study of normative and informational social influences upon individual judgment. *Journal of Abnormal and Social Psychology*, 1955, **51**, 629-636.

**FESTINGER, L., & CARLSMITH, J.** Cognitive consequences of forced compliance. *Journal of Abnormal and Social Psychology*, 1959, **58**, 203-210.

**HOVLAND, C. I., & PRITZKER, H. A.** Extent of opinion change as a function of amount of change advocated. *Journal of Abnormal and Social Psychology*, 1957, **54**, 257-261.

**KELMAN, H. C., & HOVLAND, C. I.** "Reinstatement" of the communicator in delayed measurement of opinion change. *Journal of Abnormal and Social Psychology*, 1953, **48**, 327-335.

**SCHEIN, E. H., SCHNEIER, I., & BARKER, C. H.** *Coercive pressure*. New York: Norton, 1961.

# PETITION-SIGNING AS ADJUSTMENT TO SITUATIONAL AND PERSONAL FACTORS

HARRY HELSON, ROBERT R. BLAKE,
AND JANE SRYGLEY MOUTON[1]
*Department of Psychology, University of Texas*

## A. THE PROBLEM

One of the most common methods for establishing the desires of a group with respect to proposed actions is the petition. Candidates seeking political office, groups concerned with city ordinances and zoning, and groups desiring to influence legislation at the national or international level utilize petition endorsements as evidence of public opinion. In spite of the widespread practice and importance of obtaining signatures to petitions the literature dealing with endorsement of petitions is represented by only one experimental study (4). Contrary to general belief that signatures on petitions represent the convictions of the signers, it was found in this study that the manner in which the request for an endorsement was phrased, i.e., weak or strong, and the perceived action of another individual in signing or refusing to sign the petition, significantly determined the frequency of endorsement by test *S*s. The act of signing or refusing to sign a petition cannot, therefore, be regarded as determined solely by inner conviction.

On the basis of considerable experimentation on factors operative in interpersonal relations (2) and on the basis of theoretical considerations (5) the decision to sign or not to sign a petition must be regarded as resulting from a multiplicity of simultaneously operating factors which for analytical purposes can be grouped into three main classes: (*a*) stimuli defining the character of the expected response; (*b*) contextual or background stimuli which may alter the effects of the defining stimuli; and (*c*) residuals which represent beliefs, attitudes, and all the personal considerations in terms of which individuals differ from one another with respect to the situation calling for action. The first two classes of factors–stimulus and background–refer to situational determinants of behavior while the third class points to private or personal factors which influence behavior. To predict behavior accurately the interactions of both situational and personal factors must be known.

Situational and personal determinants of behavior may be regarded as varying along continua from strong negative through neutral to strong positive depending upon whether they influence behavior toward or against designated responses. When the three sets of factors, focal and background stimuli and personal characteristics, are all of positive sign the net result is clearly indicated and there can be no doubt that the response will be assent, and if all are negative the reaction will be negative. Most interesting from the point of view of analysis are not the extreme cases in which the three classes of factors operate in the same direction, but the cases in which the three classes of factors work against one another, i.e., where some are positive and others are negative. On the personal side we may regard submissive tendency as a factor working positively toward signing since the request to sign a petition constitutes a group or person-to-person pressure. Hence it is expected that submissive individuals will tend to sign petitions under conditions where dominant individuals will be more likely to refuse to sign. The present study is therefore concerned with the interactions of positive and negative situational factors with personal tendencies toward conformity in producing assent or refusal on the part of individuals requested to sign petitions.

## B. EXPERIMENTAL PROCEDURE

Test *S*s were approached to endorse a petition under one of four conditions: (*a*) when the petition was concerned with a proposal which had previously been found to elicit 96 per cent positive responses and while seeing another individual sign; (*b*) when the same petition was presented but while seeing another individual refuse to sign; (*c*) when the petition was concerned with a proposal which previously had elicited only 15 per cent positive responses and while seeing another sign; and (*d*) the same petition while seeing another refuse to sign. With this experimental design it was possible to study the effects of combinations of positive or negative proposals with positive or negative signing actions which served as background stimuli (*cf.* [Table 3-5]).

The actual conditions of conducting the experi-

[1]The research reported here was conducted under terms of Contract No. AF18(600)-916 between the U. S. Air Force and The University of Texas in coordination with the Department of Clinical Psychology, *USAF* School of Aviation Medicine, Randolph Field, Texas.

[Table 3-5] **Stimulus and background conditions under which *S*s were approached to sign a petition**

| Petition | | Per cent signatures of two standardization groups composed of 29 each | Background conditions | |
|---|---|---|---|---|
| Proposal | Symbol | | Background subject response | Symbol |
| 1. We, students at The University of Texas, petition for the addition of floodlights to Littlefield Fountain. | $P_P$ | 96 | "Sure, I'll sign it." | $P_B$ |
| | | | "No, I'd rather not." | $N_B$ |
| 2. We, students at The University of Texas, petition to remove all soft-drink dispensing machines from University buildings. | $N_P$ | 15 | "Sure, I'll sign it." | $P_B$ |
| | | | "No, I'd rather not." | $N_B$ |

ment were as follows: students who had volunteered to take part in an experiment were met by a guide to be conducted to the experimental room. On the way to the room the experimenter for this experiment acting as a petitioner accosted the pair. Speaking first to the guide, who had been previously instructed regarding the response he should give, he requested him to sign a petition. After the guide had either assented or refused, the test *S* was requested to sign the petition. The experiment in which the test *S*s participated after being requested to sign the petition forms the second part of this study. No test *S* recognized that his reaction in the petition situation was being studied or that it had any connection with the experiment which followed.

## C. RESULTS

The number of signers of the petitions varies significantly in the four conditions as shown by the data in [Table 3-6]. When the petition concerns a proposal agreeable to the *S*s and another is seen to sign it, the number signing is 93 per cent. In this case the background action had no effect since the number signing in the standardizing condition—with no background experimenter present—was 96 per cent. The desirability of the proposal was, therefore, sufficient in itself to evoke positive action on the part of the overwhelming majority of the *S*s. When the background action is negative its power to influence *S*s against signing becomes evident, for under the $P_N B_P$ condition the number of signers decreases to 30 per cent even though exactly the same proposal is at issue.

The power of a negative background to reduce the number of signers also is evident in the fact that the per cent of signers of the negative proposal is zero when the model refuses to sign as compared with the 15 per cent who signed under the standardizing condition. The power of the positive background *S* to increase endorsements of a negative proposal appears in the $P_N B_P$ condition however, where 33 per cent signed the negative proposal. The positive action of the model *S* results in double the number who sign the negative proposal under the standardizing condition.

All differences between values in [Table 3-6] for all conditions are significant beyond the 1 per cent level of confidence as are the interactions between them. Significance of the interactions was evaluated by subtracting the total $X^2$ which is the sum of the component $X^2$'s, from the pooled $X^2$ in accordance with the method described by Snedecor (6, pp. 188 ff.). Not only do the *S*s behave significantly differently with regard to the content of the petitions but they also behave differently with respect to the two petitions when they see another sign or refuse to sign the petitions. These results are in accordance with the hypotheses underlying the present study.

From the results for the two conditions involving like signs in proposal and background action, i.e., both either positive or negative, we may conclude that

[Table 3-6] **Frequency of petition signing as a function of proposal and social background (values in parentheses are per cents)**

| Proposal | Background | | | |
|---|---|---|---|---|
| | Sign $B_P$ | | Refuse $B_N$ | |
| | Sign | Refuse | Sign | Refuse |
| Positive $P_P$ | 14 (93) | 1 (7) | 9 (30) | 21 (70) |
| Negative $P_N$ | 10 (33) | 20 (67) | 0 (0) | 15 (100) |

sufficiently compelling conditions give rise to almost uniform behavior on the part of test *S*s. In the two situations which were so compelling that almost everyone behaved in the same way, either signing or refusing to sign the petition, no personality differences among individuals appeared. Only when situational factors are conflicting do personality factors contribute decisively in the determination of action. In the present study the hypothesis was advanced that in situations involving both positive and negative situational factors, individuals with stronger conforming tendencies would sign the petitions more often than individuals with stronger tendencies toward the maintenance of social independence. Being approached by someone to sign a petition, in other words, constitutes a social induction which highly conforming individuals are less able to resist than are less conforming individuals. Accordingly, in order to obtain direct measures of conformity, all test *S*s were given the *A-S* Reaction Study (1) and also were subjected to social pressures while performing three different tasks. In the three experimental tests of conformity the *S*s were required to report the number of metronome clicks, to give answers to arithmetic problems, and to state their attitudes with respect to Thurstone-Chave statements regarding war and peace (7), after hearing four other *S*s give responses to the same items in the three tasks. Social pressures were created in that the non-test *S*s gave incorrect judgments of clicks and arithmetic problems on six of nine trials of each of these tasks and expressed attitudes at wide variance from those by a standardizing group with respect to the Thurstone-Chave statements. Complete conformity in the three tasks would be denoted by a score of 6 and complete independence by a score of zero. The procedure and content of the three tasks are described in greater detail elsewhere (3). Performance on these tasks and on the *A-S* Reaction Study provide four measures of susceptibility to social pressures, with results as shown in [Table 3-7].

[Table 3-7] **Mean conformity scores on *A-S* reaction study and on three tasks for signing and non-signing *S*s**

| Conformity tests | Negative proposal positive background $P_N B_P$ | | Positive proposal negative background $P_P B_N$ | |
|---|---|---|---|---|
| | Sign | Refuse | Sign | Refuse |
| *A-S* Reaction | 5.50 | 4.65 | 6.00 | 4.76 |
| Metronome | 2.60 | 1.75 | 2.33 | 1.71 |
| Attitude | 2.50 | 2.75 | 2.67 | 2.52 |
| Arithmetic | 2.10 | 1.30 | 2.00 | 1.72 |

Individuals who signed the petitions when either the proposal was negative or the model refused to sign made higher conformity scores than did *S*s who did not sign as shown by the scores in [Table 3-7] for the $P_N P_B$ and the $P_P B_N$ conditions. Seven of the 8 comparisons between mean conformity scores of those who signed and those who refused to sign the petitions are in the predicted direction. In other words, Ss who complied with the petitioner's request under a negative condition also were found to be more responsive to social pressures in two of the three experimental tests of conformity and they made higher submissive scores in the *A-S* Reaction Study. The differences between those who signed and those who refused to sign are significant beyond the 1 per cent level of confidence (*cf.* [Table 3-7]).

## D. DISCUSSION

The results of the present experiment demonstrate that under certain conditions situational factors are more powerful than personal factors in determining whether or not *S*s will sign a petition. In view of the overwhelming positive response by the standardizing groups to the flood lighting proposal and their overwhelming negative response to the proposal to remove the soft-drink machines from University buildings, it may safely be assumed that the inner convictions of the test *S*s coincided with those of the standardizing groups since the test *S*s were drawn from the same population as the standardizing groups. Since 63 per cent *fewer S*s signed the positive proposal when the background was negative than when it was positive and 33 per cent *more S*s signed the negative proposal when the background was positive than when it was negative, it is evident that situational factors counterbalanced the inner convictions of a considerable proportion of the test *S*s.

The results also demonstrate that seeing another person refuse to sign a positive proposal was more effective in reducing the number of signers than seeing another sign a negative proposal was in increasing the number of signers. Does this mean that a negative element in a situation of this kind is more powerful than a positive element in its effect on behavior?

In addition to situational factors and inner convictions there is another personal factor—the tendency to conform to a request made by another individual—which determines whether or not *S*s will sign. Individuals who maintained greater independence in the face of social pressures refused to sign whenever the situation contained a negative element, whereas many of those with higher measures of conformity signed the petition even though the situation contained a strong negative element. This finding implies that even with standardized situational conditions, frequency of signing is a function of strength of conforming tendency in the individual as well as inner conviction regarding the proposal.

## E. SUMMARY

In this study it has been found that when situational factors are either all positive or all negative practically all individuals behave alike by responding positively or negatively to a request to sign a petition. Inner convictions and other personal factors seem to be outweighed by situational factors in such cases. When situational factors are in conflict, some being positive and some negative, then inner convictions and conforming tendencies determine resultant actions. Under the conditions of this study a negative element in the situation confronting the subjects exerted more influence in causing individuals to refuse to sign a petition than did a positive element in inducing them to agree to sign. Individuals signing petitions when the proposal was an unpopular one or after seeing another individual refuse to sign were found to rate significantly higher in tests of submissiveness than did individuals who refused to sign under these conditions. Even under conditions of rigid standardization of presenting petitions the mere request to sign a petition operates effectively with submissive subjects regardless of the content of the petition.

## REFERENCES

1. **ALLPORT, G. W., & ALLPORT, F. H.** *A-S* Reaction Study. Boston: Houghton-Mifflin, 1928.

2. **BLAKE, R. R., & MOUTON, J. S.** The study of social conduct within the framework of adaptation-level theory. *In* Sherif, M., & Wilson, M. O. (*Eds.*). *Emerging Problems in Social Psychology*. Third Conf. in Social Psychol., Univ. Oklahoma. (In press.)

3. **BLAKE, R. R., HELSON, H., & MOUTON, J. S.** Generality of conforming behavior as a function of factual anchorage, difficulty of task, and amount of social pressures. *J. Soc. Psychol., J. Personal.*, 1957, **25**, 294-305.

4. **BLAKE, R. R., MOUTON, J. S., & HAIN, J. D.** Social forces in petition-signing. *Southwestern Soc. Sci. Quar.*, 1956, **36** 385-390.

5. **HELSON, H.** Adaptation-level as frame of reference for prediction of psychophysical data. *Amer. J. Psychol.*, 1947, **60**, 1-29.

6. **SNEDECOR, G. W.** Statistical Methods. Ames, Iowa: Iowa State Coll. Press, 1938.

7. **THURSTONE, L. L.** (*Ed.*). Attitudes Toward War. Scale No. 2, Forms *A* and *B* (1930) and Scale No. 34, Forms *A* and *B* (1931). Chicago: Univ. Chicago Press, 1930-1931.

# THE INFLUENCE OF PICKETING ON THE PURCHASE OF TOY GUNS

MICHAEL LUPFER, JANE KAY, AND SARA ANN BURNETTE
*Department of Psychology, Memphis State University*

## A. INTRODUCTION

The degree to which picketing represents an effective social influence in altering attitudes and behavior has been difficult to assess because its effect usually cannot be isolated from the concurrent impact of other factors (e.g., the influence of labor strikes and pressure groups) affecting the attitude or behavior espoused by the picketers. However, an issue prompting pickets occasionally creates a situation in which the effect of picketing can be assessed almost immediately, without being seriously confounded by other factors. For the past several years, the sale of realistic "toy guns" for children has been an issue of public controversy. The marketing of these toys has been decried (4, 5, 6), and pickets protesting the manufacture and sale of such toys have been reported (1, 7). In rebuttal, the Toy Manufacturers of the U.S.A. has issued a statement denying a correlation between adult violence and childhood exposure to war toys (3, 4).

The controversy over the sale of toy guns provided a credible issue and natural setting for testing the effectiveness of picketing as a form of social influence. The situation represented by the following study possessed two merits not ordinarily found where picketing occurs: The latency between the independent variable (exposure to the picket) and the dependent variable (purchase of toy guns) was brief, and the dependent variable was measured easily and unobtrusively.

## B. METHOD

**1. Subjects and Setting** The *S*s were 452 toy buyers at a large discount department store in Memphis, Tennessee,[1] from 9-11 a.m. during the period December 17-19 and 21-23, 1965. The department store is located in a working-class section of the city, though the manager of the store stated that the store's customers come from all segments of the city's population. There were 309 female and 143 male toy buyers, a toy buyer being any individual who purchased at least one toy at one of the three toy department cash registers in the store.

**2. Stimulus Materials** Two picket signs, measuring 28 inches by 22 inches and reading "Toy Guns Today Mean Real Guns Tomorrow," were used. Each sign was composed of a red background with bright yellow letters, except the word "mean" which was orange. The letters were approximately 2¾ inches high and 2 inches wide. Two black silhouettes (12 inches high), one a cowboy and the other a "real" gun, appeared in the upper left-hand and lower right-hand corners of each sign.

**3. Experimental Procedure** Permission to picket was obtained from the department store with the understanding that the signs would be implicit in meaning: i.e., that no explicit statement urging customers not to buy toy guns would be made.

The study was conducted over a period of six mornings, picketing occurring on the second, fourth, and sixth mornings and no picketing occurring on the first, third and fifth mornings. Alternation of picketing and nonpicketing provided a control for variation in sales as Christmas approached.

Three male and two female undergraduate psychology majors, all in their early twenties, served as picketers.[2] They dressed casually but conventionally to prevent any reinforcement of negative stereotypes of picketers. Though only two students picketed at any given time, all five picketed approximately equal periods of time during the course of the study. They held signs and stood on either side of the entrance-exit doors of the store. Since there was but one entrance, all customers had to pass the signs to enter the store.

The students arrived at the store each morning before it opened to make sure that no person entered the store without an opportunity to see the signs or to pass through the registers without being counted. Each day, observers inside the store were posted at each of the three toy cash registers (the only places in the store where toys could be purchased) and inconspicuously tallied the number of persons who bought toys, the number of toy buyers whose purchases included toy guns (other "war toys" such as

[1]The authors wish to thank Corondolet department store for its cooperation in this study.

[2]The authors acknowledge, with many thanks, the assistance of James Bradley, Thomas Floyd, and Donald Trotter, who served as picketers.

cannons and grenades were not tabulated), and the sex of the buyer.

The picketers offered no information to customers. If asked any questions, they answered, "We are a group who feel toy guns today mean real guns tomorrow." No group affiliations or rebuttals to comments were given.

## C. RESULTS

The frequency table of toy buyers who did and did not purchase guns on picketing and nonpicketing mornings is presented in [Table 3-8]. The obtained chi-square value indicates a significant relationship between picketing and the purchase of toy guns, specifically that picketing depressed the sale of toy guns.

Subsequent analyses suggested that male and female toy buyers did not differ in their tendency to buy toy guns, regardless of whether picketing did or did not occur. On picketing mornings, seven male and 10 female toy buyers bought guns, while 63 male and 135 female toy buyers did not, yielding a chi-square value of .68 ($p > .30$). On nonpicketing mornings, 13 male and 22 female toy buyers bought guns, while 60 male and 142 female toy buyers did not, yielding a chi-square value of .78 ($p > .30$).

**[Table 3-8] Number of toy buyers who bought and did not buy guns on picketing and nonpicketing mornings**

| Condition | Toy buyers who bought guns | Toy buyers who did not buy guns |
|---|---|---|
| Picketing | 17 | 198 |
| Nonpicketing | 35 | 202 |

NOTE: $\chi^2 = 5.16, p < .05$.

## D. DISCUSSION AND CONCLUSIONS

The evidence supports the hypothesis that picketing which implicitly protests the purchase of toy guns for children depresses the sale of these toys and that this relationship is consistent for both males and females. This study, unlike the research of Blake's Texas group, was not conducted to test a theoretical prediction, though the results are consistent with Blake's general findings on the effectiveness of prohibitions, such as a poster forbidding entry to a building; a sign prohibiting drinking from a fountain; or a command to stop a designated activity (2).

The data do not indicate whether picketing served as more than a temporary inhibitor on the actions of potential gun buyers. Observation over a longer period of time might provide some clarification to this question. Furthermore, increasing the period of observation to afternoon and evening hours would embrace a wider spectrum of shoppers, particularly males, and allow for the simultaneous variation of several factors: e.g., the sex and general appearance of the picketers, the wording of the picket signs. The period of observation yielding useful data would always be limited, however, since more than half the yearly sale of toys occurs during the pre-Christmas period (7).

The evidence also gives no answer to the question of whether any basic attitude change resulted from exposure to picketing. While attitudinal measures would have been desirable, the investigators feared that questioning toy buyers, essential for an assessment of attitude change, would have seriously contaminated the behavioral measure.

## REFERENCES


1. **BIGART, H.** ACLU charges police harassment in December 17 arrest of 14 children picketing New York City toy manufacturer to protest Christmas sale of war toys. *The New York Times*, January 9, 1967, 22.
2. **BLAKE, R. R., & MOUTON, J. S.** The experimental investigation of interpersonal influence. In A. D. Biderman & H. Zimmer (Eds.), *The Manipulation of Human Behavior.* New York: John Wiley, 1961. Pp. 216-276.
3. **BUZBEE, W.** Who bombed Santa's workshop? *The New York Times Magazine*, December 12, 1965, 87+.
4. **FULLER, J. G.** Trade winds: Influence of military toys on children. *Saturday Rev.*, 1965, **48**(52), 7.
5. **HONAN, W. H.** Merry bang-bang (and happy new year). *The New Republic*, 1965, **153**(26), 11-12.
6. ———. Christmas (ka-pow!) again. *The New Republic*, 1966, **155**(25), 7-8.
7. **SLOANE, L.** Toy makers say only 5% of playthings are guns. *The New York Times*, December 14, 1965, 63+.

# A FIELD EXPERIMENT ON THE COMPARATIVE EFFECTIVENESS OF "EMOTIONAL" AND "RATIONAL" POLITICAL LEAFLETS IN DETERMINING ELECTION RESULTS

GEORGE W. HARTMANN[1]

## THE EMERGENCE OF POLITICAL PSYCHOLOGY

Political psychology as a separate branch of scientific inquiry is all but non-existent. As an art or practice, however, it has long ranked among the essentials of statecraft and is now a powerful and flourishing factor in the intricate world of affairs. Dictatorships and democracies make different, but apparently equally extensive, use of it in the process of molding public opinion and shaping attitudes. Like all technologies, political psychology may be employed for a variety of ends–it is a "tool" skill for attaining efficiently the goals established by some sort of systematic or unformulated political philosophy.

By the very nature of the field which gives it its name, political psychology is bound to have close relations with advertising and salesmanship, two regions of modern commercial life in which applied psychology has been conspicuously influential. The practices of publicity, propaganda, and intentional indoctrination are the very life-blood of political activity and other "institutional" behavior–remove them and the human interests supporting even the worthiest of movements lose most of their power to affect the course of group conduct or even to maintain their own coherence. He who lacks control over the required stimuli cannot obtain the desired responses.

Despite the serious need for an organized corpus of knowledge about political psychology–which in this generation of large-scale "conflict" promises to become the most important single division of social psychology–the phrase itself is barely found in current usage. The available information and techniques comprising it are loosely distributed in incoordinated fragments among experienced politicians, reflective journalists, and copy-writers, curious social scientists and an occasional laboratory man whose versatility or heterodoxy have allowed him to be sensitive to a broader range of interests. This is a strange circumstance when one recalls that American political parties, "machines" and individual candidates annually spend unascertained millions either to get or to hold public office with its associated benefits. A substantial fraction of this sum is undoubtedly sheer waste, not only from the standpoint of positive social gain, but even from the point of view of the seekers for power, irrespective of motive. If the direct and indirect expenditures involved in incessant campaigning were correctly totalled, they would probably approach in the aggregate the amount spent on public education in the United States. To enhance the efficiency of the latter process we have developed an army of educational psychologists and allied specialists, but neither the professions nor the universities recognize such an individual as the "political psychologist."

However, if psychologists on the basis of Strong's law can recommend that the small business man spread his modest budget for a little advertising over a number of periodicals rather than concentrating all in one journal, why should they not be able to guide a minority political party in using its limited funds to secure the maximum number of votes?[2] The social utility in both cases may be low, but it is surely no lower in the competitive political field of a democracy than in the competitive business sphere of our economic system. The politician would like to know more exactly the relative vote-getting strength of an equal expenditure of time, money, and effort on newspaper, billboard, radio, personal interview, and speech-making publicity, but the psychologist has given him little or no help in this or related matters.[3] So far as the writer knows, the present study is the first experimental[4] attempt to develop a *rapproche-*

[1] Performed while serving as a post-doctoral Fellow of the Advanced School of Education, Teachers College, Columbia University.

[2] The Psychological Corporation through its national network of regional representatives is ideally organized to do such work.

[3] Perhaps an exception should be made of W. H. Wilke's "An experimental comparison of the speech, the radio and the printed page as propaganda devices." Archives of Psychology, 1934, No. 169.

[4] "Experimental" at least in the sense that deliberate intervention in a pre-election situation was planned. This distinguishes it from the post hoc researches of the type reported by Stuart Rice in his Quantitative Methods in Politics, Knopf, 1928.

*ment* between the two fields of endeavor on other than insecure laboratory analogies.

## WILL "APPEALS TO REASON" OR APPEALS TO THE EMOTIONS WIN MORE VOTES?

Both Gestalt theory and the doctrine of the "total situation" have shown that the capacity of apparently "identical" stimuli to evoke certain desired responses is dependent upon the setting, context, or "manner" in which they occur. Will an appeal, request, or command to vote for a certain party, policy, issue, or individual be more influential when it accompanies or follows a logical exposition of the case or when it appears with or after an emotional approach to the unanalyzed existing loyalties of the voter? The question as phrased implies an extreme dichotomy and opposition between the two types of mental process, whereas it is more likely that the real "contrast" is between two appeals containing various combinations of rationality and emotionality. The contrast here proposed is between a complex fusion of excitement, resentment, vague enthusiasms, strongly aroused fears and hopes, and a calm, orderly, and restrained presentation of either concrete proposals or abstract objectives. It does not take a high degree of psychological sophistication to bet (other things being equal) on the greater strength of the "emotional" attack with any random sample of the American population. However, it is important to remember that this prediction rests exclusively upon theoretical and empirical considerations, and not upon the measured findings of any deliberately devised experiment on the problem of political behavior under complex motivation. It is this kind of confirmation which the investigation here reported seeks to supply.[5]

## THE 1935 ELECTION SITUATION IN PENNSYLVANIA

The possibility of a really effective test was provided by the local and state elections held in Pennsylvania on November 6, 1935. At the time, many municipal and county offices were to be filled, as well as two important state-wide judgeships. Because it met certain extraneous considerations, such as ease of access for the experimenter, the use of voting machines, which are generally believed to enhance, if they do not guarantee, the accuracy of the poll, etc., the city of Allentown in Lehigh county was chosen as the scene of operations. For a similar variety of reasons the Socialist party in that community was made the beneficiary of the special appeals whose relative potency was being measured. The local Democratic and Republican parties were so closely matched that any publicity which would have favored one rather than the other would have created an intolerably delicate situation for an experimenter whose motives could hardly have been made clear or acceptable to a suspicious populace.[6] The Socialist party, on the other hand, was admirably suited to this purpose, since it was universally agreed that its candidates were not likely to win in this area; its exaltation of principles and ideals over individual standard bearers made possible more sharply defined contrasts without the danger of wounding personal feelings.

## PREPARATION OF THE MOTIVATING STIMULI

The next task was the construction of the contrasting leaflets. This was much harder than anticipated because a search through Socialist propaganda "literature" gave types of printed appeals which were too mixed and "impure" in style, content, and length to meet the prescribed conditions. Consequently, the experimenter wrote the texts for three pairs of emotional and rational leaflets of the desired brevity. These were submitted to thirty rank-and-file adults in Allentown; the pair finally used was the pair overwhelmingly adopted by them as the most "liked". Inspection showed that the rejected leaflets had a more involved sentence structure, heavier vocabulary burden, and lower persuasiveness than those retained. Six competent psychologists agreed that in the pair finally selected, one—the academic "test" involving some reflective judgment—was predominantly "reasonable" in character, and the other—an intimate family letter—mainly "sentimental".

Five thousand copies of each of the two appeals were printed on heavy white paper in identical typography in the form of a four-page (one sheet folded) leaflet, the cover pages bearing the titles, "Try this test on yourself" (=rational) and "Will you answer this letter?" (=emotional), respectively. The two inside pages are reproduced below. The last or back page simply bore a straightforward list of the party

[5] Similar researches could be built around such pairings as the relative effectiveness of constructive vs. destructive political appeals, emphasis upon "ideas" versus personalities, the use of praise and blame, the strength of group vs. self interests, material vs. "spiritual" incentives, and even the specific advantages of placards with and without the portraits of candidates. Our existing knowledge of these matters is exceedingly shaky.

[6] The present writer was the 1935 Socialist candidate whose vote appears in the tables below. This union of psychologist and "politician" explains how the present study came into being.

candidates with the respective city, county, and state offices opposite their names.

You've heard of intelligence tests, haven't you? Well, we have a little examination right here which we are sure you will enjoy taking, even if you didn't care much for school when you were a youngster. The beauty of this test is that you can score it yourself without any teacher to tell you whether you passed or failed.

This is how it works. First read each one of the seven statements printed below. If you *approve* the idea as it stands, *underline* the word AGREE; if you *disapprove* of the idea, underline the word DISAGREE. Simple, isn't it? All right, then. Get your pencil ready. All set? Go!

1. We would have much cheaper electric light and power if this industry were owned and operated by the various governmental units for the benefit of all the people. AGREE–DISAGREE.
2. No gifted boy or girl should be denied the advantages of higher education just because his parents lack the money to send him to college. AGREE–DISAGREE.
3. The Federal Government should provide to all classes of people opportunity for complete insurance at cost against accident, sickness, premature death and old age. AGREE–DISAGREE.
4. All banks and insurance companies should be run on a non-profit basis like the schools. AGREE–DISAGREE.
5. Higher income taxes on persons with incomes of more than $10,000 a year should be levied immediately. AGREE–DISAGREE.
6. The only way most people will ever be able to live in modern sanitary homes is for the government to build them on a non-profit basis. AGREE–DISAGREE.
7. Many more industries and parts of industries should be owned and managed co-operatively by the producers (all the workers) themselves. AGREE–DISAGREE.

Have you answered them all? Fine. Now go back and count the number of sentences with which you AGREED. Then count the number with which you DISAGREED. *If the number of agreements is larger than the number of disagreements, you are at heart a Socialist*–whether you know it or not!

Now that you have tested yourself and found out how much of a Socialist you really are, *why don't you try voting for the things you actually want?* The Republicans and Democrats don't propose to give these things to you, because a mere look at their records will show that they are opposed to them. Do you get the point?

HELP BUILD THE AGE OF PLENTY!

**VOTE:** | SOCIALIST | X |

Allentown, Pennsylvania
November 1, 1935

Dear Mother and Father:

We youngsters are not in the habit of giving much thought to serious things. You have often told us so and we admit it.

But while we like to play football and have a good time dancing and cause you a lot of amusement as well as worry with our "puppy loves," we sometimes think long and hard. You ought to know what many of us young folks are quietly saying to ourselves.

Our future as American citizens in 1940 looks dark. We want jobs–and good jobs, too–so that we can help in the useful work of the world. But we know that many of our brightest high-school and college graduates find it absolutely impossible to get any kind of employment. We also know that this condition is not temporary, but that it will last as long as we stick to harmful ways of running business, industry and government.

We want to continue our education, but we haven't the heart to ask you to make that sacrifice. With Dad working only part-time on little pay and Mother trying to make last year's coat and dress look in season, we feel we ought to pitch in and help keep the family's neck above water. But we can't. The world as it is now run has no use for us.

Many of our teachers know what is wrong, although we can see that most of them are afraid to say what they really think. Luckily, the text-books and school magazines keep us in touch with new ideas, and we have learned to read between the lines of the ordinary newspaper. Please don't be frightened if we tell you what we have decided!

*We young people are becoming Socialists.* We have to be. We can't be honest with ourselves and be anything else. *The Socialist Party is the only party which is against all wars*–and we have learned from our history courses what awful wars have taken place under both Republicans and Democrats. We refuse to be slaughtered (like Uncles Bob and Charles were in 1918) just to make profits for ammunition manufacturers.

*The Socialist Party seeks to create a world in which there will be no poverty.* In our science classes we learn how power machinery and other modern inventions make it possible for all of us to have enough of all the goods and services we need. Yet look at our town with its unpainted shacks, suffering parents, half-starved children! We might have everything, but we continue to live on next to nothing.

It is all so unnecessary. You have had to lead a poor workingman's life, because you and most of the workers and farmers of this country have regularly voted for either the Republican or Democratic parties, between which there is no real difference. These old machines are not for us.

*The youth of 1935 want to Build a Better America,* in which there will be no poverty, no fear of unemployment, no threat of war. We ask you to follow the lead of the Socialist Party this year because that is the most direct way for you to *help hasten the day when Peace and Plenty and lasting Prosperity will be the lot of all men.* Good parents such as you desire these things for us. But we can never have them as long as you are controlled by your old voting habits.

We are profoundly earnest about this. Our generation cannot enjoy the beauty and justice of the *New America* if you block our highest desires. There was a time when you too were young like us. We beg you in the name of those early memories and spring-time hopes to *support the Socialist ticket in the coming elections!*

Your Sons and Daughters

**VOTE:** | SOCIALIST | X |

## COMPOSITION OF THE TESTING POPULATION

Having settled upon the differential stimuli, the next step was the mapping out of the city into experimental and control areas. The variations in the size of the wards, density of population, assessed real-estate valuation, previous voting habits, and presumptive socio-economic status made the problem of establishing "comparable" groups unexpectedly difficult. While it is not pretended that all the obstacles were overcome, a feasible apportionment consisted in matching wards 2, 9, and 10 (=the emotional) with wards 3, 4, 5, and 7 (=the rational); the remaining twelve wards (there are nineteen in all) were simple "controls". The two experimental regions consequently had the nature of adjacent islands in a large control sea. [Table 3-9] contains some of the relevant data concerning these three areas which may be used in interpreting the results.

## APPLICATION OF THE STIMULUS PATTERNS

The stimulation plan consisted in distributing the two sets of leaflets in their assigned districts so that every family residing therein would be affected. The distributors were interested adults, all party members, who discharged their task by giving the recipient the leaflet with a polite request that it be read when convenient. If no one was at home to receive the leaflet in this manner, it was simply thrust under the door. About one-half of the prospective voters was given the leaflet in person; the other half presumably found it upon returning home. The material was all distributed between Monday and Thursday of the week preceding Election Day. Apart from a few radio talks, which affected the entire city uniformly, no other campaign activity or proselytizing was carried on during this season.

## RESULTING CHANGES IN THE PROPORTION OF VOTES RECEIVED IN THREE AREAS

The reaction to such stimulation with a specific purpose can be tested only at the ballot-box, *i.e.*, the final measure of belief or conviction is the readiness and willingness to act. Here we need to know not only the present vote, but also the base-line or reference vote of the preceding year. This has to be calculated in terms of percentages because of the fluctuating participation of the electorate in successive years. Schematically, a clear-cut check would be provided if in 1934 the Socialist vote in Allentown as a whole were 4 per cent of the total for all parties and if in 1935 it were 5 per cent in the rational wards, 6 per cent in the emotional wards, and 3 per cent in the control wards (assuming statistically reliable differences). This comparison made it necessary to contrast figures for the state-wide "heads of the tickets" which in 1934 were the governor and in 1935 the judge of the Supreme Court. Other offices fluctuate slightly from the figures for the party candidates for these leading positions. [Table 3-9] contains the necessary data for an appraisal of the effect of the two kinds of propaganda.

## ANALYSIS OF THE TABULAR RECORD

The first item to be noted is that the total vote cast increased by 3,594, or 16.69 per cent, from 21,533 in 1934 to 25,127 in 1935. This decided increase in public participation is a fact which complicates the remaining calculations. The official Allentown registration list contained 34,424 names–17,236 Democrats, 15,001 Republicans, and 187 Socialists. The Socialists polled about three and one-half times as many ballots as they had registered adherents, while the other two parties received from two-thirds to four-fifths of their overt registration. This is a common American phenomenon, since economic discretion probably causes many Socialist sympathizers to enroll on the other lists. Even in the nearby city of Reading, which has had Socialist administrators and consequently greater party prestige, the Socialist vote normally trebles its registration.

The second fact to be observed is that the Socialist vote in Allentown as a whole (and even in the control wards where there was no definite "activity") rose pro-

[Table 3-9] **Comparative increase in voting behavior under differential stimulation**

| Ward | Vote for Governor, 1934 | | | Vote for Supreme Court Judge, 1935 | | | Assessed valuation per capita | Inhabitants per acre |
|---|---|---|---|---|---|---|---|---|
| Rational | Democrat | Republican | Socialist | Democrat | Republican | Socialist | | |
| 3 | 384 | 378 | 4 | 518 | 496 | 14 | $1,663.64 | 32.51 |
| 4 | 402 | 347 | 10 | 374 | 381 | 8 | 2,786.19 | 44.08 |
| 5 | 283 | 209 | 14 | 320 | 321 | 19 | 3,094.01 | 40.70 |
| 7 | 484 | 556 | 20 | 575 | 650 | 24 | 1,478.73 | 41.40 |
| | 1553 | 1490 | 48 | 1787 | 1848 | 65 | 2,070.12 (Mean) | 38.44 (Mean) |
| Per cent of party total | 14.38 | 14.56 | 9.62 | 14.63 | 15.08 | 9.95 | | |
| Raw increase | | | | 234 | 358 | 17 | | |
| Percentage increase | | | | 15.07 | 24.03 | 35.42 | | |
| Emotional | | | | | | | | |
| 2 | 497 | 311 | 30 | 541 | 302 | 33 | 1,581.26 | 29.44 |
| 9 | 618 | 284 | 16 | 666 | 337 | 29 | 851.69 | 43.89 |
| 10 | 1188 | 623 | 64 | 1282 | 828 | 103 | 615.82 | 38.37 |
| | 2303 | 1218 | 110 | 2489 | 1467 | 165 | 871.72 (Mean) | 37.28 (Mean) |
| Per cent of party total | 21.32 | 11.90 | 22.04 | 20.37 | 11.97 | 25.27 | | |
| Raw increase | | | | 186 | 249 | 55 | | |
| Percentage increase | | | | 8.08 | 20.44 | 50.00 | | |

**[Table 3-9] – Continued.**

| Ward | Vote for Governor, 1934 | | | Vote for Supreme Court Judge, 1935 | | | Assessed valuation per capita | Inhabitants per acre |
|---|---|---|---|---|---|---|---|---|
| Control | Democrat | Republican | Socialist | Democrat | Republican | Socialist | | |
| 1 | 502 | 408 | 25 | 512 | 422 | 39 | $ 941.34 | 11.82 |
| 6 | 591 | 177 | 23 | 782 | 114 | 18 | 624.80 | 15.97 |
| 8 | 1383 | 1371 | 101 | 1635 | 1835 | 110 | 721.53 | 24.06 |
| 11 | 1264 | 2358 | 28 | 1430 | 2648 | 47 | 1,202.87 | 20.23 |
| 12 | 605 | 419 | 51 | 665 | 606 | 49 | 1,089.54 | 3.36 |
| 13 | 748 | 1206 | 19 | 730 | 1399 | 22 | 1,264.51 | 18.83 |
| 14 | 577 | 208 | 48 | 626 | 277 | 64 | 704.56 | 6.35 |
| 15 | 507 | 436 | 25 | 551 | 472 | 32 | 1,021.68 | 2.01 |
| 16 | 341 | 186 | 13 | 468 | 268 | 22 | 556.76 | 4.85 |
| 17 | 160 | 408 | 1 | 167 | 428 | 2 | 2,380.04 | 2.24 |
| 18 | 67 | 158 | – | 83 | 171 | 1 | 447.78 | 10.50 |
| 19 | 200 | 190 | 7 | 291 | 303 | 17 | 773.89 | 13.42 |
| | 6945 | 7525 | 341 | 7940 | 8943 | 423 | 946.19 (Mean) | 7.58 (Mean) |
| Per cent of party total | 64.30 | 73.54 | 68.34 | 65.00 | 72.96 | 64.78 | | |
| Raw increase | | | | 995 | 1418 | 82 | | |
| Percentage increase | | | | 14.33 | 15.86 | 24.05 | 1,088.08 (City Mean) | 10.17 (City Mean) |
| Party total | 10,801 | 10,233 | 499 | 12,216 | 12,258 | 653 | | |
| Per cent of all ballots | 50.16 | 47.52 | 2.32 | 48.62 | 48.78 | 2.60 | | |
| Raw increase | | | | 1415 | 2025 | 154 | | |
| Percentage increase | | | | 13.10 | 19.79 | 30.86 | | |

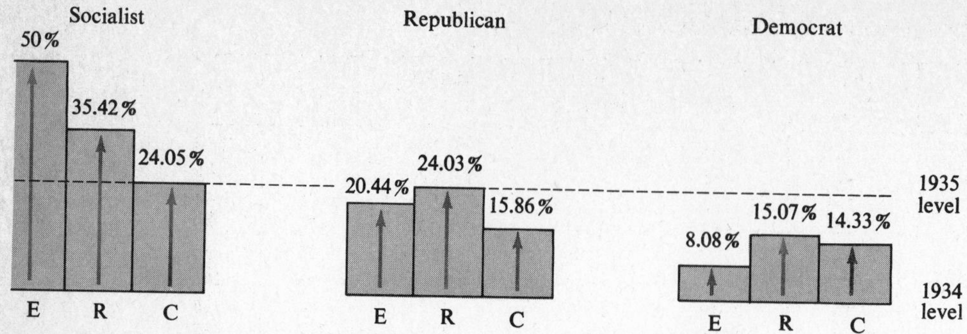


[FIGURE 3-1] Rough schema indicating differential gains in voting preference under various types of stimulation. Although all parties received more votes in 1935 than in 1934, the Socialists gained relatively more in the areas where "emotional" (E) and "rational" (R) appeals were used; (C) stands for "control" district.

portionately more than did that of the other parties.[7] With about 17 per cent more general participation in 1935 than in 1934, the total Socialist vote increased 30.86 per cent, the Republican 19.79 per cent, and the Democrat 13.10 per cent, indicating a relative loss for the last party despite an absolute gain. The crucial detail for our purpose is that the Socialist vote in the "emotional" wards rose 50 per cent, in the "rational" 35.42 per cent, and in the control 24.05 per cent—all differences large enough to be reliable even though no single adequate measures of this are applicable. This is wholly in harmony with the predicted outcomes and is a gratifying confirmation of the general hypothesis. The relations may be seen more clearly from an inspection of [Figure 3-1].

Although the use of percentages rather than absolute figures may create a faulty emphasis, these diagrams nevertheless portray best the main finding of this study, viz., that specific "revealed" propaganda definitely accelerates a tendency already present. This general "secular" trend, of course, may in turn be due to widespread contributory propaganda of a more diffuse sort.

The efficacy of these two leaflets may be brought out more fully by comparing the actual with the predicted increases of each party's total vote in the various regions under consideration. This has been done in [Table 3-10].

If the $\frac{\text{Actual}}{\text{Expected}}$ ratio is 1.00, this means that the two values coincide; if it is less it means that the party involved obtained less than its proportionate share; if more than 1.00, the party affected gained "unduly". Since they are based upon the same raw data, these computations tell essentially the same story conveyed by [Figure 3-1]. The increase in the Socialist vote in the "rational" and "emotional" areas was about two or three times, respectively, its probable gain if these stimuli had been omitted.

## SOME NECESSARY PRECAUTIONS AND CORRECTIONS

In order to correct for the inevitable exaggerative effect which such phrases as "per cent of gain" evidently produce, [Table 3-11] has been prepared. This should effectively dispel the spurious impression of a "landslide" suggested by some types of comparison.

If we select the most favorable showing—that made in the "emotional" district—we see that the effect of the leaflet has been to make one voter out of every twenty-five support the Socialist ticket where before only one person in thirty-three had done so. Had no leaflets been distributed at all, the entire Socialist vote presumably would have been 619 (*i.e.*, 499 plus 499 x 24.05, the control rate of increase); if the superior emotional leaflet had been spread evenly throughout the town, the probable total would have been 749 (*i.e.*, 499 plus 499 x .50); actually, under the mixed conditions obtaining where most of the community was the "control", the total was 653.

Because of the selective treatment which these leaf-

[7] Does this mean that the larger the total participation in balloting, the greater will be the relative minority vote? Is it not possible that the customary non-voters are more plastic in their political convictions, and that they contain a proportionately larger number of protest and opposition voters who usually refrain from exercising the franchise because of a sense of futility? In this case, only severe social crises will bring them out. Cf. the extraordinarily high rate of suffrage utilization in Germany from 1918 to 1933.

**[Table 3-10] How the three parties fared in three differently treated areas**

| Party | District | 1934 vote | 1935 vote | Expected increase | Actual increase | A-E | A/E |
|---|---|---|---|---|---|---|---|
| Socialist | Rational | 48 | 65 | 8 | 17 | 9 | 2.13 |
| | Emotional | 110 | 165 | 18 | 55 | 37 | 3.06 |
| | Control | 341 | 423 | 57 | 82 | 25 | 1.44 |
| | Entire City | 499 | 653 | 83 | 154 | 71 | 1.86 |
| Democrat | Rational | 1553 | 1787 | 259 | 234 | - 25 | .94 |
| | Emotional | 2303 | 2489 | 384 | 186 | -198 | .48 |
| | Control | 6945 | 7940 | 1159 | 995 | -164 | .86 |
| | Entire City | 10801 | 12216 | 1803 | 1415 | -388 | .78 |
| Republican | Rational | 1490 | 1848 | 249 | 358 | 109 | 1.44 |
| | Emotional | 1218 | 1467 | 203 | 249 | 46 | 1.23 |
| | Control | 7525 | 8943 | 1256 | 1418 | 138 | 1.13 |
| | Entire City | 10233 | 12258 | 1708 | 2025 | 317 | 1.17 |

NOTE: The "Expected increase" column is obtained by multiplying the 1934 vote by the coefficient of increase in public participation, viz., 16.69.

**[Table 3-11] Per cent which socialist vote is of total for all parties in different sections of Allentown**

| | 1934 | 1935 |
|---|---|---|
| Control wards | 2.30 | 2.44 |
| Rational wards | 1.55 | 1.76 |
| Emotional wards | 3.03 | 4.00 |
| Entire city | 2.32 | 2.60 |

lets received, they may be presumed to be above the average of their kind. Nevertheless, even these relatively good broadsides have an "efficiency" of but one-half of 1 per cent, since it took 10,000 leaflets to produce 72 additional votes in the emotional and rational wards combined. Moreover, about half of these added votes were "in the bag" anyhow because of the general situation. It may be estimated that one person in 200 who would not otherwise have voted Socialist was impelled to do so by virtue of the motivation directly traceable to these leaflets. Since it took an absolute commercial minimum of one cent per leaflet for printing and delivery, it will be seen that even this cheap form of legitimate political propaganda costs about three dollars for each additional party voter it secures.[8] To be sure, this stimulation probably has some deferred propaganda value in the sense that cumulative increments at some later date may be made to function more readily because of the "summation of stimuli" involved.

## CONFIRMATORY POST-ELECTION INTERVIEWS

About two weeks after Election Day, personal interviews were arranged with 45 householders (22 men and 23 women) chosen at random from different streets in the rational and emotional districts. It seemed desirable to supplement the objective record of the polls with some qualitative clues as to the way in which the personalities of the voters had been affected by these appeals. Four simple questions were asked of each interviewee with the results shown in [Table 3-12].

Incomplete as this evidence is, it shows plainly the greater impressive and retentive effect of the sentimental appeal. It is axiomatic that a piece of "printed salesmanship" must be attended to and remembered before the message it contains can achieve the end desired by the purveyor. This the emotional leaflet did much more decisively than the rational one, even though both produced more pure "good will" than immediately significant action. As soon as reasonable certainty was attained on these points, the interviews were discontinued, since additional cases did not promise to yield any new information.

## SOME WEAKNESSES AND OBJECTIONS

Although this study bears the formal pattern of the familiar parallel-group experiment, it rests upon an exceedingly imperfect matching of the contrasted populations. The mean density of population in the emotional and rational wards was purposely kept

[8]Cf. the expenditure estimate given in the third paragraph of this article. Congressional and legislative limitations on campaign expenditures are notoriously ineffective because of the many exemptions provided, the failure to include "voluntary" services, etc. The full cost per major party vote is many times that of the minority vote.

**[Table 3-12] Responses obtained in follow-up interviews for determining the impressiveness of two types of campaign literature**

| Question (given orally) | Reply |
|---|---|
| 1. Do you remember receiving any Socialist literature recently? | 29 out of 45 answered "Yes" |
| 2. What was its nature? | 8 out of 12 in the emotional wards said, "An open letter"; only 7 out of 33 in the rational wards knew it was a pamphlet or folder, and only one said it contained "questions" |
| 3. Did the literature you read influence you to vote for any Socialist candidates? | Four said it made them "split" their votes for the first time; no effect on others |
| 4. What did you think of the Socialist literature you saw? | 24 said they were "not interested"; 6 said it contained "good principles"; 4 said "very good"; 2 said they would never read any Socialist material; 1 said it was "too deep, he couldn't understand it"; 8 others expressed some degree of favor |

practically identical, but the latter region has more than twice the per capita real-estate valuation of the former (tax exempt property is excluded in these calculations). In matching for one factor, we have unmatched for another. Are not the preexisting attitudes of prospective Socialist voters strongly affected by their economic status?

The answer, of course, is a qualified "Yes", but this does not mean that there is an inverse relation between receptivity to the Socialist appeal and financial well-being. Observation indicates that the correlation is zero or slightly positive. Both the well-to-do and the poor may be persuaded to vote Socialist, although they may respond differentially to a specific approach.[9] The control group occupies the same financial level as the "emotional" population, but because of the absence of stimulation no comparable voting increase occurred. To be sure, the rational group did not gain as much as the emotional one, but this was not due to its superior economic position—these people were simply bombarded with an inferior instrument.[10] Absolute assurance that this interpretation is correct can be obtained only by reversing the appeals in another community.

Admittedly, pure experimental conditions are hard to maintain in a study of this sort, but it is an unscientific counsel of despair to refrain from using to best advantage whatever approximations thereto one can achieve. Election results are not the outcomes of single stimulation—they resemble more a complex resultant of intricate forces. Thus, energetic Socialist propaganda would undoubtedly call forth more effort from the other parties, but that would probably occur only where they sensed a genuine threat to their position, which was not the case in this city.

## CONCLUSIONS

There seems to be no escape from the decision that the emotional political appeal is a better vote-getting instrument than the rational approach, at least in the sense in which these terms describe the essential difference between the two leaflets reproduced above. The sentimental open letter integrates itself easily with such strong permanent central attitudes as parental affection and the desire for a "better life". It employs a familiar literary form, is concrete in imagery, "breathes sincerity", and is not obviously or even basically untrue. It is interesting because it digs deeply into the inner personality and links Socialism with some vital needs.

The "intelligence test", on the other hand, is straightforward, matter of fact, and unexpectedly manoeuvres the reader into an acknowledgment that he is more of a Socialist than he realizes.[11] Save for a faint inferiority feeling which this form may create, these features are positive advantages, although they

---

[9] It may be necessary to remind the reader that the Socialist vote does not come primarily from the "disinherited" or underprivileged. A glance at the returns from poverty-stricken areas, both urban and rural, shows this plainly. Socialist sympathizers in the universities are proportionately greater than among the general public; American labor unions are still strongly non-Socialist, if not anti-Socialist; and Dr. George Gallup of the American Institute of Public Opinion found that 82 per cent of the people now on relief voted Democratic in 1932.

[10] As a matter of fact, the per capita valuation per resident is a misleading index to the apparent wealth of the rational group. These wards are in the downtown business section where rented apartments above the ground floors are the commonest type of housing. The buildings are largely owned by persons living in the control wards.

[11] The seven propositions which appear in this appeal are items favored by a definite majority of sample Pennsylvania populations. Hence, the high probability of obtaining a preponderance of "Agrees" from a new random selection. Otherwise, they would have been too risky to use. With many individuals, of course, these statements definitely prejudice the case "against" rather than "for".

evidently do not outweigh the factors of strength in the other leaflet. Thus the ancient educational maxims of the Herbartians are vindicated anew in the field of political psychology! Those ideas will be most readily assimilated by the voter which fit in with his present "apperceptive mass", which are joined with some prepotent wants, which meet him on his own level and lead him on from where he is.

From a certain point of view, this investigation may be considered a research in "political pedagogy". Thorndike has repeatedly insisted that "education is a process of changing human beings for the better", and much of current educational technique consists in discovering and applying ways for making these modifications more efficiently. Political propaganda for good or ill does more to influence people's knowledge and attitudes in the field of the social sciences than all the formal educational apparatus of our time. Since so many desirable social changes are not made because the public refuses to admit that they would constitute an improvement, it is important for educational statesmanship to know what *means* of persuasion will increase the probability of realizing these *ends*. The present problem is just one aspect of this larger issue.

## SUMMARY

During the election campaign of 1935, the city of Allentown, Pennsylvania, was divided for experimental purposes into three types of wards: 1, an "emotional" area in which all the resident adults received leaflets written in vigorous advertising style urging support of the Socialist ticket; 2, a "rational" region, in which a more academic type of persuasion was used; and 3, a control district where nothing was distributed. The increase in the minority party vote was greatest in the emotional wards, next largest in the rational wards, and lowest in the control wards. These facts may constitute a significant beginning for an experimentally grounded political psychology and pedagogy.

# CHAPTER FOUR

# THE EFFECTS OF SOCIAL STATUS

The research in this area is concerned with classification of others according to some criterion of worth. People of low status are considered not to have the valued characteristics attributed to persons of high status. To a great extent, status is determined by the person making the evaluation, not by the person being evaluated. As expected, status can be defined in many ways; hence, the studies reported in this chapter do not share the same criteria of status. Status of an individual has been defined experimentally by the make of car he drives (Doob & Gross), his type of dress (Bickman; Lefkowitz, Blake, & Mouton) and by sociometric ratings (Harari & McDavid). For our purpose, the most important aspect of the study of status is to determine how it affects psychological variables such as honesty, conformity, and aggression.

Doob and Gross (page 98) examined the effect of status by staging a common situation: a car in front of us does not move when the traffic light turns green. Most drivers honk their horns in response to this delay. What is of interest in this study is that honking was a function of the make of the car. More honking occurred when the car was of low status.

Doob and Gross also mentioned that in two cases, instead of honking at the car, the subject ran into it. This occurred only with the low-status car. In most laboratory experiments, the experimenter can control the situation. However, in field situations, the subject may not always respect the status of the experiment or the experimenter. In a number of studies reported in this book, the experimenters exposed themselves to possible dangers (e.g., Kohn & Williams, Chapter 9). Since real-life situations are indeed real, these events may be unavoidable. Thus, in conducting field experiments, one must try to anticipate the unexpected because of the wide variety of people and situations dealt with.

Doob and Gross's article is also important because it studies an area of behavior which has not been frequently investigated: driving behavior. Although most of us spend a great deal of time in the car and much of our economy is based on it, the social scientist has not studied driving behavior extensively. In Chapter 3, Barch has shown how conformity is important in driving behavior. Davis (in Chapters 5 and 9) stresses the importance of interaction in a public vehicle. Shor (Chapter 9) presents a model showing how people with different expectations may cause accidents. There is much potential here for important research. What are the most effective ways to control speeding? Would certain types of signs, unmarked cars, radar traps, or educational campaigns produce the desired effects?

What role other than giving tickets for traffic violations, can police serve in preventing accidents? Social psychology has developed techniques and knowledge which might offer help with these problems. The research on persuasion and conformity appears to be especially relevant to this concern.

The studies by Bickman and by Lefkowitz, Blake, and Mouton show how others' dress can affect our behavior. In the study by Bickman (page 102), persons who appeared to be of low status were treated more dishonestly than those of apparently higher status. Feldman's study (Chapter 2), in which he found the social class of the cheater to be of some significance, is related to this finding. Unlike Feldman, Bickman found that only the social class of the person who was deceived was important. Lefkowitz et al. (page 105) found that a person dressed to look low status was much less effective than a high-status person in influencing people to follow him across a street, when the "Wait" sign was operating. Lefkowitz et al. do not report any findings about the low-status person's being hit by cars more often than others, as Doob and Gross found with their low-status car.

Manner of dress has received little attention, even though it may play a large role in our everyday behavior. When interaction is at a superficial level, we are likely to use others' appearance in making decisions about how we should behave. The military and police have always considered appearance to be of prime concern. Probably more hours in the army are spent polishing boots and brass than in learning how to fight. Only recently have some police forces felt that they should move away from the military image. Thus, in some towns, the police are wearing blue blazers instead of their usual uniforms. It would be interesting to determine whether any loss of status was incurred with the change of dress.

Vidulich and Wilson's research (page 108) manipulates status by presenting the experimenter as either a graduate student or a faculty member. Manipulations like these have been tried in the laboratory (Thibaut & Riecken, 1955), but not in a field situation. In measuring conformity to the experimenter's humor, Vidulich and Wilson found not only that status of the experimental confederate was important, but also that the structure of the situation determined the degree of social influence. Status was ineffective in prompting students to laugh in a library. This finding is relevant to the question of field experiments versus laboratory experiments. If location, with its attendent norms, is important in the field, then it probably is important in the laboratory. Thus, we can see how the social situation of the laboratory can influence the subject's behavior in unintended ways.

The last study in this chapter is Harari and McDavid's (page 113) study on "finking." They defined status sociometrically; i.e., students rated each other on who they thought could best represent the school. As with the previous findings, the behavior of the high-status person is viewed differently from that of the low-status person. The students did not "fink" on the child as often when he was of high status. This finding could be related to Hollander's (1967) concept of idiosyncrasy credit. According to Hollander, the higher the status of an individual, the more likely the group members are to allow that person to deviate from group expectancy before applying sanctions. Thus, the children would be reluctant to "fink" on the higher-status child's idiosyncratic behavior (i.e., behavior which violates group norms), because of the credit that had accrued to him because of his admirable qualities. Pepitone (1958) also presents a model which relates attribution of causality to status. Pepitone maintains that higher status persons are seen as being more internally motivated, having good intentions, and being more justified in their behavior. All the research in this chapter would support such a model.

In their conclusion, Harari and McDavid stress the necessity for debriefing their subjects. In their experiment, after the data have been collected, the subjects are told the true nature of the experiment, and any questions that they may have are answered. In most laboratory experiments, this is done as a matter of course. However, in most field experiments, there is no attempt to debrief the subjects. There are a number of reasons for this. In laboratory experiments, there are rarely more than 100 subjects involved, while there may be thousands in some of the field experiments in this book. It would be an impossible task to inform all these subjects of the details of the experiment. In addition, we question the necessity and wisdom of informing people about the details of an experiment that they did not know they were in.

## REFERENCES

**PEPITONE, A.** Attributions of causality, social attitudes, and cognitive matching processes. In R. Tagiuri and L. Petrullo (Eds.), *Person perception and interpersonal behavior.* Stanford: Stanford University Press, 1958.

**THIBAUT, J., & RIECKEN, H.** Some determinants and consequences of the perception of social causality. *Journal of Personality,* 1955, **2,** 113-133.

# STATUS OF FRUSTRATOR AS AN INHIBITOR OF HORN-HONKING RESPONSES[1]

ANTHONY N. DOOB AND ALAN E. GROSS
*Departments of Psychology, University of Toronto and University of Wisconsin*

## A. INTRODUCTION

Subjects may consciously attempt to present themselves in a favorable manner, they may cooperate with the experimenter or interviewer, and their reactions may be affected by the measurement process itself. In reviewing a number of such problems, Webb *et al.* (6, pp. 13-27) point out that some of these sources of contamination can be avoided when field data are collected from people who are unaware that they are subjects participating in an experiment. Although field procedures can reduce demand and reactivity effects, experimental manipulations outside of the laboratory may gain realism at the expense of control. The study reported here is an attempt to investigate unobtrusively some effects of frustration in a naturalistic setting without sacrificing experimental control.

Modern automobile traffic frequently creates situations which closely resemble classical formulations of how frustration is instigated. One such instance occurs when one car blocks another at a signal-controlled intersection. Unlike many traffic frustrations, this situation provides a clearly identifiable frustrator and a fairly typical response for the blocked driver: sounding his horn. Horn honking may function instrumentally to remove the offending driver and emotionally to reduce tension. Both kinds of honks may be considered aggressive, especially if they are intended to make the frustrator uncomfortable by bombarding him with unpleasant stimuli.

One factor that is likely to affect aggressive responses is the status of the frustrator (2, 3). The higher a person's status, the more likely it is he will have power to exercise sanctions, and although it is improbable that a high status driver would seek vengeance against a honker, fear of retaliation may generalize from other situations where aggression against superiors has been punished.

Aggression is not the only kind of social response that may be affected by status. High status may inhibit the initiation of any social response, even a simple informational signal. Although it is difficult in the present study to distinguish informational from aggressive motivation, it is hypothesized that a high status frustrator will generally inhibit horn honking.

## B. METHOD

One of two automobiles, a new luxury model or an older car, was driven up to a signal-controlled intersection and stopped. The driver was instructed to remain stopped after the signal had changed to green until 15 seconds had elapsed, or until the driver of the car immediately behind honked his horn twice. Subjects were the 82 drivers, 26 women and 56 men, whose progress was blocked by the experimental car. The experiment was run from 10:30 a.m. to 5:30 p.m. on a Sunday, in order to avoid heavy weekday traffic.

**1. Status Manipulation** A black 1966 Chrysler Crown Imperial hardtop which had been washed and polished was selected as the high status car.[2] Two low status cars were used: a rusty 1954 Ford station wagon and an unobtrusive gray 1961 Rambler sedan. The Rambler was substituted at noon because it was felt that subjects might reasonably attribute the Ford's failure to move to mechanical breakdown. Responses to these two cars did not turn out to be different, and the data for the two low status cars were combined.

**2. Location** Six intersections in Palo Alto and Menlo Park, California, were selected according to these criteria: *(a)* a red light sufficiently long to insure that a high proportion of potential subjects would come to a complete stop behind the experimental car before the signal changed to green, *(b)* relatively light traffic

[1] We wish to thank Tina Fox and Mike Rosenberg, the observers in the field experiment, and Lorraine Soderstrum of Foothill College, Los Altos Hills, California, who made her class available for the questionnaire experiment. The first author was supported by a Public Health Service Predoctoral Fellowship.

[2] We have labeled this operation a "status manipulation" because a large expensive car is frequently associated with wealth, power, and other qualities which are commonly regarded as comprising high status. However, it could be argued that Chrysler is potentially inhibiting not because it is a status symbol, but because of some other less plausible attribute (e.g., physical size).

so that only one car, the subject's, was likely to pull up behind the experimental car, and *(c)* a narrow street so that it would be difficult for the subject to drive around the car blocking him. Approximately equal numbers of high and low status trials were run at each intersection.

**3. Procedure** By timing the signal cycle, the driver of the experimental car usually managed to arrive at the intersection just as the light facing him was turning red. If at least one other car had come to a complete stop behind the experimental car before the signal had turned green, a trial was counted, and when the light changed, an observer started two stop watches and a tape recorder. Observers were usually stationed in a car parked close to the intersection, but when this was not feasible, they were concealed from view in the back seat of the experimental car. High and low status trials were run simultaneously at different intersections, and the two driver-observer teams switched cars periodically during the day. Drivers wore a plaid sport jacket and white shirt while driving the Chrysler, and an old khaki jacket while driving the older car.

*a. Dependent measures* At the end of each trial, the observer noted whether the subject had honked once, twice, or not at all. Latency of each honk and estimated length of each honk were recorded and later double-checked against tape recordings.

*b. Subject characteristics* Immediately after each trial, the observer took down the year, make, and model of the subject's car. Sex and estimated age of driver, number of passengers, and number of cars behind the experimental car when the signal changed were also recorded.

## C. RESULTS AND DISCUSSION

Eight subjects, all men, were eliminated from the analysis for the following reasons: four cars in the low status condition and one in the high status condition went around the experimental car; on one trial the driver of the experimental car left the intersection early; and two cars in the low status condition, instead of honking, hit the back bumper of the experimental car, and the driver did not wish to wait for a honk. This left 38 subjects in the low status condition and 36 in the high status condition.

Although the drivers of the experimental cars usually waited for 15 seconds, two of the lights used in the experiment were green for only 12 seconds; therefore 12 seconds was used as a cutoff for all data. There were no differences attributable to drivers or intersections.

**[Table 4-1] Field experiment (mean latency of first honk in seconds)**

| Frustrator | Sex of driver | |
|---|---|---|
| | Male | Female |
| Low status | 6.8 (23) | 7.6 (15) |
| High status | 8.5 (25) | 10.9 (11) |

NOTE: Numbers in parentheses indicate the number of subjects.

The clearest way of looking at the results is in terms of the percentage in each condition that honked at least once in 12 seconds. In the low status condition 84 per cent of the subjects honked at least once, whereas in the high status condition, only 50 per cent of the subjects honked ($\chi^2 = 8.37$, $df = 1$, $p < .01$). Another way of looking at this finding is in terms of the latency of the first honk. When no honks are counted as a latency of 12 seconds, it can be seen in [Table 4-1] that the average latency for the new car was longer for both sexes. ($F = 10.71$, $p < .01$).

Thus, it is quite clear that status had an inhibitory effect on honking even once. It could be argued that status would have even greater inhibitory effects on more aggressive honking. Although one honk can be considered a polite way of calling attention to the green light, it is possible that subjects felt that a second honk would be interpreted as aggression.[3]

Forty-seven per cent of the subjects in the low status condition honked twice at the experimental car, as compared to 19 per cent of the subjects in the high status condition ($\chi^2 = 5.26$, $df = 1$, $p < .05$). This difference should be interpreted cautiously because it is confounded with the main result that more people honk generally in the low status condition. Of those who overcame the inhibitions to honk at all, 56 per cent in the low status condition and 39 per cent in the high status condition honked a second time, a difference which was not significant. First-honk latencies for honkers were about equal for the two conditions. The overall findings are presented in [Table 4-2].

[3] Series of honks separated by intervals of less than one second were counted as a single honk.

**[Table 4-2] Number of drivers honking zero, one, and two times**

| Frustrator | Honking in 12 seconds | | |
|---|---|---|---|
| | Never | Once | Twice |
| Low status | 6 | 14 | 18 |
| High status | 18 | 11 | 7 |

NOTE: Overall $\chi^2 = 11.14$, $p < .01$.

Sex of driver was the only other measure that was a good predictor of honking behavior. In both conditions men tended to honk faster than women ($F$ = 4.49, $p < .05$). The interaction of status and sex did not approach significance ($F = 1.17$). These data are consistent with laboratory findings (1) that men tend to aggress more than women.

Most experiments designed to study the effects of frustration have been carried out in the laboratory or the classroom, and many of these have employed written materials (2, 5).

It is undoubtedly much easier to use questionnaires, and if they produce the same results as field experiments, then in the interest of economy, they would have great advantage over naturalistic experiments. However, over 30 years ago, LaPiere warned that reactions to such instruments "may indicate what the responder would actually do when confronted with the situation symbolized in the question, but there is no assurance that it will" (4, p. 236).

In order to investigate this relationship between actual and predicted behavior, an attempt was made to replicate the present study as a questionnaire experiment. Obviously, the most appropriate sample to use would be one comprised of motorists sampled in the same way that the original drivers were sampled. Because this was not practicable, a questionnaire experiment was administered in a junior college classroom.

Subjects were 57 students in an introductory psychology class. Two forms of the critical item were included as the first of three traffic situations on a one-page questionnaire: "You are stopped at a traffic light behind a black 1966 Chrysler (gray 1961 Rambler). The light turns green and for no apparent reason the driver does not go on. Would you honk at him?" If subjects indicated that they would honk, they were then asked to indicate on a scale from one to 14 seconds how long they would wait before honking. Forms were alternated so that approximately equal numbers of subjects received the Chrysler and Rambler versions. Verbal instructions strongly emphasized that subjects were to answer according to what they actually thought they would do in such a situation. No personal information other than sex, age, and whether or not they were licensed to drive was required.

After the questionnaire had been collected the class was informed that different kinds of cars had been used for the horn-honking item. The experimenter then asked subjects to raise their hands when they heard the name of the car that appeared in the first item of their questionnaire. All subjects were able to select the correct name from a list of four makes which was read.

[Table 4-3] **Questionnaire experiment (mean latency of honking in seconds)**

| Frustrator | Sex of subject | |
|---|---|---|
| | Male | Female |
| Low status | 9.1 (18) | 8.2 (10) |
| High status | 5.5 (13) | 9.2 (14) |

NOTE: Numbers in parentheses indicate the number of subjects.

One subject (a female in the high status condition) failed to mark the honk latency scale, and another subject in the same condition indicated that she would go around the blocking car. Both of these subjects were eliminated from the analysis, leaving 27 in the high status condition and 28 in the low status condition. The results were analyzed in the same manner as the latency data from the field experiment. Means for each condition broken down by sex are presented in [Table 4-3]. Males reported that they thought that they would honk considerably sooner at the Chrysler than at the Rambler, whereas this was slightly reversed for females (interaction of sex and status $F = 4.97$, $p < .05$). Eleven subjects, six males in the low status condition and five females in the high status condition indicated that they would not honk within 12 seconds.

It is clear that the behavior reported on the questionnaire is different from the behavior actually observed in the field. The age difference in the samples may account for this disparity. Median estimated age of subjects in the field was 38, compared to a median age of 22 in the classroom. In order to check the possibility that younger males would indeed honk faster at the high status car, the field data were reanalyzed by age. The results for younger males, estimated ages 16 to 30, fit the general pattern of the field results and differed from the results of the classroom experiment. In the field, young males honked sooner at the Rambler than at the Chrysler ($t$ = 2.74, $df = 11, p < .02$).

Unfortunately, because these two studies differed in both sample and method, it is impossible to conclude that the differences are due to differences in the method of collecting data. However, it is clear that questionnaire data obtained from this often used population of subjects do not always correspond to what goes on in the real world.

## REFERENCES


1. **BUSS, A. H.** Instrumentality of aggression, feedback, and frustration as determinants of physical aggression. *J. of Personal. & Soc. Psychol.*, 1966, **3**, 153-162.
2. **COHEN, A. R.** Social norms, arbitrariness of frustration, and status of the agent in the frustration-aggression hypothesis. *J. Abn. & Soc. Psychol.*, 1955, **51**, 222-226.
3. **HOKANSON, J. E., & BURGESS, M.** The effects of status, type of frustration and aggression on vascular processes. *J. Abn. & Soc. Psychol.*, 1962, **65**, 232-237.
4. **LAPIERE, R. T.** Attitudes vs. actions. *Social Forces*, 1934, **13**, 230-237.
5. **PASTORE, N.** The role of arbitrariness in the frustration-aggression hypothesis. *J. Abn. & Soc. Psychol.*, 1952, **47**, 728-731.
6. **WEBB, E. J., CAMPBELL, D. T., SCHWARTZ, R. D., & SECHREST, L.** *Unobtrusive Measures: Nonreactive Research in the Social Sciences.* Chicago, Ill.: Rand McNally, 1966.

# THE EFFECT OF SOCIAL STATUS ON THE HONESTY OF OTHERS[1]

LEONARD BICKMAN
*Department of Psychology, Smith College*

## A. INTRODUCTION

It is commonly assumed that the manner in which people dress tells us something about them. A number of studies done in the United States have shown that the attire of a person affects our impression of him (1, 2, 4, 8). However, except for the Lefkowitz, Blake and Mouton (4) study, none of the research was conducted in natural settings, nor was it concerned with anything other than impressions. In contrast, the present study takes place in the natural environment where the stimulus person and subject actually interact.

From previous research, we can tentatively conclude that people judge others by their clothing along a status continuum. In addition, one study (4) has pointed out that this status judgment can affect overt conformity behavior. The present study is concerned with how the dress of a stimulus person will affect the honesty of others. That is, will a stimulus person's status, as reflected in his dress, influence the subject's attempt to keep something that does not belong to him?

## B. METHOD

**1. Subject** Two hundred and six persons who happened to use specified phone booths located in Grand Central Station and Kennedy Airport in New York City were the subjects of this experiment. Eighty-five percent of the subjects were white, and fifteen percent nonwhite. Forty-six percent of the subjects were male and fifty-four percent female. The average age of the subjects was estimated to be 35 years. Forty-three percent of the subjects were judged to be of low status and the remainder of high status, according to a criterion explained below.

### 2. Procedure

*a. Variation of perceived status* The apparent social status of the three male and three female stimulus persons was varied by the type of clothing they wore. The high-status males wore suits and ties. When they were simulating low-status persons, they dressed as workers, i.e., wore work clothes and carried something that would identify them as workers, e.g., flashlight, lunch pail, six foot rule. The high-status females were clothed in neat dresses and either wore or carried dress coats. As low-status women they wore skirts and blouses and were generally unkempt in appearance.

*b. The situation* The stimulus person entered a designated phone booth, placed a dime on the shelf in front of the phone, and then left. After a subject entered the phone booth, the stimulus person observed the subject to see if he took or used the dime. The dime was in such an obvious position that most subjects noticed the dime. The subjects who, from the stimulus person's observation, never noticed the dime were not included in the data analysis.

After a subject had been in the phone booth for two minutes the stimulus person approached him. It was felt that approaching the subject while he was picking up the dime might make him feel that he had been seen. Occasionally, the subject would finish the call in less than two minutes. If this occurred, the stimulus person approached the subject upon completion of his call.

When the stimulus person approached the subject, he tapped on the phone booth door and said: "Excuse me, Sir (Miss). I think I might've left a dime in this phone booth a few minutes ago. Did you find it?" The stimulus person then recorded whether the dime was returned or not. In addition, the subject's status (as determined by dress), perceived age, race, and sex were noted. These characteristics were determined by a consensus of agreement between the experimenter and an observer who was stationed close by.

## C. RESULTS

**1. Perception of Stimulus Persons** Pictures of the six stimulus persons in both status conditions were shown to twenty-eight student judges. The judges were asked to rate each stimulus person as being of either high or low status. All the judges agreed that the stimulus persons dressed as low-status persons

[1] The author would like to thank James Fox, Glenda Freeman, Kenneth Kleinman, Jackie Lindenbaum, Les Raphael, and Allyne Ziontz for acting as stimulus persons in this study. In addition, I appreciate the assistance of Ira Prager in planning the study and Donald Reutener's helpful comments on the manuscript.

appeared to be of low status and those dressed as high-status persons appeared to be of high status. This finding provides evidence for the validity of the status manipulation.

**2. Perception of Subjects** There was complete agreement between the stimulus person and the observer with regard to the subject's sex, race, and social status. Status was defined by the same dress characteristics used in the experimental manipulation. The age estimates were highly correlated ($r = .87$).

**3. The Effect of Status on Honesty** When the stimulus person was dressed in low-status attire, 38 percent of the subjects returned the dime. However, when the stimulus person was dressed in high-status attire, 77 percent of the subjects returned the dime. This difference is highly significant ($\chi^2 = 31.63, p < .001$, 1 *df*).

No relationship was found between the tendency to return the dime and the sex, race, age, or status of the subject. In addition, the sex of the stimulus person did not affect the proportion of subjects returning the dime. Thus, the only factor that was found to be significant in this study was the mode of dress (status) of the person whose dime was taken.

## D. DISCUSSION

The results of the present study showed that a person's honesty was dependent upon the person with whom he was interacting. When the subjects thought they were dealing with a high-status person, they returned the dime more than twice as often as when they perceived the stimulus person to be of low status. These results should be interpreted in the context of the situation studied.

In the present experiment the subject was free to act without any external constraints. That is, he was anonymous, not caught in the act of pocketing the dime, and only a small amount of money was involved. The subject was never accused of having taken the dime. Instead he was asked if he had seen it. Since the stimulus person appeared to be uncertain as to whether he had actually left a dime in that specific phone booth, the subject might have felt that the stimulus person would not know that he was lying if he said that he had not seen the dime.

That the low-status person was treated differently may not be surprising given the findings of previous research (3, 6, 7). However, what does appear surprising is that, in a situation involving money, the low-status person should be treated more dishonestly. A single dime is a small amount of money, but it certainly should mean more to a person who appears to be poor than to a well-dressed person. Thus, it is not obvious that the apparently low-status person should be the one to lose his dime more often.

However, there may not have been a conscious attempt on the part of the subject to deceive the low-status person. In the present experiment, the stimulus person interrupted the subject while the latter was in the midst of a telephone conversation. When the high-status stimulus person approached the phone booth, the subject might have interpreted the interruption by this well-dressed person as meaning that he had something important to say. Thus, he might have paid more attention to the content of the stimulus person's message and returned the dime more often. However, when interrupted by a person appearing to be of low status, the subject might have attempted to rid himself of this annoyance simply by saying "no" to him without really paying attention to what he was saying.

Since most of the previous research in this area has been carried out in the classroom or laboratory using questionnaires, it would be interesting to compare the results of the present field experiment with results obtained using a questionnaire technique.

The best sample of subjects to use in the questionnaire study would be one composed of people sampled in the field experiment. Since this was not feasible, a questionnaire was given to 66 Smith College students.

Two forms of the questionnaire were devised, describing the experimental situation. In one form the person asking for the dime was described as a well-dressed middle-class person. In the other version, given to different subjects, the person was described as a poorly-dressed working-class person. The subjects were asked to predict the probability of their returning the dime on a scale from 0 to 100. They were also asked to predict the probability of others' returning it. After the subjects made their judgments, it was made certain that they perceived the status of the stimulus person on the questionnaire. All subjects correctly recalled the description of that person.

The results showed that the subjects who received the "high-status" questionnaires thought they would return the dime with an average probability of 94 percent. They predicted that others would return it with a 71 percent average probability. The subjects who received the "low-status" questionnaires reported they would return the dime with an average probability of 96 percent and others with a 72 percent probability. Thus, there was no difference between the two status descriptions in either the subjects' prediction of their own behavior or in the prediction of others' behavior.

Although the subjects in the questionnaire sample differed from those in the field study in age, social class, and sex, it was found that none of these factors affected the results of the field study. The disparity between the results of the questionnaire study and the field study suggests that there should be some caution in extrapolating the results of similar questionnaire studies to actual behavior.

Unlike the laboratory experimenter who deals on his own terms and in his own laboratory with the average college sophomore (5), the field experimenter must deal with the environment as it is. If the research is to remain unobtrusive, the experimenter must adapt his methods to fit reality rather than vice versa. However, coming to terms with the environment and the people that inhabit it can have its problems. Passersby do not always respect the right to conduct undisturbed research. For example, we encountered a number of women at Grand Central Station who somewhat interfered with our research. It seems that there are some individuals who earn their livelihood by going from phone booth to phone booth looking for change left by others. The experimenters found it somewhat difficult to explain to these women that they were not to take all our dimes because we were conducting a social-psychological experiment in a phone booth in Grand Central Station.

## E. SUMMARY

The present study is concerned with the effect of dress of a stimulus person on the honesty of others. Two hundred and six persons were approached in phone booths by a stimulus person and asked if they had found a dime which the stimulus person had left in the booth a few minutes earlier. When the stimulus person was dressed to appear to be of high status, 77 percent of the subjects returned the dime. However, when he was poorly dressed only 38 percent of the subjects returned the dime.

## REFERENCES

1. **DOUTY, H.** The effect of clothing on perceptions of persons in single contact situations. *Dissertation Abstracts,* 1963, **24**, 1269-1270.

2. **HAMID, P.** Style of dress as perceptual cues in impression formation. *Perceptual & Motor Skills,* 1968, **26**, 904-906.

3. **HEIDER, F.** *The psychology of interpersonal relations.* New York: Wiley, 1958.

4. **LEFKOWITZ, M., BLAKE, R. R., & MOUTON, J. S.** Status factors in pedestrian violation of traffic signals. *Journal of Abnormal and Social Psychology,* 1955, **61**, 704-706.

5. **SCHULTZ, D. P.** The human subject in psychological research. *Psychological Bulletin,* 1969, **72**, 214-228.

6. **SECORD, P. F., BACKMAN, C. W., & EACHUS, H. T.** Effects of imbalance in the self-concept on the perception of persons. *Journal of Abnormal and Social Psychology,* 1964, **68**, 442-446.

7. **THIBAUT, J., & RIECKEN, H. W.** Some determinants and consequences of the perception of social causality. *Journal of Abnormal and Social Psychology,* 1952, **47**, 770-777.

8. **TRIANDIS, H. C., LOH, W. D., & LEVIN, L. A.** Race, status, quality of spoken English, and opinions about civil rights as determinants of interpersonal attitudes. *Journal of Personality and Social Psychology,* 1966, **3**, 468-472.

# STATUS FACTORS IN PEDESTRIAN VIOLATION OF TRAFFIC SIGNALS

MONROE LEFKOWITZ, ROBERT R. BLAKE, AND JANE SRYGLEY MOUTON
*The University of Texas*

A social factor of importance in determining the reaction a given prohibition will evoke—whether conformance or violation—is the respondent's knowledge of the behavior the restriction has produced in others (1). More people will conform when they see others conforming to a restriction, while knowledge that violations occur will increase the probability of infraction. The validity of these statements for a typical situation involving a prohibition has been demonstrated by an experiment dealing with reactions to signs forbidding entry to a building (2). When test subjects saw that another person violated the sign, they also violated it significantly more frequently than when they saw that another person had reacted in compliance with the prohibition.

## PROBLEM

The power of others to increase or decrease the strength of a prohibition is probably a function of "who the others are." Blake and Mouton (1) proposed that the perceived status of the person whose behavior serves as a model will be an important factor in determining the rate of violation. "High status figures known to violate a given law will have greater influence in weakening it than if only low status people are known to be violators. The same holds for conformance. When high status individuals are known to accept the prohibition it should have the effect of making the law more acceptable than if only low status people are known to conform."

The present paper is concerned with testing the validity of the statements relating status of the violator who serves as a model to the reaction a prohibition provokes in others. Perceived status quality of the person whose behavior toward a prohibition served as model for others was systematically varied. The basic hypothesis was that a naive subject facing a prohibition will more likely violate or conform when a high status person serves as a model for conformance or violation than when a low status person does so.

## EXPERIMENTAL SITUATION

### Prohibition Situation

The prohibition was a pedestrian traffic signal that flashed from "wait" to "walk" alternatively with the red, amber, and green signals regulating the flow of motor traffic. During every fifty-five second interval, the "wait" signal flashed for forty seconds and the "walk" for fifteen. Observations were made during the "wait" signal when the sign forbade movement across the street.

A counterbalanced design was employed with respect to daily time periods for observations and locations of the "wait-walk" signals. Data were collected on three successive afternoons during the hours from 12 to 1, 2 to 3, and 4 to 5 respectively. The "wait-walk" signals were located at three street corners at right angles to the main thoroughfare in the central commercial section of Austin, Texas. An observer located approximately 100 feet away from the corner recorded the data. Police officers were not on duty at the locations during the time intervals when data were collected, but arrangements for conducting the experiment had been made with the Traffic Department of the Austin Police Department.

### Subjects

With the exception of children and physically handicapped people, the 2,103 pedestrians passing the three locations during the three test intervals served as subjects.

### Covariations in Perceived Status of and Violation by the Model

Two aspects of social background were covaried in the experimental design suggested by Helson's adaptation-level theory (3). One was the behavior of an experimenter's model who either complied with or violated the "wait" signal. The second was the perceived status of the experimenter's model. The experimenter's model was a 31-year-old male. By changing his clothing the model's perceived status was either high or low. For half the conformance reactions and half the violation responses, the experimenter's model was dressed in clothing intended to typify a high status person, with a freshly pressed suit, shined shoes, white shirt, tie and straw hat. Well-worn scuffed shoes, soiled patched trousers and an unpressed blue denim shirt served to define the model as a low status person for the remaining half of the conforming and violating conditions. The rate of pedestrian violation observed during the same time intervals and at the same test locations with the experimenter's model absent served as the neutral or control condition.

The experimental design permitted both social background factors to be varied simultaneously. For example, at 12:00 noon on one day the experimenter's model, dressed in one status attire, conformed to the "wait" stimulus by crossing the street when the signal changed to "walk." The procedure was repeated for each of five trials, with the number of subjects conforming or violating recorded. Following these trials, pedestrians were observed for five additional trials under the neutral condition in which the experimenter's model was absent. The experimenter's model returned to the scene dressed in the other status attire and violated the "wait" signal by crossing the street once at approximately the midpoint of each "wait" interval for the same number of trials. The inverse order for conforming and violating trials was followed the next day, and so on.

### Criteria for Scoring Violation

Two criteria were used in assessing whether pedestrians were violating the "wait" signal. Only subjects standing with the experimenter's model before he crossed the street were included in the data. Pedestrians reaching or passing the white line in the center of the street while the signal still flashed "wait" were recorded as violators. By using the center line as the criterion for scoring violation and conformity, errors of judgment as to pedestrian intent were reduced to a minimum. All others meeting the first criterion but not the second were recorded as conforming with the prohibition.

## RESULTS

Results from the several experimental and control conditions are presented in [Tables 4-4 and 4-5]. Examination of column totals demonstrates that the presence of a model of either high or low perceived status complying with the signal prohibition did not increase the rate of pedestrian conformance beyond that observed for the control condition. Since the rate of conformance under neutral conditions was so

[Table 4-4] **Reactions of test subjects to experimental treatments and control conditions**

| Status attire of experimenter's model | Reactions of experimenter's model: Conforming | | Control‡ | | Violating | | Total | |
|---|---|---|---|---|---|---|---|---|
| | Pedestrian conforms | Pedestrian violates | Pedestrian conforms | Pedestrian violates | Pedestrian conforms | Pedestrian violates | Pedestrian conforms | Pedestrian violates |
| High $N$* | 351 | 3 | 347 | 3 | 250 | 40 | 948 | 46 |
| %† | 99 | 01 | 99 | 01 | 86 | 14 | 95 | 05 |
| Low $N$ | 420 | 1 | 395 | 5 | 276 | 12 | 1091 | 18 |
| % | 100 | 00 | 99 | 01 | 96 | 04 | 98 | 02 |
| Total $N$ | 771 | 4 | 742 | 8 | 526 | 52 | 2039 | 64 |
| % | 99 | 01 | 99 | 01 | 91 | 09 | 97 | 03 |

‡The entries in the high and low status rows represent control observations made under conditions identical with the observations for the high and low status conditions except that the experimenter's model was absent.
*The unequal $N$'s are due to slight variations in the flow of pedestrians under counterbalanced test conditions.
†Figures rounded to the nearest per cent.

[Table 4-5] **$\chi^2$ values for differences between conditions**

| Conditions | $\chi^2$ | $df$ | Level of significance |
|---|---|---|---|
| Conforming model vs. control | 1.30 | 1 | – |
| Violating model vs. control | 48.04 | 1 | .01 |
| High status violating model vs. control | 44.59 | 1 | .01 |
| Low status violating model vs. control | 3.88 | 1 | .05 |
| High status condition: violating model vs. conforming model | 44.56 | 1 | .01 |
| Low status condition: violating model vs. conforming model | 16.22 | 1 | .01 |
| Violating condition: high status model vs. low status model | 16.61 | 1 | .01 |

high (99 per cent), the present study did not permit a valid test of the proposition that seeing another person conform increased rate of conformity ($\chi^2 = 1.30$, 1 *df*). However, the presence of a model of either high or low perceived status violating the prohibition increased the pedestrian violation rate above that for the control condition. The $\chi^2$ (48.04, 1 *df*) between control and experimental conditions is significant beyond the 1 per cent level of confidence. This finding is consistent with results from the comparable part of the experiment dealing with the violation of a sign forbidding the entry of a building (2).

The relationship between status and violation is shown in cell frequencies across rows of [Table 4-4]. When a perceived high status model was seen to violate the prohibition, 14 per cent of pedestrians violated the signal restricting movement. The $\chi^2$ of 44.59 (1 *df*) for the difference in pedestrian violation between the high status violation and the control condition, and the $\chi^2$ of 44.56 (1 *df*) for the difference between perceived high status violation and perceived high status conformance are both significant beyond the 1 per cent level. The results demonstrate that when a high status person violated a prohibition, there was a significant increase in the rate of violation by pedestrians. An examination of differences in pedestrian violations that were provoked by a violating person of low status contrasted with both a low status person who conforms ($\chi^2 = 16.22$, 1 *df*) and also with the control condition where the low status person was absent ($\chi^2 = 3.88$, 1 *df*) leads to the conclusion that the low status violator increased the pedestrian violation rate beyond that typical for either of the other two conditions. Such findings demonstrate that with a person whose perceived status quality was either high or low acting as a model by violating a prohibition, the pedestrian violation rate was increased significantly beyond that occurring when the model either conformed or was absent.

From the standpoint of the hypothesis stated in the introduction, the significant comparison is that between violation rates when the status of the violator was shifted from low to high. Changing the status of the violator from low to high through creating differences in attire increased pedestrian violations from 4 per cent to 14 per cent. The $\chi^2$ of 16.61 (1 *df*) for this difference in violation rate is significant at the 1 per cent level. Such findings point to the conclusion that if a situation contains a violator, a significantly greater number of pedestrians will violate the signal when the status model is high rather than low. This finding confirms the prediction given in the introduction. The behavior of others is not of equal weight in determining the readiness to violate a prohibition. Rather the higher the status of the perceived violator the greater the reduction in conformance to a prohibition by pedestrians in the same situation.

## SUMMARY

Pedestrians violated the prohibition of an automatic traffic signal more often in the presence of an experimenter's model who violated the prohibition than when the latter conformed or was absent. Significantly more violations occurred among pedestrians when the nonconforming model was dressed to represent high social status than when his attire suggested lower status.

## REFERENCES

1. **BLAKE, R. R., & MOUTON, JANE S.** Present and future implications of social psychology for law and lawyers. *Symposium Issue, Emory Univ. J. Public Law,* 1955, **3**, 352-369.

2. **FREED, A. M., CHANDLER, P. J., MOUTON, JANE S., & BLAKE, R. R.** Stimulus and background factors in sign violation. *J. Pers.,* 1955, **23**, 499.

3. **HELSON, H.** Adaptation-level as a basis for a quantitative theory of frames of reference. *Psychol. Rev.,* 1948, **55**, 297-313.

# THE ENVIRONMENTAL SETTING AS A FACTOR IN SOCIAL INFLUENCE

ROBERT N. VIDULICH AND DONNA JEAN WILSON
*Departments of Psychology*
*Memphis State University and Louisiana State University*

## A. INTRODUCTION

It is a commonplace that human social behavior always occurs within the context of some environment and is affected by the physical and social constraints and supports of that environment. That the physical environment setting of a human interaction is of importance, in particular, in determining the extent of social influence that occurs in that setting is the concern of the present report.

With one exception, students of the influence process have concerned themselves only with dimensions of the "social environment." As the reviews of Blake and Mouton (1) and Campbell (2) indicate, a sizeable body of evidence has accumulated on the variable aspects of the person or group with whom the experimental subject is in interaction, and the importance of such factors as group size and unanimity, and model age, sex, and status is acknowledged by all researchers on social influence. In the single published study which has experimentally varied a *nonsocial* (physical) environmental dimension, Freed, Chandler, Mouton, and Blake (3) found sign violation to be a function of both degree of social pressure and strength of sign prohibition. This suggests that the functioning of negative behavioral norms in a "prohibition situation" is important in determining the behavior that occurs in such a setting *independent of social pressures* to act in a certain manner.

The possibility of comparing influence effectiveness across different environments has been hampered by the lack of an experimental technique that would permit the instigation of surreptitious social influence attempts *for a single behavioral class* in *diverse* physical-social environmental settings. The technique for studying amusement influence recently reported in this journal by Vidulich and Bayley (4) appeared to provide the vehicle for such studies.

Briefly, this technique employs a highly reliable behavioral rating procedure to quantify changes in the intensity of normal amusement responses to nonhumorous stimuli, during influence attempts by a model occurring without *S*'s awareness. It can be used in any interaction situation or environmental setting in which amusement can occur, and is, therefore, "situationally free." Other field experiments using this technique have examined the relevance of the variables of source status and subject sex (4), and minority group membership (5) to the influence process, yielding highly reliable findings which compare favorably to laboratory studies of these variables.

For the present investigation, the authors assumed that a normative range of behavioral acts for any particular physical setting has been defined socially for the individual. The typical person has learned these norms and knows what behaviors are and are not usually permissible in a given setting. The authors, for example, cook, wash dishes, mix drinks, and occasionally eat in their kitchens, but do not usually sleep, relieve themselves, or play chess there (even though it is technically possible to do so). Also, for many behavioral settings, a variety of different, and sometimes opposite, behaviors are normatively possible, depending upon the momentary socially defined function of the setting. To change the environmental example, a school gymnasium may serve as a sports arena at one time with its occupants shouting, laughing, and being otherwise boisterous, whereas such behaviors would be frowned upon when the identical space was being used as an auditorium or assembly room. Finally, it may be noted that, in different settings, different degrees or intensities of the same behavior class are normative. One can only whisper in many churches during services, but can shout at full force on a basketball court; one may express only quiet amusement in a library but may laugh explosively in a recreational lounge.

The present research was designed specifically to examine the importance of the environmental setting of social influence attempts for the success of such attempts, using the previously described amusement influence technique. If the behavioral norms for two different settings have no consequences for attempts to influence amusement behavior, the extent of influence in these settings should not be dissimilar. If, however, differentially successful influence attempts were noted across the two settings, these could be attributed to the settings themselves.

Since the independent variables of model (or source) status, and model sex relative to the sex of the *S*, have been repeatedly shown to be relevant to influence effectiveness (1, 2), and additionally to provide some replicative data on the amusement influence technique itself, the consequences of these variables were also examined in the present study.

## B. METHOD

**1. Subjects and Settings** Subjects were 40 male and 40 female undergraduate students at Louisiana State University during the spring of 1965. *S*s were selected from those sitting alone in two University settings having distinctly different norms regarding talking and the expression of amusement—the University Union coffee shop and lounge, and main reading areas in the University Library. At all hours, much loud talking and laughing may be observed in the former setting, while even low level speech and mild expressions of amusement are actively discouraged in the latter. Both environments are heavily used by students and faculty and are often so overcrowded that people who are not acquainted with one another frequently sit together. Permission to use library tables within sight and hearing of the librarians' desks was obtained prior to the study.

**2. Rating Scale** The following seven-point behavioral Amusement Rating Scale (ARS), developed by Vidulich and Bayley (4), was used to quantify different levels of amusement:

(Rating 1) *No reaction or negative reaction,* involving no movement of the muscles of the face, downward turning of the corners of the mouth, shaking of the head horizontally, or verbalizations indicative of lack of amusement.

(Rating 2) *Low intensity smile* involving only the facial muscles in the vicinity of the corners of the mouth.

(Rating 3) *High intensity smile* involving most of the facial muscles and usually causing wrinkling of the skin beside the eyes.

(Rating 4) *Smile with positive comment,* such as "oh, that's very funny," or "that's good."

(Rating 5) *Low intensity laugh* involving minor bodily movement, especially of the head and shoulders. Sound is either absent or scarcely audible.

(Rating 6) *Medium intensity laugh* involving moderately vigorous bodily movements and clearly audible sound.

(Rating 7) *High intensity laugh* (roar) involving both vigorous bodily movements and loud sustained sounds; sometimes attended by striking of objects, the subject's own person, or another person.

In prior analyses, this scale was shown to have very high interrater reliability, ranging from .82 to .97 with various raters (4).

**3. Stimulus Materials** Stimuli for the experiment consisted of 10 cartoons in a published cartoon collection[1] previously identified as nonamusing (ratings of "1" on the ARS) on the basis of rated behavioral responses of 16 students (4).

**4. Procedure** The experimenter (*E*), an attractive, outgoing and socially facile 25-year-old white female,[2] dressed in a skirt and blouse and loafers (relatively low status condition) or in a dress or suit and pumps (relatively high status condition), entered the experimental setting carrying books, notebooks, and the book of cartoons. When the setting was the coffee shop she bought a cup of coffee or a soft drink; in the library she selected a book or journal from a nearby shelf. Each time she sat with the first obviously undergraduate student she saw seated alone at a table, and initiated a conversation with the *S*, using whatever introductory gambit seemed appropriate. In the coffee shop, for example, she would light a cigarette for herself, and, offering one to the *S*, would comment on whatever the student happened to be reading or studying, asking "What course is that for?" "What's that you're reading?" etc. In this context, she would introduce herself as either Dr. Bales of the English Department (high status condition) or as Sandra Bales, a graduate student in English (low status condition). In the course of the conversation, *E* would glance at one or two of the cartoons, laugh, and comment to *S* that she had just been loaned the cartoon book by a student and was looking at it for the first time.

Sharing the cartoons with *S*, a baseline of *S*'s amusement response was determined by casually showing five of the preselected cartoons to *S*, one at a time, each time commenting "Look at this one," or "How about this?" "Do you think this is funny?" etc. Care was taken during this Phase A to avoid influencing *S*'s amusement reaction through any reaction of *E*. In Phase B of the experimental session, *E*

[1] *Starke Parade.* Garden City, New York: Doubleday, 1959. The full-page cartoons on the following pages were used: 8, 9, 15, 36, 37, 51, 63, 109, 123, and 132.

[2] The authors acknowledge, with many thanks, the cooperative assistance of Mrs. Sandra Schmuckler, who served as the *E* in this study.

laughed (at level "6" on the ARS) upon presentation of five additional preselected unfunny cartoons.

The 10 cartoons were presented to each *S* in randomized order to eliminate possible serial presentation effects. All 10 responses to the cartoons were rated independently by *E* and another rater, who had entered the setting while *E* was establishing rapport with *S*, using the ARS. The *E* excused herself a reasonable length of time after presentation of the last cartoon and moved to another location. The entire procedure took about 20 minutes per *S*.

Throughout the interaction between *E* and *S*, no *S* appeared to become aware that he was being used as an experimental *S*, of the status ruse, or to connect *E* with the other rater. All *S*s except one (a male student in the library who asked not to be disturbed) immediately talked freely with *E*. Only three *S*s left before all 10 cartoons had been displayed, each for plausible reasons, such as getting to a class. So realistic and natural were the established interactions that several *S*s approached *E* on campus several days following the experimental session to ask how she was, and often continued the conversations begun during the experiment. Subjects were not informed of the nature of the experiment at any time, and no rumors about an experiment such as this were ever heard on campus.

**5. Raters and Rating Procedure** The *E* (Rater A) and a female graduate student (Rater B), each of whom had been trained in the use of the ARS for approximately four hours, served as raters. Rater B entered the setting several minutes after *E*. Sitting in a nearby chair or at an adjacent table, she unobtrusively and independently rated *S*'s amusement responses to the cartoons without *S*'s awareness. After excusing herself from *S*, *E* went to an isolated area and formally recorded her previously noted independent ratings.

## C. RESULTS

Independent ratings of amusement behavior were obtained from two raters for each of the 10 cartoons for each of the 80 *S*s. The obtained product-moment reliability coefficient of .98 for the 800 pairs of ratings indicates almost perfect agreement between the two raters about the level of expressed amusement for any given response, and compares favorably with prior rater reliability estimates obtained with the ARS (4).

Given this high reliability, the two raters' ratings were combined yielding a mean rating for each experimental phase (A and B) for each *S*. Mean baseline (Phase A) responses for the eight treatment conditions (males or females with high or low status model in the library or Union setting) were practically identical, and did not differ significantly from one another. During Phase A, males in interaction with a high status model in the Union expressed the lowest average baseline amusement, at the level of 2.61 on the ARS; females in interaction with a high status model in the Union produced the highest mean baseline response, at the level of 2.79 on the ARS, with the other treatment groups being intermediate.

**[Table 4-6] Analysis of variance of difference scores**

| Source of variation | *df* | *MS* | *F* |
|---|---|---|---|
| Environment (E) | 1 | 18.72 | 31.20* |
| Status (St) | 1 | 43.36 | 72.27* |
| Sex (S) | 1 | .30 | .50 |
| (St × E) | 1 | .23 | .38 |
| (St × S) | 1 | .33 | .55 |
| (E × S) | 1 | .15 | .25 |
| (St × E × S) | 1 | 2.12 | 3.53 |
| Within | 72 | .60 | |
| Total | 79 | | |

*Significant beyond the .01 level.

To measure the effects of environmental setting, model status, and subject sex on change in expressed amusement intensity during influence attempts, the mean rated amusement response was also determined for each *S* for the second group of five cartoons presented during Phase B. The response measure used in the triple classification analysis of variance [Table 4-6] was the difference between Phase A and Phase B rated amusement intensity for each *S*.

From [Table 4-6] it is evident that the environmental setting of influence attempts was a highly significant factor in the amount of change in amusement response that occurred. For all *S*s combined, there was approximately twice as much expressed amusement during Phase B in the Union (mean change = 1.96) than in the library (mean change = .99). This environmental effect was noted for both sexes: in the library, male *S*s (mean change = 1.01) and female *S*s (mean change = .98) expressed about half as much amusement under influence as they did in the Union (male mean change = 2.07; female mean change = 1.86). Furthermore, the relative extent of change in amusement response intensity in the two settings was independent of the status of the model with whom *S*s were in interaction. With a high status model, library mean change was 1.68 and Union mean change was 2.75; when in interaction with a low status model, library mean change was .31 as compared to a Union mean change of 1.17.

The extent of change in rated amusement intensity was also highly significantly related to the social status of the model attempting influence. For this variable, the ratio of change is on the order of 3:1. For all *S*s, the mean change in amusement intensity with a high status model was 2.22, while the mean change with a low status model was .74. This effect was noted in both settings (library-high status mean change = 1.68, library-low status mean change = .31; Union-high status mean change = 2.75, Union-low status mean change = 1.17). Male and female *S*s were consistent in their responses to models of differing social status independent of the setting of the interaction (male-high status mean change = 2.26, male-low status mean change = .82; female-high status mean change = 2.17, female-low status mean change = .66).

Male *S*s (mean change = 1.54) and female *S*s (mean change = 1.41) did not differ significantly from each other in extent of influenceability. This finding was consistent for all model status and environment treatment conditions.

## D. DISCUSSION

It seems clear from these data that attempts at socially influencing amusement behavior are of reduced effectiveness when they occur in contradiction to the behavior norms for an environmental setting. In the library setting, with its well established norms against any type of loud, noisy, or distracting behavior, *minimal* change in *S*s' amusement responses occurred, even when the influencing model was of high perceived status. Only two of the 40 *S*s (both exposed to a high status model) influenced in the library expressed amusement at an audible level (an average rating of 5.5 or above on the ARS) during Phase B of the experiment; in the Union, on the other hand, 21 of 40 *S*s behaved audibly under influence. Thus, in the library, those amusement responses that did occur following influence attempts were still predominantly within the range of the normative nonaudible and "nondisturbing" behavior for that setting. This suggests that, while social influences on behavior may take place, their extent is restricted by the norms of the environmental setting.

It should be emphasized also that the factors of the physical settings of potential influence interactions, and the social pressures for conformity occurring in these settings, are independent of each other for the extent of influence which transpires. The data, in this respect, correspond closely with the findings of Freed *et al.* (3) on prohibitory sign violation. Both sets of data support the view that the norms of the physical setting of an influence interaction function as a constant, defining the extent of influence that can occur as a function of model and subject variables.

Unlike the Freed *et al.* study, the setting of which contained a *visible* specification of the behavior norm (in the form of a sign prohibiting entrance to a building), the present study dealt only with *inferred* behavior norms for the two settings used. The similarity of the two sets of findings indicates that normative behavior is not necessarily specified by the existence of *actual,* physically present, indicators of norms in the form of prohibitory signs, police, or other authority, and the like. *Cognitive* norms–those expectancies about allowable behavior in a given setting–are of equal or perhaps even greater importance, since in most settings no actual normative indices are present.

Finally, let us turn briefly to a comparison of the findings on the variables of model status and subject sex in the present study and in the original investigation using the amusement influence technique (4). In both studies, the importance of model status in determining the extent of influence is marked, even though the sex of the influencing model was different in the two researches. The extent of influence attributable to the female high or low status model in the present study closely approximated that found with male models in the original experiments. Also, in neither investigation was there noted a significant subject sex variation; male and female *S*s responded similarly to influence attempts in both studies. Thus, the present findings provide a substantial replication of the original findings on this new field experimental technique for studying social influence.

## E. SUMMARY

The present study examined the relevance of the physical environmental setting to social influence, using the amusement influence technique of Vidulich and Bayley. In two settings with divergent behavioral norms about expression of overt amusement–University library reading rooms and a University Union–the extent of influence was shown to be independently a function of the norms of the setting and the perceived status of the influencing model. Subject sex was not related to influenceability. The results are interpreted as indicating that the physical setting of an influence interaction delimits the extent of influence that can occur as a function of other, social or personal, variables.

## REFERENCES

1. **BLAKE, R. R., & MOUTON, J. S.** Conformity, resistance, and conversion. In I. A. Berg & B. M. Bass (Eds.), *Conformity and Deviation.* New York: Harper, 1961. Pp. 1-37.

2. **CAMPBELL, D. T.** Conformity in psychology's theories of acquired behavioral dispositions. In I. A. Berg & B. M. Bass (Eds.), *Conformity and Deviation.* New York: Harper, 1961. Pp. 101-142.

3. **FREED, A., CHANDLER, P. J., MOUTON, J. S., & BLAKE, R. R.** Stimulus and background factors in sign violation. *J. Personal.*, 1955, **23**, 499.

4. **VIDULICH, R. N., & BALY, G. A.** A general field experimental technique for studying social influence. *J. Soc. Psychol.*, 1966, **69**, 253-263.

5. ——. Social influence among members of majority and minority groups. Unpublished research report, Louisiana State University, Baton Rouge, 1965.

# SITUATIONAL INFLUENCE ON MORAL JUSTICE: A STUDY OF "FINKING"

HERBERT HARARI[1]
*San Diego State College*

JOHN W. McDAVID
*University of Miami*

Piaget's notion of moral relativism with respect to peer-group standards was investigated by placing children in a situation in which they were questioned by an adult about their knowledge of a simulated transgression by a peer which they had witnessed earlier. Under these circumstances, every subject was willing to incriminate the guilty confederate. However, the presence of an innocent peer deterred subjects from making such accusations, which suggested an implicit peer norm against "finking" by a colleague. Furthermore, this norm applied selectively to reporting guilt of a high-status peer, with no restraint against a low-status peer. The results suggest that situational conditions affect overt manifestations of overt justice, which in turn advises caution in interpreting results of investigations that utilize different operations for assessing conscience.

Piaget has described the course of moral development in the child as a gradual progression from an absolute and rigid sense of justice (*moral realism*) to a flexible sense of equity which involves consideration of mitigating circumstances (*moral relativism*), suggesting that moral relativism dominates the moralistic judgments of the child by the time of preadolescence (Piaget, 1932). That peer-group standards of morality exert conditional effects upon the child's sense of justice has been suggested indirectly in several experimental investigations of conscience and moralism (Crane, 1958; Luria, Goldwasser, & Goldwasser, 1963; MacRae, 1954). Two studies by Durkin (1959a, 1959b), in which second-, fifth-, and eighth-grade children were questioned about their response to an event of aggression toward them by a peer, failed to show evidence of progression from absolutistic toward relativistic moral concepts. In interpreting her data, Durkin suggested that eighth-graders may be relatively more sensitive than younger children to peer-disapproval of "tattling" to an authority.

Questioning by adult authority with respect to transgression committed by a peer is a fairly common occurrence in a child's life. From an adult point of view, albeit somewhat oversimplified, the ensuing conflict in the child is whether to be moral (and "fink" on the peer) or not; failure to reveal the transgression may thus be conceived as "wrong." However, because of peer group pressure the child may conceive it "right" to deviate from adult moral standards. The conflict then becomes not whether or not to be moral—but how to decide between two contending moral principles: not to lie (or disobey), or not to "fink." In order to investigate some of the conditions which may temper the preadolescent's basic sense of "right" and "wrong," the present study was designed to place children in a situation in which they had knowledge of a moral transgression (theft) by a peer and were questioned by an adult about this knowledge. The influence of the guilty peer, presence of the guilty peer when the subject was questioned, and presence of other nonguilty peers when the subject was questioned were all investigated as conditions which might affect the child's willingness to report his knowledge of the transgression to an authority.

## EXPERIMENT I

**Subjects** Subjects in this study were 48 middle-class children (27 boys and 21 girls) in two junior high school history classes. Their ages ranged from 12 years 6 months to 13 years 6 months, and they were all in either seventh or eighth grade. Two additional students (a boy and a girl) from the same history classes were employed as confederates.

**Procedure** In order to simulate a realistic event of moral transgression, a contrived "theft" was arranged during regular classes. By arrangement, the teacher was called from the room to take an important telephone call. During her absence, a pre-instructed confederate student arose from his seat ostensibly to dispose of his chewing gum into a wastebasket; as he did so, the student scooped up $.75 in silver coins which had been left on a small table at the front of the room, saying "Hey, look; how about that!" He pocketed the money and returned to his seat before the teacher reentered the room. Shortly after the teacher had returned and the classroom activities had been resumed, she received a prearranged call on the local intercom telephone and engaged in a cryptic conversation for a few seconds, repeating, "I don't know," several times. Somewhat later during the class, a messenger entered the classroom to request that students be called from the room one by one for interviews concerning casting a school talent show. As subjects left the room, either singly or in pairs, with the messenger, they were intercepted in the corridor by the experimenter and diverted into an empty office for the experimental interrogation.

The interrogation itself consisted of a simple set of three direct questions, asked in a nonthreatening but business-like manner: (*a*) "Do you know whether someone took some change (about $.75) left near Mrs. X's desk today?" (*b*) "Do you know who took it?" (*c*) (If so) "Who took it?" Data were tabulated according to whether the first two questions were answered "yes" or "no," and whether the subject named the guilty confederate in response to the third question. Following the interrogation, the subjects were told that the entire situation was an experimental game, and they were sent to the playground to remain until the end of the period for a more complete explanation of the afternoon's events.

**Manipulation of Variables** Status of the guilty confederate was determined by means of a sociometric questionnaire administered approximately a week before the experiment itself. Subjects were requested to "list five people whom you consider worthy to represent the group at a planned discussion seminar, banquet, and dance for representatives from all of the schools in this area." The student receiving the greatest number of mentions, an eighth-grade girl, was selected as the high-status experimental confederate; the student receiving the lowest number of mentions (none), a seventh-grade boy, was selected as the low-status experimental confederate. These confederates played the role of the guilty thief in the simulation described above, one in each of two comparable history classes. For half of the subjects in each class, the guilty confederate was present during the interrogation; for the other half, the guilty confederate remained in the classroom and was absent during the interrogation. Half the subjects were questioned individually (apart from the presence or absence of the guilty confederate); the other half were interrogated in pairs, with the critical experimental subject accompanied by a second student from the same class (who was subsequently questioned in the same manner, but for whom data were not recorded). Subjects were debriefed at the end of the interrogation by being told that it was a game of "how to perceive people accurately." The role of the confederates was also revealed.

The three experimental variables thus generated eight combinations of situational conditions, with six subjects treated to each combination. (See [Table 4-7].)

All three questions were asked of each subject, except when a "no" answer to an earlier question automatically implied negative answers to subsequent questions.

## RESULTS AND DISCUSSION

Affirmative answers indicate willingness of the subject to report his observation of the simulated theft to a questioning authority. Since the theft occurred openly before the entire class, an absolute sense of moral justice would be expected to lead subjects to answer all three questions truthfully in the affirmative. [Table 4-7] summarizes the frequency of affirmative answers to each question under each of the eight experimental conditions. These data are self-demonstrative; however, Fisher exact-probability tests (Siegel, 1956) of differences between all possible comparison pairs reveal that on the first two questions, affirmative answers occurred significantly less frequently under the high-status thief/accused absent/questioned-in-pairs condition than under any other condition ($p < .05$). With respect to the third question (naming the guilty party), affirmative answers occurred significantly less frequently in the high-

**[Table 4-7] Proportions of affirmative ("confession") answers to three interrogations about the simulated theft, according to experimental conditions**

| Question | Status of thief | Experimental condition | | | |
|---|---|---|---|---|---|
| | | Guilty thief present | | Guilty thief absent | |
| | | Questioned alone | Questioned in pairs | Questioned alone | Questioned in pairs |
| Knowledge of theft | High | 6/6 | 5/6 | 6/6 | 0/6* |
| | Low | 6/6 | 5/6 | 6/6 | 5/6 |
| Knowledge of guilty person | High | 6/6 | 5/6 | 5/6 | 0/6* |
| | Low | 6/6 | 5/6 | 6/6 | 5/6 |
| Name the thief | High | 5/6 | 1/6* | 4/6 | 0/6* |
| | Low | 6/6 | 5/6 | 5/6 | 5/6 |

*$p < .05$.

status thief/questioned-in-pairs conditions (regardless of whether or not the guilty confederate was present) than under other conditions ($p < .05$).

Further specific differences with respect to admitting knowledge of the simulated theft were a function of whether or not the high-status guilty peer was or was not present during interviewing. When the high-status guilty confederate was *absent* during interrogation, none of the subjects interviewed admitted any knowledge of the theft, presumably because the circumstances would imply that there was no other existing evidence against the thief, so that the implicit peer norm against "ratting" on a colleague was exercised fully. In contrast, the presence of the high-status guilty confederate sitting quietly in a desk beside the experimenter during interrogation apparently suggested that some evidence might already exist to incriminate the thief. Under these conditions, most of the subjects were willing to acknowledge that they knew of the theft and even to admit that they could identify the thief. Only when subjects were brought to the third question, demanding that they stand before the guilty confederate and identify him by name, did the norm against "finking" on a high-status peer exercise an influence, leading most of the subjects interrogated under these circumstances to refuse to identify the thief directly.

It is important to call attention to the fact that this interpretation of differences in "finking" on high-status and low-status peers was subject to some confounding in the present study. The status differentiation of the two confederates was clearly established through the earlier sociometric investigation. The sex variable was presumably of little relevance to the perceived status of these people, since the high-status person (a girl) received equal numbers of nominations from boy and girl classmates, and since the low-status person (a boy) received no nomination at all from either sex. Furthermore, the distribution of boys and girls among the eight experimental subgroups was approximately equal, and there was no evidence that the behavior of boys and girls differed during the interrogation. Nevertheless, since the high-status confederate was a girl, and the low-status confederate a boy, it might be argued that differential application of the peer-group standard against "finking" may be a function not of *status* as such, but of *sex*. Conceivably, there are standards against "finking" against a girl which do not apply to the question of "finking" against a boy. Another possible artifact was that the different behavior of the two groups might have reflected a different classroom atmosphere, rather than the status of the thief. To clarify these issues, a second, similar experiment was conducted.

## EXPERIMENT II

**Subjects** Subjects in this study were 56 middle-class boys whose ages ranged from 11 to 13 and who belonged to one of two youth groups attached to a suburban community center.

**Procedure** The simulated event of moral transgression was arranged during the weekly meeting of each respective youth group. The adult advisor of the groups (in both cases the same individual) brought a tape recorder and put it on the table in front of her. In answer to queries, she told the group that the tapes were very important inasmuch as they included the program outline for various youth groups for the entire year. By arrangement, the advisor was then called from the room to take an important telephone call. The preinstructed confederate went ostensibly to dispose of his chewing gum into a wastebasket; as he did so, he went to the table, plugged in the tape recorder, and started to sing into the microphone in a clowning manner before unplugging the recorder, putting it back, and exclaiming: "I must have erased some of this tape!" The advisor then came back with her assistant and told the boys that she had to leave for about ½ hour. She left, taking the tape recorder with her. Shortly after, the assistant received a prearranged call and engaged in a cryptic conversation for a few seconds, repeating "I don't know" several times. Subjects were then called from the room, either singly or in pairs, under the same pretext (casting of a talent show) that had been used in Experiment I.

From this point on Experiment II follows closely the pattern of Experiment I. Status of the guilty confederate had been determined a week earlier by the same sociometric measure used in Experiment I. The interrogation also was essentially the same, consisting of the following three questions: (*a*) "Do you know whether someone fooled around with my tape recorder tonight?" (*b*) "Do you know who did it?" (*c*) (If so) "Who did it?" Data tabulation was identical to that in Experiment I, as was the debriefing procedure.

## RESULTS AND DISCUSSION

[Table 4-8] summarizes the frequency of affirmative answers to each question under each of the eight experimental conditions. Fisher exact-probability tests (Siegel, 1956) of differences between all possible comparison pairs reveal that affirmative answers to the third question (naming the guilty party) occurred significantly less frequently in the two high-status thief/questioned-in-pairs conditions (regardless of whether or not the guilty confederate was present) than other conditions ($p < .05$).

The data from both experiments leave little doubt

[Table 4-8] **Proportions of affirmative ("confession") answers to three interrogations about the simulated tape erasure, according to experimental conditions**

| Question | Status of transgressor | Experimental condition | | | |
|---|---|---|---|---|---|
| | | Guilty transgressor present | | Guilty transgressor absent | |
| | | Questioned alone | Questioned in pairs | Questioned alone | Questioned in pairs |
| Knowledge of recorder manipulation | High | 7/7 | 7/7 | 7/7 | 5/7 |
| | Low | 7/7 | 7/7 | 7/7 | 7/7 |
| Knowledge of guilty person | High | 7/7 | 5/7 | 7/7 | 5/7 |
| | Low | 7/7 | 7/7 | 7/7 | 7/7 |
| Name the transgressor | High | 7/7 | 1/7* | 5/7 | 0/7* |
| | Low | 7/7 | 7/7 | 7/7 | 7/7 |

$^*p < .05$.

as to the fact that the simulated transgressions were clearly observed by the subjects and interpreted by them as moral transgressions. Under certain circumstances, every subject interviewed was willing to accuse and incriminate a guilty confederate. When questioned alone, a situation in which the manner of the adult interrogator implies an expectation of moral righteousness and truthfulness, almost all the subjects questioned were willing to confess their full knowledge of the transgression or even to identify the transgressor by name. However, the presence of a peer who also witnessed the simulated transgression appears to deter subjects from making such accusations and identification of the transgressor. The status of the guilty peer seems to be a crucial variable in this context: the implicit peer-group norm against "finking" seems to apply selectively to the question of reporting the guilt of a respected and esteemed classmate, with no evidence of restraint against reporting and identifying a low-status guilty peer. There was pronounced reluctance to identify the high-status transgressor directly by name regardless of whether the guilty person was or was not actually present during the interrogation, and regardless of the transgression (theft versus tape erasure).[1]

The data reported here represent only a limited definition of the particular kinds of situational conditions which may operate in conjunction with an individual's internalized "conscience" or sense of moral justice. The situation in both experiments differed somewhat as to the nature of the experimenter-subject relationship and the seriousness of the transgression. Furthermore, it can be argued that naturalistic classes (groups to which the high- or low-status transgressors belonged) rather than individual subjects constituted the units of sampling. The possibility that the tendency to lie or to inform was due to initial differences between these classes therefore exists. Nevertheless, the present study showed the general effect of status variation to hold constant across two experiments of somewhat different type, thus minimizing the possibility of unwarranted generalization. In the long run, however, it may be more advisable to employ ad hoc groups in the laboratory in order to allow the manipulation of the status of the transgressor, while at the same time ruling out the likelihood of any more than random differences between the groups to which the transgressors belong.

Finally, a word of caution. The risk of cost to the subject (e.g., loss of self-esteem to the informer when the deception is revealed) in this type of study cannot be ruled out. In the present study, subjects' reaction during the comprehensive debriefing procedure, as well as reports by the adult authorities involved, seemed to indicate otherwise. Evidently, the entire episode was subsequently viewed as an amusing game, devoid of any dramatic or anxiety-producing aftereffects. As a rule, however, studies involving manipulation in areas such as group pressure, divided loyalties, or informing on malefactors almost inevitably run the risk of inflicting some costs on the subjects involved. Every effort should be made to keep such costs at a minimum.

[1] It is assumed that those who deny knowledge of a transgression and/or transgressor will also refuse to identify the transgressor. Still, the conservative reader might argue that the conflict between obeying and informing can be analyzed only from responses to the third question, provided that all those who responded negatively to the first two questions are eliminated as subjects. When this was done, the results remained practically unchanged: in Experiment I, the high-status thief/questioned in pairs/guilty-thief-present condition still yielded significantly less ($p < .05$) affirmative answers than any condition involving the low-status transgressor; in Experiment II, there was no change at all.

## REFERENCES

**PIAGET, J.** *The moral judgment of the child.* London: Kegan Paul, 1932.

**CRANE, A. R.** The development of moral values in children. IV. Preadolescent gangs and the moral development of children. *British Journal of Educational Psychology,* 1958, **28,** 201-208.

**DURKIN, D.** Children's acceptance of reciprocity as a justice principle. *Child Development,* 1959, **30,** 289-296. (a)

**DURKIN, D.** Children's concept of justice: A comparison with the Piaget data. *Child Development,* 1959, **30,** 59-67. (b)

**LURIA, Z., GOLDWASSER, M., & GOLDWASSER, A.** Response to transgression in stories by Israeli children. *Child Development,* 1963, **34,** 271-280.

**MACRAE, D. A.** A test of Piaget's theories of moral development. *Journal of Abnormal and Social Psychology,* 1954, **49,** 14-18.

**SIEGEL, S.** *Nonparametric statistics.* New York: McGraw-Hill, 1956.

# CHAPTER FIVE

# RACIAL PREJUDICE

The study of racial prejudice has always occupied much of the effort of social psychologists; the paper by LaPiere, in this chapter, is one of the earliest in this book.

Although it is frequently mentioned in secondary sources (Lindzey & Aronson, 1968), LaPiere's article is rarely read as a primary source. This phenomenon is characteristic of psychology, which always opts for the present, good or bad, over the past (Allport, 1960). However, this is a great loss. LaPiere's article is a prime example of early writing that still deserves to be heeded. As an example, in addition to noting the "new" problems of experimenter bias and demand characteristics, he points out the uselessness of accurately collecting irrelevant facts. These problems remain with us, as is noted by Levy (1961), who feels that psychologists stay in their laboratories because they concern themselves with techniques rather than problems.

LaPiere also stressed the disparity between verbal and overt behavioral response, which can be generalized to the disparity between laboratory experiments and field experiments; that is, the way someone behaves in a laboratory does not necessarily indicate how he will behave in the field, when his responses have real consequences. LaPiere shows surprising sophistication about control; for example, he sent questionnaires to unvisited establishments in the same area as the visited ones, to check out the effect of the visit.

McGrew's study (page 128) comes to the same conclusion as LaPiere's: little relationship exists between verbal attitude and real behavior in the area of race prejudice. However, it is difficult to draw firm conclusions. LaPiere used Chinese and McGrew used blacks, LaPiere checked verbal attitude by a mailed questionnaire and McGrew by telephone, and LaPiere found negative verbal attitude but positive behavioral response, while McGrew found positive verbal attitude but negative behavioral response. It is possible that negative responses to blacks are primarily triggered by visual cues. The current focus on civil rights may lead to socially desirable responses having little relation to the subject's real feelings. At one time, too, blacks were considered exotic, as the Chinese may have been in LaPiere's time (Catton, 1965).

The study by Selltiz (page 130) is a well-controlled experiment which also tested practices in contrast to beliefs and found, as did LaPiere's study, that restaurant owners deny they discriminate. They may be telling the truth; it may be that their employees initiate the discrimination rather than carry out the owners' policies. There is support for the visibility hypothesis, in the attempt to reduce the visibility of black patrons by providing them with an obscure table and hurrying them.

Linn (1965) has written a thoughtful paper which reviews verbal attitudes compared with overt behavior in the area of race. He feels that "statements or predictions of racial behavior based on attitude measurements have little reliability unless first validated empirically (p. 353)." The lack of correlation between attitude and behavior does not necessarily obviate their relationship; for example, Merton (1957) talks about the social and psychological mechanisms that intervene between attitudes and behavior. Many of these mechanisms are spelled out by Wicker (1969) in another article in this field. Although he notes, in an exhaustive review of the experimental literature of the area, that "only rarely can as much as 10% of the variance in overt behavioral measures be accounted for by attitudinal data (p. 65)." He also points out that there are many factors which affect the correlation between a measured attitude and behavior. For example, there are many personal and situational factors responsible for behavior disparate with attitude. However, most of these factors can be subsumed, as Wicker notes, under the rubric of "the expected and/or actual consequences of various acts (p. 73)." Competing motives, alternative behaviors available, and normative prescriptions for behavior are just a few of the many mediators between attitude and behavior elucidated by Wicker.

The article by Parker (page 139) is a more up-to-date extension of the work by LaPiere and Selltiz; that is, it concerns itself not with whether blacks are allowed entrance, but with how accepted they really are in integrated settings. His findings support those of other workers. For example, Dollard (1957) spoke of the caste system in which the lowest-class white feels himself to be superior to the highest-class black. Also, studies of communication in experimentally created hierarchies (Kelley, 1951; Cohen, 1958) found that low-status subjects communicate significantly more to high-status subjects than vice versa. Parker's finding, that blacks sat separately from whites more often than would be expected by chance, tends to support Heider's (1958) basic notion that "like attracts like." It is also interesting to note that the only integrated activities which did *not* fail were those centered on religion. This agrees with Sherif's conclusion (see Chapter 6) that a superiordinate goal is required to draw conflicting groups together.

The article by Campbell, Kruskal, and Wallace (page 146) contains a much more sophisticated method than Parker's for determining behavioral referents of attitudes. Their method is the chief asset in the article, because of its heuristic value for generating other studies. For example, Bickman has used it to measure faculty-student relationships. At the same time, however, the article by Campbell et al. illustrates the fragility of some research findings in the face of historical events. That is, if the same results were obtained on repetition of the experiment, the greater separation now could possibly indicate pro-black attitudes on the part of blacks more than anti-black attitudes on the part of whites. Campbell et al.'s suggestion of a study of the "flow" of seat choosing may help in answering this question. Do blacks move toward blacks or away from whites? Do whites move toward whites or away from blacks?

The Davis, Seibert, and Breed article (page 155) is a careful, self-critical study and illustrates the development of an index of social measurement. Of particular interest are the facts that not white males but black females violate precedence, and that the young violate precedence more than the old. The article is also a fine empirical study of the kind needed to develop a sociology of public transit [see Davis & Levine, Chapter 9]. Other articles useful in the development of such a sociology are those by Allen and by Piliavin, Rodin and Piliavin in Chapter 2.

The paper by Gaertner and Bickman (page 162) not only studies the prejudice whites have toward blacks, but also tries to determine if blacks discriminate against whites. It is becoming increasingly important to be able to assess how the black man reacts to individual whites.

## REFERENCES

**ALLPORT, G. W.** The open system in personality theory. *Journal of Abnormal and Social Psychology.* 1960, **61**, 301-311.

**CATTON, B.** *Terrible swift sword: the centennial history of the Civil War.* Vol. 2. New York: Doubleday, 1965.

**COHEN, A. R.** Upward communication in experimentally created hierarchies. *Human Relations,* 1958, **11**, 41-53.

**DOLLARD, J.** *Caste and class in a southern town.* New York: Doubleday, 1957.

**HEIDER, F.** *The psychology of interpersonal relations.* New York: Wiley, 1958.

**KELLEY, H. H.** Communication in experimentally created hierarchies. *Human Relations,* 1951, **4**, 39-56.

**LEVY, L. H.** Anxiety and behavior scientists' behavior. *American Psychologist,* 1961, **16**, 66-68.

**LINDZEY, G., & ARONSON, E.** (Eds.) *Handbook of social psychology.* (2nd ed.) Cambridge, Mass.: Addison-Wesley, 1968.

**LINN, L. S.** Verbal attitudes and overt behavior: A study of racial discrimination. *Social Forces,* 1965, **43**, 353-364.

**MERTON, R. K.** *Social theory and social structure.* (Rev. ed.) New York: The Free Press, 1957.

**WICKER, A. W.** Attitudes versus actions. *Journal of Social Issues,* 1969, **25**, 41-78.

# ATTITUDES VS. ACTIONS

RICHARD T. LAPIERE
*Stanford University*

By definition, a social attitude is a behavior pattern, anticipatory set or tendency, predisposition to specific adjustment to designated social situations, or, more simply, a conditioned response to social stimuli.[1] Terminological usage differs, but students who have concerned themselves with attitudes apparently agree that they are acquired out of social experience and provide the individual organism with some degree of preparation to adjust, in a well-defined way, to certain types of social situations if and when these situations arise. It would seem, therefore, that the totality of the social attitudes of a single individual would include all his socially acquired personality which is involved in the making of adjustments to other human beings.

But by derivation social attitudes are seldom more than a verbal response to a symbolic situation. For the conventional method of measuring social attitudes is to ask questions (usually in writing) which demand a verbal adjustment to an entirely symbolic situation. Because it is easy, cheap, and mechanical, the attitudinal questionnaire is rapidly becoming a major method of sociological and socio-psychological investigation. The technique is simple. Thus from a hundred or a thousand responses to the question "Would you get up to give an Armenian woman your seat in a street car?" the investigator derives the "attitude" of non-Armenian males toward Armenian females. Now the question may be constructed with elaborate skill and hidden with consummate cunning in a maze of supplementary or even irrelevant questions yet all that has been obtained is a symbolic response to a symbolic situation. The words "Armenian woman" do not constitute an Armenian woman of flesh and blood, who might be tall or squat, fat or thin, old or young, well or poorly dressed–who might, in fact, be a goddess or just another old and dirty hag. And the questionnaire response, whether it be "yes" or "no," is but a verbal reaction and this does not involve rising from the seat or stolidly avoiding the hurt eyes of the hypothetical woman and the derogatory stares of the other street-car occupants. Yet, ignoring these limitations, the diligent investigator will jump briskly from his factual evidence to the unwarranted conclusion that he has measured the "anticipatory behavior patterns" of non-Armenian males towards Armenian females encountered on street cars. Usually he does not stop here, but proceeds to deduce certain general conclusions regarding the social relationships between Armenians and non-Armenians. Most of us have applied the questionnaire technique with greater caution, but not I fear with any greater certainty of success.

Some years ago I endeavored to obtain comparative data on the degree of French and English antipathy towards dark-skinned peoples.[2] The informal questionnaire technique was used, but, although the responses so obtained were exceedingly consistent, I supplemented them with what I then considered an index to overt behavior. The hypothesis as then stated *seemed* entirely logical. "Whatever our attitude on the validity of 'verbalization' may be, it must be recognized that any study of attitudes through direct questioning is open to serious objection, both because of the limitations of the sampling method and because in classifying attitudes the inaccuracy of human judgment is an inevitable variable. In this study, however, there is corroborating evidence on these attitudes in the policies adopted by hotel proprietors. Nothing could be used as a more accurate index of color prejudice than the admission or nonadmission of colored people to hotels. For the proprietor must reflect the group attitude in his policy regardless of his own feelings in the matter. Since he determines what the group attitude is towards Negroes through the expression of that attitude in overt behavior and over a long period of actual experience, the results will be exceptionally free from those disturbing factors which inevitably affect the effort to study attitudes by direct questioning."

But at that time I overlooked the fact that what I was obtaining from the hotel proprietors was still a "verbalized" reaction to a symbolic situation. The response to a Negro's request for lodgings might have

[1] See Daniel D. Droba, "Topical Summaries of Current Literature," *The American Journal of Sociology*, 1934, p. 513.

[2] "Race Prejudice: France and England," *Social Forces*, September, 1928, pp. 102-111.

been an excellent index of the attitude of hotel patrons towards living in the same hotel as a Negro. Yet to ask the proprietor "Do you permit members of the Negro race to stay here?" does not, it appears, measure his potential response to an actual Negro.

All measurement of attitudes by the questionnaire technique proceeds on the assumption that there is a mechanical relationship between symbolic and non-symbolic behavior. It is simple enough to prove that there is no *necessary* correlation between speech and action, between response to words and to the realities they symbolize. A parrot can be taught to swear, a child to sing "Frankie and Johnny" in the Mae West manner. The words will have no meaning to either child or parrot. But to prove that there is no *necessary* relationship does not prove that such a relationship may not exist. There need be no relationship between what the hotel proprietor says he will do and what he actually does when confronted with a colored patron. Yet there may be. Certainly we are justified in assuming that the verbal response of the hotel proprietor would be more likely to indicate what he would actually do than would the verbal response of people whose personal feelings are less subordinated to economic expediency. However, the following study indicates that the reliability of even such responses is very small indeed.

Beginning in 1930 and continuing for two years thereafter, I had the good fortune to travel rather extensively with a young Chinese student and his wife.[3] Both were personable, charming, and quick to win the admiration and respect of those they had the opportunity to become intimate with. But they were foreign-born Chinese, a fact that could not be disguised. Knowing the general "attitude" of Americans towards the Chinese as indicated by the "social distance" studies which have been made, it was with considerable trepidation that I first approached a hotel clerk in their company. Perhaps that clerk's eyebrows lifted slightly, but he accommodated us without a show of hesitation. And this in the "best" hotel in a small town noted for its narrow and bigoted "attitude" towards Orientals. Two months later I passed that way again, phoned the hotel and asked if they would accommodate "an important Chinese gentleman." The reply was an unequivocal "No." That aroused my curiosity and led to this study.

In something like ten thousand miles of motor travel, twice across the United States, up and down the Pacific Coast, we met definite rejection from those asked to serve us just once. We were received at 66 hotels, auto camps, and "Tourist Homes," refused at one. We were served in 184 restaurants and cafes scattered throughout the country and treated with what I judged to be more than ordinary consideration in 72 of them. Accurate and detailed records were kept of all these instances. An effort, necessarily subjective, was made to evaluate the overt response of hotel clerks, bell boys, elevator operators, and waitresses to the presence of my Chinese friends. The factors entering into the situations were varied as far and as often as possible. Control was not, of course, as exacting as that required by laboratory experimentation. But it was as rigid as is humanly possible in human situations. For example, I did not take the "test" subjects into my confidence fearing that their behavior might become self-conscious and thus abnormally affect the response of others towards them. Whenever possible I let my Chinese friend negotiate for accommodations (while I concerned myself with the car or luggage) or sent them into a restaurant ahead of me. In this way I attempted to "factor" myself out. We sometimes patronized high-class establishments after a hard and dusty day on the road and stopped at inferior auto camps when in our most presentable condition.

In the end I was forced to conclude that those factors which most influenced the behavior of others towards the Chinese had nothing at all to do with race. Quality and condition of clothing, appearance of baggage (by which, it seems, hotel clerks are prone to base their quick evaluations), cleanliness and neatness were far more significant for person to person reaction in the situations I was studying than skin pigmentation, straight black hair, slanting eyes, and flat noses. And yet an air of self-confidence might entirely offset the "unfavorable" impression made by dusty clothes and the usual disorder to appearance consequent upon some hundred miles of motor travel. A supercilious desk clerk in a hotel of noble aspirations could not refuse his master's hospitality to people who appeared to take their request as a perfectly normal and conventional thing, though they might look like tin-can tourists and two of them belong to the racial category "Oriental." On the other hand, I became rather adept at approaching hotel clerks with that peculiar crab-wise manner which is so effective in provoking a somewhat scornful disregard. And then a bland smile would serve to reverse the entire situation. Indeed, it appeared that a genial smile was the

[3] The results of this study have been withheld until the present time out of consideration for their feelings.

most effective password to acceptance. My Chinese friends were skillful smilers, which may account, in part, for the fact that we received but one rebuff in all our experience. Finally, I was impressed with the fact that even where some tension developed due to the strangeness of the Chinese it would evaporate immediately when they spoke in unaccented English.

The one instance in which we were refused accommodations is worth recording here. The place was a small California town, a rather inferior auto-camp into which we drove in a very dilapidated car piled with camp equipment. It was early evening, the light so dim that the proprietor found it somewhat difficult to decide the genus *voyageur* to which we belonged. I left the car and spoke to him. He hesitated, wavered, said he was not sure that he had two cabins, meanwhile edging towards our car. The realization that the two occupants were Orientals turned the balance or, more likely, gave him the excuse he was looking for. "No," he said, "I don't take Japs!" In a more pretentious establishment we secured accommodations, and with an extra flourish of hospitality.

To offset this one flat refusal were the many instances in which the physical peculiarities of the Chinese served to heighten curiosity. With few exceptions this curiosity was considerately hidden behind an exceptional interest in serving us. Of course, outside of the Pacific Coast region, New York, and Chicago, the Chinese physiognomy attracts attention. It is different, hence noticeable. But the principal effect this curiosity has upon the behavior of those who cater to the traveler's needs is to make them more attentive, more responsive, more reliable. A Chinese companion is to be recommended to the white traveling in his native land. Strange features when combined with "human" speech and action seems, at times, to heighten sympathetic response, perhaps on the same principle that makes us uncommonly sympathetic towards the dog that has a "human" expression in his face.

What I am trying to say is that in only one out of 251 instances in which we purchased goods or services necessitating intimate human relationships did the fact that my companions were Chinese adversely affect us. Factors entirely unassociated with race were, in the main, the determinant of significant variations in our reception. It would appear reasonable to conclude that the "attitude" of the American people, as reflected in the behavior of those who are for pecuniary reasons presumably most sensitive to the antipathies of their white clientele, is anything but negative towards the Chinese. In terms of "social distance" we might conclude that native Caucasians are not averse to residing in the same hotels, auto-camps, and "Tourist Homes" as Chinese and will with complacency accept the presence of Chinese at an adjoining table in restaurant or cafe. It does not follow that there is revealed a distinctly "positive" attitude towards the Chinese, that whites prefer the Chinese to other whites. But the facts as gathered certainly preclude the conclusion that there is an intense prejudice towards the Chinese.

Yet the existence of this prejudice, very intense, is proven by a conventional "attitude" study. To provide a comparison of symbolic reaction to symbolic social situations with actual reaction to real social situations, I "questionnaired" the establishments which we patronized during the two year period. Six months were permitted to lapse between the time I obtained the overt reaction and the symbolic. It was hoped that the effects of the actual experience with Chinese guests, adverse or otherwise, would have faded during the intervening time. To the hotel or restaurant a questionnaire was mailed with an accompanying letter purporting to be a special and personal plea for response. The questionnaires all asked the same question, "Will you accept members of the Chinese race as guests in your establishment?" Two types of questionnaire were used. In one this question was inserted among similar queries concerning Germans, French, Japanese, Russians, Armenians, Jews, Negroes, Italians, and Indians. In the other the pertinent question was unencumbered. With persistence, completed replies were obtained from 128 of the establishments we had visited; 81 restaurants and cafes and 47 hotels, auto-camps, and "Tourist Homes." In response to the relevant question 92 per cent of the former and 91 per cent of the latter replied "No." The remainder replied "Uncertain; depend upon circumstances." From the woman proprietor of a small auto-camp I received the only "Yes," accompanied by a chatty letter describing the nice visit she had had with a Chinese gentleman and his sweet wife during the previous summer.

A rather unflattering interpretation might be put upon the fact that those establishments who had provided for our needs so graciously were, some months later, verbally antagonistic towards hypothetical Chinese. To factor this experience out responses were secured from 32 hotels and 96 restaurants located in approximately the same regions, but uninfluenced by this particular experience with Oriental clients. In this, as in the former case, both types of questionnaires were used. The results indicate that neither the type of questionnaire nor the fact of previous experience had important bearing upon

[TABLE 5-1] **Distribution of results from questionnaire study of establishment "policy" regarding acceptance of Chinese as guests**

Replies are to the question: "Will you accept members of the Chinese race as guests in your establishment?"

| | Hotels, etc., visited | | Hotels, etc., not visited | | Restaurants, etc., visited | | Restaurants, etc., not visited | |
|---|---|---|---|---|---|---|---|---|
| Total | 47 | | 32 | | 81 | | 96 | |
| | 1* | 2* | 1 | 2 | 1 | 2 | 1 | 2 |
| Number replying | 22 | 25 | 20 | 12 | 43 | 38 | 51 | 45 |
| No | 20 | 23 | 19 | 11 | 40 | 35 | 37 | 41 |
| Undecided: depend upon circumstances | 1 | 2 | 1 | 1 | 3 | 3 | 4 | 3 |
| Yes | 1 | 0 | 0 | 0 | 0 | 0 | 0 | 1 |

*Column (1) indicates in each case those responses to questionnaires which concerned Chinese only. The figures in columns (2) are from the questionnaires in which the above was inserted among questions regarding Germans, French, Japanese, etc.

the symbolic response to symbolic social situations.

It is impossible to make direct comparison between the reactions secured through questionnaires and from actual experience. On the basis of the above data it would appear foolhardy for a Chinese to attempt to travel in the United States. And yet, as I have shown, actual experience indicates that the American people, as represented by the personnel of hotels, restaurants, etc., are not at all averse to fraternizing with Chinese within the limitations which apply to social relationships between Americans themselves. The evaluations which follow are undoubtedly subject to the criticism which any human judgment must withstand. But the fact is that, although they began their travels in this country with considerable trepidation, my Chinese friends soon lost all fear that they might receive a rebuff. At first somewhat timid and considerably dependent upon me for guidance and support, they came in time to feel fully self-reliant and would approach new social situations without the slightest hesitation.

The conventional questionnaire undoubtedly has significant value for the measurement of "political attitudes." The presidential polls conducted by the *Literary Digest* have proven that. But a "political attitude" is exactly what the questionnaire can be justly held to measure; a verbal response to a symbolic situation. Few citizens are ever faced with the necessity of adjusting themselves to the presence of the political leaders whom, periodically, they must vote for—or against. Especially is this true with regard to the president, and it is in relation to political attitudes towards presidential candidates that we have our best evidence. But while the questionnaire may indicate what the voter will do when he goes to vote, it does not and cannot reveal what he will do when he meets Candidate Jones on the street, in his office, at his club, on the golf course, or wherever two men may meet and adjust in some way one to the other.

The questionnaire is probably our only means of determining "religious attitudes." An honest answer to the question "Do you believe in God?" reveals all there is to be measured. "God" is a symbol; "belief" a verbal expression. So here, too, the questionnaire is efficacious. But if we would know the emotional responsiveness of a person to the spoken or written word "God" some other method of investigation must be used. And if we would know the extent to which that responsiveness restrains his behavior it is to his behavior that we must look, not to his questionnaire response. Ethical precepts are, I judge, something more than verbal professions. There would seem little to be gained from asking a man if his religious faith prevents him from committing sin. Of course it does—on paper. But "moral attitudes" must have a significance in the adjustment to actual situations or they are not worth the studying. Sitting at my desk in California I can predict with a high degree of certainty what an "average" business man in an average Mid-Western city will reply to the question "Would you engage in sexual intercourse with a prostitute in a Paris brothel?" Yet no one, least of all the man himself, can predict what he would actually do should he by some misfortune find himself face to face with the situation in question. His moral "attitudes" are no doubt already stamped into his personality. But just what those habits are which will be invoked to provide him with some sort of adjustment to this situation is quite indeterminate.

It is highly probable that when the "Southern

**[TABLE 5-2] Distribution of results obtained from actual experience in the situation symbolized in the questionnaire study**

| Conditions | Hotels, etc. | | Restaurants, etc. | |
|---|---|---|---|---|
| | Accompanied by investigator | Chinese not so accompanied at inception of situation* | Accompanied by investigator | Chinese not so accompanied at inception of situation |
| Total | 55 | 12 | 165 | 19 |
| Reception very much better than investigator would expect to have received had he been alone, but under otherwise similar circumstances | 19 | 6 | 63 | 9 |
| Reception different only to extent of heightened curiosity, such as investigator might have incurred were he alone but dressed in manner unconventional to region yet not incongruous | 22 | 3 | 76 | 6 |
| Reception "normal" | 9 | 2 | 21 | 3 |
| Reception perceptibly hesitant and not to be explained on other than "racial" grounds | 3 | 1 | 4 | 1 |
| Reception definitely, though temporarily, embarrassing | 1 | 0 | 1 | 0 |
| Not accepted | 1 | 0 | 0 | 0 |

*When the investigator was not present at the inception of the situation the judgments were based upon what transpired after he joined the Chinese. Since intimately acquainted with them it is probable that errors in judgment were no more frequent under these conditions than when he was able to witness the inception as well as results of the situation.

Gentleman" says he will not permit Negroes to reside in his neighborhood we have a verbal response to a symbolic situation which reflects the "attitudes" which would become operative in an actual situation. But there is no need to ask such a question of the true "Southern Gentleman." We knew it all the time. I am inclined to think that in most instances where the questionnaire does reveal non-symbolic attitudes the case is much the same. It is only when we cannot easily observe what people do in certain types of situations that the questionnaire is resorted to. But it is just here that the danger in the questionnaire technique arises. If Mr. A adjusts himself to Mr. B in a specified way we can deduce from his behavior that he has a certain "attitude" towards Mr. B and, perhaps, all of Mr. B's class. But if no such overt adjustment is made it is impossible to discover what A's adjustment would be should the situation arise. A questionnaire will reveal what Mr. A writes or says when confronted with a certain combination of words. But not what he will do when he meets Mr. B. Mr. B is a great deal more than a series of words. He is a man and he acts. His action is not necessarily what Mr. A "imagines" it will be when he reacts verbally to the symbol "Mr. B."

No doubt a considerable part of the data which the social scientist deals with can be obtained by the questionnaire method. The census reports are based upon verbal questionnaires and I do not doubt their basic integrity. If we wish to know how many children a man has, his income, the size of his home, his age, and the condition of his parents, we can reasonably ask him. These things he has frequently and conventionally converted into verbal responses. He is competent to report upon them, and will do so accurately, unless indeed he wishes to do otherwise. A careful investigator could no doubt even find out by verbal means whether the man fights with his wife (frequently, infrequently, or not at all), though the neighbors would be a more reliable source. But we should not expect to obtain by the questionnaire method his "anticipatory set or tendency" to action should his wife pack up and go home to Mother, should Elder Son get into trouble with the neighbor's daughter, the President assume the status of a dictator, the Japanese take over the rest of China, or a Chinese gentleman come to pay a social call.

Only a verbal reaction to an entirely symbolic situation can be secured by the questionnaire. It may indicate what the responder would actually do when confronted with the situation symbolized in the question, but there is no assurance that it will. And so to call the response a reflection of a "social attitude" is to entirely disregard the definition commonly given for the phrase "attitude." If social attitudes are to be conceptualized as partially integrated habit sets which will become operative under specific circumstances and lead to a particular pattern of adjustment they must, in the main, be derived from a study of humans behaving in actual social situations. They must not be imputed on the basis of questionnaire data.

The questionnaire is cheap, easy, and mechanical. The study of human behavior is time consuming, intellectually fatiguing, and depends for its success upon the ability of the investigator. The former method gives quantitative results, the latter mainly qualitative. Quantitative measurements are quantitatively accurate; qualitative evaluations are always subject to the errors of human judgment. Yet it would seem far more worth while to make a shrewd guess regarding that which is essential than to accurately measure that which is likely to prove quite irrelevant.

# HOW "OPEN" ARE MULTIPLE-DWELLING UNITS?[1]

JOHN M. McGREW
*Department of Psychology, State University of New York at Buffalo*[2]

## A. INTRODUCTION

Although New York State law prohibits discrimination in multiple-dwelling units–i.e., dwellings inhabited by four or more residents–and the State Commission on Human Rights had received no complaints regarding suspected discrimination, it was popular opinion that discriminatory practices still existed. Therefore, an empirical investigation of such practices seemed useful to develop data having both general interest and practical value. In regard to the latter, information concerning the "openness" or availability of various apartments could be used by potential Negro renters; discriminating landlords could be effectively handled by the proper authorities; and, finally, such action could open housing still further.

On a more general plane, it was thought that the data would provide evidence for one of two points of view: the notion originating with William G. Sumner (7) that "stateways cannot change folkways," or the conclusion of Deutsch and Collins (2) that "official policy, executed without equivocation, can result in large changes of behavior and attitudes despite initial resistance to that policy."

The study was also seen to bear upon the contradiction between verbal attitude and behavior, as originally suggested by LaPiere (4).

LaPiere's data showed that while hotel proprietors expressed negative attitudes toward the Chinese people, they exhibited positive behavior towards a Chinese couple. In the present investigation, it was hypothesized that the reverse situation would occur: i.e., apartment landlords would express positive attitudes towards Negroes, by a willingness to rent to them, but would, in practice, exhibit negative attitudes, by discriminating against a Negro couple.

A final question posed was derivable from the theory of "No Social Equality" (5). Myrdal noted that although interracial marriages are viewed negatively by white Americans, there was much more ostracization in the case of a Negro male married to a white female, than in the case of a white male married to a Negro female. Hence, it was hypothesized that a Negro male-white female couple would be less able to obtain an apartment than a white male-Negro female couple.

## B. METHOD

Ten multiple-unit apartment dwellings, located in the central and suburban areas of Buffalo and which advertised vacancies, were selected. The student experimenters (*E*s) were divided into white (W) and Negro (N) couples, who visited a given apartment in a white-Negro-white or ABA order, approximately an hour apart.

In the case of the interracial couples, five of the 10 apartments were studied. The white male-Negro female (WN) couple visited a given apartment and was followed, approximately an hour later, by the Negro male-white female (NW) couple. Both couples visited the five apartments prior to the W and N couples.

Prior to the day of the experiment, all of the student couples participated in a workshop. During the course of these sessions, the importance of minimizing between-couple manner differences was stressed. For this purpose, each couple was instructed to dress neatly, preferably shirts and ties for the men and skirts and blouses for the women; couples were instructed to mention that they had no children; the girls were requested to purchase wedding bands; and, finally, all of the couples were asked to inform the landlord, after the sought information was obtained, that the apartment was unsuitable.

Besides requesting that the apartment be shown to them, each couple determined the rental and the willingness of the landlord to rent. Several weeks later, each landlord was telephoned and asked if he would rent to a Negro couple (verbal attitude) and if he were acquainted with the State law barring discrimination in multiple-dwellings.

## C. RESULTS

The data showed that, at the time sampled, some discrimination was taking place. That is, in four cases, the landlord refused to show the vacant apartment to the Negro couple and, in one case, increased the rental. Furthermore, in six cases, the landlord refused to rent the apartment to a Negro couple and offered a variety of excuses, such as "there is a long waiting list," "a 30-day notice" or "60-day notice" is needed, or "the apartment is already rented."

[1] Acknowledgment to the Housing Sub-Committee of the Civil Rights Committee at the University of Buffalo. Sincere appreciation to Drs. R. G. Hunt and B. Levinson for their valuable suggestions on presenting this paper.

[2] Formerly The University of Buffalo.

In order to determine the statistical significance of these findings, Fisher's Exact Probability Test (6) was computed on the information obtained by the couples. In each instance, the null hypothesis was that there were no differences in the responses received by the W and N couples. Although there were no significant treatment differences in regard to the landlord's willingness to show the apartment or the amount of rental requested, there was a racial difference obtained in the case of the landlord's willingness to rent the apartment ($p$ = .02). Since this difference was in the expected direction–that is, W couples more readily obtained the apartments than N couples –the one-tailed significance level is .01.

The telephone inquiry revealed that for the six landlords who refused to rent to a Negro couple, their verbal attitude was not consistent with actions. Furthermore, four of the six landlords claimed unfamiliarity with the State law. In the first instance, the difference was significant at the .05 level and, in the latter case, $p > .05$. Both of these comparisons were tested by Fisher's formula.

In the case of the interracial couples, no differences were observed.

When the data obtained from the interracial couples are compared to those obtained from the Negro couples, however, it appears that three apartments attainable by the interracial couples were unattainable by the Negro couples. Fisher's Test was computed for these differences and found to be not significant.

## D. DISCUSSION AND CONCLUSIONS

The data seem to indicate that, at the time sampled, statute had not been effective in producing simple compliance, thus supporting the notion that "stateways cannot change folkways." Although the data further show that 66 per cent of the discriminating landlords claimed no knowledge of the law, it is not discernible whether this is just a "claim" or suggestive of inadequate channels of communication extant between the proper authorities and those concerns which manage public housing. Future research could possibly eliminate this likely error of interpretation by indicating whether or not the proper authorities have, in fact, informed public housing managers of their obligation in upholding nondiscriminatory practices where laws, to that effect, exist.

When verbal attitudes concerning discriminatory practices were compared with behavior, the data were consistent with the now classic suggestion of LaPiere. His original data, however, indicated negative verbal attitude, yet positive action towards a Chinese couple; the present data reverse that trend. Namely, the results indicated positive verbal attitude but negative behavior in the situation. On the one hand, these findings seem consistent with the prevailing attitudes surrounding interracial housing as recently indicated in a nation-wide survey (3). On the other, the results seem to provide one of the first instances of what Campbell (1) has called "inconsistency."

Campbell criticizes the LaPiere study because it confused correlational inconsistency with situational threshold differences. The net result, Campbell argues, is an exaggeration of the inconsistency present. According to Campbell, "inconsistency would be represented if those who refused face to face accepted by questionnaire, or if those who accepted by questionnaire refused face to face. There is no report that such cases occurred" (1, p. 160).

The present data seem to provide evidence for *both* types of inconsistency and suggest the relative unimportance of verbal attitude content, concerning the racial issue, when behavior is to be predicted.

Finally, there seemed to be no treatment differences between the interracial couples and, as a consequence, some question is raised about Myrdal's (5) formulation. The small number of apartments sampled, however, does not allow for broad generalizations. Such a trend does merit further research and especial concern should be given to the differences between interracial couples and Negro couples.

## REFERENCES

1. **CAMPBELL, D. T.** Social attitudes and other acquired behavioral dispositions. In *Psychology: A Study of a Science. (Vol. 6)*, S. Koch, *Ed.* New York: McGraw-Hill, 1964. Pp. 94-172.

2. **DEUTSCH, M., & COLLINS, M. E.** The effect of public policy in housing projects upon interracial attitudes. In *Readings in Social Psychology,* Maccoby, *et al., Eds.* New York: Holt, Rinehart & Winston, 1958..

3. **HARRIS, L.** How whites feel about Negroes: A painful dilemma. *Newsweek,* Oct. 21, 1963, pp. 44-55.

4. **LAPIERE, R.** Attitudes vs. actions. *Soc. Forces,* 1934, **13,** 230-37.

5. **MYRDAL, G.** An American Dilemma. New York: Harper, 1962.

6. **SIEGEL, S.** Nonparametric Statistics for the Behavioral Sciences. New York: McGraw-Hill, 1956.

7. **SUMNER, W. G.** Folkways. New York: Ginn, 1940.

# THE USE OF SURVEY METHODS IN A CITIZENS CAMPAIGN AGAINST DISCRIMINATION

CLAIRE SELLTIZ*

In 1950 a group of citizens of New York City, working with limited and unpaid professional assistance, organized and carried out a campaign to reduce discrimination in restaurants in an area around the United Nations building. The event is of interest to social science because the group evaluated its success by a systematic comparison of restaurant practices before and after the campaign. While a number of communities have undertaken "self-surveys" of discriminatory practices, this is the only case known to the writer in which the results of the undertaking have been objectively measured.

The project was carried out by the Committee on Civil Rights in East Manhattan. The Committee was organized in the spring of 1949, "to compare public practices now existing in East Manhattan and those principles upon which our democracy was founded." The Committee is composed of representatives of 23 affiliated organizations, plus a few individual members-at-large. About half of the member groups represent specific minorities or have as their primary concern the reduction of discrimination and prejudice. The others represent broad community interests; they include such groups as branches of the American Association of University Women, of Americans for Democratic Action, of the Welfare and Health Council of New York City, and the Uptown Chamber of Commerce.

Both the organizational representatives and the members-at-large are more or less ordinary citizens. Although above average in education and in concern with problems of civil rights, they are not especially prominent in the community. They include, for example, housewives, school teachers, a public relations consultant, an editor, a photographer, a salesman, a biochemist, a group worker, a personnel director, an attorney, and a few persons working professionally in the field of intergroup relations. In addition to these "ordinary citizens," CCREM enlisted a number of prominent persons as sponsors and several social scientists as technical consultants.

In selecting its first project, CCREM recognized two criteria: the importance to the life of minority group members of practices in the area, and feasibility of investigating them.

Employment and housing were considered more important than public accommodations in their effects on the lives of minority group members, but they presented serious problems by way of gathering accurate information. Committee members were generally skeptical of the trustworthiness of information from interviews with persons responsible for policy and practices. Nor were they more favorably inclined to basing their conclusions on information from people opposed to discrimination and presumably in a position to know the facts. They wanted to come out with findings which could not be successfully challenged. Thus, they wanted to test practices—specifically, by determining whether majority group and minority group members, matched in all other relevant respects, would be treated alike in a given situation.

The fields of housing and employment seemed too formidable for such testing by the as yet inexperienced Committee. Public accommodations seemed to be much easier to tackle by this approach. The Committee recognized that this field is less crucial than others in its bearing on the lives of minority group members, but nevertheless it seemed sufficiently important to merit investigation. It was, therefore, decided that the Committee's first survey would deal with the practices of eating places—with the further simplification of limiting the study to one minority group, Negroes.

To reduce the scope of the project still further, the Committee decided to cover only the eastern half of midtown Manhattan, with its high concentration of restaurants. At the time, it seemed likely that a similar group would investigate the practices of eating places in west midtown. An area of about 150 square blocks was selected—from Fifth Avenue to the East

*The project reported here was carried out by a group of citizens, all volunteers. Limitations of space make it impossible to give credit to all those who participated. Among the lay participants, however, special mention should be made of Mr. Snowden T. Herrick and Mrs. Edna A. Merson, who served as chairmen of the Committee. A number of social scientists served as technical consultants: Drs. Kenneth B. Clark, Dan Dodson, Samuel H. Flowerman, Herbert Hyman, Patricia Kendall, Sophia M. Robison and the author. Miss Selltiz is currently a Research Associate at the Research Center for Human Relations at New York University.

River, and from Thirty-fourth Street to Fifty-ninth Street. This neighborhood was especially interesting because it includes the site of the United Nations building, with its personnel from many lands.

## PREPARING FOR THE INITIAL SURVEY

**Development of the Measuring Instrument** In the course of the discussions which led to the selection of eating places as the subject of the first survey, it had been decided that two teams—one consisting of two Negroes, the other of two white persons—would go to each restaurant, ostensibly as ordinary diners. Starting from the assumption that democratic practice requires the giving of equal service to all persons regardless of race, discrimination was defined as any inequality between the treatment accorded the two teams, unless there seemed reason to believe that the difference in treatment was due to some factor other than the difference in race.

The measuring instrument, then, must be such as to provide accurate comparison of the treatment given the two teams. It took the form of a questionnaire report to be filled out separately by each team after they had left the restaurant. Emphasis was placed on objective information which could easily be subjected to statistical analysis rather than on subjective or narrative reports.

The first step in preparing the questionnaire was to list the possible ways in which discrimination might be shown. The most obvious, of course, would be refusal to serve the Negro team. In view of the New York State Civil Rights Law, such refusal might be expressed deviously rather than forthrightly, by claiming, for instance, that reservations were necessary, or by simply keeping the Negroes waiting indefinitely. Short of refusal to serve the minority team, the following possible milder forms of discrimination were listed:

1. Evidences of confusion at the appearance of the Negro team or of hesitation about admitting them, such as a hasty conference between headwaiter and waiter, shifting of waiters, etc.
2. Directing the Negro team to a table in an undesirable location: one which would be considered poor by most customers, regardless of race (tables near the kitchen, near a lavatory, etc.); or one which placed the Negroes out of view of other diners (tables in a back corner, on a balcony, in a separate room, etc.).
3. Poor service: markedly slower than that given other customers; markedly faster than that given other customers, in an apparent attempt to get the Negroes out of the restaurant as quickly as possible; rudeness by restaurant employees; statements that items of food ordered were not available when in fact they were.
4. Inferior food: excessive amounts of salt or other spices added to the food served the Negro team; decayed food; etc.
5. Overcharges.

Questions were framed to get the information necessary to judge whether or not each form of discrimination had been practiced. Wherever possible, the questions called for short factual answers: "When did you enter the restaurant?" "When were you seated?" "Did you pick your own table, or were you assigned by a restaurant employee?" "Was the table assigned to you located in any of the following places . . . ?" A few questions called for evaluations or subjective impressions; for example, "Did you feel you were being hurried as compared with other persons served by the same waiter?" Such questions were followed by attempts to get the evidence on which such judgments were based: "What made you feel that way?" or "State your reasons" or "Please describe."

In order to make possible an analysis of characteristics of restaurants which might be related to discrimination, the questionnaire called for information on the following points: price of dinner, nationality of cuisine, location of restaurant, number of employees, race of employees, extent of occupancy at the time of the test.

**Pilot Survey of Luncheonettes** At about the time the questionnaire was being put into final form, two students from the New York School of Social Work of Columbia University volunteered to conduct a pilot survey. Luncheonettes and drug stores serving food were selected for this pilot study, which took place in the period May 8-29, 1950. The procedures and findings have been reported fully by the two students who took responsibility for this part of the survey;[1] only a brief summary will be given here. Forty-nine of the 227 luncheonettes and drug stores in the area (that is, approximately one-fifth of the total number) were tested. No discrimination of any kind was found in any of the places tested; in every case the treatment given the Negro team was substantially the same as that given the majority team.

---

[1] Phyllis Landa and Gerard Littman, "A Pilot Study to Test Discriminatory Practices against Ethnic Minority Groups in Public Eating Accommodations: An Audit to Determine the Degree of Discrimination Practiced against Negroes in Luncheonettes." Unpublished thesis, New York School of Social Work of Columbia University, 1950.

This pilot test indicated the need for only minor revisions in the testing instructions and report form. However, it revealed serious organizational and administrative problems–in recruiting testers, making assignments, filling out and returning report forms, supervising progress, etc.–and led to much more careful planning of these aspects in the survey of restaurants proper.

**Selecting the Sample of Restaurants to Be Tested** Since no complete list of restaurants was available, a complete enumeration was made during the winter and spring of 1950 by volunteers who walked through every block in the area, recording each eating place–its name, address, price range, and any other relevant information which could be secured. The enumeration produced a list of 771 eating places within the area–including restaurants proper, luncheonettes, drug stores, cafeterias, bars and grills, cocktail lounges and night clubs.

In view of the findings of the pilot study, the 227 luncheonettes and drug stores were removed from the list. As the Committee proceeded in its deliberations, its originally ambitious plans were gradually whittled down by realistic considerations. It was finally decided that limitations of personnel and funds made it impossible to test an adequate sample of the remaining 544 eating places; some categories would have to be omitted from the survey. Cafeterias were dropped on the ground that their practices were probably quite similar to those of luncheonettes, in which no discrimination had been found. It was decided also to omit bars and grills, cocktail lounges, and night clubs, on the grounds that these were not primarily eating places and that they presented special problems in testing.

Hence, the survey concentrated on restaurants proper, of which there were 364 listed in the area, ranging in price of an average meal from 75¢ to $10.00. It was decided to stratify on the basis of price, the variable most suspected of being relevant to the likelihood of discrimination.

The cards on which the data about each restaurant had been entered were arranged in order of the estimated price of an average meal. At the beginning of the week scheduled for testing, teams were available for 47 tests. It was decided to reduce the population about which statements were to be made, rather than to reduce the accuracy of the findings, by using less than a 25 percent sample. This was done by narrowing the price range to be covered, focusing on restaurants in the middle of the range. The median card was selected as the first case in the sample; the other cases were selected by taking, alternately, every fourth card above and every fourth card below the median. As additional teams were set up during the week, the sample was expanded. The final sample consisted of 62 restaurants, constituting 25 percent of the 248 restaurants with average prices from $1.30 to $3.75.

**Recruiting and Training the Testers** The volunteers who carried out the tests were recruited from the member organizations of CCREM, from other interested organizations, and from among friends of Committee members. There were 153 testers in all: 68 Negroes and 85 white persons, from 25 different organizations. All the testers were of pleasing appearance, quiet in manner, well but not ostentatiously dressed. All the minority group members were judged to be recognizably Negro; persons so light-skinned that they were not likely to be identified as Negroes by restaurant personnel were asked not to participate.

In both the minority and the control groups, there were twice as many women as men. More than 80 percent of each group were between the ages of 21 and 45. The testers were distinctly above average in education and socio-economic status. The great majority (90 per cent of the control testers and 76 percent of the Negro testers) had attended college. Only one (a member of the control group) had not attended high school. Of the minority group, 34 percent were engaged in professional or semiprofessional work, 25 percent had clerical or sales jobs, and 16 percent were students. Of the control group, 49 percent were engaged in professional or semiprofessional work, 21 percent had clerical or sales jobs and 14 percent were housewives.

An intensive training session was held the evening before testing began. The training instructions had four main themes: an injunction that all testers approach the situation open-mindedly, without preconceptions that they would either find or not find discrimination; the need for all teams to follow the same standardized procedures, so that the results would be comparable; the importance of remaining passive regardless of the treatment given the minority team, in order not to affect the practices of the restaurant and thus invalidate the test results; and the necessity for careful but unobtrusive noting of details of time, location, etc.

## THE INITIAL SURVEY

The testing took place on six nights during the period June 16-23, 1950, omitting Saturday and Sunday. All tests were conducted during the dinner hour, with teams entering the restaurants between 6:30 and 7:30 p.m.

The basic procedure was very simple: a Negro team and a white team went to each restaurant, and the treatment given the two teams was compared. The white team had two functions: first, to serve as a control against which the treatment given the Negro team could be measured; second, to observe, insofar as they could, the treatment given to the Negro team.

As far as possible, the two teams were matched except in skin color. If the Negro team consisted of two men, the white team going to the same restaurant consisted of two men; similarly, both teams might consist of two women, or of a man and a woman. With few exceptions, both teams were of about the same age. Since the entire group of testers was quite homogeneous in socio-economic level, in dress, and in general social behavior, no special effort was made to match teams on such factors as these.

The two teams assigned to a given restaurant separated before reaching the vicinity of the restaurant they were to test. The minority team entered the restaurant first so that there could be no question as to which team was entitled to be seated first and no possibility that the white team might be given a more desirable table simply because they had arrived first. The minority team was followed closely—less than a minute later—by the control team. All testers had been given general instructions as to the type of meal to order; to eliminate possible differences in time needed to prepare food or possible differences in treatment related to the prices of the meals ordered within a given restaurant.

Each team left the restaurant as soon as its two members had finished eating, still without giving any indication of acquaintance with the other team, and returned to the Committee's headquarters. There the two members of each team jointly filled out the team's report form, without discussing their experiences with the opposite team or indeed with anyone else until the form had been completed. The questionnaire was checked for completeness and clarity by a member of the Committee. Then the two teams who had tested a given restaurant came together, and a member of the Committee compared the two reports, asking for details on any points which were not clear or where the reports differed. At this time, most disagreements between the teams (and there were very few) were resolved by discussion; in the two or three cases where there was genuine disagreement as to what had happened or why it had happened, the supervisor wrote a detailed report of the versions given by each team. Final judgment as to whether the two teams had in fact been given approximately equal treatment was left to a committee of eight coders.

**Description of the Restaurants Tested** As stated earlier, 62 restaurants were tested, constituting 25 percent of all the restaurants within the geographic area and price range previously described. The sample was checked against the enumeration in terms of price and location and was found to be representative, except for a slight underrepresentation of one corner of the area.

Of the 62 restaurants tested, 39 served American food and 23 specialized in foreign dishes (11 French, 8 Italian, 2 French-Italian, one German, one Swedish). At the time the teams entered, 42 percent of the restaurants were less than half full, 21 percent were about half full, 21 percent were about three-quarters full, 11 percent were about full but with no people waiting, and five percent had people waiting for tables. About one-third had less than five waiters or other visible service staff, another third had from five to nine, and another third had 10 or more. About three-fourths of the restaurants had a headwaiter or hostess. Only nine of the 62 had any non-white employees who were visible, that is, waiters, bus boys, etc.

**Deciding Whether Discrimination Had Occurred** As has been stated, the questionnaire, the training of testers, and the testing procedures were all designed to secure objective information and to minimize the effects of possible bias on the part of the testers. The judgment as to whether the treatment reported actually showed inequality, and hence discrimination, was left to eight members of the Committee who served as coders. Preliminary classification was done by coders working in pairs; finally the whole group of coders, acting as a committee, reviewed all the tests and made the final decisions as to whether or not there had been clear inequality of treatment.

The decisions of the coders as to whether the minority team had received discriminatory treatment in a given restaurant were based on their judgment as to whether the facts reported indicated clearly that the minority team was treated less well than the control team and that the inferior treatment could not reasonably be considered accidental. In reaching their decisions, the coders took into account such factors as whether discriminatory treatment was manifested in more than one way (thus lessening the likelihood that any given action might have been accidental), whether both teams reported the treatment as unequal, etc. The final decision rested on the convincingness of the evidence reported. Whenever there was reason to believe that inferior treatment given the minority group might have been accidental, the case was not considered one of discrimination even if both teams reported that the minority was given less good treatment.

**Findings** In no restaurant was the minority team refused service, nor was there any attempt to avoid serving them by such devices as saying that reservations were needed or by making them wait indefinitely without being given a table. However, in 26 restaurants (42 percent of those tested; $Op = 6.3$) the minority team was given treatment so clearly inferior to that given the control team as to be considered discriminatory. In no case was the control team treated less well than the minority team.

*Types of discriminatory treatment* Unequal treatment was of two general types: assignment of the Negro team to a table in an undesirable location, and giving poorer service to the Negro team than to the control team. [Table 5-3] shows the number of restaurants in which each of these types of discriminatory treatment was encountered.

In about 70 percent of the restaurants, the testers were assigned to tables by a headwaiter or other restaurant employee. In these restaurants where tables were assigned, there was a marked tendency to give the minority team a less desirable table than the control team. The control teams were given undesirable tables in nine of the 62 restaurants tested, whereas the minority teams were given undesirable tables in 28 of the 62 restaurants. In each case, in addition to rating the desirability of the table given each team, the testers rated the comparative desirability of the two tables. In only one case was the control team reported as having a less desirable table than the minority team. In 17 restaurants the minority teams were given clearly less desirable tables than the controls even though other tables were available.

**[TABLE 5-3] Types of discriminatory treatment, initial survey**

| | Number of restaurants |
|---|---|
| Less desirable location only | 5 |
| Poorer service or rudeness only | 9 |
| Both less desirable location and poorer service | 12 |
| | 26 |

In no case did the control team report being treated rudely, being made to wait out of turn for a table, receiving unduly slow service, or other evidence of reluctance to serve them. In contrast, there were 21 cases in which the minority team was given such clearly inferior service that the restaurants were classified as discriminatory. In 19 of these cases, the minority team was treated rudely by one or more restaurant employees; in seven of these 19, they were also made to wait considerably longer for service than diners at nearby tables. In three restaurants the minority team was hurried to the point of inconvenience, although nearby diners were not hurried.

*Characteristics of discriminatory restaurants* The only observed characteristic in which the restaurants which discriminated differed significantly from those which did not discriminate was price.[2] As shown in [Table 5-4], discrimination was encountered in one-seventh of the restaurants in the $1.30-$1.99 price range, and in slightly more than half of those where the average price of the meal was between $2.00 and $3.99.

When price was held constant, no significant differences in frequency of discrimination were found between American and foreign restaurants, between restaurants with and without headwaiters, nor among the geographic sections of the survey area. There was no relation between the size of the visible staff and the occurrence of discrimination, nor between the occupancy of the restaurant and the occurrence of discrimination.

## THE ACTION PROGRAM

The next question was: What steps should be taken to reduce—or, hopefully, eliminate—discriminatory practices? CCREM enunciated two principles: that its

[2] Where the number of cases and the lowest expected theoretical frequencies were sufficiently large, probabilities were calculated by Chi-square. Where the number of cases or the theoretical frequencies were too low to justify the use of Chi-square, probabilities were calculated by Fisher's exact test for fourfold tables and multiplied by two to make them comparable to a two-tailed test such as Chi-square. The difference in the frequency of discrimination between restaurants in the $1.30 to $1.99 price range and those in the $2.00 to $3.99 range, as shown in [Table 5-4], is significant beyond the one percent level ($p = .003$). With regard to all of the other characteristics considered, as described in the following paragraph, the statistical tests indicated that the obtained differences in frequency of discrimination between restaurants in different categories might be expected to occur by chance more than eight times in 100 ($p$'s ranged from .09 to .70).

**[TABLE 5-4] Frequency of incidents of discrimination in restaurants in various price ranges–initial survey**

| Price of average meal | Number tested | Number with incidents | Percent of incidents to number tested |
|---|---|---|---|
| $1.30 - 1.99 | 21 | 3 | 14 |
| $2.00 - 2.99 | 26 } 41 | 15 } 23 | 58 } 56 |
| $3.00 - 3.99[3] | 15 | 8 | 53 |

approach would be "educational" and persuasive rather than militant, and that it would attempt to enlist broad community support for a change in practices. There was no assumption that this approach would necessarily be the most effective one under all circumstances, but it seemed promising, and it seemed the one most appropriate for a group representing such a range of organizations as CCREM's affiliates.

**Activities Directed toward the Restaurant Field** The Committee turned its attention first toward the organizations of persons with responsibility for policies and practices in restaurants; associations of restaurant owners and unions of restaurant employees. There were nine such organizations operating in the area at the time: seven management associations, and two union groups (one of which was a Joint Board representing 12 hotel and restaurant unions). Representatives of CCREM held one or more conversations with the officers of each of these organizations. Within four months after the first contact, all of the groups had signed pledges of equal treatment to all patrons both in seating and in service.

The next step was to send a letter to the owner or manager of each of the 364 restaurants in the area, informing him of the survey findings and of the organizational pledges, and enclosing an individual pledge for his signature. This letter was followed by three others during the next year. A total of 127 pledges were signed and returned, representing approximately one-third of the restaurants in the area. Eleven of the owners added notes expressing their sympathy with the campaign and offering to help.

A more direct personal approach seemed called for in the case of restaurants which had been found to discriminate. A fundamental policy of the Committee was that no individual restaurant would be named in any public discussion of the survey findings, since the sample had been selected randomly and was assumed to be representative of all restaurants in the area. This did not, however, rule out the possibility of individual conferences with the managers of restaurants where discrimination had been encountered.

The Committee planned to talk individually with the managers of each of the restaurants in which discrimination had been found. This program was not completed, largely because of lack of personnel; most of the Committee members have full-time jobs and are not able to visit restaurants at the odd day-time hours when restaurateurs are free. The interviews which were carried out, however, were of considerable interest and showed a wide range of reactions. At one extreme was the manager of a small relatively inexpensive hotel restaurant. She seemed completely cooperative, expressed surprise at the Committee's report of the treatment received in her restaurant, and volunteered to issue instructions to her employees that all patrons were to be treated alike. At the other extreme was the owner of a small "exclusive" French restaurant in the upper price bracket, who denied that discrimination had occurred in his restaurant and was generally hostile toward the Committee members. There were two conversations with this owner, and two follow-up tests of his restaurant; the final one showed no discrimination.

**Activities Directed toward the Community** The decision to adopt a persuasive approach toward the restaurant industry had entailed a decision not to publicize the survey findings until some progress could be reported–or until the Committee was satisfied that no progress was going to be achieved through persuasion. The Committee's first press release was issued immediately after the signing of pledges by all the restaurant unions and management associations; it reported not only the survey findings but the restaurant industry's pledge to eliminate discrimination. This story was carried in three major New York City newspapers and in two Negro papers with national circulation; it led to mention of the survey or personal appearances of CCREM members on five broadcasts over four radio stations. Later, 10,000 copies of a popular pamphlet about the survey and the follow-up action program, entitled "Have You Heard What's Cooking?", were distributed.

CCREM's conception of its work with the community, however, focused on direct appeals to individuals in organizations rather than on broadside appeals through the mass media. The first step along

[3] The prices actually paid differed slightly from the estimates based on the enumeration. This is why the upper price limit here is higher than that reported in the selection of the sample.

these lines was a meeting, in April 1951, of those who had participated in the initial test, to inform them of the success in securing pledges from the restaurant organizations and to discuss further plans. This was followed by reports and sociodramatic presentations at meetings of 10 groups affiliated with CCREM or interested in its work.

### THE FINAL SURVEY

A re-test was carried out in the spring of 1952 to determine what changes, if any, had taken place in the almost two years since the initial test.

**Selecting the Sample** The major question in planning the re-survey was whether to re-test the same restaurants used in the first audit or to select another representative sample of restaurants in the area. Retesting the old sample had great research advantages because of the greater confidence that any changes found would not reflect chance sampling variations, and because of the possibility of detailed analysis of the characteristics of restaurants which had changed their practices. On the other hand, taking a new sample was attractive for a number of practical reasons. Information about a new sample, when added to that from the original audit, would give data about the practices of a larger total number of restaurants; this was particularly important if subsequent action was to be taken with regard to those which discriminated. Further, testing a new sample would increase the number of restaurants which had at least once had the experience of serving Negro customers. And, incidentally, the members of the Committee would find a new batch of restaurants more interesting.

Resources were not great enough to allow for re-testing the entire old sample and a sufficiently large new sample to give reliable results, so a compromise was adopted. It was decided to re-test all the restaurants which had been found discriminatory in the first survey and half of those which had been found non-discriminatory, and to test a new sample of 50 restaurants. In the analysis, the non-discriminatory restaurants would be weighted so that they would account for their proper proportion of an original sample.

No sampling procedure was needed, of course, to identify the old discriminatory restaurants; all 26 of them were to be tested. The cards of the 36 which had not discriminated in 1950 were arranged in order of price, and every other one selected. One of these turned out to have gone out of business, leaving 17 to be tested. The enumeration cards which has been prepared in the winter and spring of 1950 were used as the basis for selection of the new sample. After the cards for the 62 restaurants in the original sample and those of a few which were known to have gone out of business were removed, there were 175 cards within the price range covered by the initial survey. From these cards, arranged in order of price, a sample of 50 restaurants was selected by taking every fifth card, then every tenth one of the remaining cards.

**Procedures** The tests were carried out at the dinner hour during the period of March 21 to April 1, 1952, omitting Saturday and Sunday. Training, testing, reporting and coding procedures were essentially the same as in the first audit, except for minor changes designed to insure greater clarity in the reports.

In this second audit there were 272 testers: 130 minority group members, 142 in the control group. They came from about 40 different organizations. Although only 37 of the 272 had taken part in the initial survey, as a group they were very similar to the 1950 testers in age, sex, education, and occupation.

**Description of the Restaurants Tested** A total of 93 restaurants were tested. The old sample, of course, remained the same in such characteristics as geographical location, nationality of food, size of staff, and character of staff. The new sample differed slightly in some of these characteristics.

The geographic distribution of the restaurants tested again differed slightly from that of the total population of restaurants within the area. Again about two-thirds of the restaurants tested served American food, one-third specialized in foreign dishes, mostly French or Italian. Again, about one-third of the restaurants had less than five waiters or other visible staff, one-third had from five to nine, and one-third had 10 or more. Approximately 80 percent had a headwaiter or hostess. Again, only a very few restaurants had any visible non-white employees.

As might be expected, prices had risen; whereas the prices paid per meal in the first test had ranged from $1.30 to $3.99, they now ranged from $1.37 to $4.77. Since the percentage increases were fairly consistent, it was possible to set up new categories which included approximately the same proportions of restaurants as those in the first survey. The two sets of categories are shown in [Table 5-5].

**[TABLE 5-5] Price categories, 1950 and 1952**

| | 1950 | 1952 |
|---|---|---|
| "Lower priced" | $1.30 - 1.99 | $1.37 - 2.27 |
| "Medium priced" | $2.00 - 2.99 | $2.28 - 3.37 |
| "Higher priced" | $3.00 - 3.99 | $3.38 - 4.77 |

**[TABLE 5-6][4] Types of discriminatory treatment, final survey**

| | Number of restaurants |
|---|---|
| Less desirable location only | 6 |
| Poorer service or rudeness only | 2 |
| Both less desirable location and poorer service | 7 |
| | 15 |

Although no relation between the occurrence of discrimination and the fullness or emptiness of the restaurant had been found in the first survey, the hypothesis had been offered that restaurant business might be worse (or better) in 1952 than it had been in 1950, and that this might account for any difference found in the prevalence of discrimination. The extent of occupancy during the two audits, however, was found to be almost identical.

In summary, the second sample was similar in all major aspects to the one originally tested, both being fairly representative of all restaurants in the given price range within the geographical area bounded by Fifth Avenue, the East River, 34th Street and 59th Street.

**Findings** As in 1950, in no restaurant was the minority team refused service. More important, there was a marked reduction in the number of restaurants where the minority team encountered discriminatory treatment. In only 16 percent of the restaurants was the minority team given treatment clearly inferior to that of the control team.[5] This figure (16 percent) was the same both for the restaurants which were being re-tested and for the new sample. The difference between this proportion and that found in the first survey–42 percent–is significant at the one-percent level.

*Types of discriminatory treatment* Again the two major types of discrimination encountered centered around location of tables and quality of service. [Table 5-6] shows the frequency of occurrence of these two types of treatment.

*Characteristics of discriminatory restaurants* The initial survey had shown markedly greater incidence of discrimination among the restaurants in the middle and upper part of the price range tested than among those in the lower part of the price range. [Table 5-7] shows the percentages of restaurants in each price range which discriminated in 1950 and in 1952.

Obviously there was no decrease in the proportion of lower-priced restaurants which discriminated; however, the original low frequency of discrimination in this price range left relatively little room for improvement. The drop in discrimination for both the middle- and upper-priced restaurants is significant at the one-percent level.

The small number of restaurants in which discrimination occurred during the re-test makes it impossible to carry out any statistical analysis of characteristics related to discrimination. Factors such as nationality of cooking, presence of head waiter, size of staff, geographic location, and occupancy were inspected, but no trends sufficient to establish significance in such a small number of cases appeared.

**COMMENT**

The drop in discrimination between the first and second surveys provides interesting evidence of the ease and speed with which discriminatory practices can be changed under favorable conditions. There is no assumption that the work of CCREM was exclusively responsible for the marked reduction of discrimination in Manhattan restaurants. The period between the two tests was marked by a general liberalizing of practices with regard to minority groups in many areas of living. Moreover, just before the second survey there had been a change in New York State law, providing for more effective enforcement of the law forbidding discrimination in public accommodations which had long been in existence. Although the

**[TABLE 5-7] Frequency of incidents of discrimination in restaurants in various price ranges–initial and final surveys**

| Price range | 1950 Percentage which discriminated | 1952 (total sample, weighted) Percentage which discriminated |
|---|---|---|
| Lower | 14 | 14 |
| Middle | 58 | 17 |
| Upper | 53 | 15 |

[4] This table, as well as all subsequent discussion which deals only with the discriminatory restaurants, is based on the 15 restaurants in which discrimination occurred; in view of the small number of cases, the two formerly non-discriminatory restaurants which now showed discrimination have not been weighted.

[5] In one case the reporting was not sufficiently clear to permit a decision as to whether there had been discrimination. This case was dropped from the analysis. The present figure is based on the 92 cases which could be coded, with the non-discriminatory cases from the original sample weighted (doubled) to account for their proper proportion.

new law had not yet gone into effect at the time of the re-survey, it is possible that the news of its passage may have affected restaurant practices. It remains to be seen whether a program of objective fact-finding, followed by educational and persuasive action directed toward the persons responsible for policy and practices in the area and an attempt to enlist community support for the change in practices, can be effective in areas where discrimination is more strongly supported by economic considerations and personal prejudice. CCREM intends to put this question to the test as it turns its attention to the field of private housing.

# THE INTERACTION OF NEGROES AND WHITES IN AN INTEGRATED CHURCH SETTING

JAMES H. PARKER
*Michigan State University*

*Abstract*
Data on interracial interaction were collected by participant observation from the first church in the American Baptist Convention to adopt a policy of racial integration. It was found that the 38 most active members were not discriminatory in the rate at which they conversed with members of the other race. A number of factors are offered to explain this highly successful experiment in racial integration. Seating patterns of the whole congregation, however, showed a significant amount of segregation. Also, it was found that social class was not related to the propensity to initiate interracial interaction, either among Negroes or whites.

A process of racial and class integration has been going on in the First Baptist Church, Chicago, Illinois, since 1942. It has been beset by many problems of finances, strong race prejudice and an unstable community setting, but it has survived. It was the first church in the American Baptist Convention to adopt a policy of integration. It admitted Japanese-Americans into an all-white congregation when we were at war with Japan and all Japanese were "suspects" in this country. No sooner had the Japanese been assimilated into the church when an influx of Negroes invaded the neighborhood and soon entered the church. Through all this the racially integrated nature of the church remained intact. One rarely finds a voluntary social situation in which race differences exist, therefore it seemed to present a good opportunity to explore the extent to which the church was "really" integrated and the reasons that the church had survived and racial integration flourished.

## THE PROBLEM AND HYPOTHESES

The literature has little to tell us about the interaction of persons in desegregated institutions having voluntary membership. Some literature dealing with quasi-voluntary integrated settings[1] such as public housing, work situations and clerk-customer relations, indicate that people tend to adapt to a *fait accompli* and through increased interracial contact develop more positive behaviors and attitudes toward the other race. However, the question of whether real integration can be achieved in a society so full of race hatred such as our own, has never been adequately tested. It was this investigator's intent to find out if real integration was possible in a voluntary membership organization such as a church where the climate would appear to be most favorable for such a development.

Along with this general objective were subsidiary aims which included the following. First, we wished to find out what characteristics of the church membership and the community aided the church in maintaining its integrated character. Second, we wished to discover if the social class of the members was related to their tendency to interact with members of the other race. Several studies which indicated that prejudice and discrimination were positively related to economic insecurity have been reviewed by Gerhart Saenger.[2] A study was found referring to Negro attitudes toward whites, using class as a variable. This study done by Frank and Margaret Westie[3] indicated that substantially the same relationship exists with respect to class and race attitudes among Negroes as among whites. They reported that the higher the status of Negroes, the less their social distance toward whites. Based on this literature it was hypothesized

[1] Morton Deutsch and Mary Collins, *Interracial Housing: A Psychological Evaluation of a Social Experiment* (Minneapolis: University of Minnesota Press, 1951); Marie Jahoda and Patricia West, "Race Relations in Public Housing," *Journal of Social Issues,* 7 (1951), pp. 132-139; Daniel M. Wilner, Rosabelle Walkley, and Stuart W. Cook, *Human Relations in Interracial Housing: A Study of the Contact Hypothesis* (Minneapolis: University of Minnesota Press, 1955); John Harding and Russell Hogrefe, "Attitudes of White Department Store Employees Toward Negro Co-Workers," *Journal of Social Issues,* 3 (1952), pp. 18-28; Gerhart Saenger and Emily Gilbert, "Customer Reactions to the Integration of Negro Sales Personnel," *International Journal of Opinion and Attitude Research,* 4 (1950), pp. 57-76.

[2] Gerhart Saenger, *The Social Psychology of Prejudice* (New York: Harper & Bros., 1953), p. 279.

[3] Frank Westie and Margaret Westie, "The Social Distance Pyramid: Relationships between Caste and Class," *American Journal of Sociology,* 63 (September 1957), pp. 190-196.

that a positive association would be found between social class and interracial interaction.[4]

## THE OBSERVATIONAL AND STATISTICAL METHODS

The basic data for this study were secured by field observations at the First Baptist Church. The writer and his wife attended social functions at the church for eight months; collecting a total of 608 observations on a group of 38 subjects. These observations consisted of noting who the subjects initiated interactions with, that is, the number of times the subjects initiated interactions with Negroes and the number of times with whites. Also some observations consisted of timing the interactions of nine individuals, and making seating charts by race both at Sunday worship services and weekly Wednesday night suppers.

An average of 14 initiations were observed and written down for each subject. The procedure used in observing was to determine beforehand four or five individuals who would be observed at a certain function. No social group function was observed that had fewer than 40 percent or more than 60 percent white participants. This rule was made in order to control for bias in the number of people of both races available for interaction. On the average there was no consistent tendency for more whites or more Negroes to be at these functions. In 75 percent of the situations there was only a slight imbalance with a few (3 or 4) extra whites or Negroes. If we had sampled all events regardless of the racial composition we probably would have found different interaction patterns. For example, if 80 percent of the people present were Negroes, there would undoubtedly be more interaction directed toward Negroes.

**Computations of Ratios** After the observations were collected for an individual, an interracial interaction ratio was computed. The ratio was arrived at by dividing the number of interactions initiated by this person with the other race by the total number of interactions we observed this individual initiating. This gave us the proportion of the time we observed the subject initiating interaction with the other race:

$$\text{Interracial Interaction Ratio} = \frac{\text{Initiations to other race}}{\text{Total initiations observed}}$$

**Interracial Conversation Length Ratio** On a sample of nine of the subjects, the lengths of the initiated conversations were measured to determine if frequency of interactions was an adequate measure of the quantity of interactions. The conversation length ratio was arrived at as follows:

$$\text{Conversation Length Ratio} = \frac{\text{Average length of conversations initiated by subject to other race}}{\text{Average length of conversations initiated by subject to both races}}$$

Eighty-three conversations were timed with a stopwatch and at least three conversations were timed involving each of the four possible interaction patterns (such as Negro initiating to white).[5]

**Information on Status** Another variable of major importance was occupational status. In most cases information on occupational status could be found in the church records; even then it was checked by asking the individual or his friends to confirm it. If no record was available, the individual was asked his occupation and that of his spouse. The occupations were rated by using Duncan's NORC Transform Scale.[6]

**Statistical Techniques** The Rank Correlation Test[7] (both one- and two-tailed depending on whether or not the direction was postulated) was used when both variables were clearly ordinal. When one or both of the variables were nominal the *Chi*-Square Test of Independence[8] was used to determine if a significant relationship existed.

**Accuracy and Reliability** The interaction data may be considered fairly accurate because of several factors. First, duplicate observations by two observers on

[4] In the preliminary analysis we found a number of variables to be unrelated to rates of interracial interaction: social adeptness of respondent, age of respondent, Negro's lightness of skin color, three social-psychological characteristics of respondents (acceptance of others, adaptation to new situations, and ease of relating to others), sex of the respondent, and racial balance in Negro respondent's neighborhood.

[5] We found a positive association between the length of conversation with other race and propensity to initiate interaction with other race (*.01* level of significance) which indicates that the interracial interaction ratio is a good measure of conversation volume.

[6] Otis Dudley Duncan, "A Socio-Economic Index for all Occupations," in *Occupations and Social Status,* Albert J. Reiss, Jr. (New York: The Free Press, 1961).

[7] W. Allan Wallis and Harry V. Roberts, *Statistics: A New Approach* (Glencoe, Illinois: The Free Press, 1956), p. 603.

[8] Helen M. Walker and Joseph Lev, *Statistical Inference* (New York: Holt, Rinehart & Winston, 1953), p. 93.

about 18 individuals proved highly compatible. Second, the interracial interaction ratios for individuals changed very little as more observations were gathered. Finally, it is extremely doubtful that any of the subjects knew they were being studied. After the field work was completed, we divulged the fact that we had been observing interaction, and all members showed genuine surprise and lack of previous knowledge.

The validity of occupation as an index of class position has been demonstrated by several researchers as being the best single measurement. The validity of propensity to initiate interracial interaction as an index of interpersonal acceptance is questionable. However, at the very minimum, it measures the degree of interracial contact.

## THE POPULATION

At the time of the study, the racial composition of the membership was 71 percent Negro, 25 percent white, and four percent Oriental. Of the total church population of 290, occupational status of 144 persons was known. Sixty-nine percent of these people are classified as managerial and professional, 19 percent are skilled and unskilled workers, and 12 percent are clerical workers. Negroes and whites have about the same occupational distribution.

## THE SAMPLE

Our observations of interracial interaction rates were collected from the 38 most active persons in the church. About 55 percent of these people are managerial or professional, 20 percent are clerical workers, and the remaining 25 percent are unskilled or skilled workmen. The most active group then is roughly proportional with respect to occupation to the half of the population whose occupation is known. "Most active" was rated on the basis of attendance at social functions and church services, and the amount of responsibility taken in the work of the church. Careful study of church attendance and individual activity records was made in order to determine the most active group in the church. To have a wider spread of socioeconomic status it was necessary to add some who were less active than those left out. The bias was in overrepresenting the lower-status group. We chose the most active members as subjects because it was easier to observe them, and because they were more committed to the church.

## THE FINDINGS

Both the Negroes and the whites initiated conversations with each other close to 50 percent of the time. [Table 5-8] indicates that whites talked to Negroes in 41 percent of their initiations and Negroes initiated conversations with whites in 49 percent of their initiations. Even though whites interacted with Negroes less frequently than would be expected by chance (tested by the *Chi*-Square Test of Independence, at the *.05* level), 41 percent still indicates a high degree of integration. In short, we find that interaction between the races was almost as integrated as one could expect. This should be a rewarding finding for those who are interested in finding out how to integrate racially or culturally diverse groups.

The standard deviation of the individual interracial interaction ratios present something of a problem however. Although the average rate of interracial interaction of Negroes and whites was close to 50 percent, there were many low interracial interactors and many high ones. Therefore, there is a lot of dispersion within the racial groups that has not been explained.

[Table 5-8] shows that there was no association between social class of a subject and his propensity to initiate interracial interaction. Why didn't we find any association between social class and interracial interaction? The explanation probably lies in two directions. First, the previous studies dealt with random samples of very large populations. Attitudes in these samples were supposedly a cross-section of this large parent population. On the other hand, in this study the population was very select with respect to attitudes. The people in the church were there because they were not violently opposed to interracial interaction. In fact, we might say that the population was to some extent *self-selective* with respect to racial attitudes. The second thing to consider in explaining the unexpected results is the differences in indices used in this and previous studies. The studies done previously, employed attitude items which are unreliable in predicting actual behavior in a given interracial situation.

In order to test the self-selective hypothesis we looked at the length of time each respondent had belonged to the church and compared the interracial interaction of persons who had joined before integration with those who had joined after integration. As we suspected, [Table 5-9] shows an association indicating that white people who joined before integration engaged in less interracial interaction. Of course we also found that age showed a negative association with interracial interaction. The question remains, then, whether it is merely age or self-selectivity that affects the interracial interaction rates. The fact that we did not find any correlation with age among Negroes

**[TABLE 5-8] Frequency of initiating interracial interaction by class and race**

| | White subjects | | Negro subjects | |
|---|---|---|---|---|
| | No. of initiations observed | % of interracial initiations (interracial interaction ratio) | No. of initiations observed | % of interracial initiations (interracial interaction ratio) |
| Low status (0-50) | 24 | .25 | 21 | .76 |
| | 23 | .22 | 9 | .55 |
| | 10 | .40 | 18 | .50 |
| | 13 | .15 | 16 | .31 |
| | 9 | .33 | 25 | .36 |
| | No. of | Mean .27 | No. of | Mean .49 |
| | subj. = 5 | stand. dev. .10 | subj. = 6 | stand. dev. .12 |
| Middle status (51-70) | 26 | .54 | 12 | .75 |
| | 19 | .47 | 16 | .69 |
| | 9 | .44 | 11 | .36 |
| | 12 | .42 | 7 | .29 |
| | 17 | .65 | 12 | .17 |
| | 17 | .29 | 18 | .50 |
| | No. of | Mean .47 | No. of | Mean .46 |
| | subj. = 6 | stand. dev. .12 | subj. = 6 | stand. dev. .23 |
| High status (71-90) | 25 | .33 | 6 | .17 |
| | 25 | .68 | 7 | .71 |
| | 11 | .73 | 21 | .48 |
| | 6 | .33 | 12 | .75 |
| | 6 | .33 | 16 | .37 |
| | 8 | .38 | 7 | .29 |
| | 13 | .38 | 16 | .81 |
| | | | 23 | .65 |
| | No. of | Mean .45 | No. of | Mean .53 |
| | subj. = 7 | stand. dev. .19 | subj. = 8 | stand. dev. .24 |
| | Total initiations = 255 | Mean for white subj. = .41 | Total initiations = 270 | Mean for Negro subj. = .49 |

Mean for Negro and white subjects = .46
Standard deviation for all subjects = .18
Total number of subjects = 38
Total number of interactions observed = 525

would lead us to suspect that the crucial factor is self-selectivity.

## OTHER INDEXES OF INTERRACIAL CONTACT

One of the surprising results, then, was that whites in the sample talked to Negroes 41 percent of the time, on the average, and Negroes talked to whites 49 percent of the time. If Negroes and whites had no racial preference as to with whom they wished to talk, this is what we could expect. Either these people are making a tremendous effort to talk to those whom they do not like or else race is not an important factor. In order to find out whether this color blindness is more apparent than real, we decided to examine other indexes of interracial contact that might add some depth to this study of racial contact.

**Seating Patterns** The easiest and most obvious measurement to investigate was seating habits. If there was a significant amount of segregation in seating we might have some doubt about the apparent racial integration revealed in the interaction data. However, if the seating patterns are found to be nonsegregated with respect to race, it would encourage us to believe that race is not much of a factor in relationships between people in the church.

*Seating patterns at Sunday services* The first seating study was made in the Sunday morning church services, giving a population of many more people than the original sample of 38.

For five Sundays the race and position of nearly every person in the church was charted. Only once

**[TABLE 5-9] Frequency of initiating interracial interaction by race and length of membership**

| White subjects | | Negro subjects | |
|---|---|---|---|
| Interracial interaction ratios | Length of membership (years) | Interracial interaction ratios | Length of membership (years) |
| .33 . . . . . . | 4 | .50 | 6 |
| .38 . . . . . . | 5 | .78 | 6 |
| .25 . . . . . . | 10 | .55 | 2 |
| .38 . . . . . . | 11 | .69 | 3 |
| .42 . . . . . . | 8 | .71 | 3 |
| .54 . . . . . . | 32 | .75 | 4 |
| .29 . . . . . . | 24 | .43 | 2 |
| .22 . . . . . . | 25 | .75 | 2 |
| .40 . . . . . . | 25 | .76 | 7 |
| .33 . . . . . . | 64 | .36 | 1 |
| .65 . . . . . . | 14 | .17 | 7 |
| .33 . . . . . . | 12 | .31 | 2 |
| .47 . . . . . . | 7 | .17 | 8 |
| .44 . . . . . . | 7 | .50 | 3 |
| .68 . . . . . . | 7 | .48 | 7 |
| .73 . . . . . . | 5 | .65 | 7 |
| .15 . . . . . . | 20 | .37 | 5 |
| .33 . . . . . . | 5 | .36 | 3 |
| | | .29 | 6 |
| | | .29 | |

*Substantive Hypothesis 1:* The longer the church membership for whites the lower the interracial interaction ratio.
*Substantive Hypothesis 2:* The shorter the church membership of a Negro, the lower the interracial interaction ratio.
*Null Hypothesis:* Length of membership has no effect upon the interracial interaction ratio.
*Results:* Using the Rank Correlation Test we tested the null hypothesis and found levels of significance of *.001* and *.147* for whites and Negroes respectively. Therefore we accepted Substantive Hypothesis 1 and rejected Substantive Hypothesis 2.

was the entire population charted, because of the difficulty of observation. Sometimes the first 12 rows were charted, at other times the last 15 rows, depending upon the position of the observer. The sections that were charted were broken up into four equal quadrants. The proportions of Negroes and whites in each quadrant was computed and compared with the expected proportion. Using the *Chi*-Square Test of Independence we tested the null statistical hypothesis that the proportions of whites in these quadrants were equal enough so that any differences might be explained by chance. [Table 5-10] shows null hypothesis can be rejected. Negroes and whites in church services are sitting apart from each other more than we would expect by chance.

*Seating at Wednesday night suppers and worship services* The second seating study was carried out at Wednesday night church suppers and worship services, with the population very nearly identical to the sample of 38 persons for whom we measured interaction rates.

We tested the null hypothesis that the proportion of whites at each table or on each side of the room would be equal to what we would expect by chance. Using the *Chi*-Square Test of Independence, [Table 5-11] shows that in only two of the seven events were Negroes and whites sitting apart more than we would expect by chance.

*Discussion of the results of seating studies* In the Sunday services, we find a significant amount of segregation, whereas at Wednesday night suppers we do not. Since the population of the Wednesday night suppers was roughly comparable to our original population in which we measured interracial integration, the data on seating merely reinforces our belief that the most active group exhibits a disregard for race in making sociometric choices.

**[TABLE 5-10] Seating by race at church service—five Sundays**

| Service No. | Quadrant | No. of subjects | Actual proportion of whites | Expected proportion of whites |
|---|---|---|---|---|
| 1 | 1 | 22 | .41 | .34 |
| | 2 | 26 | .27 | .34 |
| | 3 | 22 | .45 | .34 |
| | 4 | 21 | .24 | .34 |
| 2 | 1 | 25 | .52 | .31 |
| | 2 | 28 | .07 | .31 |
| | 3 | 26 | .42 | .31 |
| | 4 | 13 | .23 | .31 |
| 3 | 1 | 18 | .39 | .21 |
| | 2 | 19 | .21 | .21 |
| | 3 | 18 | 0.00 | .21 |
| | 4 | 13 | .15 | .21 |
| 4 | 1 | 29 | .31 | .27 |
| | 2 | 20 | .25 | .27 |
| | 3 | 24 | .38 | .27 |
| | 4 | 23 | .13 | .27 |
| 5 | 1 | 34 | .30 | .22 |
| | 2 | 36 | .11 | .22 |
| | 3 | 33 | .30 | .22 |
| | 4 | 34 | .18 | .22 |

Expected proportion of whites is the ratio of whites to the total number of people in the church.
*Null Hypothesis:* There are no significant differences in the proportions of whites in each quadrant.
*Results:* Using the *Chi*-Square Test of Independence we found the following significance levels: *.001*, *.001*, *.001*, *.01*, and *.05*. We tested each Sunday seating separately. We rejected the null hypothesis, therefore, and would say that seating segregation exists here.

[TABLE 5-11] **Seating by race at Wednesday supper and worship service**

| Event | Expected proportion of whites | Actual proportion of whites | *n* | Level of significance *Chi*-square Test of Independence |
|---|---|---|---|---|
| Supper | .54 | Table 1 = .50<br>Table 2 = .56 | 12<br>16 | .75 |
| Worship | .75 | Left = .90<br>Right = .40 | 11<br>5 | .10 |
| Worship | .75 | Left = .80<br>Right = .70 | 10<br>10 | .75 |
| Supper | .63 | Table 1 = .59<br>Table 2 = .67 | 17<br>18 | .75 |
| Supper | .36 | Table 1 = .50<br>Table 2 = .13<br>Table 3 = .57 | 16<br>16<br>17 | .005 |
| Supper | .63 | Table 1 = .79<br>Table 2 = .33 | 19<br>9 | .025 |
| Worship | .63 | Left = .67<br>Right = .58 | 12<br>12 | .75 |

As a check on the possibility that the late arrival of Negroes might account for the segregation in the Sunday services, we performed the following test. On a predetermined Sunday we measured the proportion of whites in the front rows and the proportion in the rear rows at different times prior to and during the service. The proportion of whites in the front rows increased as the service proceeded, therefore the time of seating did not explain the tendency of Negroes to sit near the rear and whites toward the front of the sanctuary. In order to prove that "time of seating" was important we would have expected that the Negroes coming in late would disproportionately fill up the rear rows.

The larger population at Sunday services apparently is not as racially integrated as the 38 most active in the church or those who appear at the Wednesday night suppers (largely made up of the 38). Nevertheless there was considerable mixing of the two racial groups at the services and after church.

We can therefore conclude that the people who are more involved in the life of the church are more racially integrated. Why do we find this? Could it be a result of the fact that high involvement in organizational affairs is related to high commitment to organizational goals? In this case the prime organizational goal is racial integration and it may well be that the more active members are more conscientious in creating an integrated setting. A second explanation might be that only people who are comfortable in interracial settings are likely to become highly involved in an integrated institution. A third alternative explanation is the possibility that the more a person is involved in interracial situations the more likely it is he will feel comfortable in interacting with people of a different race. It is impossible to choose among these explanations but it may be that all three factors are having an effect.

## CONDITIONS THAT FOSTER EQUALITY IN INTERRACIAL CONTACTS WITHIN AN ORGANIZATION

Both the frequency of interracial interaction and the seating patterns of this sample of 38 subjects suggest that a remarkable amount of racial integration has been achieved. Because of the importance in modern societies of lessening racial tension, it is our object in the rest of the article to discuss the possible conditions in this church and its location that account for the pattern of equality in interracial contacts.

From interviews with members, ministers of this and other integrated churches, and further data on the social organization of the church, we found that the following five conditions seemed to be of basic importance for the development of this pattern of equality.

*First,* the area in which the church is located has adopted patterns of integration. Racial integration is practiced in stores, on buses, at work situations, and in other churches and voluntary associations. Therefore, to mingle with other races is not deviant behavior in Hyde Park.

*Second,* the people in the church are free to leave if association with other races disturbs them too much. Therefore, only those who are willing to mingle with other races remain. Even if there are people in the church who are prejudiced, the church as a whole will be free of rabid racists.

The *third factor* is the status composition of the membership. We have seen that this is a fairly high-status church. It is probable that this could have several effects. First, it would provide a more skilled and dependable leadership than a lower-class church would. Second, the church would not have to deal with so many financial problems as a lower-class church would. Good leadership and financial solvency obviously aid in maintaining the solidarity of an institution. The fact that several South Side integrated churches have been very unsuccessful, were made up largely of lower-class people, and had severe financial problems, gives some support to this hypothesis.

The *fourth factor* is the exceptional leadership that this church has had in its ministers. The fact that the leadership has been strongly oriented toward a liberal view of race relations is likewise important. A written history of the church shows what a powerful force it had in Dr. Morikawa, the minister who steered the church through its initial integrated period.[9] The woman who wrote the history told this writer that it was Dr. Morikawa who convinced her and many others of the equality of all men. The fact that he has since risen to a high position in the denomination further testifies to his leadership abilities. The succeeding minister likewise had many strong leadership capabilities and was later promoted to a high position within the church hierarchy.

The *fifth factor* is strong common interest that crosses racial lines, i.e., familiarity and interest in religious thought, discussion and worship. The following evidence bears out this assertion. The listed activities that have succeeded were oriented around the study of the Bible, the common worship, or religious discussion whereas those activities that failed were not.

*Successful Activities*

1. Wednesday Night Suppers and Worship Services
2. Women's Bible Study Group
3. Bible Encounter Group
4. Sunday School
5. Sunday Worship Services

*Unsuccessful Activities*

1. Women's Circle Groups
2. Men's Club
3. Youth Program
4. Boy Scouts
5. Young Adults Group

There are, no doubt, many other reasons for the successful integrated nature of this institution, but the last and perhaps most important factor is the 20 years of experience in integration. Not only has learning taken place, but there is also a history of positive experiences and problems met and dealt with in common.

[9] Mary A. Marx, "How Did Integration Come About and How Does It Work in the First Baptist Church of Chicago," (unpublished paper).

# SEATING AGGREGATION AS AN INDEX OF ATTITUDE *

DONALD T. CAMPBELL
*Northwestern University*

WILLIAM H. KRUSKAL
*University of Chicago*

WILLIAM P. WALLACE
*Northwestern University*

An index of "aggregation," computed as the departure from randomness in the number of classroom Negro-white seating adjacencies, is examined as a tentative index of interracial attitudes. In the three schools studied, significant aggregation by race was found. Two schools selected on *a priori* grounds showed an expected difference in degree of aggregation. All schools also showed significant aggregation by sex. Control analyses examining the effect of class size, proportion of Negroes, and proportion of vacant seats do not indicate artifacts in these respects. The index of seating aggregation is judged worthy of further exploration.

The social sciences are at present overdependent upon voluntary verbal self-description by questionnaire or interview. This method is subject to weaknesses, such as voluntary or unconscious distortion, self-consciousness, reactive effects upon attitudes, and awkwardness of administration. More important, even though voluntary verbal self-description eventually be judged the best of all methods, every method contains systematic irrelevancies which can only be ascertained through a strategy of joint application of methods as different as possible.[1] It is in the service of developing such other measures that this study of seating aggregation is presented.

Where seating in a classroom is voluntary, the degree to which the Negroes and whites present sit by themselves rather than mixing randomly is a presumptive index of the degree to which acquaintance, friendship, and preference are affected by race. Such voluntary clustering by race will be termed "aggregation," as opposed to the enforced separation connoted by the term "segregation."

Just as an attitude questionnaire has its irrelevant components such as response sets, social desirability factors, social class differences in willingness to use hostile vocabulary for any purpose, etc., so such a measure as seating aggregation is distorted by factors irrelevant to the concept of interest. Observation of the high degree of racial clustering or aggregation at the typical annual banquet of a society dedicated to removing racial barriers reflects no doubt the biased opportunities for prior acquaintance rather than the racial attitudes of the persons involved. So too in a classroom, the tendency to sit with friends from one's neighborhood and previous schools provides a bias perhaps more directly reflecting acquaintance opportunity than lack of good will. None the less, if within a classroom there are marked shifts in aggregation from time to time, these might reflect shifts in interracial fear and good will superimposed on the baseline provided by prior acquaintance opportunity. Or if two schools drawing from the same community provide markedly different aggregation indices, these differences might be attributed to attitudinal factors. The illustrative data of the present study are primarily of this latter case.

**The Aggregation Index** Among the many possible ways one might measure aggregation, we chose to base a measure on the number of Negro-white seating adjacencies, that is, the number of pairs of row-wise adjacent seats, one of which is occupied by a Negro

*The contributions of Donald T. Campbell and William P. Wallace to the preparation of this paper were supported by Project C998 Contract 3-20-001 with the Media Research Branch, Office of Education, U.S. Department of Health, Education and Welfare, under the provisions of Title VII of the National Defense Education Act. William H. Kruskal's work was carried out in the Department of Statistics, University of Chicago, under partial sponsorship of the Statistics Branch, Office of Naval Research. Reproduction in whole or part is permitted for any purpose of the United States government.

[1] Eugene J. Webb, Donald T. Campbell, Richard D. Schwartz, and Lee Sechrest, *Unobtrusive Measures: A Survey of Unconventional and Nonreactive Measures for Social Research.* Chicago: Rand McNally, 1966.

student, the other by a white student. (Seats separated by an aisle, and seats with empty seats in between, are not considered to be adjacent.) The number of adjacencies by itself, however, is not suitable as an index. For one thing, it is clearly influenced by the total number of students and by the proportions of Negro and white students. Some kind of baseline and yardstick are necessary. In principle, a realistic stochastic model for the seating of students should be used, but not enough is known about the phenomenon to warrant work on such a model. Instead, we have used a baseline and yardstick corresponding to expected number and standard deviation of adjacencies derived from a randomness assumption, namely that the seats were randomly chosen as regards race, but that the pattern of occupied seats was fixed. Details are given in the Appendix.

The index used was

$$I = (A - EA)/\sigma_A,$$

where

A = observed number of adjacencies
EA = expected number of adjacencies under randomness
$\sigma_A$ = standard deviation of number of adjacencies under randomness

The expressions for EA and $\sigma_A$ are in terms of

N = total number of students in a class
M = number of Negro students
N − M = number of white students
K = number of groups of row-wise contiguous students (including isolates)
$K_1$ = number of students with no one next to them (isolates).

In these terms

$$EA = 2\,\frac{M\,(N-M)}{N\,(N-1)}(N-K)$$

$$\sigma_A{}^2 = 2\,\frac{M\,(N-M)}{N(N-1)}\,(2N - 3K + K_1)$$

$$+\,4\,\frac{M\,(M-1)\,(N-M)\,(N-M-1)}{N\,(N-1)\,(N-2)\,(N-3)}$$

$$[(N-K)\,(N-K-1) - 2\,(N - 2K + K_1)]$$

$$4\,\frac{M^2\,(N-M)^2}{N^2\,(N-1)^2}\,(N-K)^2.$$

[Figure 5-1] shows a typical seating chart from the study. In this case

$N = 22, M = 6, K = 10, K_1 = 4, A = 1, EA = 4.99$ and $\sigma_A = 1.51$.

$$I = \frac{1 - 4.99}{1.51} = -2.64.$$

Negative values of I indicate more aggregation than under randomness, and positive values indicate less aggregation than that under randomness.

**Data Sources** The data of major interest come from classrooms observed at two colleges in the Fall of 1963 and 1964. These two colleges had in a previous unpublished study provided the two extremes of most prejudiced and least prejudiced white students in a comparison of five colleges scattered over the nation, including one southern white college. Both were located in the same northern metropolis. Both consisted entirely of commuter students. Both had substantial minorities—as colleges go—of Negro students. Both had unbiased administrative policies and Negro faculty members. One, which we shall call Downtown U., was by reputation militantly liberal on the race issue. The other, which we shall call Normal U., attracted primarily students seeking teaching credentials, and apparently of predominantly traditional, nonintegrationist attitudes. Also available were seating charts for classes from Normal U. in 1951 and for 1963 from a Junior College which was located in this same northern metropolis. The basic data pool is

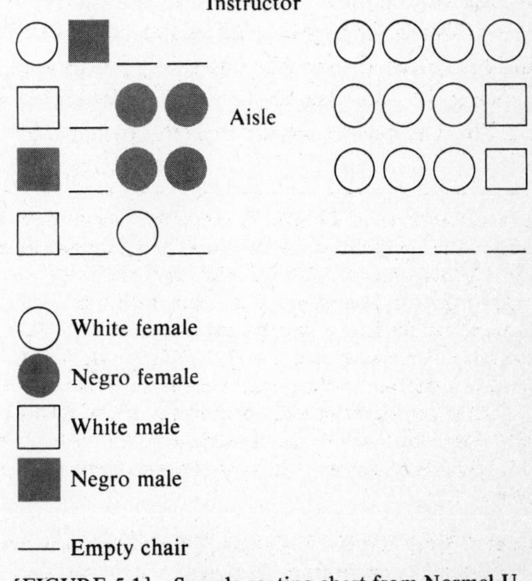


[FIGURE 5-1] Sample seating chart from Normal U., 1964.

[TABLE 5-12] **Basic data pool**

| | Number of classes | | | Of Negroes | | Of whites | | Percentage | |
|---|---|---|---|---|---|---|---|---|---|
| | Total | All of one race | All of one sex | Male | Female | Male | Female | Negro | Female |
| Downtown U. 1963-1964 | 23 | 2 | 1 | 34 | 24 | 335 | 160 | 10% | 33% |
| Normal U. 1963-1964 | 20 | 0 | 0 | 49 | 103 | 164 | 215 | 29% | 60% |
| Junior College 1963 | 12 | 1 | 0 | 59 | 79 | 106 | 23 | 52% | 38% |
| Normal U. 1951 | 19 | 0 | ? | 89 | | 435 | | 17% | ? |

described in [Table 5-12]. In this table the 1963-1964 data have been pooled. Inspection showed no trends within this period.

The 1963-1964 data were collected by an observer who entered the classroom as though a student and from a convenient vantage point prepared the seating chart. The 1951 observations were made by the administrator of a test while the test was being taken by the students, no record being made of the sex of the students. It must be noted that the observations on any one class were collected by a single observer. Consequently, difficulties in observer identification of Negro and white students present an unchecked source of error. Although it is presumed this problem produces a negligible error, it would be desirable to have several observers in each classroom to assess interobserver variation, and if possible to check these against self-identification.

Any errors of identification almost certainly lead to underestimation of the number of Negroes present, given the current U.S. norms. This would make the expected number of adjacencies too low in classrooms where Negroes are in the minority. The number of observed Negro-white adjacencies would be overestimated where a Negro-Negro adjacency was recorded as an NW, and underestimated where an NW was recorded as a white-white adjacency. If aggregation occurs to the same degree among the potential passers on whom errors have been made, the net error would probably be one of overestimation of Negro-white adjacencies, which, when combined with the downward error of expected adjacencies, leads the computed indices to be underestimates of aggregation. There is no reason to believe that in the present data such errors have been distributed in any systematic manner. (The dichotomous recording made should be more accurately described as Negro and non-Negro, as there were a few oriental students who were classified as white.)

The courses sampled covered a variety of liberal arts classes. The selection of classes was haphazard but not random. During a class hour the experimenter observed as many classes as he could, selecting the classes to be observed systematically on the basis of their location, e.g., the second class sampled in a given hour would be one located near the first class sampled. This selection method was judged to be sufficiently unrelated to observed characteristics that statistical procedures based on randomness might be tentatively used. Approximately three class hours were needed for the collection of the data from each school. This gives rise to the possibility that some students may have been observed in more than one classroom. The possibility of some dependence between classrooms thus cannot be ruled out, but is judged to be of minor importance. Observations at both schools were made within a week of each other in both 1963 and 1964, with no incidents of racial relevance occurring during the period of observation.

## RESULTS

**The Generality of Aggregation by Race** [Table 5-13] shows the basic results for the class indices. (Classes not having members of both races have been omitted.) All schools have a negative mean index, indicating fewer Negro-white seating adjacencies than would be expected by chance. Using the $t$ test all of these means are statistically significantly different from zero at the $p < .01$ level. Most individual classes show negative indices, although there are a few that do not.

**School Differences in Aggregation** The distributions of the aggregation-index values for each school appear in [Figure 5-2]. In [Figure 5-2], D.U. refers to the Downtown U., 1963-1964 samples, N.U. refers to the Normal U., 1963-1964 samples, J.C. refers to the Junior College, and N.U. '51 refers to the Normal U.,

[TABLE 5-13] **Racial aggregation indices**

| | Downtown U. 1963-1964 | Normal U. 1963-1964 | Junior College 1963 | Normal U. 1951 |
|---|---|---|---|---|
| Mean index | −.81 | −1.50 | −1.41 | −1.05 |
| Standard deviation | .81 | .98 | 1.46 | 1.53 |
| *t* from zero index | 4.50 | 6.82 | 3.20 | 3.00 |
| Number of classes | 21 | 20 | 11 | 19 |
| Number of classes with positive indices | 3 | 1 | 2 | 6 |

NOTE: Differences in numbers of classes from [Table 5-12] reflect discarding of classes with M or N-M equal to zero.

1951 sample. The two schools of major interest show a statistically significant difference in aggregation indices in the expected direction. The Downtown U. mean of −.81 was significantly less negative than the Normal U. mean of −1.50 with a $t$ of 2.46, 39 degrees of freedom, $p < .02$ (two-sided test of significance). The difference was in the same direction and to about the same degree in the 1963 and 1964 data taken separately. The utility of the index as a measure of attitude thus receives some confirmation.

The degrees of differentiation that the index provides is, however, by no means as sharp as that

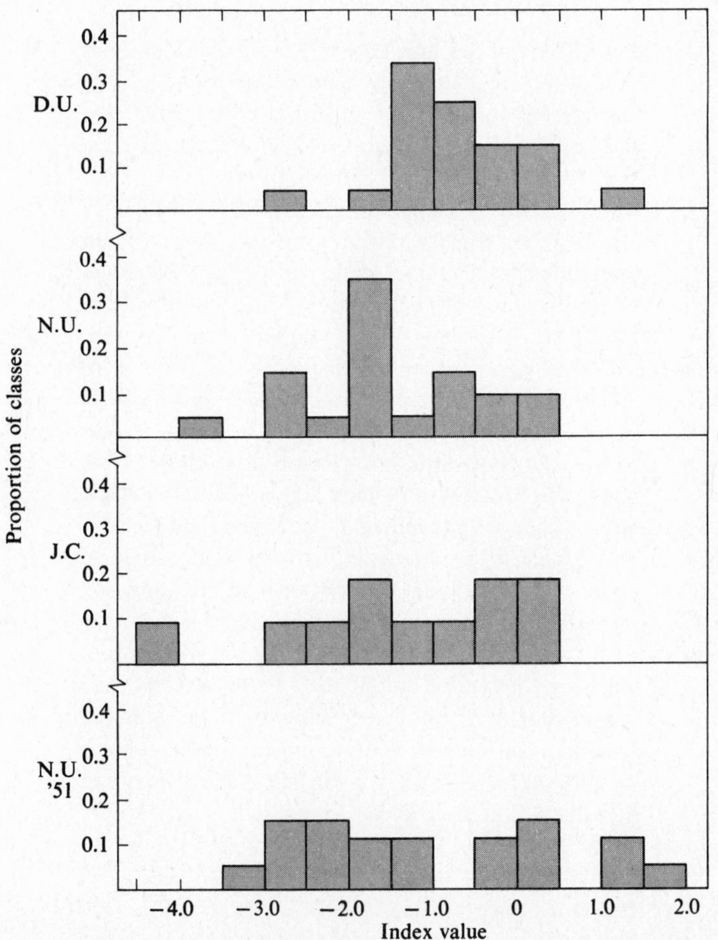


[FIGURE 5-2] Distribution of index values for D.U., N.U., J.C., and N.U. '51.

provided by the earlier unpublished questionnaire data. In 1951, anonymous questionnaire data on attitudes toward Negroes were collected from six classes at Downtown U. and nine at Normal U. When means are computed for the white students in each class, the two schools show no overlap on either a direct attitude scale or a multiple choice information test scored for anti- and pro-Negro bias in the alternatives selected.[2] The $t$ ratios for the difference between the two schools, computed for an $n$ of classes, were 5.74 for "direct" scores and 8.62 for "indirect" scores, these values being much larger than the $t$ of 2.46 for the aggregation index even though fewer classes were involved. Different years, different classes, and different constructs are involved. It is, of course, presumptive to assume that had anonymous questionnaire data been collected in 1963-1964 the differences would have remained as large as they were in 1951, but this is the only comparison available. Since no measures of anti-white attitudes were taken from the 1951 Negro students, only the white data have been examined. The aggregation index is presumably a joint product of the dislikes and fears of both Negroes and whites. (In more refined data collection, the total sequence of seat-taking might be examined in such a way as to isolate actions symptomatic of white attitudes from those symptomatic of Negro attitudes.) The lesser degree of prejudice-differential for the aggregation index might be regarded as another illustration of a recurrent observation in northern settings that overt actions are less prejudiced than anonymous questionnaire responses.

**Aggregation Changes over Time** For Normal U. the difference between the 1951 data and that for 1964 was not statistically significant. Corresponding attitude test data from the school for the time trend is not available, although general public opinion surveys show a decrease in prejudice for this decade.[3] The direction of shift for the index is counter to this national trend. While the proportion of Negroes attending Normal U. increased between 1951 and 1964, this proportion seems, as shown below, to be unrelated to bias.

**Aggregation by Sex** As is commonly noted, classroom seating shows aggregation by sex. The computation of indices for sex aggregation was thought to be of value both as a check on the index and to provide a comparison for the racial aggregation indices. [Table 5-14] shows the basic values for the indices of aggregation by sex. (Sex was not recorded in the 1951 data from Normal U., and classes have been omitted which did not have members of both sexes.) The general finding is one of significant sex aggregation in all schools.

Within the classrooms there is significant aggregation by sex and there is significant aggregation by race. However, the difference between sex and race aggregation is not statistically significant when computed by a paired-sample $t$ test on the 51 classes for which both indices were available (Race mean = $-1.20$, Sex mean = $-.99$, $t = 1.24$, df = 49, $p < .25$). Since pooling across schools may be inappropriate, the analyses were repeated considering each school separately. None of the resultant $t$'s approached statistical significance.

**Joint Effect of Sex and Race** The following analysis asks whether or not the number of adjacencies is particularly low when the adjacency crosses both race and sex. That is, do adjacencies between Negro men and white women or between Negro women and white men occur still less frequently than do adjacencies between persons differing on race alone, or on sex alone. No adequate approach to this problem was found. What has been explored are fragmented indices, paying attention only to the two subgroups involved, and treating all other persons as though they were empty seats. This analysis has been limited to those classes providing persons in all four race-sex subgroups. (Downtown U. contributed three classes, Normal U., 1963-1964 contributed eleven classes, and the Junior College contributed three classes to this analysis.) [Table 5-15] shows the results of this analysis. While the two indices crossing both race and sex average lower (more negative) than either of the other pairs, they both fall within the range of indices provided by the other subgroups. Using class-by-class paired-sample $t$'s for the averages of these pairs, no significant differences were found (cross Sex & Race *vs.* cross Race $t = 1.85$; cross Sex & Race *vs.* cross Sex, $t = 1.53$; cross Sex *vs.* cross Race, $t = .20$, df = 16 in each case). Thus while a slight trend toward a joint effect was present, it did not approach usual standards for statistical significance. This approach has inadequacies on logical grounds, and a better approach is being sought.

[2] This test was an improved version of tests reported in brief in Donald T. Campbell, "The Indirect Assessment of Social Attitudes," *Psychological Bulletin,* **47** (January, 1950) p. 21, and in Robert E. Rankin and Donald T. Campbell, "Galvanic Skin Response to Negro and White Experimenters," *Journal of Abnormal and Social Psychology,* **51** (July, 1955), p. 32.

[3] Herbert H. Hyman and Paul B. Sheatsly, "Attitudes on Desegregation," *Scientific American,* **211** (July, 1964) pp. 16-23.

[TABLE 5-14] **Aggregation indices for sex**

| | Downtown U. 1963-1964 | Normal U. 1963-1964 | Junior College 1963 |
|---|---|---|---|
| Mean index | −.90 | −1.36 | −.77 |
| Standard deviation | 1.36 | .98 | 1.18 |
| *t* from zero index | 3.10 | 6.18 | 2.26 |
| Number of classes | 22 | 20 | 12 |
| Number of classes with positive indices | 4 | 2 | 4 |

**Control Analyses** It is very difficult to achieve descriptive indices of degree of effect which are comparable with assurance across heterogeneous conditions of size and proportion. For this reason, certain control analyses have been done. It is possible that the index might not be comparable between two classes varying widely in the proportion of Negroes present. Computing the correlation between this proportion and the resulting index for each of the four samples the following correlation coefficients were obtained: Downtown U., 1963-1964, $r = -.21$; Normal U., 1963-1964, $r = +.37$; Junior College, $r = -.13$; Normal U., 1951, $r = +.13$. None of these coefficients reached a usual level of statistical significance.

Class size is somewhat more problematic. The correlation between the aggregation index and class size for the four samples were as follows: $r = -.18$ for Downtown U., 1963-1964; $r = -.17$ for Normal U., 1963-1964; $r = -.75$ for the Junior College; and $r = -.14$ for Normal U., 1951. Of the above correlations, only that in the Junior College reached statistical significance ($p < .01$, df = 10). All of the correlations were negative, which suggests that larger classes show more racial aggregation. Larger classes probably come from freshmen and sophomore courses, and the correlation may thus indicate improved race relations as a function of maturity, familiarity, etc. Unfortunately, course levels were not recorded. The class size correlations with aggregation by sex did not approach statistical significance ($r = +.01$ for Downtown U., 1963-1964; $r = -.11$ for Normal U., 1963-1964; $r = -.18$ for the Junior College). These latter results do not support an interpretation that the aggregation index is artificially influenced by class size. In any event, the class size correlation does not affect the interpretation of the Downtown U.-Normal U. aggregation differences, as the 1963-1964 mean sizes for these two are 26.33 and 26.55 respectively, and the class-size correlations within these schools did not reach an acceptable level of statistical significance.

In some respects the index neglects features that might artificially affect the number of Negro-white adjacencies. Thus no use is made of the number of vacant seats nor their possible location so as to buffer Negro-white adjacency. Undoubtedly in many instances a shortage of seats increases Negro-white adjacencies in a manner not reflecting the preferences of the persons involved. As a partial check on this, the proportion of empty seats was correlated with the race aggregation index. The resulting correlations were +.12 for Downtown U., +.24 for Normal U., 1963-1964, and +.55 for the Junior College. The correlations are not statistically significant and are in the opposite direction from that expected, showing the larger the proportion of empty seats the less aggregation. For sex aggregation, these correlations were −.04, +.18, and −.49 for Downtown U., Normal U., 1963-1964, and the Junior College respectively. None of these correlations reached statistical significance. Thus neglect of empty chairs does not in these data

[TABLE 5-15] **Aggregation indices with fragmented classes**

| | Cross race & sex | | Cross race | | Cross sex | |
|---|---|---|---|---|---|---|
| | MN-FW | MW-FN | MN-MW | FN-FW | MN-FN | MW-FW |
| Mean index | −1.20 | −1.26 | −.66 | −1.21 | −.60 | −1.34 |
| Average subclass size | 15.00 | 17.59 | 14.82 | 17.76 | 9.47 | 23.12 |
| Number of classes | 17 | 17 | 17 | 17 | 17 | 17 |
| Number of classes with positive index | 1 | 4 | 6 | 3 | 5 | 2 |

appear to have produced misleading effects. Another feature which an ideal index might attend to is the number or proportion of row-ends where no adjacency is possible. Thus an arrangement of the same number of chairs into a pattern of many short rows reduces the opportunities for adjacency in comparison with an arrangement of fewer longer rows. This attribute varied so little in the present study that no control correlation has been computed. Even though empty seats and row ends probably do not distort the present data, the development of a more complex index which would take these into account seems desirable.

## DISCUSSION

While there is no indication that the index is of high precision or purity, the results do encourage further exploration. The index might be used, for example, as a before-and-after measure in studies of class presentations designed to improve race relations. One of the most needed studies is the examination of shifts in the degree of mutual trust. A cooperating group of instructors could easily produce a daily series of seating charts in classes in which written classroom work takes place. The index can also be applied in any other situation in which unidimensional adjacency can be noted. One recurrent class of situations of this type is in the waiting lines for cafeterias, theater tickets, time-clock punching, etc. For waiting lines, the formula is simpler, as K becomes 1, and the number of adjacencies become one less than the number of runs, a much studied topic.[4]

The adjacency index is but one of a larger class of potential aggregation indices. Consider a school playground in which many of the pupils can be identified as participating in activity groups, be they baseball games, hopscotch, penny-pitching, etc. Utilizing children so classified, one could examine racial composition in terms of a contingency table in which columns were Negro and white, and in which each play group constituted a row. In a similar way, ethnic bias in isolates versus group-involved could be computed. A time-series of such indices from multiracial schoolyards might provide an index of changing tensions.

Another way of conceptualizing aggregation is in terms of the steepness of the interracial boundary—and note that the schoolroom and the school yard indices must come from essentially boundary conditions; they are not available for either all white or all Negro schools. If one considers, for example, the residences, sidewalks, stores and public services on a street which crosses the Negro-white boundary at right angles, the more aggregation there is, the "steeper" the racial boundary, i.e., the narrower the transition area in which there is mixed racial presence, the more nearly the shift is from 100% Negro to 100% white, without blocks, stores, sidewalk segments, etc., which have both Negroes and whites present. For presences for which daily decisions and changes are possible, such as shopping for groceries, an increase in the steepness of the boundary might indicate an increase in tension, as Negroes feel reluctance to shop in predominantly white stores and as whites feel reluctance to shop in predominantly Negro ones. Such considerations move us close to the sociological literature on city indices of segregation computed from census data.[5]

## APPENDIX—COMBINATORIAL DERIVATION[6]

Suppose that there are K unbroken sequences of row-wise contiguous occupied seats, containing $n_1$, $n_2$, . . . , $n_K$ seats respectively. Each end of a sequence is bounded by either an empty seat or a row end. Let $N = \sum_{i=1}^{K} n_i$ be the total number of occupied seats.

Consider random arrangements of two kinds of units, M of one and N-M of the other, over the occupied seats. In our case, there are M Negro students and N-M white students. Let a random variable corresponding to each seat take the value 0 or 1 as the seat is occupied by a Negro or white student. Then the random variables of interest, arranged in the K sequences, are

$$X_1, X_2, \ldots, X_{n_1};$$
$$X_{n_1+1}, X_{n_1+2}, \ldots, X_{n_1+n_2};$$
$$\vdots$$
$$X_{N-n_K+1}, X_{N-n_K+2}, \ldots, X_N.$$

[4] K. A. Brownlee, *Statistical Theory and Methodology in Science and Engineering,* Second Edition, Wiley, New York, 1965, pp. 224-232, and Samuel S. Wilks, *Mathematical Statistics,* Wiley, New York, 1962, pp. 144-150.

[5] Otis Dudley Duncan and Beverly Duncan, "A Methodological Analysis of Segregation Indexes," *American Sociological Review,* 20 (April, 1955); Otis Dudley Duncan, Ray P. Cuzzort, and Beverly Duncan, *Statistical Geography,* Glencoe, Illinois: The Free Press, 1961; Linton C. Freeman and John Pilger, "Segregation: a Micro-Measure Based upon Compactness," Residential Segregation Study, Maxwell School of Citizenship and Public Affairs, Syracuse, New York, October 19, 1964; Linton C. Freeman and John Pilger, "Segregation: A Micro-Measure Based upon Well-Mixedness," Residential Segregation Study, Maxwell School of Citizenship and Public Affairs, Syracuse University, February 12, 1965.

[6] The development of the aggregation index as presented in the appendix is by William H. Kruskal.

Note that the sum of all N X's is N-M. It is assumed that all $\binom{N}{M}$ ways of assigning M 0's and N-M 1's to the N X's are equally likely. That is, the model is one of complete randomness conditionally on the given pattern of occupied seats.

The statistic of major interest is the number of adjacencies, A, which may be written

$$\begin{aligned} A = &|X_1 - X_2| + \ldots + |X_{n_1 - 1} - X_{n_1}| \\ &+ |X_{n_1+1} - X_{n_1+2}| + \ldots + |X_{n_1+n_2-1} - X_{n_1+n_2}| \ldots + \\ &\cdot \\ &\cdot \\ &\cdot \\ &+ |X_{N-n_K+1} - X_{N-n_K+2}| + \ldots \\ &+ |X_{N-1} - X_N|, \end{aligned}$$

with the convention that if any sequence contains a single member ($n_i = 1$), no corresponding absolute difference appears in the sum. For convenience set $U_i = |X_i - X_{i+1}|$, so that

$$\begin{aligned} A = &\{U_1 + \ldots + U_{n_1 - 1}\} + \{U_{n_1+1} + \ldots \\ &+ U_{n_1+n_2-1}\} + \ldots + \{U_{N-n_K+1} + \ldots \\ &+ U_{N-1}\}. \end{aligned}$$

Each $U_j$ takes the values 0 and 1; 1 means an adjacency, and 0 a non-adjacency.

The next step is to compute some first and second moments in order to obtain the expectation and variance of A, EA and $\sigma_A{}^2$. These results may be regarded as a specialization of work by P. A. P. Moran or as a generalization of standard manipulations in the study of runs.[7]

Clearly, $EU_j = \text{Prob}\{X_j \neq X_{j+1}\} = 2\dfrac{M(N-M)}{N(N-1)}$, since $\text{Prob}\{X_j = 1 \text{ and } X_{j+1} = 0\} = \text{Prob}\{X_j = 0 \text{ and } X_{j+1} = 1\} = \dfrac{M}{N}\dfrac{N-M}{N-1}$.

Hence $EA = 2\dfrac{M(N-M)}{N(N-1)}(N-K)$.

Since $U_j = U_j^2$, $E(U_j^2)$ is also $2\dfrac{M(N-M)}{N(N-1)}$.

Next turn to $E(U_jU_{j+1})$. A convenient way of finding this is to notice that $(U_j - U_{j+1})^2$ takes the values 0 and 1, the latter if and only if $X_j \neq X_{j+2}$. This event has the same probability as $X_j \neq X_{j+1}$. Hence

$$E(U_j - U_{j+1})^2 = 2EU_j^2 - 2E(U_jU_{j+1}) = EU_j^2,$$

so that

$$E(U_jU_{j+1}) = \tfrac{1}{2}EU_j = \frac{M(N-M)}{N(N-1)}.$$

Finally, we need $E(U_jU_k)$ with $|j-k| > 1$. A conditional argument provides this readily, for $E(U_jU_k) = \text{Prob}\{U_j = U_k = 1\}$. Given $U_j = 1$, one Negro student and one white student are already sitting in seats j and j + 1. Hence the *conditional* expectation of $U_jU_k$ (remember that $|j-k| > 1$) is just $EU_k$ but with M diminished by one and N by 2, i.e.,

$$2\frac{M-1}{N-2}\;\frac{N-M-1}{N-3}$$

But $\text{Prob}\{U_j = U_k = 1\} = \text{Prob}\{U_k = 1|U_j = 1\}$ $\text{Prob}\{U_j = 1\}$. Hence the desired expectation is

$$\left[2\frac{M-1}{N-2}\;\frac{N-M-1}{N-3}\right]\left[2\frac{M}{N}\;\frac{N-M}{N-1}\right] = 4\frac{M(M-1)}{N(N-1)}\;\frac{(N-M)(N-M-1)}{(N-2)(N-3)}.$$

Since $E(U_jU_k)$ does not depend on j,k when $|j-k| > 1$, we may as well write it $E(U_jU_{j+2})$ for simplicity of notation.

Turn now to $E(A^2)$. From the expression for A in terms of sums of U's, we see that

$$\begin{aligned} E(A^2) = &(\text{number of } U_j\text{'s in sum}) \times E(U_j^2) \\ &+ \text{number of } U_jU_{j+1} \text{ products possible} \\ &\times E(U_jU_{j+1}) \\ &+ (\text{number of } U_jU_k,\ |j-k| > 1, \text{ products possible}) \\ &\times E(U_jU_{j+2}). \end{aligned}$$

There are clearly N − K $U_j$'s in the sum. Ask next how many $U_jU_{j+1}$ products are possible, and to this end set

$K_1$ = number of X sequences with just one member,
$K_2$ = number of X sequences with just two members,
$K*$ = number of X sequences with more than two members,

so that $K = K_1 + K_2 + K*$. $K_1$ is the number of isolates and $K_2$ the number of isolated pairs.

Only the K* sequences (those with more than two X's) give rise to $U_jU_{j+1}$ products, and the $i^{th}$ of these sequences gives rise to $2(n_i - 2)$ such products. (The factor 2 is there because, for example, both $U_1U_2$ and $U_2U_1$ must be counted.) Summing $2(n_i - 2)$ over the K* sequences, we get

[7] P. A. P. Moran, "The Interpretation of Statistical Maps," *Journal of the Royal Statistical Society,* Ser. B, 10 (1948), pp. 243-251.

$$2[(N - K_1 - 2K_2) - 2K*] = 2[N - 2K - K_1].$$

Now how many products of form $U_jU_{j+2}$ are there? Each of the $K_2$ sequences contributes $N - K - 1$ such products, so from that source we obtain a total of $K_2$ $(N - K - 1)$. The $i^{th}$ $K*$ sequence contributes $2(N - K - 2) + (n_i - 3)(N - K - 3)$ $U_jU_{j+2}$ products, to give a total from this source of

$$2K*(N - K - 2) + (N - K_1 - 2K_2 - 3K*)(N - K - 3),$$

which may be expressed as

$$(N - K - 1)(N - K - K_2) - 2(N - 2K + K_1).$$

Adding the prior $K_2(N - K - 1)$ gives the final number of $U_jU_{j+2}$ products

$$(N - K)(N - K - 1) - 2(N - 2K + K_1).$$

(As a check, note that the total number of all three kinds of products is, correctly, $(N - K)^2$.)

Putting these results together, we have

$$\sigma_A^2 = 2\frac{M(N - M)}{N(N - 1)}(N - K) + 2(N - 2K + K_1)\frac{M(N - M)}{N(N - 1)}$$

$$+ 4[(N - K)(N - K - 1) - 2(N - 2K + K_1)]$$

$$\frac{M(M - 1)(N - M)(N - M - 1)}{N(N - 1)(N - 2)(N - 3)}$$

$$- 4\frac{M^2(N - M)^2}{N^2(N - 1)^2}(N - K)^2$$

$$= 2\frac{M(N - M)}{N(N - 1)}(2N - 3K + K_1)$$

$$+ 4\frac{M(M - 1)(N - M)(N - M - 1)}{N(N - 1)(N - 2)(N - 3)}$$

$$[(N - K)(N - K - 1) - 2(N - 2K + K_1)]$$

$$- 4\frac{M^2(N - M)^2}{N^2(N - 1)^2}(N - K)^2.$$

Various partial checks may be made. For example, the formulas are symmetric in M and N – M. Again, if $N = K = K_1$, i.e., if all the units are isolates, A must be zero; EA and $\sigma_A^2$ do indeed properly turn out to be also zero. Again, if $K = 1$ and $K_1 = 0$, A is just one less than the number of runs in a sequence of N objects of two kinds, so that the above results may be compared with well-known formulas[8]

$$EA = \frac{2M(N - M)}{N}$$

$$\sigma_A^2 = \frac{2M(N - M)[2M(N - M) - N]}{N^2(N - 1)}$$

After algebraic simplification, this specialization does provide a consistency check. Finally, our results may be derived as special cases of those given by Moran.[9]

Depending on the relative magnitudes of M, N, N – M, K, and $K_1$, approximations to the rather lengthy variance formula may be worked out. One may also consider asymptotic normality of A.

---

[8] For example, see p. 570 of W. Allen Wallis and Harry V. Roberts, *Statistics, a New Approach,* Glencoe, Illinois: Free Press, 1956.

[9] P. A. P. Moran, *op. cit.*, p. 245.

# INTERRACIAL SEATING PATTERNS ON NEW ORLEANS PUBLIC TRANSIT*

MORRIS DAVIS
*University of Illinois*

ROBERT SEIBERT
*Tulane University*

WARREN BREED
*Tulane University*

As the result of a federal court order, legally enforceable segregation on New Orleans public transit ended on May 31, 1958. Prior to that time no Negro had been permitted to sit forward of any white on NOPSI buses.[1] While in many respects the patterns of practice had not required maximum racial separation–e.g., whites and Negroes rode the same buses, entered and exited by the same doors, and occupied a single, physically undivided compartment–they had resulted in a perfect racial ordering of seated passengers.[2] To the extent, then, that whites continued to sit in front of Negroes even after the court order went into effect, legal desegregation would have failed to bring about full *de facto* integration. Indeed, a particular bus could be ranked along the dimension segregation-integration according to the prevalence of interracial mixing by its passengers.

An attempt was made during April and May of 1964 to assess the degree of actual integration on NOPSI vehicles by charting the seating arrays on a sample of bus cross-sections and adducing certain indices from these data. Three graduate students rode buses on 11 of the 39 transit lines during both morning and afternoon peak periods. Routes were selected so as to include a variety of lines passing through different kinds of neighborhoods.[3] At twelve minute intervals during a given run seating patterns were recorded on mimeographed charts. Two of the students (and occasionally all three) would ride the same bus, one sitting in front and one further back, their overlapping observations providing a reliability check.[4]

Three variables were coded: race, dichotomized into Negro and All Others (the latter being overwhelmingly white and so referred to hereinafter); sex; and age, trichotomized as under 16 years, 17 to 45, and over 45. The last characteristic was, of course, most open to estimation errors. Attempts to record other theoretically interesting kinds of data–for example, type of clothing as an indicator of class–were abandoned during a pretest as unreliable. No interviewing was conducted.

Eighty-seven vehicle cross-sections were charted

---

*The first named author was supported while at Tulane University by U.S. Public Health Service Grant CH 00098, from the Division of Community Health Services.

[1] Throughout this paper the term *buses* refers to diesel and gasoline buses, trolley coaches, and/or streetcars. Almost all intracity public transit in New Orleans is provided by New Orleans Public Service, Inc. (NOPSI), a utility that also furnishes both gas and electricity within the city. NOPSI is a wholly owned subsidiary of Middle South Utilities, a New York based holding company.

[2] During the spring of 1957 students in an undergraduate sociology course had ridden the buses, observing behavior under legally segregated seating, and engaging passengers in conversations about possible desegregation. At no time did a student observe a Negro sitting ahead of a white. A few moderating activities were encountered–e.g., a white passenger moving forward the sign that demarked the limits of the white and Negro "sections" so that Negro standees could sit, or a Negro arguing with a bus driver–but in general segregated seating seemed to have been accepted by both races among the transit riders.

[3] The lines studied were Freret and Magazine (trolley buses); Canal and St. Charles (streetcars); and Tchoupitoulas, Broad, Metairie, Hayne, Esplanade, and Claiborne (gasoline and diesel buses).

[4] The students were Miss Gay Brannon, Mr. Muhammed Tayyarah, and Mr. Seibert. Standees were omitted. The ratio of passengers to seats varied between .05 and 1.32 at the times of observation.

during the test period.[5] Each diagram showed the exact placement of every seated passenger at the time of sampling, and specified his race, sex, and estimated age. Time, date, name of line, and weather condition were also noted, though these do not figure in this article. From the diagrammed data we have computed the extent of *de facto* integration (or segregation) on New Orleans public transit, its variations as a bus becomes more crowded or as its racial composition becomes more one-sided, and finally the age and sex characteristics of those whites and Negroes who are sitting in what may be considered an integrated position and who, therefore, may also be considered agents of social change.

These computations should not be thought of as proceeding automatically from the data. For while it is clear that an absolutely segregated bus would at the least have all whites sitting ahead of all Negroes[6] and that an absolutely integrated bus would be one on which information about race were of no help in predicting seating patterns, it is not obvious how one can measure *degrees* of segregation-integration on a bus or compare the amount on one vehicle to that on another. One reason for the difficulty is that there are no physical barriers that separate a "white compartment" from a "Negro compartment." There are no vestigial dividing lines either. If some Negroes sit in front of (or beside) some whites, just who has entered whose "section"? An analyst who wishes conceptually to partition the bus must introduce his own cutting lines, and there is no ultimately satisfactory way for him to do that.

A second problem derives from the fact that even among adjacent persons degrees of interaction may differ. Sitting side by side seems behaviorally unlike sitting front to back, or diagonally tangent, or across the aisle from; and sitting side by side on transverse seats is probably different from the same relation on lengthwise seats. Furthermore, passengers do not always sit immediately next to each other, especially on relatively empty buses. Vacant seats, it would appear, somewhat reduce the impact of integration.[7] One is tempted, of course, to suggest some sort of weighting for these various interpersonal relationships (see note 12), but it is doubtful whether the participants' ratings would agree with ours.

Since it is not obvious how one is to assess degrees of segregation-integration, we have tried some four different summarizing measures. Each of them computes the number of persons who violate the old pattern of white precedence over Negroes. A "perfectly integrated" bus is then defined as one on which half the seated passengers are precedence violators.[8] The measures may be labelled and defined as follows:

Method 1. The Traditional Definition. Starting from the front of the bus, all whites and the first

---

[5] There is some slight lack of independence among some pairs of these 87 cross-sections. A typical bus line (all of those sampled except Broad, Metairie, and Hayne) runs from the outskirts of New Orleans to downtown Canal Street where it loops, has a virtually complete turnover of passengers, and returns to its starting point. The observers, who remained on the bus during its entire inbound-outbound run, usually charted four cross-sections on a given trip, two going toward and two away from downtown. While the inbound recordings may be considered totally independent from the outbound ones, those taken in the same direction on the same vehicle would involve some redundancy in passengers. There was, however, a surprising amount of turnover even along a route, probably to be accounted for by the low fare (10 cents) and frequent service of the buses. It was not uncommon, in fact, for a bus to have taken in on its way to or from town more than twice as many fares as its average passenger load. Though the cross-sections were not totally independent, then, they were sufficiently so for the purposes to which they are put here.

[6] At the most, in traditional New Orleans terms, it would mean that whites would sit from the front and Negroes from the back, and that no whites would be standing. Had white patronage of buses declined precipitously after the court order, the NOPSI system itself would have become segregated in the sense of being virtually a Negro mode of transportation. As [Table 5-19] shows, however, whites and Negroes each composed about half the total complement of transit users. Negroes are obviously over-represented (they comprised only about 37 per cent of the city's population in 1960), but income level could easily explain the difference. More crucially, whites are still major utilizers of the buses. And while revenue passengers did decline 23 percent from 1957 to 1963 on NOPSI lines, that is not too dissimilar from the 17 per cent decline in the U.S. generally. Buses that service predominantly white (or Negro) neighborhoods tend, of course, to have predominantly white (or Negro) passenger loads; but this is an obvious function of their routes. (The statement needs modifying because of checkerboard patterning, the movement of maids to and from white districts, etc.; but the trend is clear enough.) For that reason our concept of segregation of buses relates not to the proportion of whites or Negroes riding but to their configuration. Fortunately, as the text remarks, this was also the traditional meaning of transit segregation in the New Orleans community.

[7] They do not rob the concept of all meaning, however, for under the old rules a Negro could not sit in front of a white no matter how much space separated them.

[8] This definition and the reason for employing the term *precedence violators* are explained further in our discussion of [Table 5-16].

Negro follow the old style of precedence, but any whites seated further back than the first seated Negro are precedence violators.

Method 2. The Split Half. Any Negroes seated in the front half of the bus and any whites in the back half are precedence violators.

Method 3. The Proportional Break. The percentage of seated passengers who are white is calculated. Any Negroes seated in that proportion of seats from the front and any whites in the remaining seats are precedence violators.

Method 4. The Perfect Rank Order. The number of seated whites is tabulated. Any Negroes who are seated among that number of passengers from the front and any whites beyond that number are precedence violators.[9]

All four methods have shortcomings. Findings under Method 1 can be massively affected by the behavior of a single individual. A solitary Negro on the first seat can be the difference between a bus that totally follows or totally violates precedence. Method 2 is imperfect since it overestimates the amount of apparent precedence violation on any crowded bus in which the racial balance departs from unity. A bus on which all seats were occupied, Negroes comprised three-quarters of the passengers, and all whites sat ahead of all Negroes, would under this method supposedly have one out of each four riders violating precedence. Method 3 suffers from a similar, though oppositely caused, defect. On a lightly patronized bus in which Negroes sat behind whites but all persons sat relatively near the front, the extent of precedence violation would again be severely over-reported.[10] Even Method 4, the measure we think is both simplest to compute and conceptually most justifiable, particularly because it does not require "sectioning" of the buses, has at least two partial faults. First, it results in double counting: every Negro who sits in front of a white causes one of the last whites also to be considered a precedence violator. Second, if a Negro sits adjacent to a white at the front of the bus, it is not that white but another further back who is deemed to violate precedence. Neither of these faults, however, seems to damage Method 4 as markedly as their various flaws do the first three methods.[11]

The four methods[12] yield the distributions of segregation-integration on bus cross-sections by per cent of precedence violating passengers given in [Table 5-16]. As mentioned above, on a single "perfectly integrated" bus only 50 per cent of the riders should be precedence violators. If the figure were 100 per cent, then perfect reverse segregation would have occurred.[13] Over a series of buses, however, passenger distributions might well depart from the midpoint for various idiosyncratic reasons, the array of cross-sections perhaps assuming a bell curve. The series itself could still be considered perfectly integrated so long as the curve were not markedly skewed to the left. Such "statistical integration" clearly does not obtain with our data, otherwise the number of cross-sections within the 80-100 per cent range of precedence violation would approximate that within the 0-19 per cent range. Comparing column 6 to columns 1 and 2, one may see that no cross-section shows any extreme

[9] For all four methods any person who is ambiguous is not considered a precedence violator. For example, a white in the same cross row as the first Negro is considered under Method 1 not to be violating precedence.

[10] The difficulties in Methods 2 and 3 would not be obviated by employing any derivative ratios, such as the Duncans' index of difference (Otis D. Duncan and Beverly Duncan, "Residential Distribution and Occupational Stratification," *American Journal of Sociology*, 60 [March, 1955], p. 494). For as crowded buses became mono-racial, their index would tend to decline with a middle cutting point; and, of course, no index *per se* can solve the problem of how to establish consistent cutting points from one relatively empty bus to another. Analogous comments apply to the transactional indices employed by Karl Deutsch and James V. Toscano in their studies of intra- and inter-community flow patterns: see Philip E. Jacob and Toscano, *The Integration of Political Communities*, Philadelphia: Lippincott, 1964, chs. 3 and 4.

[11] One could even justify the anomalies. After all, Negroes sitting in front of whites do implicate at least some whites as well as themselves in the violation of precedence, yet the white person sat beside seems less an agent of change than its object.

[12] We also attempted a fifth Method (Cluster Analysis) in which the total number of bi-racial and mono-racial adjacencies were measured and compared. Weightings were made in accordance with our *a priori* assumptions about the meanings of such interactions. Thus, sitting beside someone on a crosswise double seat was weighted 3; sitting beside someone on a lengthwise seat was weighted 2; sitting front to back, 2; sitting diagonally tangent, 1; and aisles and the center doorway were deemed to obliterate any interactions that crossed them. This mode of analysis was dropped after a 25 per cent computation sample, however, largely because its results were grossly affected by empty seats.

[13] This explains why we have used the awkward phrase "precedence violators" to refer to individual passengers. As inelegant as the term is, it at least keeps us from the apparent paradox of stating that a perfectly integrated bus has only 50 per cent of its passengers integrated.

**[TABLE 5-16] Segregation-integration on bus cross-sections by percentage of precedence violating passengers (four methods)**

| Method | Percentage of passengers violating precedence in cross-sections | | | | | | |
|---|---|---|---|---|---|---|---|
| | 0 | .01-19 | 20-39 | 40-59 | 60-79 | 80-100 | Total |
| 1 | 17 | 40 | 22 | 7 | 1 | 0 | 87 |
| 2 | 1 | 29 | 32 | 22 | 3 | 0 | 87 |
| 3 | 7 | 40 | 27 | 10 | 3 | 0 | 87 |
| 4 | 14 | 49 | 20 | 4 | 0 | 0 | 87 |

NOTE: Figures in the cells of [Tables 5-16, 5-17, and 5-18] refer to bus cross-sections, not to individual passengers. Row 1, column 3, for example, shows that 22 cross-sections, out of the 87 observed, had between 20 and 40 per cent of their passengers violating precedence according to the rationale of Method 1.

reverse segregation, while (depending on the method employed) somewhere between 30 and 63 out of the 87 exhibit high degrees of the usual brand. And as column 4 indicates, relatively few buses (between 4 and 22) individually approach an integrated condition. Any assertions about the precise amount of segregation-integration depend, of course, on which measure one deems most adequate; but as a scanning of [Table 5-16] would show, Methods 1 and 4, the vernacular notion and the methodologically most defensible index, yield rather similar results.[14]

We had expected that the "true degree" of integration on NOPSI buses would be greatest as they were most equally balanced racially, and that as they became more exclusively white or Negro, marked segregation would rapidly develop. Further, we imagined that high segregation would be more characteristic of a bus in which whites were relatively few in number than where they predominated. The grounds for our reasoning were these: that as a race becomes a smaller and smaller minority on a vehicle, it is placed in an increasingly more "threatening" situation; that the average threat per bus is least when the two races are evenly balanced; and that minorities of whites see themselves more threatened than similar minorities of Negroes. [Table 5-17], which cross-tabulates the distributions in [Table 5-16] (Methods 1 and 4 only) by the percentage of passengers who are white, confirms this interpretation. The data take a general wedge shape, with evenly balanced buses showing the most integration, mono-racially dominated buses the least, and buses with few whites exhibiting rather more

[14] Rank order correlations (Spearman's rho) are as follows. Methods 1 and 2 = .44; 1 and 3 = .52; 1 and 4 = .76; 2 and 3 = .47; 2 and 4 = .53; 3 and 4 = .75.

**[TABLE 5-17] Segregation-integration on bus cross-sections by percentages of precedence violating and of white passengers (methods 1 and 4 only)**

| | Per cent white | Percentage of passengers violating precedence in cross-sections | | | | | | |
|---|---|---|---|---|---|---|---|---|
| | | 0 | .01-19 | 20-39 | 40-59 | 60-79 | 80-100 | Total |
| Method 1 | 80-100 | 7 | 6 | 2 | 2 | 0 | 0 | 17 |
| | 60-79 | 4 | 8 | 8 | 1 | 1 | 0 | 22 |
| | 40-59 | 2 | 9 | 9 | 4 | 0 | 0 | 24 |
| | 20-39 | 2 | 11 | 3 | 0 | 0 | 0 | 16 |
| | 0-19 | 2 | 6 | 0 | 0 | 0 | 0 | 8 |
| | Total | 17 | 40 | 22 | 7 | 1 | 0 | 87 |
| Method 4 | 80-100 | 7 | 8 | 2 | 0 | 0 | 0 | 17 |
| | 60-79 | 3 | 9 | 8 | 2 | 0 | 0 | 22 |
| | 40-59 | 1 | 13 | 8 | 2 | 0 | 0 | 24 |
| | 20-39 | 1 | 13 | 2 | 0 | 0 | 0 | 16 |
| | 0-19 | 2 | 6 | 0 | 0 | 0 | 0 | 8 |
| | Total | 14 | 49 | 20 | 4 | 0 | 0 | 87 |

[TABLE 5-18] **Segregation-integration on bus cross-sections by percentage of precedence violating passengers and degree of crowding (methods 1 and 4 only)**

| | Degree of crowding | Percentage of passengers violating precedence in cross-sections | | | | | | |
|---|---|---|---|---|---|---|---|---|
| | | 0 | .01-19 | 20-39 | 40-59 | 60-79 | 80-100 | Total |
| Method 1 | High | 2 | 12 | 6 | 3 | 0 | 0 | 23 |
| | Medium | 9 | 22 | 9 | 2 | 1 | 0 | 43 |
| | Low | 6 | 6 | 7 | 2 | 0 | 0 | 21 |
| | Total | 17 | 40 | 22 | 7 | 1 | 0 | 87 |
| Method 4 | High | 2 | 18 | 3 | 0 | 0 | 0 | 23 |
| | Medium | 7 | 24 | 11 | 1 | 0 | 0 | 43 |
| | Low | 5 | 7 | 6 | 3 | 0 | 0 | 21 |
| | Total | 14 | 49 | 20 | 4 | 0 | 0 | 87 |

NOTE: "High" means from 35 to 51 seated passengers; "medium," from 18 to 34; and "low," less than 18. Most buses have 51 seats.

segregation than those with few Negroes. (See columns 3 and 4 especially.) Methods 1 and 4 differ slightly, but both demonstrate these phenomena clearly.[15]

We had also thought that, as buses became more crowded and sorting out was more troublesome, the observance of segregated patterns would tend to break down. [Table 5-18], which cross-tabulates the data in [Table 5-16] by the degree of crowding, does not, however, confirm these suppositions. The degree of integration changes only slightly as the bus population increases, the trend from low to medium being particularly ambiguous. It is our *post hoc* guess that these results stem from two opposite sorts of motives; and that as a bus becomes more crowded and segregation is more difficult to keep in operation, it also becomes more important to uphold segregation, since a crowded bus provides a more "threatening" environment. Integration on crowded public transit means adjacent seating, shoulder to shoulder and hip to hip, rather than just occupying a seat in the vicinity of the other race, and it means performing that act before a larger audience. Ease and threat, thus, would work in contrary directions on NOPSI buses, their effects tending to wash out in the observed data.

Those persons who violated precedence may be considered agents of social change, since it is they who are breaking with tradition. [Table 5-19] gives the number of white and Negro males and females for each of our three age divisions who did and did not violate precedence.[16] Among the whites it was the males, and among Negroes the females, who did so most frequently. Older persons, both white and Negro, violated precedence less than others of their sex and race, while the contrary tended to be true for the younger riders. The gap between youths and elders was particularly wide among the Negroes.

On their face the data in [Table 5-19] seem to "make sense." The fact that the legal rules had changed only six years earlier would account for the greater propensity of youths to integrate and the more uniformly traditional behavior of their elders. The rate reversal by sex between whites and Negroes was also to be expected, if only that in many aspects of Southern life it has long been easiest and least stressful for white males and Negro females to perform in somewhat less-than-caste-like roles. That Negroes exhibited greater ranges of precedence violation than whites might have been foreseen, too, since among legally disadvantaged Negroes some subsections (like youths) felt able to exercise their new prerogatives, while others (like grown men) would still practice their traditional reticence.

In our attempt to measure the actual degree of segregation-integration on New Orleans public transit

[15] Methods 2 and 3 are omitted from this Table, and from the next also, since their findings are contaminated either by racial dominance or by degree of crowding, the very dimensions we are examining here.

[16] The white and Negro totals in Column 1 differ solely because more of the former tended to be in ambiguous situations. See note 9. Only those persons who are considered precedence violators under Method 4 are included in this Table.

[TABLE 5-19] **Seated passengers, violators and non-violators of precedence, by race, sex, and age N = 2074**

| Total | Violators of precedence | Non-violators of precedence | Total |
|---|---|---|---|
| White males | 76 (16.2) | 394 | 470 |
| Age 1-16 | 6 (16.2) | 31 | 37 |
| 17-45 | 44 (19.4) | 202 | 246 |
| 46+ | 26 (13.9) | 161 | 187 |
| White females | 53 ( 9.1) | 532 | 585 |
| Age 1-16 | 21 (15.2) | 117 | 138 |
| 17-45 | 22 ( 7.7) | 265 | 287 |
| 46+ | 10 ( 6.2) | 150 | 160 |
| All whites | 129 (12.2) | 926 | 1055 |
| Negro males | 45 (11.6) | 344 | 389 |
| Age 1-16 | 6 (27.3) | 16 | 22 |
| 17-45 | 32 (11.7) | 242 | 274 |
| 46+ | 7 ( 7.5) | 86 | 93 |
| Negro females | 138 (21.9) | 492 | 630 |
| Age 1-16 | 26 (38.8) | 41 | 67 |
| 17-45 | 83 (20.5) | 322 | 405 |
| 46+ | 29 (18.3) | 129 | 158 |
| All Negroes | 183 (17.9) | 836 | 1019 |
| Total | 312 (15.0) | 1762 | 2074 |

NOTE: Figures in parentheses give the percentages violating precedence in each row.

some six years after a court desegregation order, we have dealt largely with gross seating patterns of whites and Negroes and with the effects that differing racial proportions and degrees of crowding have had on these configurations. We have also glanced at those individuals among the transit population who acted as "agents of social change." In addition, we have extensively discussed some of the methodological difficulties involved in defining and operationalizing the notions of segregation and integration on buses. It is both tempting and difficult to speculate about the general import that these findings and methods might possess.

The difficulty stems not just from our having made a limited number of observations in one city during a brief period of time. Most case studies face *that* problem. A much more serious obstacle is the lack of theoretically relevant prior knowledge about what a bus is sociologically like. Familiar concepts from such subfields as collective behavior, small groups, and organizational research do not seem particularly appropriate. A complement of bus passengers does not appear aptly labelled a crowd or audience or movement; its often large and shifting numbers engage in too little face-to-face discussion to fall easily within the confines of micro-sociology; and it lacks that degree of structured authority and institutionalized goals typically associated with formal organizations. Furthermore, passenger loads on buses are of many kinds. One need list only a coast-to-coast express bus, a commuter bus from the suburbs, a jammed city bus in the rush hour, and a relatively deserted one on the early a.m. "owl service," a tourist bus, and a school bus—not to mention Steinbeck's Wayward Bus—to show how heterogeneous the category really is. A typology of buses would be useful. Indeed, what is needed is a sociology of public transit.

Not knowing what a bus is fundamentally like makes it difficult to generalize to other behavioral situations. Could one predict from observations of interpersonal behavior on a long distance bus how the passengers would regroup at a lunch counter at which the bus stops en route? The similarity of the two settings is apparent in many respects, but there may well be crucial differences. So too, we several times observed a white and a Negro woman talking together at a NOPSI bus stop, only to separate once they boarded the vehicle. Transportation obviously provides its users with a special ambiance, though many other clusterings (e.g., a patients' waiting room in a medical building) may still be partly comparable.

While our findings can be extended to other situations only with caution, our methods—in particular, the measures and their underlying rationale—can be

terns of helping behavior than, say, a black person raised in the Virgin Islands, or in New England. Nevertheless, the "Southern Negro" dialect was selected because it seemed to typify the conception whites have of black speech. An attempt was made to select stimulus persons (victims) who were perceived to be nearly equivalent in terms of social class and other characteristics. The effectiveness of the manipulations of the caller's dialect (i.e., race) was assessed by asking college students to listen to recordings of the actors' experimental sessions and then rate each voice in terms of race, sex, social class, and personality characteristics. Data relevant to these ratings will be presented in the section on results. Seven black men and seven white men were used as callers.

To ensure that both male and female subjects would be home to receive the calls, the study was conducted between the hours of 6:30 and 9:30 P.M. If anyone identified by voice characteristics as being under 18 years of age answered, the caller apologized for reaching the wrong number and hung up. When an adult (someone over 18) answered, the caller repeated the following:

> *Caller:* Hello, . . . Ralph's Garage. This is George Williams. . . . Listen, I'm stuck out here on the parkway, and I'm wondering if you'd be able to come out here and take a look at my car?
>
> *Subject's expected response:* This isn't Ralph's Garage. You have the wrong number.
>
> *Caller:* This isn't Ralph's Garage! Listen, I'm terribly sorry to have disturbed you, but listen, . . . I'm stuck out here on the highway, and that was the last dime I had! I have bills in my pocket, but no more change to make another phone call. Now I'm *really* stuck out here. What am I going to do now?
>
> *Subject:* . . . (Subject might volunteer to call the garage. If he does not, caller goes on.)
>
> *Caller:* Listen, . . . do you think you could do me the favor of calling the garage and letting them know where I am? I'll give you the number. They know me over there.
>
> Prod A: Oh, brother. Listen, I'm stuck out here. Couldn't you *please* help me out by simply calling the garage for me? (Pleadingly.)
>
> Prod B: Listen, if *you* were in my situation, wouldn't you want someone to help you?

If after prod B the subject refused to place the call but did not hang up, he was relieved of any concern he may have had for the stranded motorist when the caller reported: "Oh, one second. . . . Here comes a police car. I think he will be able to give me a hand."

If the subject agreed to help, the victim gave him a telephone number to call. In fact, the subject's call was received by an assistant acting as the garage attendant. The assistant assured the subject that the victim would be helped immediately and graciously thanked him for his helpfulness.

To identify which subjects actually helped, the following procedures were employed. Firstly, black and white callers gave the subjects different telephone numbers to call. Secondly, each time a subject agreed to call, the caller changed his location on the parkway (e.g., Shore Parkway and Bay Ridge Rd., Shore Parkway and Coney Island Ave., etc.) rotating eight different locations. At the "garage" the subject was asked for the location of the stranded motorist. Finally, the time at which the call to the subject was completed, along with the time at which subject's call was received at the "garage," was recorded.

Only if the subject actually called the garage was he credited with a "help" response. If the subject refused to help after prod B, or hung up after the caller said " . . . and that was the last dime . . . " a "no help" response was scored. However, if the subject hung up before the word "dime," a "premature hang-up" response was recorded and was considered separately from the "help" and "no help" categories.

## RESULTS

**A. Perceived Characteristics of the Black and White Callers** As was noted earlier, college students were asked to listen to tape recordings of the callers' performances of the experimental dialogue. After they heard the dialogue they were asked to rate the caller along a number of dimensions. The students were very accurate in identifying the racial identity of these various callers. The white callers were perceived as white by 92 percent ($N = 89$) of the students; the black callers were perceived as black by 97 percent ($N = 97$).

In addition, the panel of judges perceived social and personality differences between the black and white callers. Although blacks were perceived to be of lower social class ($t = 2.57$, $p < .01$) and less education ($t = 1.97$, $p < .05$), both groups were judged as being lower-middle class and as having completed a high school education. Thus, although the difference was statistically significant, both groups of callers fell into the same overall categories. Furthermore, blacks were perceived as more good-natured ($t = 2.13$, $p < .05$); whites were perceived as somewhat older ($t = 3.55$, $p < .001$): the blacks were perceived as approximately 26 years old and the whites as about 28 years

**[TABLE 5-20] The frequency with which blacks and whites extended assistance to black and white victims**

| | White subjects | | Black subjects | |
|---|---|---|---|---|
| | White v. | Black v. | White v. | Black v. |
| Frequency help | 164 | 125 | 167 | 145 |
| Frequency no help | 88 | 111 | 82 | 95 |
| Percent help | 65% | 53% | 67% | 60.4% |

old. Again, this difference does not appear to be meaningful for this study. In general both groups of callers were judged favorably on characteristics such as good nature, friendliness, courtesy, reliability, truthfulness, and sincerity. They were also perceived as somewhat careless and anxious.

Although minor social-class differences were perceived between the black and white callers, which may confound the variable of race, these ratings may in fact represent a realistic appraisal of the relative social status of blacks and whites in our society.

**B. The Effects of the Race of the Victim Upon the Elicitation of Helping Behavior** The results indicated that whites helped black victims less frequently than white victims, which supports the hypothesis that the social-responsibility norm would be violated more frequently for blacks than for whites among whites. However, blacks extended relatively equivalent levels of assistance to each of the stranded motorists. In addition, there was a nonsignificant trend for black subjects to help white victims somewhat more frequently than black victims.

Specifically, [Table 5-20] indicates that when whites were called, the white victim was helped 65 percent of the time, whereas the black victim was helped only 53 percent of the time. This difference of 12 percent favoring the white victim was greater than could be reasonably expected by chance ($\chi^2 = 7.40, p < .01$, 1 df).

Blacks assisted the white caller 67 percent of the time and the black caller 60.4 percent of the time. However, the 6.6 percent difference favoring the white victim does not reach an acceptable level of significance ($\chi^2 = 2.34, p < .20$).

The interpretation of the findings changes somewhat when the sex of the subjects is considered. [Table 5-21] reveals that among whites both males and females helped the black victim less frequently than the white victim. Interestingly, the black male subjects gave equivalent levels of assistance to the black and white victims. That is, 68 percent of the black males helped the black victim and 69 percent helped the white victim. However, among black female subjects the white victim was assisted somewhat more frequently than the black victim: 66 percent of the black females

**[TABLE 5-21] The frequency with which blacks and whites, males and females, helped the black and white victims**

| | Male *S*s | | | |
|---|---|---|---|---|
| | White male *S*s | | Black male *S*s | |
| | White v. | Black v. | White v. | Black v. |
| Frequency help | 71 | 57 | 59 | 59 |
| Frequency no help | 26 | 40 | 26 | 28 |
| Percent help | 73% | 59% | 69% | 68% |
| | Female *S*s | | | |
| | White female *S*s | | Black female *S*s | |
| | White v. | Black v. | White v. | Black v. |
| Frequency help | 93 | 68 | 108 | 86 |
| Frequency no help | 61 | 71 | 55 | 66 |
| Percent help | 60% | 49% | 66% | 57% |

helped the white victim; only 57 percent helped the black victim ($\chi^2 = 3.12, p < .10$, 1 df). Thus, black males were the only group of subjects to extend equivalent levels of assistance to each of the stranded motorists.

Ignoring race of subjects and victims, the stranded motorists were assisted by 67 percent of the male subjects and by only 58 percent of the female subjects. The difference of 9 percent in the frequency with which males and females helped is unlikely to be due to chance ($\chi^2 = 7.35, p < .01$, 1 df).

**C. Premature Hang-Ups (i.e., Hanging Up Before Help Was Solicited)** Recall that the subjects were categorized as "help" or "no help" only after the stranded motorist had the opportunity to say, " . . . and that was my last dime." Before hearing the word "dime," the subject could believe that he had simply received a wrong-number telephone call, to which the only appropriate response would be to inform the caller of his error. However, once he heard the word "dime," the subject could be expected to realize that the caller needed further assistance.

Regardless of whether the subject eventually helped or not, a "no premature hang-up" response was recorded if the subject remained on the phone following the word "dime."

Inspection of [Table 5-22] indicates that whites hung up prematurely as frequently on the white as on the black victims ($\chi^2 = 1.68$, NS). However, there was a tendency for the blacks to hang up prematurely 4.7 percent more frequently on black than on white victims ($\chi^2 = 3.45, p < .10$, 1 df). Overall, whites hung up prematurely more frequently than blacks. That is, 14.2 percent of the white subjects but only 9.4 percent of the black subjects hung up prematurely on the experimenters ($\chi^2 = 6.07, p < .02$, 1 df).

If we take into account the sex of the subject, we find that there was a tendency for the white males to hang up prematurely more frequently on the black victim than on the white victim ($\chi^2 = 3.54, p < .10$, 1 df). However, although the white females did not hang up more often on the blacks than the whites, there was a tendency for the black females to do so ($\chi^2 = 3.65, p < .10$, 1 df). Overall, females hung up prematurely more often than males. That is, 14 percent of the females, as compared to 5 percent of the males, responded by hanging up prematurely ($\chi^2 = 18.41, p < .001$, 1 df).

**DISCUSSION**

In this nonreactive study it appears that whites discriminated against blacks in a situation which can be characterized as "distant" on a Bogardus Social Distance Scale. It was observed that in an encounter, not face-to-face, with a stranger requesting that a phone call be made in his behalf, a "black voice" lowered by an amount that is statistically significant the frequency of success in eliciting help from white residents of the New York City area. However, black subjects did not appear to discriminate against whites, which confirms the findings of public-opinion polls. Somewhat surprising, but approached with caution because of the low level of statistical significance, was the unpredicted finding that black females also tended to help the white victim more frequently (9 percent) than the black victim.

Thus, it appears that among whites, the social-responsibility norm was violated more frequently for the black victim than for the white victim. It should be stressed, however, that for 88 percent of the white subjects, the race of the victim did not affect helping behavior. Therefore, the race of the victim (inferred from his dialect) has a small but detectable influence upon helping behavior.

If in fact the social-responsibility norm was purposefully violated more frequently for the black victim than for the white victim, then it is reasonable to

**[TABLE 5-22] The frequency with which blacks and whites hung up prematurely when called by black and white stranded motorists**

| | Whites | | Blacks | |
|---|---|---|---|---|
| | White v. | Black v. | White v. | Black v. |
| Frequency premature hang-ups | 47 | 34 | 19 | 32 |
| Frequency no premature hang-ups | 252 | 236 | 249 | 240 |
| Percent premature hang-ups | 15.7% | 12.6% | 7.1% | 11.8% |

conclude that attitudes toward the victim can simply and directly affect the willingness to help—i.e., the motivation to act in accord with the social-responsibility norm. The bystander's dislike and hostility toward the person in need can be expressed by purposefully remaining passive. In a civilized society not helping is perhaps an adaptively effective expression of aggression toward the victim, because the bystander avoids many of the distasteful consequences so often involved in the overt, direct expression of hostility (e.g., legal penalties or threat to personal safety). Since subjects in the wrong-number situation had no reason to believe that they were not anonymous, there was no threat of negative social sanctions if they chose to violate the social-responsibility norm. This would seem to be a condition most conducive for the elicitation of overt behavior in accord with the subject's attitude.

On the other hand, perhaps when attitudes toward the victim mediate the elicitation of helping behavior they operate in a passive and less direct fashion than that hypothesized above. These attitudes toward the victim (or strangers in general) may affect the bystander's interpretation of the situation in terms of whether or not help is needed, rather than in terms of his own obligation to help. In the present study, it is possible that blacks received less help than whites because the subject might have assumed that the black person did not really need his help. But if the bystander maintains a favorable attitude toward the victim, perhaps he is more likely to believe the victim is in need of assistance. Ambiguous situations, too, complicate the matter. Milgram and Hollander (1964) point out that the bystanders who witnessed the murder of Kitty Genovese did not completely comprehend what was happening. They faced an ambiguous, frightening, and confusing situation. Thus, while one person may have thought that he was witnessing a murder, another may have thought it was a lovers' quarrel. Perhaps in ambiguous situations a favorable attitude toward a victim increases the importance of the decision regarding whether or not help is needed. Under this circumstance there should be a greater concern about what the consequences would be if it is decided, incorrectly, that help is not needed.

It seems reasonable to assume that the social-responsibility norm first becomes salient when the bystander interprets the situation as one in which the victim needs help. A study by Bickman (1969) indicated that a second bystander can decrease the frequency of helping behavior or delay the onset of helping behavior by providing the subject with a definition of the situation suggesting that help is not needed. A reasonable interpretation of this finding is that the saliency of the social-responsibility norm is lowered when the subject accepts the suggestion that help is not needed. With respect to the present study, attitudes toward the victim might have differentially affected the saliency of the social-responsibility norm: that is, for some subjects the social-responsibility norm might not apply to blacks.

Additionally, negative attitudes toward the victim's "kind" might make one more likely to believe that the victim's circumstances, although unfortunate, are well deserved or due to some fundamental flaw in the victim's character. Schopler and Matthews (1965) have shown that helping behavior is more likely when the "dependent other" is perceived to be a victim of circumstances beyond his control than when he is perceived to be personally responsible for his dependency. If the victim's circumstances are believed to represent just reparation, then perhaps the bystander tends to believe that his help is not only unnecessary but unwarranted. Consistent with this notion is Lerner's principle of the "need to perceive a just world." Lerner and Simmons, (1965) observed that subjects derogated a martyred victim to a greater extent than less nobly motivated victims. Thus subjects cognitively made an "unjust" situation "just." This type of mechanism could have been operating in the present situation.

## APPLICATION OF THE WRONG-NUMBER TECHNIQUE

The wrong-number technique may also be used to investigate the effects of different amounts and types of interracial contact on the level of discrimination as indicated by the frequency of helping behavior. Thus, one could compare integrated with segregated housing areas. In addition, we can study whether discrimination is more prevalent in one city than in another: for example, a comparison of the results of the present study with studies conducted in the Deep South seems called for.

Other studies using this technique are in progress. An investigation of whether the sex of the victim is important in determining the subject's response is being conducted: will a black woman get more help than a black man? In addition, the political affiliations of the subjects are being considered. Will members of different political parties, with their different ideologies (conservatives versus liberals), behave in different ways?

The usefulness of this method is not limited to the

study of attitudes of one group toward another. At the present time many other aspects of helping behavior are being studied. For example, the manner in which the victim asks for help is under investigation, to determine whether help is more likely when the victim requests or demands it. In addition, the relationship between the sex of the victim and the sex of the subject is being investigated. The wrong-number technique, then, can be used to study a variety of problems.

## REFERENCES

**BERKOWITZ, L.** A laboratory investigation of social class and national differences in helping behavior. *International Journal of Psychology,* 1966, **1**, 231-242.

**BERKOWITZ, L., & DANIELS, L.** Affecting the salience of the social responsibility norm: Effects of past help on the response to dependency relationships. *Journal of Abnormal and Social Psychology,* 1964, **68**, 275-281.

**BERKOWITZ, L., KLANDERMAN, S., & HARRIS, R.** Effects of experimenter awareness and sex of subject and experimenter on reactions to dependency relationships. *Sociometry,* 1964, **27**, 327-339.

**BICKMAN, L.** Effect of the presence of others on bystander intervention in an emergency. Unpublished doctoral dissertation, The City University of New York, 1969.

**BICKMAN, L., & HENCHY, T.** *Beyond the Laboratory: Field Research in Social Psychology.* New York: McGraw-Hill, 1971.

**BRYAN, J. H. & TEST, M. A.** Models and helping: Naturalistic studies in aiding behavior. *Journal of Personality and Social Psychology,* 1967, **6**, 400-407.

**LERNER, M. J. & SIMMONS, C. H.** Observer's Reaction to the "innocent victim": compassion or rejection? *Journal of Personality and Social Psychology,* 1966, **4**, 203-210.

**MARX, GARY.** *Protest and Prejudice.* New York: Harper Torchbooks, 1969.

**MILGRAM, S. & HOLLANDER, P.** Paralyzed witnesses: The murder they saw. *Nation*, 1964, **198**, 602-604.

**ORNE, M. T.** On the social psychology of the psychological experiment: with particular reference to demand characteristics and their implications. *American Psychologist,* 1962, **17**, 776-783.

**PILIAVIN, I. M., RODIN, J. & PILIAVIN, J. A.,** Good Samaritanism: An Underground Phenomenon? *Journal of Personality and Social Psychology,* 1969, **13**, 289-299.

**SCHOPLER, J., & MATTHEWS, M.** The influence of perceived causal locus of partner's dependence on the use of interpersonal power. *Journal of Personality and Social Psychology,* 1965, **2**, 609-612.

**SCHULTZ, D. P.** The human subject in psychological research. *Psychological Bulletin,* 1969, **72**, 214-228.

**WICKER, A.** Attitudes versus actions: The relationship of verbal and overt behavioral responses to attitude objects. *Journal of Social Issues,* 1969, **XXV**, 41-78.

# CHAPTER SIX

# COLLECTIVE BEHAVIOR

Although collective behavior has always been a crucial concern of social psychologists (Allport, 1954; Milgram & Toch, 1969), most of the articles in this chapter, with the exception of the article by Sherif, are recent. We expect this area to increase in importance because of the increased population density, the increased waiting in lines to receive goods and services, and the increased difficulty of establishing territory for the individual.

The first article, by Sommer and Becker, discusses a reason for field studies which is totally different from those previously enumerated: the field is the only place where territorial behavior should be studied. This is because the work on human territoriality follows directly from work on animal territoriality; it is in the ecological tradition (Lorenz, 1966; Tinbergen, 1953). The study by Sommer and Becker is a good combination of questionnaire and field work, such as was suggested by Festinger (1953). The questionnaires were used to generate hypotheses which were then tested in the field. Again, as in Chapter 3, in the article by Hofling et al., and in the study by Mann and Taylor in this chapter, there was a disparity between verbal response and actual behavior. In general, the work by Sommer and Becker is a good example of field research from its inception, through hypotheses generating from questionnaires, to checking the hypotheses and alternative explanations by further experimentation.

The second article in this chapter, by Felipe and Sommer, while another good field experiment, also exemplifies the fact that field studies, too, can run into ethical problems just a laboratory experiments can (Baumrind, 1964; Milgram, 1964). Intruding into the personal space of mental patients may be a questionable procedure. It is also conceivable that personal space may vary across racial lines. (See Davis, Seibert, & Breed, Chapter 5.)

The article by Mann and Taylor (page 187) represents a first attempt at understanding the psychology of an increasingly important part of our lives: lines. It also provides us with a good example of the search for alternative explanations and the reduction of them through further experimentation. However, there are some problems with the control in their study; i.e., a *line* by definition should be *waiting* for something. The weaker results of the field experiment, compared with the study of real football lines, are evidence of what happens when people are not involved or motivated, or when they know they are in an experiment. There is also some evidence of the operation of reactance motivation, when disappointed subjects toward the end of the line report greater fondness for chocolate than other subjects. (Also see Regan & Brehm, Chapter 8.)

The study by Milgram, Bickman, and Berkowitz (page 196) is similar to the preceding one, in that it introduces an area of study and a novel technique. The area of crowd formation should increase in importance, especially with some urban planners (incredibly) urging *greater* density in our urban centers (Blake, 1969). This study also illustrates that field studies can be used for hypothesis testing and model building. Practically, it is also of great importance to know what makes a crowd gather; this knowledge may aid in dispersing a crowd (Mann & Taylor, page 187).

The final article in the chapter, Sherif's (page 199), is a classic in the field of social psychology. It is both an ingenious field experiment and a good demonstration of psychological principles. It demonstrates how the usual methods of attempting to reduce intergroup prejudice (Katz, Sarnoff, & McClintock, 1956) have little hope of success. (See Parker, Chapter 5.)

The area of collective behavior is one which is expected to grow in importance, and one which is particularly amenable to field techniques. It is hoped that the techniques developed by Milgram et al. and by Mann and Taylor will encourage others to be innovative and to investigate what really should be one of the most studied areas in social psychology and, indeed, will have to be as population density increases.

## REFERENCES


**ALLPORT, G. W.** The historical background of modern social psychology. In G. Lindzey (Ed.) *Handbook of social psychology.* Vol. 1. Cambridge, Mass: Addison-Wesley, 1954, pp. 3-56.

**BAUMRIND, D.** Some thoughts on ethics of research: after reading Milgram's "Behavioral study of obedience." *American Psychologist*, 1964, **19**, 421-423.

**BLAKE, P.** The island nobody knows. *New York*, 1969, **2**, 62-63.

**KATZ, D., SARNOFF, I., & MCCLINTOCK, C.** Ego defense and attitude change. *Human Relations*, 1956, **9**, 27-45.

**LORENZ, K.** *On aggression.* New York: Bantam, 1966.

**MILGRAM, S.** Issues in the study of obedience: a reply to Baumrind. *American Psychologist*, 1964, **19**, 848-852.

**MILGRAM, S., & TOCH, H.** Collective behavior: crowds and social movements. In G. Lindzey & E. Aronson (Eds.), *The handbook of social psychology.* Reading, Mass.: Addison-Wesley, 1969, Vol. 4, 517-610.

**TINBERGEN, N.** *Social behavior in animals.* New York: Wiley, 1953.

# TERRITORIAL DEFENSE AND THE GOOD NEIGHBOR

ROBERT SOMMER[1] AND FRANKLIN D. BECKER
*University of California, Davis*

A series of questionnaire and experimental studies was designed to explore how people mark out and defend space in public areas. The use of space is affected by instructions to defend actively the area or retreat, by room density, and by the location of walls, doors, and other physical barriers. Under light population pressure, most markers are capable of reserving space in a public area, but more personal markers have the greatest effect. As room density increases, the effect of the marker is seen in delaying occupancy of the area and in holding onto a smaller subarea within the larger space. Neighbors play an important part in legitimizing a system of space ownership.

The concept of human territoriality is receiving increased attention. In addition to the popular books by Ardrey (1961, 1966), a number of social scientists have become impressed with the utility of the concept (Altman & Haythorn, 1967; Esser et al., 1965; Hall, 1966; Lipman, 1967; Lyman & Scott, 1967). Hediger (1950) defined a territory as "an area which is first rendered distinctive by its owner in a particular way and, secondly, is defended by the owner." When the term is used by social scientists to refer to human behavior, there is no implication that the underlying mechanisms are identical to those described in animal research. The major components of Hediger's definition are *personalization* and *defense*. Roos (1968) uses the term *range* as the total area an individual traverses, *territory* as the area he defends, *core area* as the area he preponderantly occupies, and *home* as the area in which he sleeps. Goffman (1963) makes the further distinction between a territory and a *jurisdiction*, such as that exercised by a janitor sweeping the floor of an office and keeping other people away. Territories are defended on two grounds, "you keep off" and "this space is mine." Jurisdictions are controlled only on the former ground; no claim of ownership, no matter how transitory, is made.

In a previous study, the reactions to staged spatial invasions were investigated (Felipe & Sommer, 1966). There was no single reaction to a person coming too close; some people averted their heads and placed an elbow between themselves and the intruder, others treated him as a nonperson, while still others left the area when he came too close. The range of defensive gestures, postures, and acts suggested that a systematic study of defensive procedures would contribute materially to our knowledge of human spatial behavior. Following the tradition of ecological research, the studies would be undertaken in naturally occurring environments.

## QUESTIONNAIRE STUDIES

During previous observations of library study halls Sommer (1967) was impressed by the heavy concentration of readers at the side-end chairs. Interviewing made it clear that students believed that it was polite to sit at an end chair. Someone who sat, for example, at a center chair of an empty six-chair table (three chairs on each side) was considered to be "hogging the table." There appeared to be two styles by which students gained privacy in the library areas. One method was avoidance, to sit as far away from other people as one could. The other method was offensive ownership of the entire area. To study the two methods of gaining privacy, a brief questionnaire was constructed which presented the student with table diagrams containing 6, 8, and 10 chairs, respectively (Sommer, 1967). Two forms to the questionnaire were distributed randomly within a class of 45 students. Twenty-four students received avoidance instructions: "If you wanted to be as far as possible from the distraction of other people, where would you sit at the table?" Twenty-one other students in the same class were shown the same diagrams and given the offensive display instructions: "If you wanted to have the table to yourself, where would you sit to discourage anyone else from occupying it?" Even though both sets of instructions were aimed at insuring privacy, the two tactics produced a striking difference in seats chosen. Those students who wanted to sit by themselves as far as possible from other

[1] The authors are grateful to Harriet Becker, Martha Connell, Ann Gibbs, Lee Mohr, Tighe O'Hanrahan, Pamela Pearce, Ralph Requa, Sally Robison, and Nancy Russo for their assistance.

people overwhelmingly chose the *end* chairs at the table, while those students who wanted to keep other people away from the table almost unanimously chose the *middle* chair.

When the findings were discussed with architect James Marston Fitch, his first question concerned the location of the door in regards to the table. This seemed a good question, since the preferred location for retreat or active defense should be guided by the path the invaders would take or by the most accessible escape route. The previous diagrams had depicted only a table and chairs, so it seemed necessary to undertake another study in which the entrance to the room was indicated. This conception of the study suggested that additional information could be obtained on the ecology of retreat and active defense by varying the location of walls and aisles and the table size.

## Method

The present study involved four diagrams, each one drawn on a separate 8½ x 11-inch sheet.

*Form G* showed eight rectangular six-chair tables, with a large aisle down the center and two smaller aisles along the walls. (See [Figure 6-1].)

*Form H* was the same as Form G, only the tables were set against the wall and the center aisle was wider.

*Form J* was a hybrid of G and H, with the right row of tables against the wall and the left row of tables away from the wall.

*Form I* contained one row of four-chair tables and one row of eight-chair tables, with aisles in the center and along both walls.

Four different sets of instructions were used with the forms (two defense styles and two densities), but any single subject received only one set. One form asked the subject where he would sit if he wanted to be by himself and away from other people–the retreat instructions. The other form asked where he would sit if he wanted to keep other people away from the table–the active defense instructions. In each case, the prospective room density was also indicated. On half the questionnaires, it was stated that room density was likely to be low throughout the day and very few people would be using the room, while remaining subjects were told that room density was likely to be high and many people would be using the room. All the instructions described the room as a study hall such as that already existing in the campus library, and the respondent was informed that he was the first occupant in the room, so he could take any seat he wanted. Booklets containing some combination of instructional set (Defense Style X Room Density) and two diagrams in random order were passed out randomly among 280 students in introductory psychology classes.

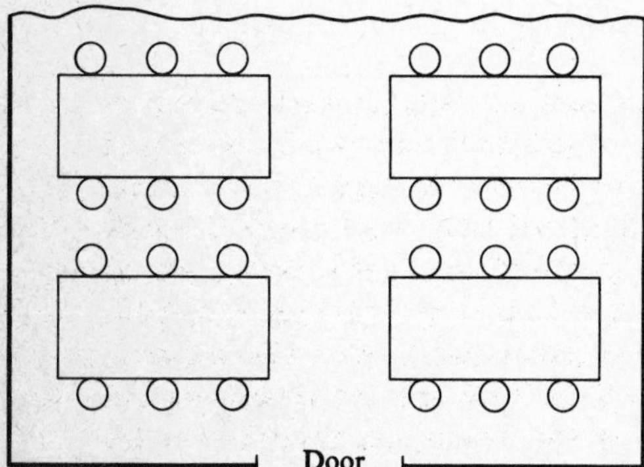


[FIGURE 6-1] Arrangement of tables and chairs in Form G.

## Results

*Hypothesis 1* stated that during the retreat condition people gravitate to the end chair closest to the wall. During the active defense condition they make greater use of the center and aisle chairs. Hypothesis 1 was confirmed beyond the .01 level. During the retreat conditions 76% of the subjects occupied a wall chair compared to 48% during the active defense condition.

*Hypothesis 2* stated that with the retreat instructions the subjects face away from the door, while they face towards the door with the active defense instructions. The data disclose a preference in all conditions for a subject to sit with his back to the door–60% of the subjects faced away from the door compared to 40% who faced towards it. However, the results were still in the predicted direction since 44% of the subjects in the active defense condition faced the door compared to 36% in the retreat condition ($p <$ .05).

Although the authors had imagined that the use of different-sized tables and the variation in wall placement would influence seating patterns, specific hypotheses had not been formulated. In all conditions there was a marked preference for chairs towards the rear of the room. Overall, 79% selected chairs in the rear half of the room. However, occupancy of the rear was significantly higher with the retreat instructions under high room density than in any of the other conditions ($p < .05$). There was also a highly significant preference for the four-chair tables when they were paired with the eight-chair tables, with 73% selecting a small table compared with 27% selecting a large table. There was a slight trend in the active defense condition to make greater use of the small tables, but this was not statistically significant.

When tables against the wall were paired with tables with aisles on both sides, 62% of the subjects selected a table against the wall compared to 38% who chose a table with aisles on both sides ($p < .001$). As an independent variable, description of the projected room density as high or low made very little difference in where people sat. However, density interacted with the defense instructions on several of the tabulations. With high density *and* retreat instructions, there was significantly greater use of (*a*) the rear half of the room, (*b*) a wall compared to an aisle table, and (*c*) the chair closest to the wall. In essence, the attribution of high room density increased the degree of physical retreat. It had no observable effects on the active defense conditions.

The results make it clear that room dimension and the location of barriers must be considered if we are to understand the ecology of spatial defense. In a library reading room, the best chair for retreat is at the rear, facing away from the door, next to a wall, and at a small table if one is available. Distance from the door protects the person against people simply walking by as well as lazy intruders who are more likely to sit in the first available chair; facing away from the door tends to minimize distraction and also displays an antipathy toward social intercourse; a wall table protects a person's entire left (or right) side; and a small table reduces the number of invaders in close proximity. At this point the authors felt they had derived many useful hypotheses from the questionnaire data which they wanted to extend using an experimental approach under natural conditions. The first experimental studies took place in two soda fountains, and the remainder took place in library areas.

## EXPERIMENTAL STUDIES

Most territories are marked and bounded in some clear way. In the animal kingdom, markers may be auditory (bird song), olfactory (glandular secretions by deer), or visual (bear-claw marks on a tree). Since humans rely almost exclusively on visual markers, the authors decided to test the strength of various markers ranging from the physical presence of a person to impersonal artifacts.

### Study 1

> The first study took place in a popular soda fountain on campus. The soda fountain was located in a converted office building which still contained a number of small rooms. Patrons would obtain their refreshments at a central counter and then repair to one of the smaller rooms to eat and chat informally. Prior to the study, the authors had been struck by the sight of students walking up and down the corridor looking for an empty room. One of the small rooms which contained three square tables, each surrounded by four chairs, was used for the study. A 20-year-old girl who appeared to be studying stationed herself at a table facing the door. On other occasions during the same hours she stationed herself down the hall so she could observe who entered the experimental room. A session took place only when the room was unoccupied at the outset.

If an all-or-none criterion of room occupancy is applied, the experimenter's defense was not very successful. During only 1 of the 10 experimental sessions was she able to keep the entire room to herself. The average length of time before the room was occupied during the experimental sessions was 5.8 minutes compared to 2.6 minutes during the control sessions, but the difference was not statistically reliable. Although the experimenter was unable to keep the room to herself, she was able to protect the table at which she studied. The remaining three seats were occupied only once during the experimental sessions compared to 13 occupancies during the control sessions ($p < .01$). It seems clear that territorial defense in a public area is not an all-or-none affair. The defender's presence may be seen in a delay in occupancy rather than an absence of invaders and in the avoidance of a subarea within the larger area.

### Study 2

> The next study took place in a more traditional open-plan soda fountain and, instead of the physical presence of the experimenter, three sorts of objects were used as territorial markers–a sandwich wrapped in cellophane, a sweater draped over a chair, and two paperback books stacked on the table. In each case the experimenter located two adjacent empty tables and arbitrarily placed a marker on one with the other as a control. Seating himself some distance away, he was able to record the duration of time before each table was occupied. The sessions all took place at moderate room density. There were 8 sessions with a sandwich marker, 13 with a sweater, and 20 with the books.

The authors were interested in whether a marker would reserve an entire table as well as the marked chair. The answer for all of the markers was affirmed. The unmarked control tables were occupied significantly sooner than were the marked tables, and the difference was significant for each of the three markers. In fact, in all 41 sessions the control table was occupied sooner or at the same time as the marked table. In only three of the sessions did anyone sit at the marked *chair*. All three were occupied by males, a finding whose significance will be discussed later. It is also interesting to examine the occupancy patterns at the two sorts of tables. The marked tables were eventually occupied by 34 lone individuals and 4 groups of 2 persons, while the unmarked tables were occupied by 18 lone individuals and 20 groups. It can be noted that a group of 2 or 3 could easily be accommodated at a marked table even assuming that the marker represented one person, yet virtually all the groups sat at unmarked tables. It is clear that the markers were able to (*a*) protect the particular chair almost totally, (*b*) delay occupancy of the entire table, and (*c*) divert groups away from the table.

**Study 3**

A similar study using books and newspapers as markers was undertaken in a dormitory study hall at a time of very light room density. Virtually all the markers proved effective in reserving the marked chair. The only exceptions were two sessions when the school paper which had been used as a marker was treated as litter and pushed aside. After more than 30 individual sessions where virtually all the markers were respected, the authors decided to move the experiments to the main university library where room density was much heavier. It seemed clear that at low densities almost any marker is effective. One qualification is that the object must be perceived as a marker and not as something discarded and unwanted by its former owner. Certain forms of litter such as old newspapers or magazines may, indeed, attract people to a given location.

The locus of study was switched to the periodical room in the university library where room density was high and pressure for seats was great. This room contained rectangular six-chair tables, three chairs to a side. The experimenter arrived at one of the six seats at a designated table at 6:50 P.M., deposited a marker, and then departed to another table at 7:00 P.M. to view any occupancy at the marked position by a student seeking space. During each session, a similarly situated empty chair which was unmarked was used as the control. There were 25 experimental sessions, each lasting 2 hours. The markers included two notebooks and a textbook, four library journals piled in a neat stack, four library journals randomly scattered on the table, a sports jacket draped over the chair, and a sports jacket draped over the chair in addition to the notebooks on the table.

If one compares the average time before occupancy of the marked and the control chairs, it is apparent that all markers were effective. Seventeen of the 25 marked chairs remained vacant the entire 2-hour period, while *all* control chairs were occupied. The average interval before the control chairs were occupied was 20 minutes. Some of the markers were more potent than others. Only one student occupied a chair that was marked either by a sports jacket or a notebook-and-text. Chairs marked by the neatly-piled journals were occupied three of the five sessions, while chairs marked by the randomly placed journals were occupied all five sessions, even though the interval in each case exceeded that of the control chairs. It is clear that the personal markers, such as the sports jacket and notebooks, were able to keep away intruders entirely, while the impersonal library-owned markers (journals) could only delay occupancy of the marked chairs.

An interesting sidelight is that eight of the nine students who sat down despite the markers were males. Since there were more females than males in the control chairs at the same time, the high incidence of males is quite significant. It may be recalled in the previous study that the only three individuals who pushed aside the marker and sat at a marked chair were also males. It is likely that some sort of dominance or risk-taking factor is at work in the decision to disregard a territorial marker. The relationship between personality characteristics and the likelihood of invading someone else's space seems an exciting topic for further investigation.

Another serendipitous finding concerns the role of the neighbor, the person sitting alongside the marked chair, in defending the marked space. In all five trials with the scattered journals, the potential invader questioned the person sitting alongside the marked chair (the neighbor) as to whether the space was vacant. Early in the 2-hour session, the neighbor unknowingly served as the protector of the space. He informed all inquisitive intruders that the space was taken, since he believed the experimenter would return in view of the marker left on the table. As time passed, the neighbor's belief that the experimenter would return to the chair began to wane. At this point he would impart his new conception of the situation to potential invaders, "Yes, somebody was sitting there, but that was over an hour ago. Maybe he's not coming back."

**Study 4**

Since the role of the neighbor seemed an important aspect of a property-ownership system, the authors decided to investigate it experimentally. The first of such studies involved two experimenters and a person sitting alongside an empty chair. One experimenter seated himself next to a stranger (the neighbor) for 15 minutes and then departed, leaving behind an open book and an open notebook upon the table as territorial markers. After a fixed interval, the second experimenter, in the role of a student looking for a chair, came and inquired about the marked space nonverbally. The nonverbal questioning was a pantomime which included catching the neighbor's eye, pulling out the chair slightly, hesitating, looking at the place markers and at the neighbor, and then back at the markers. The authors had very little experience with such nonverbal cues, but expected that the neighbor's reactions might include verbal defenses ("That seat is taken") and nonverbal defenses (moving the books to reinforce the marker). The independent variable was the length of time between the departure of the first experimenter and the arrival of the second–which was either a 5- or a 20-minute interval. Some sessions had to be terminated when the neighbor departed before the second experimenter arrived on the scene.

Overall the results were discouraging. In only 6 of the 55 trials did the neighbor respond to the nonverbal gestures of the second experimenter in what could be described as a space-defending manner, such as a statement that the seat was taken. Five of the six defensive acts occurred when the experimenter had been away 5 minutes, compared to only one defensive act when he had been away 20 minutes, but considering that there were 55 trials the difference was unimpressive.

### Study 5

The authors decided to make another attempt to see if the neighbor could be involved in property defense on a spontaneous basis–that is, if he would defend marked space without being questioned directly. Unlike in the preceding study, the "owner" attempted to establish a relationship with the neighbor prior to the "owner's" departure. There were two phases of the study; when it seemed that the first approach was not leading anywhere, another approach was used. The markers were a neat stack of three paperback books left on the table in front of a chair. The sessions took place at six-chair tables where there was at least 1 empty seat between the marker and the neighbor. The first experimenter entered the room and found the location meeting the experimental requirements (a person sitting at the end chair of a six-person table with two empty chairs alongside him–O–O–S). The experimenter (a girl) sat down on the same side of the table but one seat away (E–O–S). There were 13 trials in each of the following conditions: (*a*) The experimenter sat 5 minutes and then departed from the table, leaving her books neatly stacked on the table. During this time she did not interact with her neighbor. (*b*) Similar to Condition *a*, the experimenter sat for 5 minutes except that during the 5-minute wait, the experimenter asked the neighbor "Excuse me, could you tell me what time it is?" (*c*) Similar to Condition *a*, the experimenter sat for 5 minutes except that during the 5-minute wait the experimenter engaged the neighbor in conversation four times and, while leaving and placing the stack of three paperback books on the table, declared, "See you later." Fifteen minutes later, the second experimenter (a male) entered the room, walked directly to the marked chair, pushed the books directly ahead of him, and sat down at the table.

The results were again discouraging. In none of the 39 trials involving Conditions *a*, *b*, and *c* did the neighbor inform the intruder that the seat was taken. The authors therefore decided to strengthen the conditions by having the "owner" return and directly confront the intruder. Seven of such trials were added to Condition *a*, six to Condition *b*, and 6 to Condition *c*, making 19 trials in all when the "owner" came back and told the intruder "You are sitting in my chair." Each time she hesitated about 30 seconds to see if the neighbor would intervene, and then she picked up her books and departed. There was no verbal response from the neighbor in any of the 19 sessions. The most that occurred would be a frown or a look of surprise on the part of the neighbor, or some nonverbal communication with someone else at the table. Stated simply, despite a flagrant usurpation of a marked space, all neighbors chose to remain uninvolved. It became clear that if one wanted to study the neighbor's role in such an informal regulatory system one would have to question him directly as to whether the seat was occupied.

### Study 6

The next study employed two experimenters, a male and a female, and the same three paperback books as markers. Two different girls were used as experimenters, and the sessions occurred in two different, nearby college libraries. The experimental situation involved six-chair tables where the first experimenter (female) sat down at the same side of a table with a subject, leaving an empty chair between them (E–O–S). The goal of the study was to learn whether a greater amount of interaction between the former occupant and the neighbor would increase the neighbor's likelihood of defending the chair. Unlike in the previous study, the neighbor was questioned directly as to whether the seat was taken. There were three different instructional sets, and these took place according to a prearranged random order. In 14 trials, the first experimenter sat at the chair for 5 minutes without saying anything, deposited the marker (three paperback books), and left. Fourteen other sessions were similar except that at some time during her 5-minute stay, the first experimenter asked the neighbor for the time. Ten other sessions were similar except that the experimenter engaged the neighbor in conversation as to where to get a coke, what was happening on campus, and other minor matters. Fifteen minutes after the first experimenter departed, the second experimenter (a male) entered the room, walked over to the marked chair, and asked the neighbor "Excuse me, is there anyone sitting here?"

The results differ markedly from those in the previous study. A total of 22 out of the 38 neighbors defended the seat when questioned directly on the matter. The typical defense response was "Yes, there is" or "There is a girl who left those books."[2] However, the amount of contact between the first experimenter and the neighbor made little difference in defensive behavior. When there had been no contact, or minimal contact, between the first experimenter and neighbor the seat was protected 58% of the time, while the use of several items of conversation between the experimenter and her neighbor raised the percentage of defensive responses only to 66%. The difference between conditions is small and statistically unreliable; what is impressive is the great increase in defensive behavior when the neighbor was questioned directly. Two other parameters of the situation are (*a*) the time that the first experimenter remained in the seat before depositing her marker, and (*b*) the length of time that the first experimenter was out of room before the second experimenter approached the marked chair.

### Study 7

The final study employed two experimenters, both males, and the same three paperback books. The sessions took place at six-chair tables in the library, where the first experimenter again sat down on the same side of the table with a subject, leaving an empty chair between them (E–O–S). He remained either 5 minutes or 20 minutes, depending upon the experimental condition, and then departed, leaving on the table a neat stack of three paperback books. After a designated interval of either 15 or 60 minutes, the second experimenter entered the room and asked the neighbor whether the (marked) chair was taken. The second experimenter recorded the neighbor's reply verbatim just as soon as he was able to sit down somewhere. Since both experimenters were males, it was decided to use only male neighbors in the experiment.

The independent variables were (*a*) the length of time the first experimenter had been seated before he left his marker and departed and (*b*) the length of time the first experimenter was absent before the neighbor was questioned by the second experimenter. Some sessions were unusable since the neighbor departed before the designated time and could not be interviewed. Most of the unusable sessions occurred when the experimenter had been absent for 60 minutes. The sessions took place at times of light-to-moderate room density.

Although the design had not called for comparison of marked and unmarked chairs, it is noteworthy that the markers were effective in keeping people away. Not one of the 64 marked chairs was ever occupied. Regarding the inclination of the neighbor to defend the marked space when questioned by the second experimenter, a content analysis of the neighbor's responses to the query "Is this seat taken?" into defense and nondefense categories revealed that 44 neighbors defended the marked space by indicating that it was taken, while 20 failed to do so either by pleading ignorance or by stating that the chair was empty. The response to a direct question stands in contrast to the lack of involvement when neighbors were approached nonverbally. The length of time that the first experimenter had originally occupied the chair (his tenure period) had no effect on the willingness of the neighbor to defend the chair. However, the length of time that the previous owner was away—either 15 or 60 minutes—had a significant effect. When the former owner had been absent 15 minutes, 80% of the neighbors defended the space compared to 54% defending it when the former owner had been away a full hour ($p < .05$).

Several aspects of the results require elaboration. It is possible that initial tenure periods of 5 and 20 minutes were not sufficiently different. Yet it seems noteworthy that even with a rather impersonal marker, more than two-thirds of the neighbors defended the marked chair upon direct questioning. Most of those who didn't defend it simply pleaded ignorance ("I don't know if it's taken") rather than indicating that the seat was vacant.

After the experiments had been completed, 15 additional students in the library were interviewed on the question of how personal belongings could reserve space. Each student was asked how he would react if he saw someone intrude into a marked space, particularly if the original owner came back and claimed the space (i.e., the actual experimental situation was described to him). The replies were at variance with what the authors had actually found in such a situation. Most of the respondents maintained

[2] The neighbors' replies to the intruder's question were scored separately by two coders as indicating defense of the space ("Yes, that seat is taken") or nondefense ("No, it isn't taken" or "I don't know"). There was 100% agreement between the two raters in scoring the replies into defense or nondefense categories.

that they would indeed protect a marked space, although some of them added qualifications that they would defend the space only if the person were away a short time. Typical responses were: "I would protect the person's books and state (to the intruder) that the place was obviously taken by the presence of the books," and "Yes, I would mention that someone was sitting there." Although the majority mentioned specifically that they would protect a marked chair, in the actual situation no one had done so unless approached directly. The ethic regarding space ownership in the library exists, but is paid lip service, probably because institutional means of enforcement do not exist.

## DISCUSSION

The present article represents a small beginning toward understanding how markers reserve space and receive their legitimacy from people in the area (neighbors) and potential intruders. Psychologists have paid little attention to boundary markers in social interaction, perhaps because such markers were regarded as physical objects relegated to the cultural system (the province of the anthropologist) rather than an interpersonal system which is the true province of the social psychologist. Generally it is the geographers and lawyers who are most concerned with boundaries and markers. Since the present studies took place in public spaces, we are dealing more with norms and customs than with legal statutes. Stated another way, the situations involve an interpersonal system where sanctions are enforced by the individuals immediately present. Goffman (1963) labels the situations the authors used in the experiments *temporary territories.* It is clear that a person placing his coat over the back of a chair desires to reserve the space, and most people in the immediate vicinity will support his claim if questioned (although they will remain uninvolved if they can); such behavior meets Hediger's (1950) definition of territory presented previously as well as the more simple one provided by Noble (1939) that a territory represents "any defended area." The phenomena the present authors have studied do not belong under other available rubrics of spatial behavior, such as home range, biotope, niche, or life space. The major differences between the experimental situations and more enduring territories is that the latter are meshed with a legal-cultural framework and supported in the end by laws, police, and armies. The marked spaces in the present authors' experiments have no legal status and are supported only by the immediate social system. Occasionally it became necessary to articulate the structure of the system by "requiring" neighbors to enter the situation.

People are now spending an increasing portion of their time in public or institutional spaces, including theaters, airport lobbies, buses, schools, and hospitals, where the use of personal belongings to mark out temporary territories is a common phenomenon. The study of territories, temporary as well as enduring ones, deserves study by psychologists. There is some danger that such work will lose much of its force if some semantic clarity is not obtained. While the ethologist's definition of a territory as "any defended area" has considerable heuristic value, there is no need to assume that the mechanisms underlying human and animal behavior are identical. The paucity of data about human territorial behavior makes it most reasonable to assume that the mechanisms are analogous rather than homologous.

In conclusion, the present series of studies suggests that further investigation of spatial markers is feasible and warranted. The physical environment has for too long been considered the background variable in psychological research. The time is past when we can have theories of man that do not take into account his surroundings. Boundary markers not only define what belongs to a person and what belongs to his neighbor, but also who he is and what it means to be a neighbor in a complex society.

## REFERENCES

**ALTMAN, I., & HAYTHORN, W. W.** The ecology of isolated groups. *Behavioral Science*, 1967, **12**, 169-182.

**ARDREY, R.** *African genesis.* London: Collins, 1961.

**ARDREY, S.** *The territorial imperative.* New York: Atheneum, 1966.

**ESSER, A. H. et al.** Territoriality of patients on a research ward. In J. Wortis (Ed.), *Recent advances in biological psychiatry.* Vol. 8. New York: Plenum Press, 1965.

**FELIPE, N., & SOMMER, R.** Invasions of personal space. *Social Problems*, 1966, **14**, 206-214.

**GOFFMAN, E.** *Behavior in public places.* New York: Free Press of Glencoe, 1963.

**HALL, E. T.** *The hidden dimension.* Garden City: Doubleday, 1966.

**HEDIGER, H.** *Wild animals in captivity.* London: Butterworths, 1950.

**LIPMAN, A.** Old peoples homes: Siting and neighborhood integration. *The Sociological Review*, 1967, **15**, 323-338.

**LYMAN, S. M., & SCOTT, M. B.** Territoriality: A neglected sociological dimension. *Social Problems*, 1967, **15**, 236-249.

**NOBLE, G. K.** The role of dominance in the social life of birds. *Auk*, 1939, 263-273.
**ROOS, P. D.** Jurisdiction: An ecological concept. *Human Relations*, 1968, **21**, 75-84.
**SOMMER, R.** Sociofugal space. *American Journal of Sociology*, 1967, **72**, 654-660.

# INVASIONS OF PERSONAL SPACE

NANCY JO FELIPE AND ROBERT SOMMER
*University of California, Davis*

The last decade has brought an increase in empirical studies of deviance. One line of investigation has used the case study approach with individuals whom society has classified as deviants–prostitutes, drug addicts, homosexuals, mental patients, etc. The other approach, practiced less frequently, has involved staged situations in which one individual, usually the investigator or one of his students, violates the norm or "routine ground" in a given situation and observes the results.[1] The latter approach is in the category of an experiment in that it is the investigator himself who creates the situation he observes and therefore has the possibility of systematically varying the parameters of social intercourse singly or in combinations. From this standpoint these studies have great promise for the development of an experimental sociology following the model set down by Greenwood.[2] With topics such as human migration, collective disturbance, social class, the investigator observes events and phenomena already in existence. Control of conditions refers to modes of observations and is largely on an *ex post facto* statistical or correlational basis. On the other hand, few staged studies of deviance have realized their promise as experimental investigations. Generally they are more in the category of demonstrations, involving single gross variations of one parameter and crude and impressionistic measurement of effect without control data from a matched sample not subject to the norm violation. Of more theoretical importance is the lack of systematic variation in degree and kind of the many facets of norm violation. The reader is left with the impression that deviancy is an all-or-none phenomenon caused by improper dress, impertinent answers, naive questions, etc. It cannot be denied that a graduate student washing her clothes in the town swimming pool is breaking certain norms. But we cannot be sure of the norms that are violated or the sanctions attached to each violation without some attempt at isolating and varying single elements in the situation.

The present paper describes a series of studies of one norm violation, sitting too close to another individual. Conversational distance is affected by many things including room density, the acquaintance of the individuals, the personal relevance of the topic discussed, the cultural backgrounds of the individuals, the personalities of the individuals, etc.[3] There are a dozen studies of conversational distance which have shown that people from Latin countries stand closer together than North Americans,[4] eye contact has important effect on conversational distance,[5] introverts stand farther apart than extroverts,[6] friends place themselves closer together than strangers,[7] and so on, but there is still, under any set of conditions, a range of conversational distance which is considered normal for that situation. Several of these investigators, notably Birdwhistell,[8] Garfinkel,[9] Goffman,[10] and Sommer[11] have described the effects of intruding into this distance or personal space that surrounds each individual. The interest shown in the human spacing mechanisms as well as the possibilities of objective measurement of both norm violation and defensive

---

[1] See for example Harold Garfinkel, "Studies of the Routine Grounds of Everyday Activities," *Social Problems*, 11 (Winter, 1964), pp. 225-250.

[2] Ernest Greenwood, *Experimental Sociology*, New York: Kings Crown Press, 1945.

[3] Edward T. Hall, *The Silent Language*, Garden City, N.Y.: Doubleday, 1959.

[4] Edward T. Hall, "The Language of Space," *Landscape*, 10 (Autumn, 1960), pp. 41-44.

[5] Michael Argyle and Janet Dean, "Eye-Contact, Distance, and Affiliation," *Sociometry*, 28 (September, 1965), pp. 289-304.

[6] John L. Williams, "Personal Space and its Relation to Extraversion-Introversion," unpublished M.A. thesis, University of Alberta, 1963.

[7] Kenneth B. Little, "Personal Space," *Journal of Experimental Social Psychology*, 1 (August, 1960), pp. 237-247.

[8] Birdwhistell, R. L. *Introduction to Kinesics*, Washington, D.C.: Foreign Service Institute, 1952.

[9] Garfinkel, *op. cit.*

[10] Erving Goffman, *Behavior in Public Places*, Glencoe, Ill.: The Free Press, 1963.

[11] Robert Sommer, "Studies in Personal Space," *Sociometry*, 22 (September, 1959), pp. 247-260.

postures suggests that this is an excellent area in which to systematically study norm violations.

The present paper describes several studies of invasions of personal space that took place over a two-year period. The first was done during the summer of 1963 in a mental hospital. At the time it seemed that systematic studies of spatial invasions could only take place in a "crazy place" where norm violation would escape some of the usual sanctions applied in the outside world. Though there is a strong normative control system that regulates the conduct of mental patients toward one another and toward staff, the rules governing staff conduct toward patients (except cases of brutality, rape, or murder), and particularly higher status staff, such as psychiatrists, physicians, and psychologists, are much less clear. At times, it seems that almost anything can be done in a mental hospital provided it is called research, and one can cite such examples as psychosurgery, various drug experiments, and recent investigations of operant conditioning as instances where unusual and sometimes unproven or even harmful procedures were employed with the blessing of hospital officialdom. To call a procedure "research" is a way of "bracketing" it in time and space and thus excluding it from the usual rules and mores. This is one reason why we supposed that spatial invasions would be more feasible inside a mental hospital than outside. We had visions of a spatial invasion on a Central Park bench resulting in bodily assault or arrest on a sex deviant or "suspicious character" charge. It seemed that some studies of norm violation were deliberately on a one-shot basis to avoid such difficulties. After the first study of spatial invasions in a mental hospital had been completed, however, it became apparent that the method could be adapted for use in more typical settings. We were then able to undertake similar intrusions on a systematic basis in a university library without any untoward consequences, though the possibilities of such problems arising were never far beyond the reaches of consciousness in any of the experimental sessions.

## METHOD

The first study took place on the grounds of Mendocino State Hospital, a 1500-bed mental institution situated in parklike surroundings. Most wards were unlocked and many patients spent considerable time outdoors. In wooded areas it was common to see patients seated underneath trees, one to a bench. Because of the easy access to the outside as well as the number of patients involved in hospital industry, the ward areas were relatively empty during the day. This made it possible for the patients to isolate themselves from other people by finding a deserted area on the grounds or remaining in the almost empty wards. The invasions of personal space took place both indoors and outdoors. The victims were chosen on the basis of these criteria: the victim would be a male, sitting alone, and not engaged in any clearly defined activities such as reading, card playing, etc. All sessions took place near the long stay wards, which meant that newly-admitted patients were largely omitted from the study. When a patient meeting these criteria was located, E walked over and sat beside the patient without saying a word. If the victim moved his chair or moved further down the bench, E would move a like distance to keep the space between them about six inches. There were two experimental conditions. In one, E sat alongside a patient and took complete notes of what ensued. He also jiggled his keys occasionally and looked at the patient in order to assert his dominance. In the second experimental condition, E simply sat down next to the victim and, three or four times during the 20 minute session, jiggled his keys. Control subjects were selected from other patients seated at some distance from E but still within E's visual field. To be eligible for the control group, a patient had to be sitting by himself and not reading or otherwise engaged in an activity as well as be visible to E.

Each session took a maximum of twenty minutes. There were 64 individual sessions with different patients, 39 involved the procedure in which E took notes and 25 involved no writing.[12] One ward dayroom was chosen for additional, more intensive observations. During the daylight hours this large room was sparsely populated and the same five patients occupied the same chairs. These patients would meet Esser's[13] criteria of territoriality in that each spent more than 75 per cent of his time in one particular area.

[12] Four incomplete sessions are omitted from this total. On two occasions a patient was called away by a nurse and on two other occasions the session was terminated when the patient showed signs of acute stress. The intruder in Study One was the junior author, a 35 year old male of slight build. It is likely that invasions by a husky six-footer would have produced more immediate flight reactions.

[13] Aristide H. Esser, *et al.*, "Territoriality of Patients on a Research Ward," *Recent Advances in Biological Psychiatry*, Vol. 8, in Joseph Wortis (ed.), New York: Plenum Press, 1965.

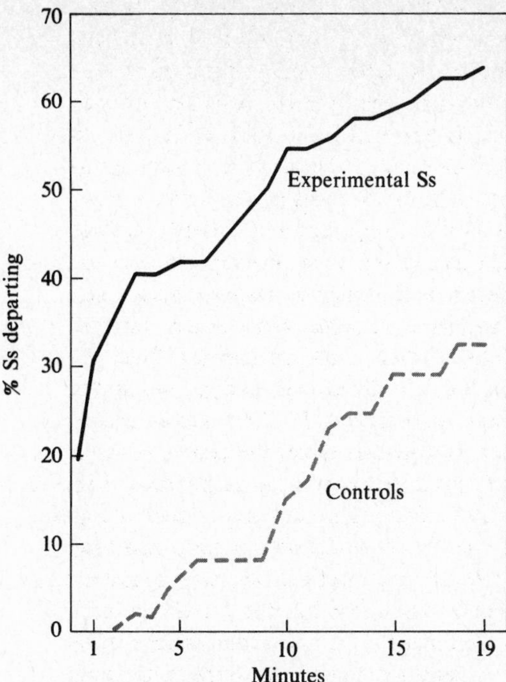


[FIGURE 6-2] Cumulative percentage of patients having departed at each one-minute interval.

## RESULTS

The major data of the study consist of records of how long each patient remained seated in his chair following the invasion. This can be compared with the length of time the control patients remained seated. [Figure 6-2] shows the cumulative number of patients who had departed at each one-minute interval of the 20 minute session. Within two minutes, all of the controls were still seated but 36 per cent of the experimental subjects had been driven away. Within nine minutes fully half of the victims had departed compared with only 8 per cent of the controls. At the end of the 20 minute session, 64 per cent of the experimental subjects had departed compared with 33 per cent of the controls. Further analysis showed that the writing condition was more potent than the no-writing condition but that this difference was significant only at the .10 level ($\chi^2 = 4.61$, df = 2). The patient's actual departure from his chair was the most obvious reaction to the intrusion. Many more subtle indications of the patient's discomfort were evident. Typically the victim would immediately face away from E, pull in his shoulders, and place his elbows at his sides. Mumbling, irrelevant laughter, and delusional talk also seemed to be used by the victim to keep E at a distance.

Repeated observation of the same patients took place on one particular ward where the patients were extremely territorial in their behavior. Five patients generally inhabited this large room and sat in the same chairs day after day. There were gross differences in the way these particular territorial patients reacted to the writer's presence. In only one case ($S_3$) was E clearly dominant. At the other extreme with $S_1$ and $S_2$, it was like trying to move the Rock of Gibraltar. E invariably left these sessions defeated, with his tail between his legs, often feeling the need to return to his colleagues and drink a cup of coffee before attempting another experimental session. $S_5$ is a peculiar case in that sometimes he was budged but other times he wasn't.

## STUDY TWO

These sessions took place in the study hall of a university library, a large room with high ceilings and book-lined walls. The room contains fourteen large tables in two equal rows. Each table is 4 x 16 feet, and accommodates six chairs on each long side. Because of its use as a study area, students typically try to space themselves as far as possible from others. Each victim was the first female sitting alone in a predetermined part of the room with at least one book in front of her, two empty chairs on either side (or on one side if she was at the end of the table), and an empty chair across from her. An empty chair was also required to be across from E's point of invasion. The second female to meet these criteria and who was visible to E served as a control. The control was observed from a distance and no invasion was attempted. Sessions took place between the hours of 8-5 on Mondays through Fridays; because of time changes between classes and the subsequent turnover of the library population, the observations began between 5 and 15 minutes after the hour. There were five different experimental conditions [see Figure 6-3].

Condition I: E walked up to an empty chair beside an S, pulling the chair out at an angle, and sat down, completely ignoring S's presence. As E sat down, she unobtrusively moved the chair close to the table and to S, so that the chairs were approximately within three inches from one another. The E would lean over her book, in which she surreptitiously took notes, and tried to maintain constant shoulder distance of about 12 inches between E and S. To use Crook's[14]

[14] J. H. Crook, "The Basis of Flock Organization in Birds," in W. H. Thorpe and O. L. Zangwill (eds.), *Current Problems in Animal Behaviour*, Cambridge: Cambridge University Press, 1961, pp. 125-149.

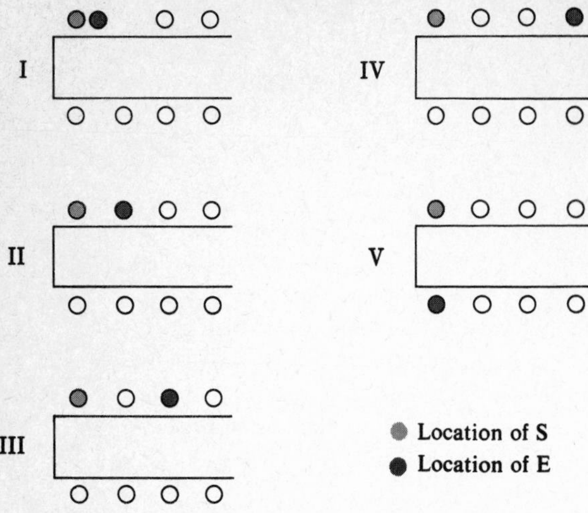


[FIGURE 6-3] Seating of intruder *vis-à-vis* victim in each experimental condition.

terms, E tried to maintain the arrival distance, and to keep the S from adjusting to a settled distance. This was sometimes difficult to do because the chairs were 18½ inches wide and an S would sometimes sit on the other half of her chair, utilizing its width as an effective barrier. However, E tried to get as close to the Ss as possible without actually having any physical contact. If the S moved her chair away, E would follow by pushing her chair backward at an angle and then forward again, under the pretense of adjusting her skirt. At no time did she consciously acknowledge S's presence. In this condition E took detailed notes of the S's behavior, as well as noting time of departure.

Condition II: E went through the same procedure, except instead of moving the adjacent chair closer to S, E sat in the adjacent chair at the expected distance, which left about 15 inches between the chairs or about two feet between the shoulders of E and S.

Condition III: One empty seat was left between E and S, with a resulting shoulder distance of approximately three and a half feet.

Condition IV: Two empty seats were left between E and S with a resulting shoulder distance of about five feet.

Condition V: E sat directly across from S, a distance of about four feet.

In all conditions E noted the time of initial invasion, the time of the S's departure (or the end of the thirty minute session, depending on which came first), and any observable accommodations to E's presence such as moving books or the chair. For the controls E noted the time the session began and the time of the C's departure if it occurred within thirty minutes after the start of the session.

## RESULTS

[Figure 6-4] shows the number of subjects remaining after successive five minute periods. Since there was no significant difference between the scores in Conditions 2-5, these were combined in the analysis. At the end of the thirty minute session, 87 per cent of the controls, 73 per cent of the Ss in the combined conditions remained, compared to only 30 per cent of the experimental Ss in Condition I. Statistical analysis shows that Condition I produced significantly more flight than any of the other conditions, while there was a slight but also significant difference between the combined conditions (2-5) and the control condition. Although flight was the most clearly defined reaction to the invasion, many more subtle signs of the victim's discomfort were evident. Frequently an S drew in her arm and head, turned away from E exposing her shoulder and back, with her elbow on the table, her face resting on her hand. The victims used objects including books, notebooks, purses, and coats as barriers, and some made the wide chair into a barrier.

## DISCUSSION

These results show clearly that spatial invasions have a disruptive effect and can produce reactions ranging from flight at one extreme to agonistic display at the other. The individual differences in reacting to the invasion are evident; there was no single reaction among our subjects to someone "sitting too close." The victim can attempt to accommodate himself to the invasion in numerous ways, including a shift in position, interposing a barrier between himself and the invader, or moving farther away. If these are precluded by the situation or fail because the invader shifts positions too, the victim may eventually take to flight. The methods we used did not permit the victim to achieve a comfortable *settled distance*. Crook[15] studied the spacing mechanisms in birds, and found three component factors that maintain individual distance, which he defined as the area around an individual within which the approach of a neighboring bird is reacted to with either avoidance or attack. A number of measurements may be taken when studying individual distance—the arrival distance (how far away from settled birds a newcomer will land), settled distance (the resultant distance after adjustments have occurred), and the distance after departure. The conditions in Study One and in Condition I of the

[15] Crook, *op. cit.*

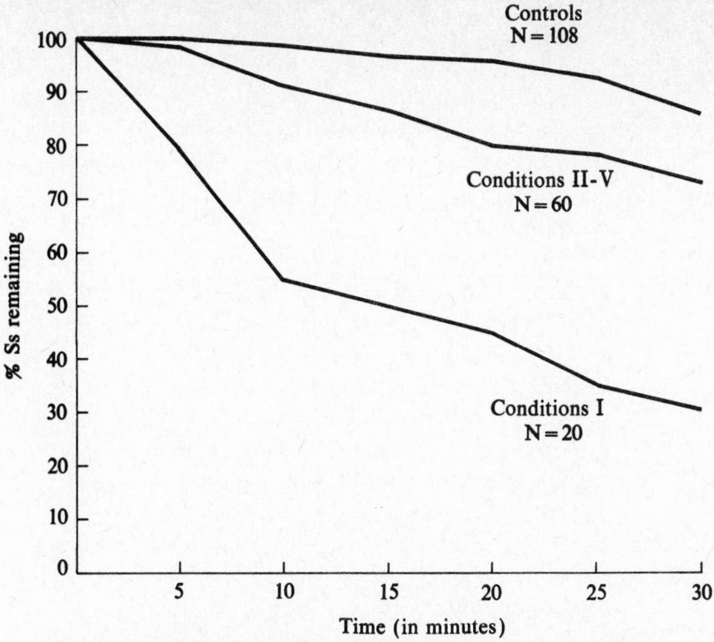


[FIGURE 6-4] Per cent of victims remaining at each five-minute interval after the invasion.

second study called for E to maintain the arrival distance, and to keep the victim from adjusting to a settled distance. In these conditions, the victim was unable to increase the arrival distance by moving away (since the invader followed him down the bench in Study One and moved her chair closer in Study Two), and the greatest number of flight reactions was produced by these conditions. McBride,[16] who has studied the spatial behaviors of animals in confinement, has found that avoidance movements and turning aside are common reactions to crowding, particularly when a submissive animal is close to a dominant animal. Literally the dominant bird in a flock has more space and the other birds will move aside and look away when the dominant bird approaches. Looking away to avoid extensive eye contact was also a common reaction in the present studies. This probably would not have occurred if a subordinate or lower status individual had invaded the personal space of a dominant or higher status individual. There was also a dearth of direct verbal responses to the invasions. Only two of the mental patients spoke directly to E although he sat right beside them, and only one of the 80 student victims asked E to move over. This is some support for Hall's view that "we treat space somewhat as we treat sex. It is there but we don't talk about it."[17]

We see then that a violation of expected conversational distance produces, first of all, various accommodations on the part of the victim. The intensity of his reaction is influenced by many factors including territoriality, the dominance-submission relationship between invader and victim, the locus of the invasion, the victim's attribution of sexual motives to the intruder (in this case all victims and intruders were like-sex individuals), etc. All of these factors influence the victim's definition of the situation and consequently his reaction to it. In the present situation the first reaction to the invasion was accommodation or adaptation: the individual attempted to "live with" the invasion by turning aside, interposing a notebook between himself and the stranger, and pulling in his elbows. When this failed to relieve the tension produced by the norm violation, flight reactions occurred.

There are other elements in the invasion sequence that can be varied systematically. We have not yet attempted heterosexual invasion sequences, or used invaders of lower social standing, or explored more

[16] Glen McBride, *A General Theory of Social Organization and Behaviour*, St. Lucia: University of Queensland Press, 1964; also McBride, *et al.*, "Social Forces Determining Spacing and Head Orientation in a Flock of Domestic Hens," *Nature*, 197 (1963), pp. 1272-1273.

[17] Hall, *The Silent Language*, *op. cit.*

than two unusual and contrasting environments. We are making a start toward using visual rather than spatial invasions, in this case staring at a person rather than moving too close to him. Preliminary data indicate that visual invasions are relatively ineffective in a library where the victims can easily retreat into their books and avoid a direct visual confrontation. There are many other types of intrusions, including tactile and olfactory, that have intriguing research potentialities. It is important to realize that the use of staged norm violations permits these elements to be varied singly and in combination, and in this sense to go beyond the methods of *ex post facto* or "natural experiments" or single-point demonstrations. It is noteworthy that the area of norm violation provides one of the most fruitful applications for the experimental method.

# QUEUE COUNTING: THE EFFECT OF MOTIVES UPON ESTIMATES OF NUMBERS IN WAITING LINES[1]

LEON MANN
*Harvard University*

K. F. TAYLOR
*University of Melbourne*

Three field studies and one field experiment examined the relationship between actual and apparent (estimated) position in long queues for football tickets, Batman shirts, and chocolate bars. Generally, there was a tendency to overestimate numbers ahead in the front part of each line, but after the "critical point" (where the supply of the commodity was likely to become exhausted) queuers tended to underestimate, or show less pessimism in, their judgments. It is postulated that the late-comer is motivated to underestimate numbers ahead in order to justify standing in line, and to reassure himself that prospects of success are still good. The significance of erroneous estimates of numbers in queues, crowds, and mobs is discussed briefly.

While there is considerable evidence that value factors influence the judgment of size (e.g. Bruner & Goodman, 1947), the effect of motives on estimates of number (numerousness) has been a neglected problem. In many social situations involving competition for a rare and valued commodity, estimates of the number of people present may have important consequences for behavior. Decisions to join or leave a crowd, to compete or to cooperate, are often based upon an estimate of the number of people who seek, for example, a seat on a bus, parking space, a theater ticket, an opportunity to address a meeting, and so on.

In this paper a program of studies is reported on estimates of number in long, real-life waiting lines. The focus of the research is the relationship between apparent (estimated) position and actual position in line in situations where *(a)* there is a limited supply of the commodity, and *(b)* priority for the commodity is determined by position in line. In brief, the authors' aim is to investigate the judgmental distortions that occur when position in line has some intrinsic value to the person.

In making predictions about the direction of distortion, there are few guidelines other than psychophysical studies involving the judgment of beans in bottles and dots arranged on cards. In general, these studies indicate a tendency toward underestimation when large numbers are involved (e.g., Bevan, Maier, & Helson, 1963; Bevan & Turner, 1964). It is difficult to generalize from these laboratory studies to the real-life waiting line, because the person in line is part of the object to be estimated. Involvement in line is likely to interfere in unpredictable ways with the judgment process. It is assumed, however, that when queuers are less than certain they will get the valued commodity there will be a tendency to underestimate numbers ahead. Underestimation allows the person to gain reassurance that there still is some possibility of success, and serves to justify the decision to join the line.

## FIELD STUDY 1: QUEUES FOR FOOTBALL TICKETS

Every August, football fans assemble in long, overnight queues outside the Melbourne Football Stadium (actually the Melbourne Cricket Ground) to buy tickets for the Australian equivalent of the World Series. Usually more people are on hand than tickets available, and since many people face a 16-hour wait and the possibility of disappointment, there is some pressure to make a realistic estimate of position in line and chances of getting tickets.

It was predicted that people in line after the "critical point," that is, where it is likely that the supply of tickets will run out, will tend to underestimate their position in line. This prediction is based on the assumption that in order to remain in the queue when there is a strong possibility of disappointment, the person must justify his presence by

[1] The research reported in this paper was partially supported by a grant to the senior author from the Comparative International Program of the Department of Social Relations, Harvard University. Research funds were also provided by the Department of Psychology, University of Melbourne. The authors acknowledge the assistance of Ruth Chaplin and Frank Nordberg in the collection and analysis of data, and express gratitude to Paul Holland for his advice on statistical matters.

distorting the numbers ahead. To test the distortion hypothesis a field study was carried out at the Melbourne Stadium.

**Procedure**

From 4:00 P.M. until 6:00 P.M. of the day before selling began, a team of eight research assistants, psychology majors from the University of Melbourne, conducted short, standard interviews with 121 people in 8 of the 22 queues outside the stadium. Each interviewer was randomly assigned a queue. Starting with the first person in line, the procedure was to approach every tenth person throughout the line. The longest line consisted of 210 people. The request was brief and informal: "I am from the University, and we are doing a study of how people feel about the queues. Would you care to answer a few questions?" Only three refusals were encountered. Questions covered attitudes toward pushing in and place keeping. Subjects were asked to estimate their position in line ("How many people are ahead of you in this queue?"), and to estimate their chances of getting a ticket.

**Results** The major interest is in the accuracy with which people estimate their position. [Figure 6-5] presents mean estimates of position as a function of actual position.[2] It may be noted that subjects in the first part of the line were extremely accurate. However, after Position 30, there was an increasing tendency to *overestimate* numbers ahead, and this continued up to Position 140, after which there was a tendency to *underestimate*. To compare accuracy of estimates at different parts of the line, a deviation score was computed for each queuer, using the formula $d = (x - t)/t$, where $x$ is the estimated position and $t$ is true position in line.

[2]"Actual" position in line is something of a misnomer, since people, especially at the front, were sometimes gathered together in knots of three and four. Thus a completely objective ordering of the queue was impossible.

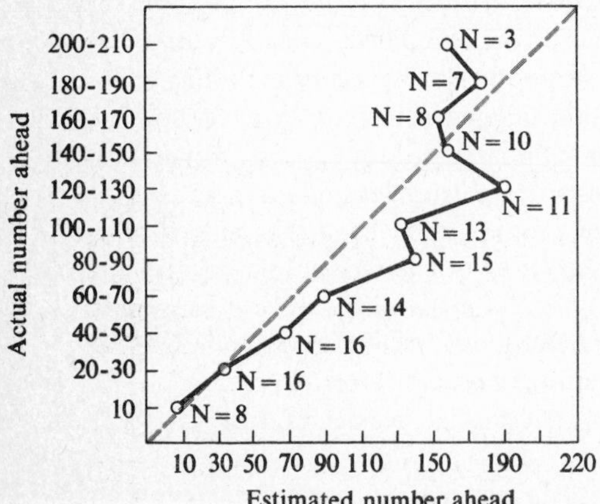


[FIGURE 6-5] Mean estimates of position in line as a function of actual position. (Data collected from eight queues, Melbourne Football Stadium, 1966. The dotted line represents perfect estimates–Field Study 1.)

**[Table 6-1] Estimates of positions in line as a function of actual position in line: Melbourne football queues**

| Actual position in line | Estimates of no. ahead in line | | |
|---|---|---|---|
| | Over-estimate | Under-estimate | Correct |
| 10–70 | 25 | 19 | 10 |
| 80–140 | 30 | 10 | 4 |
| 150–210 | 10 | 12 | 1 |

NOTE–Critical point is Position 140. $\chi^2$ overestimators, underestimators, accurates = 9.82, $df = 4$, $p < .05$; $\chi^2$ overestimators, underestimators = 5.99, $df = 2$, $p < .05$.

Since error variance at the 11 positions at which observations were pooled was not homogeneous (estimates were particularly erratic in the middle part of each line), analysis of the data by parametric statistics was not appropriate.[3] [Table 6-1] presents the number of overestimators and underestimators at the head, middle, and end of the line. A chi-square test revealed a significant association between direction of inaccuracy and position in line ($\chi^2 = 5.99$, $df = 2$, $p < .05$). Trichotomizing the sample into three equal sets rather than cutting the line by position yielded a chi-square value of 5.27 ($df = 2, p < .10$).

**Discussion** To explain the reversal in direction of judgmental distortion at Position 140, the significance of this point in the queue must be understood. Notices in the daily papers informed the Melbourne football public that a total of 12,500 tickets would be on sale to the 22 queues. Assuming that the tickets were distributed in equal numbers to each queue and that each queuer took his full allotment of four tickets,

[3]A problem associated with the scaling of subjective estimates is that identical deviation scores at different parts of the line may not be psychologically equivalent. An estimate of 25 at Position 20, which is sufficiently accurate for the queuer's purposes, yields a deviation score of 25%; an estimate of 250 at Position 200 also yields a deviation score of 25%, but could hardly be considered accurate. For this reason, judgments in the early and middle parts of the line appear more erratic than errors made toward the end of the line. To give a balanced picture of the data, throughout this paper nonparametric analyses will be presented together with parametric analyses.

the "critical point" where the ticket supply became exhausted was approximately Position 140. Looked at this way, it can be argued that the tendency to underestimate after the "critical point" was an attempt to justify participation in an almost futile activity. The queuer at Position 180 could reason that he was right to stand in line because there really were fewer people ahead than met the eye.

While a defensive or wish-fulfillment mechanism seems a reasonable explanation for the optimistic estimates of the late-comers, there are a number of equally plausible explanations. A psychophysical explanation would maintain that the observed relationship between objective and subjective position was a function of perceptual inaccuracies which occur when judgments are made at too great a distance. This explanation would discount the significance of the "critical point." Instead, it would regard the observed curve as one of a large family of curves representing the relationship between actual and assumed position in lines of different length.

Another explanation is related to the frequency of averaging errors. It could be argued that the change in direction of distortion at the so-called critical point (140) was due to a bunching of estimates at 150. People between 100 and 200 did not attempt an exact estimate to the third digit, but "rounded off" upwards (or downwards) to 150. Indeed, 9 of 62 subjects (15%) who were located in the region 100-200 gave 150 as their estimate, a larger proportion than would be expected by chance alone.

A third possibility, the self-selection interpretation, is based on the assumption that a difference exists between the sample before and after the critical point. Perhaps early-comers were by nature cautious and pessimistic and the late-comers adventurous and optimistic. A frivolous variant of this explanation is that the only people who joined the line after the critical point were either myopic or psychotic, since normal people selected themselves out and went home. Unfortunately, there are no records of the number of people who came, looked, and departed, so it is impossible to comment on personality differences between early- and late-comers. However, late-comers were as optimistic about their chances of getting tickets as people in the middle of the line; on the average late-comers estimated their chances of getting a ticket to be 84%, while middle of the line people gave 86% as their estimate. The fact that people in both parts of the line were equally optimistic about their chances suggests that the self-selection interpretation cannot be overruled as an alternate explanation.

Methodological problems plague all attempts to invoke an explanation in terms of a "critical point." It must be assumed that queuers had some concept of a danger point and knowledge of where it occurred, but when asked if they knew the number of tickets for sale to each queue, most queuers had no idea. Another problem relates to the fact that time waiting may have interfered with judgment, and of course this was correlated with position in line. Since judgment is sometimes a function of the number of people *behind* the person, the fact that the eight lines under investigation differed somewhat in length is a cause for concern. Finally, actual position was determined by the interviewer's judgment of where the respondent stood in line; it is possible that the interviewer's own biases and misperceptions shaped this continuum, and thereby influenced the nature of the relationship (see Footnote [2]). Taking into account the numerous alternate explanations and methodological problems in this field study, it cannot be concluded with any confidence that a wish-fulfillment mechanism accounts for distortions in judgment found in the latter part of the queue.

## FIELD STUDY 2: A LONG QUEUE FOR FOOTBALL TICKETS

Several weeks after completion of Field Study 1, an opportunity arose to investigate a single, long queue. As a bonus for reaching the "Grand Final" of the football series, an extra 2,000 tickets were made available to members of the Collingwood Football Club. The Collingwood queue was particularly interesting as the first people in line had taken up residence 6 days before tickets went on sale, and the mounting excitement of the series created an atmosphere of extreme urgency (see Mann, 1968).

### Procedure

Interviews were conducted from 9:00 P.M. until 11:00 P.M. on the evening before the sale of tickets. There were well over 700 people in line. Starting from the front the investigators approached an average of 2 people at intervals of 10, yielding a total of 134 respondents. Questions were identical with the set used in Field Study 1, and no refusals were encountered.

**Results** The Collingwood queue, because it differed in size from the Melbourne Stadium queues, provides another test of the wish-fulfillment hypothesis. There were 2,000 tickets available, with a limit of 4 to each member; therefore the "critical point" for obtaining the commodity was Position 500. Since most queuers knew the exact number of tickets on sale, it can be assumed there was some concept of a "critical point."

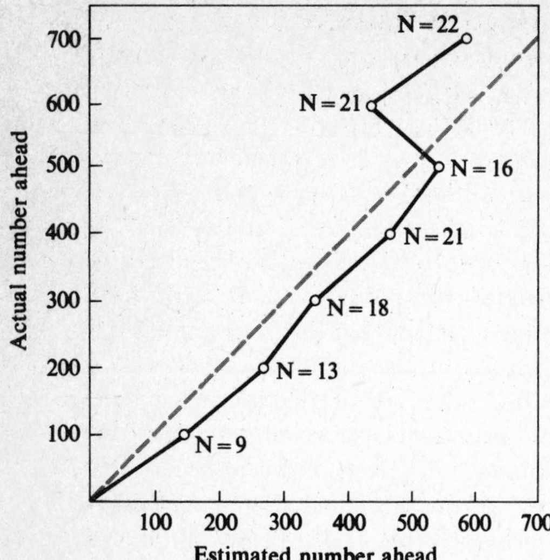


[FIGURE 6-6] Mean estimates of position in line as a function of actual position. (Data collected from a queue at the Collingwood Football Stadium, 1966. The dotted line represents perfect estimates–Field Study 2.)

[Figure 6-6] illustrates the relationship between actual and estimated position in line. There was a tendency for subjects in the first part of the queue to *overestimate* the number ahead, but toward the end of the queue there was a reversal and people tended to *underestimate* their position. It will be noted that the crossover occured near the "critical point" of 500. An analysis of variance to test the main effect of position on percentage of deviation from true length was significant ($F$ = 10.79, $df$ = 6/113, $p < .01$). The form of the relationship between true position and deviation score was essentially linear. Fifty-seven percent of the variance among the seven pooled positions was accounted for by a linear component ($F_{\text{lin}}$ = 36.95, $df$ = 1/113, $p < .001$). The numbers of overestimators and underestimators before and after the "critical point" are presented in [Table 6-2]. A chi-square test of these data revealed a significant association between direction of judgment error and position in line ($\chi^2$ = 11.69, $df$ = 1, $p < .01$).

[Table 6-2] **Estimates of position in line as a function of actual position in line: Collingwood football queue**

| Actual position in line | Estimates of no. ahead in line | | |
|---|---|---|---|
| | Over-estimate | Under-estimate | Correct |
| 1–500 | 51 | 25 | 4 |
| 501–740 | 19 | 35 | 0 |

NOTE–Critical point is Position 500. $\chi^2$ overestimators, underestimators, accurates = 15.84, $df$ = 2, $p < .001$; $\chi^2$ overestimators, underestimators = 11.69, $df$ = 1, $p < .01$.

**Discussion** The results of Field Study 2 provide some support for the hypothesis that judgmental processes are systematically distorted to reassure the person in situations where position determines right to a valued object. Field Study 2 overcomes some of the problems in the first study. It is not likely that the change from overestimation to underestimation at 500 was due to an averaging or "rounding off" error. It is reasonable to invoke a "critical point" concept since there was full knowledge of the supply of tickets and the quota for each person. Moreover, investigation of a single line (rather than a number of queues of unequal length) discounts the possibility of error due to pooling of data.

A number of difficulties remain. The "objectivity" of the investigator's judgment of subjects' actual position in line is still open to question. It is still conceivable that there were different kinds of respondents before and after the critical point. The findings do not exclude a psychophysical explanation that distortions in judgment were entirely due to perceptual rather than motivational factors. To eliminate some of the methodological problems and to examine alternative explanations for the direction of distortion, it became necessary to obtain a small queue, with a specific critical point, and no ambiguity about actual position in line.

## FIELD STUDY 3: QUEUES FOR BATMAN SHIRTS

During the August school vacation a downtown theatre in Melbourne featured a special children's program. To attract a large audience, the management announced that Batman T-shirts would be given away to the first 25 arrivals at the daily 10:00 A.M. show. At 7:00 each morning a queue formed outside the Grosvenor theatre to wait for the distribution of Batman shirts. The location of a precise critical point toward the front of a short queue offered a rare opportunity to investigate whether systematic distortions occur in situations where it is possible for judgment to be fairly accurate.

### Procedure

Queues were studied on three consecutive mornings. Starting with the first person in line, two research assistants interviewed every second or third youngster up to and including Position 50. Sixty-six interviews were conducted. Respondents were almost invariably 12 to 13-year-old boys who, with few exceptions, knew about the shirt offer and the number of shirts available. Subjects were asked to estimate the number ahead and their chances of getting a shirt. Other questions dealt with reactions to queue jumping and place keeping.

**Results** For estimates of position in line, there was a systematic difference between judgments of subjects before and after the critical point. The mean percentage deviation before the critical point was 4.30, but after the critical point the mean percentage deviation was -12.85. A *t* test on the difference between early- and late-comers in magnitude of deviation was highly significant ($t = 3.50, df = 64, p < .001$). [Table 6-3] shows that although many subjects in the first part of the queue were accurate in their judgments, there was some tendency to *overestimate* the number ahead. After the critical point this tendency was reversed, and most subjects *underestimated* their position in line. A chi-square test reveals that this difference in judgmental error before versus after the critical point was significant ($\chi^2 = 7.20$, $df = 1$, $p < .01$).

**Discussion** It seems reasonable to maintain on the basis of Field Study 3 that motives influence perceptual judgments of position, even in relatively short lines. The accuracy with which actual position in line could be determined discounts experimenter bias as an explanation for the findings. Also, the self-selection interpretation that two kinds of judges made up the line, pessimists before the critical point and chronic optimists after, can be rejected. While 20 of the 26 youngsters after the critical point underestimated their position, 9 of the 20 gave estimates that were higher than the magical number of 25. The late-comers wanted to get a shirt if possible, but whatever the outcome, they were at least guaranteed the diversion of a Tarzan movie.

**[Table 6-3] Estimates of position in line as a function of actual position in line: Grosvenor Theatre queue for Batman Shirts**

| Actual position in line | Estimates of no. ahead in line | | |
|---|---|---|---|
| | Over-estimate | Under-estimate | Correct |
| 1–25 | 14 | 9 | 17 |
| 26–50 | 6 | 20 | 0 |

NOTE–Critical point is Position 25. $\chi^2$ overestimators, underestimators, accurates = 22.44, $df = 2$, $p < .001$; $\chi^2$ overestimators, underestimators = 7.20, $df = 1$, $p < .01$.

## SUMMARY OF FIELD STUDIES

Three field studies on natural, real-life queues have revealed a tendency for subjects before a so-called "critical point" (where the commodity is likely to become unavailable) to *overestimate* the numbers waiting ahead. In contrast, subjects after the critical point tend to *underestimate* their position in line. Several explanations for this phenomenon, which depend on possible methodological or statistical flaws in the data, can be discounted if all three studies are considered together. There remain, however, two rival explanations. A wish-fulfillment explanation holds that the judgmental errors are motivated by the needs and values of late-comers who seek the commodity. The psychophysical explanation maintains that contextual (background) stimuli such as physical shape of the queue, distance from end of line, time spent waiting, etc., could be responsible. This second explanation implies that the observed relationship between actual and estimated position would have been obtained in each queue regardless of whether or not a commodity was available. It is impossible to assess the relative merits of the rival explanations without the benefit of a *control* queue, that is, a waiting line in which there is no commodity at stake. Lack of a control queue also makes it difficult to determine whether the early-comer's tendency to *overestimate* numbers ahead is due to some motivational factor (e.g., protection against the remote possibility of disappointment), or is evidence of a general judgmental habit to overestimate small numbers of stimuli (cf. Taves, 1941).

## FIELD EXPERIMENT: A QUEUE FOR CHOCOLATE BARS

The aim of the experiment was to establish two parallel queues of comparable length and composition: an experimental line in which a valued commodity was available only to some people, and a control line in which the commodity did not enter as a consideration. If the wish-fulfillment hypothesis is valid, systematic errors in judgment should be confined to the experimental line. No such distortion should be found in the control line, because position in line does not entitle the person to goods or services.

### Procedure

The field experiment (actually an experiment in the field) was carried out in a small coeducational high school in Melbourne.[4] On a regular school day, the 521 students

[4]The cooperation of the Headmaster, staff, and students of Wattle Park High School, Victoria, Australia, is gratefully acknowledged.

who served as subjects heard an announcement in their classrooms instructing them to assemble in the yard to participate in a study on how people make judgments. Students were met at the entrance of the yard by research assistants, and were directed randomly in groups of 3 and 4 into one of the two lines located approximately 60 feet apart. After the lines had been formed, the senior experimenter introduced himself, and administered the following instructions through the school public address system.

We are interested in how people make estimates or judgments. In a moment everyone will be given a card with a few simple questions on it. As soon as you get the card, read the questions carefully and write down the answers to them. Some of the questions ask you to choose one out of several possible answers. In these, check the box next to the answer which applies to you. It is very important to give your answers immediately. Don't discuss your answer with anybody else, and please hurry as we will be coming to collect the cards very quickly. When your card has been collected please wait quietly for a further announcement.

By a toss of a coin, the line to the right of the public address system became the experimental line, and the other became the control line. Starting with the first person in each line, two research assistants handed out a card (precoded for queue and position) to each student in turn.

*Experimental queue.* Cards for the experimental line read as follows:

Please try to do these questions very quickly and on your own. Each one asks you to make an estimate. Do your best, but do not worry if you are not too sure of the answer.

To create a critical point at Position 130, the following information next appeared:

We have about 130 bars of chocolate to give to the people at the front of the line. We will give one each until we have run out. Estimate your chances of getting a bar: Certain; Good; Fair; Poor; Hopeless.

Subjects then checked their responses to four standard items.

1. How many are *in front of you* in this line?
2. How many are *behind you* in this line?
3. Standing in this line is: very interesting; interesting; all right; boring; waste of time.
4. Compared with other people I like chocolate: a lot more; a bit more; about average; not as much; hardly at all.

*Control queue.* Instructions and questions for the control line were identical to those administered to the experimental line, except there was no information about the availability of chocolate, and of course no question asking subjects to estimate their chances of getting a bar. Because of the physical distance between queues, subjects in the control line were at no time aware that their counterparts in the experimental line stood to gain chocolate.

After all cards were filled in and collected, the senior experimenter thanked the staff and students for their cooperation, promised an account of the results of the study, and announced that bars of chocolate would be distributed to everyone in the school.

**Results** [Figure 6-7] shows estimates of position in the two lines as a function of actual position. In the first part of each line, there was little difference between queues; both, on the average, were quite accurate. However, just before the critical point subjects in the experimental line began to overestimate more than subjects in the control line. This pattern was reversed after the critical point, as the experimental subjects gave smaller estimates than the control subjects. Unexpectedly, there was another reversal toward the end of each queue, with experimental subjects more pessimistic than the controls.

An analysis of variance of the percentage of deviation scores revealed a significant interaction between type of queue and position in line ($F$ = 4.69, $df$ = 3/455, $p < .01$). A trend analysis of the experimental line showed that a linear component was significant ($F_{\text{lin}}$ = 5.73, $df$ = 1/234, $p < .05$).

For purposes of testing the hypothesis, a region of uncertainty was defined as 50 positions before and 50 positions after the critical point.[5] In the 50 positions *before* the critical point, the percentage of deviation in the experimental line was 32.28. In the control line the percentage of deviation in the 50 positions before 130 was 22.95, but this did not differ significantly from the experimental line mean ($t$ = .96, $df$ = 91, $p > .30$). However, in the 50 positions after the critical point subjects in the experimental line with a mean percentage of deviation of 18.73 showed less tendency to overestimate than

[5]The decision to cut at 81 and 180 was not arbitrary. Although cutting at 180 eliminates from the test the unexpected reversal in estimates after Position 200, the selection of 81 and 180 as cutoff points was not made for purposes of convenience. At Position 81 the first "run" of cautious responses to the question of getting chocolate began; up to Position 180 some optimism was still expressed that chocolate would be obtained.

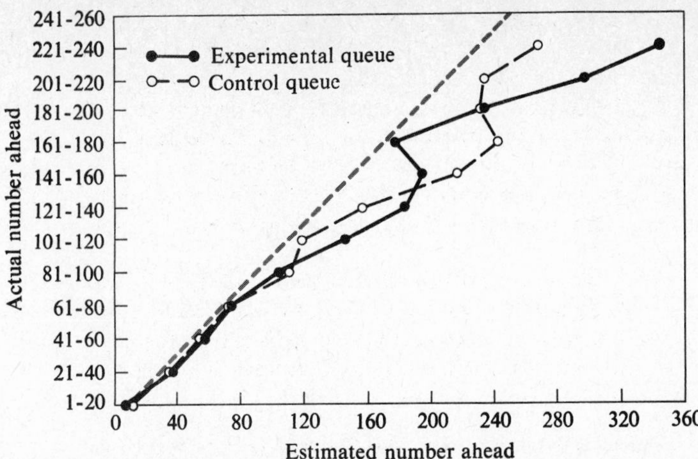


[FIGURE 6-7] Estimates of position in line as a function of actual position. (After Position 130 in the experimental queue the commodity, chocolate bars, was exhausted. No commodity was available to the control queue. The dotted line represents perfect estimates–field experiment.)

subjects in the control line whose percentage of deviation was 39.38 ($t$ = 2.01, $df$ = 82, $p < .05$). Although there was a tendency toward overestimation throughout both lines, which might be a general characteristic of judgment in queues, the pattern of results lends support to the hypothesis that motivational factors influence estimates of number. One problem remains, however, for the wish-fulfillment explanation. Relative to their counterparts in the control line, subjects in the experimental line did underestimate after the critical point, but not in absolute terms. Indeed, only a minority of experimental subjects in this region (33%) underestimated their position, and while this was greater than the percentage who underestimated in the control line (21%), the difference falls short of significance ($z$ = 1.07, $p$ = .14). It is possible that compared to football fans, queuers for chocolate were less motivated to distort their estimates. There was less pressure to justify standing in line since they were coerced initially, and, in comparison to football tickets and T-shirts, a chocolate bar is not quite the stuff fantasies are made of. Thus the data lend some support to the wish-fulfillment hypothesis but are not altogether conclusive.

Why were experimental subjects immediately before the critical point and at the end of the line so pessimistic in their estimates? Pessimism before the critical point may have been a function of a self-protective mechanism. At this stage there was some possibility that they could miss out. A pessimistic estimate safeguarded against possible disappointment because it cushioned the blow of unfulfilled expectations. The pessimism of the end people can be interpreted as a facetious response to a hopeless situation. Standing in line was futile, and this was reflected in such "estimates" as "20,000," "heaven knows," "three-quarters of the school," and so on. These interpretations are quite speculative, and there is no direct evidence which could raise their status.

*Attitudinal measures.* The late-comer in the experimental line knew that through no fault of his own he would miss out on the commodity. While he was deprived others ahead of him would probably be rewarded. Several mechanisms could have been used to reduce his feelings of disappointment. One was to reason that chocolate is distasteful (and therefore not getting the bar was no great loss). There is no evidence, however, that sweet chocolate was given a sour-grapes rationalization. Indeed it appears that unobtainable fruits were the sweetest, as the disappointed people toward the end of the experimental line expressed most liking for chocolate (see [Table 6-4]).

Another possible rationalization was to regard queueing as enjoyable. Indeed differences in attitudes toward queueing were found within and between queues ([Table 6-4]). In the control line there was an increase in dislike for queueing throughout the line (of necessity late-comers had to wait longer than early-comers before filling out the card). In the experimental line, however, after the first 80 positions there was a trend in the opposite direction, with an

**[Table 6-4] Evaluation of chocolate and of queueing as a function of position in line: Wattle Park High School queues**

| Actual position in line | Chocolate[a] | | | Queueing[b] | | |
|---|---|---|---|---|---|---|
| | Experimental queue | Control queue | *t* | Experimental queue | Control queue | *t* |
| 1–80 | 3.2 | 3.4 | <1 | 3.0 | 3.0 | <1 |
| 81–130 | 3.4 | 3.3 | <1 | 2.2 | 2.6 | 1.56* |
| 131–180 | 3.3 | 3.3 | <1 | 2.3 | 2.0 | 2.17** |
| 181–250 | 3.6 | 3.2 | 2.38** | 2.4 | 2.0 | 2.10** |

NOTE–Critical point (in experimental queue) is Position 130.
[a]Question 4: "Compared with other people, I like chocolate: a lot more (4); bit more (3); about average (2); not as much (1); hardly at all (0)."
[b]Question 3: "Standing in this line is: very interesting (4); interesting (3); all right (2); boring (1); waste of time (0)."
$^*p = .12$.
$^{**}p < .05$.

increase in liking for queueing. Subjects from 81-130, who believed they were in some danger of missing out, were least happy about waiting in line.[6] However, after the critical point, experimental subjects expressed greater liking for queueing than their counterparts in the control line.

## CONCLUSIONS

The results of three field studies and one field experiment on estimates of position in line reveal a consistent tendency on the part of queuers to err in judgment of numbers ahead. The data show that motivation exerts a significant influence on estimates of numerousness. It is an accepted convention that position in queue determines priority of service, hence number has value. When the sought-after commodity is in short supply, the late-comer is motivated to underestimate numbers ahead in order to justify standing in line, and to reassure himself that his prospects of service are still good. Since the queuer has not actually counted numbers in line before joining it, this error is probably due to non-deliberate factors rather than conscious distortion.

The field experiment provides evidence that structural as well as functional factors influence judgments of numerousness. For control subjects, position in line determined order in which question cards were distributed, but had no bearing on service as no commodity was promised or expected. Nevertheless, there was a tendency to overestimate numbers ahead in the control line, an error more pronounced at some points in the queue than at others. There is evidence that errors of underestimation predominate in judging dots and beans (Bevan et al., 1963; Bevan & Turner, 1964; Taves, 1941). The tendency to overestimate numbers of people ahead may be a function of pessimism developed through repeated experiences of disappointment and delay in earlier waiting lines. It is also likely that judgmental errors are due partly to physical immersion in the line, a perspective which limits the queuer to a worm's-eye view of the proceedings. Future research which focuses on a comparison between judges who are members and nonmembers of the line may be relevant to this problem.

The problem of erroneous estimates of queues, crowds, and mobs is of more than academic interest. The decision to join or leave a gathering is often based on the number presumed present, and when there is competition for entry or exit, panic could be a consequence of inaccurate estimates. Effective deployment of law-enforcement agents to control large crowds depends on accurate estimates of numbers. Large attendances at political and protest rallies influence public opinion and enhance the standing of a candidate. Usually there are wide discrepancies in reports of numbers at such rallies, evidence, perhaps, that motivated distortion is at work. Such errors also highlight the need for more refined techniques in crowd measurement. The application of sophisticated methods of quantification to the study of collective behavior (cf. Milgram & Toch, 1968) may stimulate new interest in this area.

[6]This corresponds to a finding in the football queues that people in the region of the critical point expressed most dissatisfaction with the method of selling tickets.

## REFERENCES

**BEVAN, W., MAIER, R., & HELSON, H.** The influence of context upon the estimation of number. *American Journal of Psychology*, 1963, **76**, 464-469.

**BEVAN, W., & TURNER, E.** Assimilation and contrast in the estimation of number. *Journal of Experimental Psychology,* 1964, **67**, 458-462.

**BRUNER, J., & GOODMAN, C.** Value and need as organizing factors in perception. *Journal of Abnormal and Social Psychology*, 1947, **42**, 33-44.

**MANN, L.** Queue culture. Unpublished manuscript, Harvard University, 1968.

**MILGRAM, S., & TOCH, H.** Collective behavior: Crowds and social movements. In G. Lindzey & E. Aronson (Eds.), *Handbook of social psychology.* (Rev. ed.) Reading, Mass.: Addison-Wesley, 1968.

**TAVES, E. H.** Two mechanisms for the perception of visual numerousness. *Archives of Psychology*, 1941, **37**, 1-47.

# NOTE ON THE DRAWING POWER OF CROWDS OF DIFFERENT SIZE[1]

STANLEY MILGRAM, LEONARD BICKMAN,[2]
AND LAWRENCE BERKOWITZ
*The City University of New York*

This study reports on the relationship between the size of a stimulus crowd, standing on a busy city street looking up at a building, and the response of passersby. As the size of the stimulus crowd was increased a greater proportion of passersby adopted the behavior of the crowd. The results of this study suggest a modification of the Coleman and James model of the size of free-forming groups to include a contagion assumption.

In a typical urban setting, when a group of people engage in an action simultaneously, they have the capacity to draw others into the crowd. The actions of the initial group may serve as a stimulus for others to imitate this action. A careful analysis of the details of crowd formation is of obvious interest to a society in which collective action plays an increasingly important part in social life. One theoretical formulation that bears on this problem is that of Coleman and James (1961).

Coleman and James assumed that there is a "natural process" by which free-forming groups acquire and lose members and thus reach specific maximum sizes. They have developed a model that generates a size distribution that closely approximates the actually observed size distribution of many thousands of groups. The central assumption of their model of acquisition and loss are "a constant tendency of a group member to break away, independent of the group, thus producing a loss rate for the group proportional to size; and an acquisition rate for each group proportional to the number of single individuals available to be 'picked up [p. 44].'" Thus the growth of a group is independent of the size of the group and dependent only upon the number of persons who are available to join the group. However, Coleman and James pointed out that "a contagion assumption—that is, an assumption that a person is more likely to join a large group than a small one [p. 44]," might be needed in their model. (Their use of the term "contagion" is not entirely accurate, since this term does not signify in any direct way that a large group is more effective in attracting new persons than a small one. It is preferable, in this connection, to use the phrase "assumption of initial group size.")

This paper reports on the effects which crowds of different sizes had on passersby, following the quantitative approach to the study of crowd behavior outlined by Milgram and Toch (1969).

A few of the basic concepts used in this study need to be clarified. First there is the *stimulus crowd.* This was provided by the investigators and varied in number from 1 to 15. If the crowd is to draw onlookers, then it must be exposed to an *available population.* The population may be finite, and thus exhaustable, or it may be continually replenished as in the present study. The population may also be in various *states of activity*, that is, sitting around (as at a beach) or moving along paths. The available population in the case of the present study consisted of the stream of pedestrians moving along a major city thoroughfare. Finally, the crowd must exhibit some sort of *observable action* that the population can imitate or in some manner respond to. In the present study the stimulus crowd stood on the pavement and looked up at the window of a nearby building. This action, or parts of it, could be adopted by the passersby. The passerby could simply look up at the building where the crowd was staring without breaking stride, or he could make a more complete imitative action by stopping and standing alongside the crowd. Analyses were undertaken for both types of responses.

In sum, the investigators wanted to see in what degree crowds, varying in size from 1 to 15 persons, and all performing the same observable action, would draw persons into their activities.

[1] This study arose out of a graduate seminar in social psychology conducted by the first author at The City University of New York. Among those who took part in the present study were Stuart Baum, Sheryl Bruder, Fay Crayne, Victor Ernoult, Susan Flinn, Bert Flugman, Henry Glickman, Michael Hoffman, Marcia Kay, Jo Lang, Elaine Lieberman, Nicholas Papouchis, Arthur Shulman, Henry Solomon, Sheila Sperber, and Mark Silverman. The study was supported by The City University of New York and by a small grant from the National Institute of Mental Health, Number 16284-01.

[2] Now at Smith College, Northampton, Massachusetts.

## METHOD

### Subjects

The subjects were 1,424 pedestrians on a busy New York City street who passed along a 50-foot length of sidewalk during thirty 1-minute trials. The study was conducted on two winter afternoons in 1968.

### Procedure

A 50-foot length of sidewalk was designated as the area of observation. At a signal, flashed from the sixth-floor window of an office building across the street from this area of sidewalk, a group of confederates (stimulus crowd) entered the middle of the observation area, stopped, and looked up at the sixth-floor window. This gaze was maintained for 60 seconds. At the end of this period the group was signaled to disperse. After the area was cleared of the gathered crowd the procedure was repeated using a different size stimulus crowd. Five randomly ordered trials were conducted for each of the six different size stimulus crowds. The stimulus crowds were composed of 1, 2, 3, 5, 10, and 15 persons. Motion pictures were taken of the observation area for the 60 seconds during which the stimulus crowd maintained its gaze at the window.

### Data Analysis

The motion pictures were analyzed to determine the total number of persons who passed through the observation area and their behavior. Pairs of judges counted the number of persons entering the field; within this group, the number of persons who looked up; and finally the number of persons who stopped.

## RESULTS

The first question is whether the number of persons who stop alongside the crowd increases as the size of the stimulus crowd increases. The data are provided in [Figure 6-8] (broken line). While 4% of the passersby stopped alongside a single individual looking up, 40% of the passersby stopped alongside a stimulus crowd of 15. An analysis of variance was performed on the mean percentage of persons who stopped alongside the crowd [Table 6-5]. This analysis indicates that the size of the stimulus crowd significantly affects the proportion of passersby who stand alongside it.

**[Table 6-5] Analysis of variance of the proportion of passersby who stop as a function of the size of the stimulus crowd**

| Source | *SS* | *df* | *MS* | *F* |
|---|---|---|---|---|
| Between | .423 | 5 | .085 | 20.63* |
| Within | .099 | 24 | .004 | |
| Total | .522 | 29 | | |

$*p < .001$.

But the influence of the stimulus crowd is not limited to those who stop and stand alongside it. For a larger number of passersby partially adopt the behavior of the crowd by looking up in the direction of the crowd's gaze, while not, however, breaking stride and standing alongside it. Here again the influence of the stimulus crowd increases along with its size. While one person induced 42% of the passersby to look up (whether or not they also stopped), the stimulus crowd of 15, all looking in the same direction, caused 86% of the passersby to orient themselves in the same direction ([Figure 6-8], solid line). An analysis of variance again confirms the difference in means ([Table 6-6]).

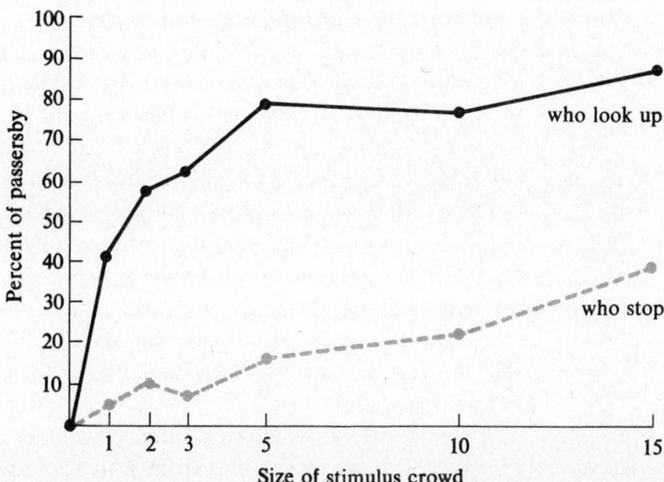


[FIGURE 6-8] Mean percentage of passersby who look up and who stop, as a function of the size of the stimulus crowd.

**[Table 6-6] Analysis of variance of the proportion of passersby who look up as a function of the size of the stimulus crowd**

| Source | *SS* | *df* | *MS* | *F* |
|---|---|---|---|---|
| Between | .628 | 5 | .125 | 16.28* |
| Within | .187 | 24 | .008 | |
| Total | .815 | 29 | | |

$*p < .001$.

A trend analysis for unequal intervals was performed on the data (Gaito, 1965). There is a significant linear trend ($F = 101.7$, $p < .01$) and a nonsignificant quadratic trend ($F = .42$) for the passersby who stopped. However, for the passersby who looked up, there are both significant linear ($F = 57.2$, $p < .01$) and quadratic ($F = 11.6$, $p < .01$) components. This bears on a recent discussion of Gerard, Wilhelmy, and Conolley (1969). In their study, conformity increased in linear fashion as a function of group size, in contrast to Asch (1951), who found a curvilinear relationship. The present study shows that a single set of group-size manipulations can generate both types of functions, depending on the specific dependent variable selected for analysis.

A comparison of those who stop and those who look up shows that while both behaviors increase with the size of the stimulus crowd, the percentage of those who only look up is always higher than those who stop, regardless of the size of the stimulus crowd. It appears that the more demanding, in time or effort, the behavior the less likely it is that the passerby will join it.

Two additional points need to be made. First, it is clear that while the effects of a precipitating group of a given size for the subsequent growth of the crowd were studied, the size of the stimulus crowd increased as soon as persons joined it. Thus, the effect of a stimulus crowd of constant size was not studied. In order to do this it would be necessary to withdraw a member of the stimulus crowd as soon as a passerby joined it.

Second, the maximum size which the crowd attains is dependent not only on the initial size of the crowd, but also on the nature of the stimulus to which the passerby is directed. In the present study, passersby were oriented by the gaze of the crowd to a scene that had no special holding power. (Pedestrians looked up to the sixth floor of an office building where some dimly perceived figures were peering back from inside. It was not a scene of compelling interest.) If, instead, an acrobat were performing on the building ledge, the interest of the scene would likely hold crowd members for a longer period of time, and the crowd would grow to a larger maximum size within a 1-minute interval (the size of the crowd at any given moment being equal to the initial stimulus crowd plus additions minus withdrawals.) There is some logical basis for joining larger crowds: all other things being equal, the larger the crowd the more likely its members are attending to a matter of interest.

The results of this study show that the number of persons who will react to, and join in, the observable behavior of a stimulus crowd is related to the size of the stimulus crowd. These findings contradict the acquisition assumption of the Coleman and James model. The acquisition rate is not, as they assume, dependent only upon the number of persons available to join the group. (For the present study, the mean number of such individuals was not significantly different for the different size stimulus crowds.) An assumption of initial group size is indeed necessary.

## REFERENCES


**ASCH, S. E.** Effects of group pressure upon the modification and distortion of judgment. In H. Guetzkow (Ed.), *Groups, leadership, and men.* Pittsburgh: Carnegie Press, 1951.

**COLEMAN, J. S., & JAMES, J.** The equilibrium size distribution of freely-forming groups. *Sociometry*, 1961, **24**, 36-45.

**GAITO, J.** Unequal intervals and unequal *N* in trend analysis. *Psychological Bulletin*, 1965, **63**, 125-127.

**GERARD, H. B., WILHELMY, R. A., & CONOLLEY, E. S.** Conformity and group size. *Journal of Personality and Social Psychology*, 1968, **8**, 79-82.

**MILGRAM, S., & TOCH, H.** Collective behavior: Crowds and social movements. In G. Lindzey & E. Aronson (Eds.), *The handbook of social psychology.* Vol. 4. (2nd ed.) Reading, Mass.: Addison-Wesley, 1969.

# SUPERORDINATE GOALS IN THE REDUCTION OF INTERGROUP CONFLICT[1]

MUZAFER SHERIF

In the past, measures to combat the problems of intergroup conflicts, proposed by social scientists as well as by such people as administrators, policy-makers, municipal officials, and educators, have included the following: introduction of legal sanctions; creation of opportunities for social and other contacts among members of conflicting groups; dissemination of correct information to break down false prejudices and unfavorable stereotypes; appeals to the moral ideals of fair play and brotherhood; and even the introduction of rigorous physical activity to produce catharsis by releasing pent-up frustrations and aggressive complexes in the unconscious. Other measures proposed include the encouragement of co-operative habits in one's own community, and bringing together in the cozy atmosphere of a meeting room the leaders of antagonistic groups.

Many of these measures may have some value in the reduction of intergroup conflicts, but, to date, very few generalizations have been established concerning the circumstances and kinds of intergroup conflict in which these measures are effective. Today measures are applied in a somewhat trial-and-error fashion. Finding measures that have wide validity in practice can come only through clarification of the nature of intergroup conflict and analysis of the factors conducive to harmony and conflict between groups under given conditions.

The task of defining and analyzing the nature of the problem was undertaken in a previous publication.[2] One of our major statements was the effectiveness of superordinate goals for the reduction of inter-group conflict. "Superordinate goals" we defined as goals which are compelling and highly appealing to members of two or more groups in conflict but which cannot be attained by the resources and energies of the groups separately. In effect, they are goals attained only when groups pull together.

## INTERGROUP RELATIONS AND THE BEHAVIOR OF GROUP MEMBERS

Not every friendly or unfriendly act toward another person is related to the group membership of the individuals involved. Accordingly, we must select those actions relevant to relations between groups.

Let us start by defining the main concepts involved. Obviously, we must begin with an adequate conception of the key term—"group." A group is a social unit (1) which consists of a number of individuals who, at a given time, stand in more or less definite interdependent status and role relationships with one another and (2) which explicitly or implicitly possesses a set of values or norms regulating the behavior of individual members, at least in matters of consequence to the group. Thus, shared attitudes, sentiments, aspirations, and goals are related to and implicit in the common values or norms of the group.

The term "intergroup relations" refers to the relations between two or more groups and their respective members. In the present context we are interested in the acts that occur when individuals belonging to one group interact, collectively or individually, with members of another in terms of their group identification. The appropriate frame of reference for studying such behavior includes the functional relations between the groups. Intergroup situations are not voids. Though not independent of relationships within the groups in question, *the characteristics of relations between groups cannot be deduced or extrapolated from the properties of in-group relations.*

Prevalent modes of behavior within a group, in the way of co-operativeness and solidarity or competitiveness and rivalry among members, need not be typical of actions involving members of an out-group. At times, hostility toward out-groups may be proportional to the degree of solidarity within the group. In this connection, results presented by the British statistician L. F. Richardson are instructive. His analysis of the number of wars conducted by the major nations of the world from 1850 to 1941 reveals that Great Britain heads the list with twenty wars—more than the Japanese (nine wars), the Germans (eight wars), or the United States (seven wars). We think that this significantly larger number of wars engaged in by a leading

[1] The main points in this paper were presented at the Third Inter-American Congress of Psychology, Austin, Texas, December 17, 1955.

[2] Muzafer Sherif and Carolyn W. Sherif, *Groups in Harmony and Tension* (New York: Harper & Bros., 1953).

European democracy has more to do with the intergroup relations involved in perpetuating a far-flung empire than with dominant practices at home or with personal frustrations of individual Britishers who participated in these wars.[3]

In recent years relationships between groups have sometimes been explained through analysis of individuals who have endured unusual degrees of frustration or extensive authoritarian treatment in their life-histories. There is good reason to believe that some people growing up in unfortunate life-circumstances may become more intense in their prejudices and hostilities. But at best these cases explain the intensity of behavior in a given dimension.[4] In a conflict between two groups—a strike or a war—opinion within the groups is crystallized, slogans are formulated, and effective measures are organized by members recognized as the most responsible in their respective groups. The prejudice scale and the slogans are not usually imposed on the others by the deviate or neurotic members. Such individuals ordinarily exhibit their intense reactions within the reference scales of prejudice, hostility, or sacrifice established in their respective settings.

*The behavior by members of any group toward another group is not primarily a problem of deviate behavior.* If it were, intergroup behavior would not be the issue of vital consequence that it is today. The crux of the problem is the participation by group members in established practices and social-distance norms of their group and their response to new trends developing in relationships between their own group and other groups.

On the basis of his UNESCO studies in India, Gardner Murphy concludes that to be a good Hindu or a good Moslem implies belief in all the nasty qualities and practices attributed by one's own group—Hindu or Moslem—to the other. Good members remain deaf and dumb to favorable information concerning the adversary. Social contacts and avenues of communication serve, on the whole, as vehicles for further conflicts not merely for neurotic individuals but for the bulk of the membership.[5]

In the process of interaction among members, an in-group is endowed with positive qualities which tend to be praiseworthy, self-justifying, and even self-glorifying. Individual members tend to develop these qualities through internalizing group norms and through example by high-status members, verbal dicta, and a set of correctives standardized to deal with cases of deviation. Hence, possession of these qualities, which reflect their particular brand of ethnocentrism, is not essentially a problem of deviation or personal frustration. It is a question of participation in in-group values and trends by good members, who constitute the majority of membership as long as group solidarity and morale are maintained.

To out-groups and their respective members are attributed positive or negative qualities, depending on the nature of functional relations between the groups in question. The character of functional relations between groups may result from actual harmony and interdependence or from actual incompatibility between the aspirations and directions of the groups. A number of field studies and experiments indicate that, if the functional relations between groups are positive, favorable attitudes are formed toward the out-group. If the functional relations between groups are negative, they give rise to hostile attitudes and unfavorable stereotypes in relation to the out-group. Of course, in large group units the picture of the out-group and relations with it depend very heavily on communication, particularly from the mass media.

Examples of these processes are recurrent in studies of small groups. For example, when a gang "appropriates" certain blocks in a city, it is considered "indecent" and a violation of its "rights" for another group to carry on its feats in that area. Intrusion by another group is conducive to conflict, at times with grim consequences, as Thrasher showed over three decades ago.[6]

When a workers' group declares a strike, existing group lines are drawn more sharply. Those who are not actually for the strike are regarded as against it. There is no creature more lowly than the man who works while the strike is on.[7] The same type of behavior is found in management groups under similar circumstances.

In time, the adjectives attributed to out-groups take their places in the repertory of group norms. The lasting, derogatory stereotypes attributed to

[3] T. H. Pear, *Psychological Factors of Peace and War* (New York: Philosophical Library, 1950), p. 126.

[4] William R. Hood and Muzafer Sherif, "Personality Oriented Approaches to Prejudice," *Sociology and Social Research*, XL (1955), 79-85.

[5] Gardner Murphy, *In the Minds of Men* (New York: Basic Books, 1953).

[6] F. M. Thrasher, *The Gang* (Chicago: University of Chicago Press, 1927).

[7] E. T. Hiller, *The Strike* (Chicago: University of Chicago Press, 1928).

groups low on the social-distance scale are particular cases of group norms pertaining to out-groups.

As studies by Bogardus show, the social-distance scale of a group, once established, continues over generations, despite changes of constituent individuals, who can hardly be said to have prejudices because of the same severe personal frustrations or authoritarian treatment.[8]

Literature on the formation of prejudice by growing children shows that it is not even necessary for the individual to have actual unfavorable experiences with out-groups to form attitudes of prejudice toward them. In the very process of becoming an in-group member, the intergroup delineations and corresponding norms prevailing in the group are internalized by the individual.[9]

## A RESEARCH PROGRAM

A program of research has been under way since 1948 to test experimentally some hypotheses derived from the literature of intergroup relations. The first large-scale intergroup experiment was carried out in 1949, the second in 1953, and the third in 1954.[10] The conclusions reported here briefly are based on the 1949 and 1954 experiments and on a series of laboratory studies carried out as co-ordinate parts of the program.[11]

The methodology, techniques, and criteria for subject selection in the experiments must be summarized here very briefly. The experiments were carried out in successive stages: (1) groups were formed experimentally; (2) tension and conflict were produced between these groups by introducing conditions conducive to competitive and reciprocally frustrating relations between them; and (3) the attempt was made toward reduction of the intergroup conflict. This stage of reducing tension through introduction of superordinate goals was attempted in the 1954 study on the basis of lessons learned in the two previous studies.

At every stage the subjects interacted in activities which appeared natural to them at a specially arranged camp site completely under our experimental control. They were not aware of the fact that their behavior was under observation. No observation or recording was made in the subjects' presence in a way likely to arouse the suspicion that they were being observed. There is empirical and experimental evidence contrary to the contention that individuals cease to be mindful when they know they are being observed and that their words are being recorded.[12]

In order to insure validity of conclusions, results obtained through observational methods were cross-checked with results obtained through sociometric technique, stereotype rating of in-groups and out-groups, and through data obtained by techniques adapted from the laboratory. Unfortunately, these procedures cannot be elaborated here. The conclusions summarized briefly are based on results cross-checked by two or more techniques.

The production of groups, the production of conflict between them, and the reduction of conflict in successive stages were brought about through the introduction of problem situations that were real and could not be ignored by individuals in the situation. Special "lecture methods" or "discussion methods" were not used. For example, the problem of getting a meal through their own initiative and planning was introduced when participating individuals were hungry.

Facing a problem situation which is immediate and compelling and which embodies a goal that cannot be ignored, group members *do* initiate discussion and *do* plan and carry through these plans until the objective is achieved. In this process the discussion becomes

---

[8] E. S. Bogardus, "Changes in Racial Distances," *International Journal of Opinion and Attitude Research*, I (1947), 55-62.

[9] E. L. Horowitz, " 'Race Attitudes,' " in Otto Klineberg (ed.), *Characteristics of the American Negro*, Part IV (New York: Harper & Bros., 1944).

[10] The experimental work in 1949 was jointly supported by the Yale Attitude Change Project and the American Jewish Committee. It is summarized in Sherif and Sherif, *op. cit.*, chaps. ix and x. Both the writing of that book and the experiments in 1953-54 were made possible by a grant from the Rockefeller Foundation. The 1953 research is summarized in Muzafer Sherif, B. Jack White, and O. J. Harvey, "Status in Experimentally Produced Groups," *American Journal of Sociology*, LX (1955), 370-79. The 1954 experiment was summarized in Muzafer Sherif, O. J. Harvey, B. Jack White, William R. Hood, and Carolyn W. Sherif, "Experimental Study of Positive and Negative Intergroup Attitudes between Experimentally Produced Groups: Robbers Cave Study" (Norman, Okla.: University of Oklahoma, 1954). (Multilithed.) For a summary of the three experiments see chaps. vi and ix in Muzafer Sherif and Carolyn W. Sherif, *An Outline of Social Psychology* (rev. ed.; New York: Harper & Bros., 1956).

[11] For an overview of this program see Muzafer Sherif, "Integrating Field Work and Laboratory in Small Group Research," *American Sociological Review*, XIX (1954), 759-71.

[12] E.g., see F. B. Miller, " 'Resistentialism' in Applied Social Research," *Human Organization*, XII (1954), 5-8; S. Wapner and T. G. Alper, "The Effect of an Audience on Behavior in a Choice Situation," *Journal of Abnormal and Social Psychology*, XLVII (1952), 222-29.

*their* discussion, the plan *their* plan, the action *their* action. In this process discussion, planning, and action have their place, and, when occasion arises, lecture or information has its place, too. The sequence of these related activities need not be the same in all cases.

The subjects were selected by rigorous criteria. They were healthy, normal boys around the age of eleven and twelve, socially well adjusted in school and neighborhood, and academically successful. They came from a homogeneous sociocultural background and from settled, well-adjusted families of middle or lower-middle class and Protestant affiliations. No subject came from a broken home. The mean I.Q. was above average. The subjects were not personally acquainted with one another prior to the experiment. Thus, explanation of results on the basis of background differences, social maladjustment, undue childhood frustrations, or previous interpersonal relations was ruled out at the beginning by the criteria for selecting subjects.

The first stage of the experiments was designed to produce groups with distinct structure (organization) and a set of norms which could be confronted with intergroup problems. The method for producing groups from unacquainted individuals with similar background was to introduce problem situations in which the attainment of the goal depended on the co-ordinated activity of all individuals. After a series of such activities, definite group structures or organizations developed.

The results warrant the following conclusions for the stage of group formation: When individuals interact in a series of situations toward goals which appeal to all and which require that they co-ordinate their activities, group structures arise having hierarchical status arrangements and a set of norms regulating behavior in matters of consequence to the activities of the group.

Once we had groups that satisfied our definition of "group," relations between groups could be studied. Specified conditions conducive to friction or conflict between groups were introduced. This negative aspect was deliberately undertaken because the major problem in intergroup relations today is the reduction of existing intergroup friction. (Increasingly, friendly relations between groups is not nearly so great an issue.) The factors conducive to intergroup conflict give us realistic leads for reducing conflict.

A series of situations was introduced in which one group could achieve its goal only at the expense of the other group—through a tournament of competitive events with desirable prizes for the winning group. The results of the stage of intergroup conflict supported our main hypotheses. During interaction between groups in experimentally introduced activities which were competitive and mutually frustrating, members of each group developed hostile attitudes and highly unfavorable stereotypes toward the other group and its members. In fact, attitudes of social distance between the groups became so definite that they wanted to have nothing further to do with each other. This we take as a case of experimentally produced "social distance" in miniature. Conflict was manifested in derogatory name-calling and invectives, flare-ups of physical conflict, and raids on each other's cabins and territory. Over a period of time, negative stereotypes and unfavorable attitudes developed.

At the same time there was an increase in in-group solidarity and co-operativeness. This finding indicates that co-operation and democracy within groups do not necessarily lead to democracy and co-operation with out-groups, if the directions and interests of the groups are conflicting.

Increased solidarity forged in hostile encounters, in rallies from defeat, and in victories over the out-group is one instance of a more general finding: Intergroup relations, both conflicting and harmonious, *affected the nature of relations within the groups involved.* Altered relations between groups produced significant changes in the status arrangements *within* groups, in some instances resulting in shifts at the upper status levels or even a change in leadership. Always, consequential intergroup relations were reflected in new group values or norms which signified changes in practice, word, and deed within the group. Counterparts of this finding are not difficult to see in actual and consequential human relations. Probably many of our major preoccupations, anxieties, and activities in the past decade are incomprehensible without reference to the problems created by the prevailing "cold war" on an international scale.

## REDUCTION OF INTERGROUP FRICTION

A number of the measures proposed today for reducing intergroup friction could have been tried in this third stage. A few will be mentioned here, with a brief explanation of why they were discarded or were included in our experimental design.

1. Disseminating favorable information in regard to the out-group was not included. Information that is not related to the goals currently in focus in the activities of groups is relatively ineffective, as many studies on

attitude change have shown.[13]

2. In small groups it is possible to devise sufficiently attractive rewards to make individual achievement supreme. This may reduce tension between groups by splitting the membership on an "every-man-for-himself" basis. However, this measure has little relevance for actual intergroup tensions, which are in terms of group membership and group alignments.
3. The resolution of conflict through leaders alone was not utilized. Even when group leaders meet apart from their groups around a conference table, they cannot be considered independent of the dominant trends and prevailing attitudes of their membership. If a leader is too much out of step in his negotiations and agreements with out-groups, he will cease to be followed. It seemed more realistic, therefore, to study the influence of leadership within the framework of prevailing trends in the groups involved. Such results will give us leads concerning the conditions under which leadership can be effective in reducing intergroup tensions.
4. The "common-enemy" approach is effective in pulling two or more groups together against another group. This approach was utilized in the 1949 experiment as an expedient measure and yielded effective results. But bringing some groups together against others means larger and more devastating conflicts in the long run. For this reason, the measure was not used in the 1954 experiment.
5. Another measure, advanced both in theoretical and in practical work, centers around social contacts among members of antagonistic groups in activities which are pleasant in themselves. This measure was tried out in 1954 in the first phase of the integration stage.
6. As the second phase of the integration stage, we introduced a series of superordinate goals which necessitated co-operative interaction between groups.

The social contact situations consisted of activities which were satisfying in themselves—eating together in the same dining room, watching a movie in the same hall, or engaging in an entertainment in close physical proximity. These activities, which were satisfying to each group, but which did not involve a state of interdependence and co-operation for the attainment of goals, were not effective in reducing intergroup tension. On the contrary, such occasions of contact were utilized as opportunities to engage in name-calling and in abuse of each other to the point of physical manifestations of hostility.

The ineffective, even deleterious, results of intergroup contact without superordinate goals have implications for certain contemporary learning theories and for practice in intergroup relations. Contiguity in pleasant activities with members of an out-group does not necessarily lead to a pleasurable image of the out-group if relations between the groups are unfriendly. Intergroup contact without superordinate goals is not likely to produce lasting reduction of intergroup hostility. John Gunther, for instance, in his survey of contemporary Africa, concluded that, when the intergroup relationship is exploitation of one group by a "superior" group, intergroup contact inevitably breeds hostility and conflict.[14]

## INTRODUCTION OF SUPERORDINATE GOALS

After establishing the ineffectiveness, even the harm, in intergroup contacts which did not involve superordinate goals, we introduced a series of superordinate goals. Since the characteristics of the problem situations used as superordinate goals are implicit in the two main hypotheses for this stage, we shall present these hypotheses:

1. When groups in a state of conflict are brought into contact under conditions embodying superordinate goals, which are compelling but cannot be achieved by the efforts of one group alone, they will tend to co-operate toward the common goals.
2. Co-operation between groups, necessitated by a series of situations embodying superordinate goals, will have a cumulative effect in the direction of reducing existing conflict between groups.

The problem situations were varied in nature, but all had an essential feature in common—they involved goals that could not be attained by the efforts and energies of one group alone and thus created a state of interdependence between groups: combating a water shortage that affected all and could not help being "compelling"; securing a much-desired film, which could not be obtained by either group alone but required putting their resources together; putting into working shape, when everyone was hungry and the food was some distance away, the only means of transportation available to carry food.

The introduction of a series of such superordinate goals was indeed effective in reducing intergroup conflict: (1) when the groups in a state of friction interacted in conditions involving superordinate goals, they

[13] E.g., see R. M. Williams, *The Reduction of Intergroup Tensions* (Social Science Research Council Bull. 57 [New York, 1947]).

[14] John Gunther, *Inside Africa* (New York: Harper & Bros., 1955).

did co-operate in activities leading toward the common goal and (2) a series of joint activities leading toward superordinate goals had the cumulative effect of reducing the prevailing friction between groups and unfavorable stereotypes toward the out-group.

These major conclusions were reached on the basis of observational data and were confirmed by sociometric choices and stereotype ratings administered first during intergroup conflict and again after the introduction of a series of superordinate goals. Comparison of the sociometric choices during intergroup conflict and following the series of superordinate goals shows clearly the changed attitudes toward members of the out-group. Friendship preferences shifted from almost exclusive preference for in-group members toward increased inclusion of members from the "antagonists." Since the groups were still intact following co-operative efforts to gain superordinate goals, friends were found largely within one's group. However, choices of out-group members grew, in one group, from practically none during intergroup conflict to 23 per cent. Using chi square, this difference is significant ($P < .05$). In the other group, choices of the out-group increased to 36 per cent, and the difference is significant ($P < .001$). The findings confirm observations that the series of superordinate goals produced increasingly friendly associations and attitudes pertaining to out-group members.

Observations made after several superordinate goals were introduced showed a sharp decrease in the name-calling and derogation of the out-group common during intergroup friction and in the contact situations without superordinate goals. At the same time the blatant glorification and bragging about the in-group, observed during the period of conflict, diminished. These observations were confirmed by comparison of ratings of stereotypes (adjectives) the subjects had actually used in referring to their own group and the out-group during conflict with ratings made after the series of superordinate goals. Ratings of the out-group changed significantly from largely unfavorable ratings to largely favorable ratings. The proportions of the most unfavorable ratings found appropriate for the out-group—that is, the categorical verdicts that "all of them are stinkers" or ". . . smart alecks" or ". . . sneaky"—fell, in one group, from 21 per cent at the end of the friction stage to 1.5 per cent after interaction oriented toward superordinate goals. The corresponding reduction in these highly unfavorable verdicts by the other group was from 36.5 to 6 per cent. The over-all differences between the frequencies of stereotype ratings made in relation to the out-group during intergroup conflict and following the series of superordinate goals are significant for both groups at the .001 level (using chi-square test).

Ratings of the in-group were not so exclusively favorable, in line with observed decreases in self-glorification. But the differences in ratings of the in-group were not statistically significant, as were the differences in ratings of the out-group.

Our findings demonstrate the effectiveness of a series of superordinate goals in the reduction of intergroup conflict, hostility, and their by-products. They also have implications for other measures proposed for reducing intergroup tensions.

It is true that lines of communication between groups must be opened before prevailing hostility can be reduced. But, if contact between hostile groups takes place without superordinate goals, the communication channels serve as media for further accusations and recriminations. When contact situations involve superordinate goals, communication is utilized in the direction of reducing conflict in order to attain the common goals.

Favorable information about a disliked out-group tends to be ignored, rejected, or reinterpreted to fit prevailing stereotypes. But, when groups are pulling together toward superordinate goals, true and even favorable information about the out-group is seen in a new light. The probability of information being effective in eliminating unfavorable stereotypes is enormously enhanced.

When groups co-operate in the attainment of superordinate goals, leaders are in a position to take bolder steps toward bringing about understanding and harmonious relations. When groups are directed toward incompatible goals, genuine moves by a leader to reduce intergroup tension may be seen by the membership as out of step and ill advised. The leader may be subjected to severe criticism and even loss of faith and status in his own group. When compelling superordinate goals are introduced, the leader can make moves to further co-operative efforts, and his decisions receive support from other group members.

In short, various measures suggested for the reduction of intergroup conflict—disseminating information, increasing social contact, conferences of leaders—acquire new significance and effectiveness when they become part and parcel of interaction processes between groups oriented toward superordinate goals which have real and compelling value for all groups concerned.

# CHAPTER SEVEN

# ATTITUDES AND BEHAVIOR

The area of attitude measurement and attitude change has always been one of the preeminent concerns of the experimental social psychologist. However, this interest does not readily extend beyond the laboratory, for attitudes have both cognitive and evaluative components (Scott, 1968) which lend themselves more easily to verbal or written response on questionnaires than to overt behavior in the field. A further complication is the fact that attempts to infer behavior from attitudes have failed (see Chapter 5). The studies in this chapter, on the other hand, attempt to infer attitudes from behavior. As *behavioral* scientists, we somehow feel more comfortable in the latter mode. Still, the studies in this chapter are the most reactive in the book. As was said above, there may be a limit to how much an "attitude" can be shown in overt behavior. Investigators, thus, depend on scale checking, hence the greater reactivity. Some of these articles are also the most difficult to read, but they serve as a good start on what can be done in the field with attitudes.

The Abelson and Miller article (page 208) is particularly timely because disagreements between parties often degenerate into name-calling and backbiting: examples are the polarization into "antisemitic" and "racist" factions during the 1968 teachers' strike in New York City, and Vice President Spiro T. Agnew's calling those who disagree with him "effete snobs" and "ideological eunuchs." Agnew also espoused "positive polarization," which, in light of Sherif's study (see Chapter 6), is a concept difficult to imagine. Thus, the route from disagreement to antagonism becomes shorter every day. This article also indicates the special problems inherent in doing experimentation in the field. In addition, although the authors consider the results more convincing when the study is done in the field, field studies can be susceptible to the same demand characteristics and reactivity as laboratory studies. However, Abelson and Miller mention, as a check on the permanence of attitude change, an after-only design which is much less reactive although similar in design to a study by Levanthal and Niles in this chapter. The authors also corroborate some findings from Allen's study (Chapter 2); i.e., when the misinformer (Allen) or the insulter (Abelson and Miller) leaves the scene of the induction, the effect of the induction still holds.

The article by Miller and Levy (page 216), although difficult to understand, is germane to the problems of studying attitudes in the field. It is somewhat reactive and illumines the difficulty of eliminating experimenter effects. It is an interesting adjunct to Abelson and Miller's study: i.e., it also deals with insult, but here, because the insult was not connected to the communicator, no "boomerang effect" ensued.

The article by Levanthal and Niles (page 226) is less reactive than the previous articles; i.e., it uses an after-only design similar to the substudy in Abelson and Miller. Like the articles in Chapter 5, the Levanthal and Niles article is concerned with the relationship between stated intentions (attitude) and behavior. However, in contrast with the consensus of the authors in Chapter 5, Levanthal and Niles found intentions and behavior to be closely related. This difference may be the result of the temporal and spatial contiguity of the available behavioral response to the stated intention in the Leventhal and Niles procedure. Linn (1965) has noted that too many studies in the area hinge on hypothetical behavioral situations.

Levanthal and Niles are also aware of the problems engendered in setting up a field study, but their greater concern with external validity and answering the common criticism of attitude experiments—that they lack behavioral measures—impels them to move to the field.

The Smith article (page 237) is an interesting example of the application of social psychological theory to applied uses. There are many control problems in the study, but it has been essentially replicated in a well-controlled study by Zimbardo, Weisenberg, Firestone, and Levy (1965). The Smith study also demonstrates a lack of understanding of dissonance theory (reviewed in Brehm & Cohen, 1962). The two-step inducement in this experiment was obviously reducing volition drastically, and the "no influence attempt with rationale," which Smith feels to be more effective than a dissonance procedure, seems in fact to be a high-dissonance condition because of the high choice involved. However, it should be noted that the latter problem is most likely the natural dilemma of the communicator in field situations; i.e., there are many situations where the amount of pressure necessary to get compliance from a sufficient number of subjects may not create the right amount of dissonance to cause a permanent change in either attitude or behavior. Thus, one gets compliance but not a permanent attitude change because of the lack of dissonance aroused.

The Milgram article (page 245) on the lost-letter technique is an example of a nonreactive field study of attitudes. Having seen the disparity between verbal accounts and actions (see Chapter 5), it is refreshing to see that "deeds" rather than words can be measured on a large scale. Milgram's ingenious technique could also fit into Chapter 9, except for the presence of so many data. It is, like Gaertner and Bickman's (Chapter 5), a very general technique which can have many variations, for example, Hornstein's lost-wallet technique in Chapter 2. The possibilities inherent in this method are increased by Milgram's use of *two* behavioral measures: whether or not the letter is mailed and whether or not it is opened. This method can also be used to map political boundaries and, in tandem with Feldman's methods (Chapter 2), could be used to investigate national character, an area much in eclipse, partly for lack of a good experimental technique. Milgram also used some noteworthy validity checks, e.g., the actual election results in wards where letters had been distributed and the check on whether or not the post office was responsible for some letters not reaching their destination. This technique has also been used by Berkowitz (1970) to study the effect of public war demonstrations on spectators. Berkowitz found that the anti-war demonstration appeared not to have counter-productive effects on the observers who were not strongly supporting the war in Vietnam.

The final article in this chapter, by Wrightsman, stems from a class project. It opens a whole new area to be investigated as people define themselves more and more with bumper stickers, buttons, and flags. Other notable aspects of Wrightsman's study are (1) the check on the differential motivation of those with various bumper stickers, (2) the check as to whether or not the sample was representative by looking at the percentages actually voting for each candidate (this check was also used by Milgram in his article in this chapter), (3) the check to see whether experimenter bias could explain the results, and (4) the check to see whether socioeconomic differences could have accounted for the results.

The interesting substudy of stop-sign violators by McCarthy demonstrates that Wallace supporters are more defiant of authority than are supporters of other candidates. But whether defiance or the "rejection of the actions of bureaucrats" accounts for Wrightsman's findings can only be answered by further research, for which Wrightsman provides an excellent beginning.

## REFERENCES

**BERKOWITZ, W. R.** Spectator responses at public war demonstrations. *Journal of Personality and Social Psychology,* 1970, **14**, 305-311.

**BREHM, J. W., & COHEN, A. R.** *Explorations in cognitive dissonance.* New York: Wiley, 1962.

**SCOTT, W. A.** Attitude measurement. In G. Lindzey & E. Aronson (Eds.) *The handbook of social psychology.* Reading: Addison-Wesley, 1968, Vol. 2, 204-273.

**ZIMBARDO, P. G., WEISENBERG, M., FIRESTONE, I., & LEVY, B.** Communicator effectiveness in producing public conformity and private attitude change. *Journal of Personality,* 1965, **33**, 233-256.

# NEGATIVE PERSUASION VIA PERSONAL INSULT[1]

ROBERT P. ABELSON AND JAMES C. MILLER
*Yale University*

A controlled experiment was performed in a field situation to test the hypothesis that an individual directly insulted by a communicator attempting to persuade him will show a "boomerang effect" by increasing the extremity of his initial attitude position. The field situation consisted of a park-bench discussion of a topical social issue, arranged by a public-opinion interviewer. Prepared experimental variations were introduced by one of the discussion partners, a confederate of the interviewer. In the critical variation, the confederate insulted the subject during discussion. In other variations, he tried to persuade but did not insult, or else simply gave certain arguments without intent to persuade. Attitude-change results supported the hypothesis of negative change in the insult condition. Other experimental variations were whether the insulter stayed or left following his last argument, and whether or not a crowd hostile to the insulter was present. No significant differences in attitude change were attributable to these variations. The mechanism for the obtained "boomerang effect" remains unexplained, although a "social equity" explanation has some plausibility.

In controlled experimental studies of attitude change, some degree of change in the direction advocated by the communicator is almost always observed, even under seemingly unfavorable conditions such as the use of communicators of very low credibility (Hovland, Janis and Kelley, 1953; Hovland, 1959; Cohen, 1964). It is extremely unusual for negative influence—the so-called "boomerang effect"—to occur, in which the mean attitude-change score differs significantly from zero in the direction *away* from the advocated position.

If the influence of persuasive communications in natural-field situations were always positive and never negative, one would be led to expect that social controversies would typically tend to resolve themselves by mutual compromise whenever audiences on opposing sides became exposed to each other's spokesmen. While such an outcome is by no means unheard of, it is obvious that there are a number of political and social issues for which considerable social disagreement persists in the face of repeated persuasive attempts by all participants. One is thus led to ask what social and attitudinal mechanisms might serve to "freeze" opinion bipolarity in large social groups. Abelson (1964), in discussing three possible mechanisms, tended to favor the "boomerang effect" as a strong explanatory principle. While it has been argued that boomerang effects are probably rare even in field situations (cf. McGuire, 1966, p. 490), it is nevertheless clear that chronic bipolarity of opinion could readily be accounted for if mutual repulsion of opinions were found to occur between opposing partisans under certain circumstances during social controversy.

What might be the circumstances that could result in negative persuasion? One interesting possibility is that when a speaker insults the listener during a persuasive attempt, the listener will react "negatively" not only in terms of his feelings toward the speaker but in terms of attitude change. This possibility has significance in field applications. Coleman (1957, p. 10), in a classic monograph reviewing psychological and sociological factors common to a number of disparate community controversies, pointed out that "A . . . change in the nature of issues as a controversy develops is the shift from *disagreement* to *antagonism.* A dispute which began dispassionately, in a disagreement over issues, is characterized suddenly by personal slander, . . . by the focusing of direct hostility." Coleman went on to discuss a number of mechanisms by which personal antagonisms typically arise, and the effects of antagonisms in rendering conflicts independent of specific issues. Although he did not comment directly on the matter, it seems a plausible conjecture that the targets of personal insults subsequently adopt more extreme attitude positions on the issues with which the insults were associated.

[1] This research was supported out of funds granted from the Rockefeller Foundation for the Yale Studies in Communication and Attitude Change. The original program under Carl I. Hovland is being continued under the direction of Irving L. Janis and the first author. We wish to thank Dennis L. Cherlin, Richard M. Goodman, and Cynthia P. Miller for their invaluable help.

The study to be reported in this paper was an attempt to discover whether, in fact, a boomerang effect could be produced by slanderous argumentation. Strict experimental procedures were employed in a natural-field situation, in an effort to avoid the possibly overconstrained, polite atmosphere of the experimental laboratory. As previously noted, boomerang effects are very infrequent in the laboratory. The only previous studies deliberately designed to find a boomerang effect[2] are those of Cohen (1962) and Berscheid (1966), although there have been scattered and largely unanticipated post hoc findings of boomerang effects in particular experimental subgroups (e.g., Kelley and Volkhart, 1952; Mann, 1965).

The hypothesis of the present study was not that personal insult is the only way to produce a boomerang effect, but merely that it is one of the effective ways. That insults should have negative persuasive effectiveness is by no means a foregone conclusion, however. Insults have previously been found to have certain limited positive effects in attitude-change research by Weiss and Fine (1956) and by Norman Miller.[3] Weiss and Fine found that insulted subjects were more likely to accept later communications urging a punitive point of view toward juvenile delinquents. Miller found a slight facilitating effect of a snide reference to obesity on the subsequent persuasibility of overweight women, as though guilt prodded them into obliging docility. However, the insult in this latter study was delivered "accidentally," and the communicator could not be held accountable for it. In the Weiss and Fine study, the communicator was presumably completely unaware of the prior insult. In the present study, the insults were designed to come directly and intentionally from the communicator.

While a boomerang effect from intentional personal insults seems intuitively plausible, it is not obvious what the psychological mechanism might be (if indeed the effect occurs). In considering possible mechanisms, it is important to select those which might explain negative attitude change, not merely zero change. The present study, designed primarily to verify the hypothesized boomerang effect in a natural-field situation, was also intended as a preliminary probe of two possible boomerang mechanisms: a "social equity" mechanism, and an "imagined supporter" mechanism.

The "social equity" mechanism might operate as follows. Participation in a communication situation represents a social "investment" (cf. Homans, 1961), a willingness to expose one's views to challenge, in return for which a certain level of social "reward" in the form of social acceptance or approval is considered appropriate. If social equity is violated by virtue of gratuitous insults from the other party, the victim attempts to redress the inequity in some fashion, very possibly by "withdrawing his investment" and adopting a more extreme version of his original position. It is as though the victim says, "I'll show you. If you're going to insult me when I give you a chance to change my opinions, I not only won't change them, I'll make them more objectionable to you."

This theoretical "derivation" is much more loose and informal than in other, more clear-cut recent applications of social equity theory (Adams, 1965), and it is not completely clear what experimental manipulations would be germane to these conjectures. One seemingly important variable is whether the communicator remains in the social situation after his insulting argumentation. Reprisal by boomeranging would seem to make less sense for the victim if his tormentor has left the scene. Accordingly, we arranged in our experiment for the insulter to leave immediately after his performance for half the subjects, and to remain on the scene for the other half. This manipulation was intended as a tentative exploration of the "social equity" explanation.

The "imagined supporter" mechanism involves a completely different kind of explanation. In giving his insults during persuasive argument, the attacker conveys the impression that people arguing his particular side of the issue are obnoxious individuals. The victim, harassed and confronted with an obviously bad opinion model, may cast about in his memory for a good opinion model, a reference person whose views may be adopted the more effectively to ward off hostile arguments. The chances are that his "imagined supporter" will be someone whose views are well crystallized and highly polarized, i.e., someone probably more extreme in his opinions than the victim himself. It is as though the victim says, "Well, if a lout like you has those opinions, they can't be right.

[2] Cohen demonstrated a boomerang effect in the communicator's position rather than the listener's. Communicators, upon finding that their attempts to persuade a peer have produced large negative attitude change, subsequently move their own positions farther from that of the peer.

[3] "Defaming and agreeing with the communicator as a function of communication extremity, emotional arousal, and evaluative set," unpublished manuscript.

The good people I know don't believe those things at all. In fact, I can recall someone proving the exact opposite."

In an attempt to test the "imagined supporter" mechanism, an experimental condition was designed in which the victim could be provided with a determined group of onlookers whom the victim could easily imagine to be extreme partisans on his side of the issue. This condition was applied for half the subjects, while for the other half there were no onlookers.

In sum, then, the present experimental study was designed to test whether personal insults during persuasion would in fact produce a boomerang effect, and if so, to explore two possible explanatory mechanisms. Irrespective of the explanatory mechanism, a demonstration of the occurrence of such an effect would counterbalance the dominant impression of universally pliant communication audiences in laboratory attitude-change studies, and would fill an important missing link in the understanding of bitter community controversies. Additionally, the procedures by which we were able to introduce the appropriate experimental manipulations in a field situation are of special methodological interest, particularly in view of the potential artifacts which may sometimes endanger the validity of laboratory studies (cf. Aronson and Carlsmith, 1967).

## METHOD

### Subjects

Subjects were 80 persons, of heterogeneous ages and backgrounds, sitting on park benches in Washington Square Park in New York City on weekend afternoons in the summer of 1963. They were selected by a confederate of the experimenter who sat down near them, posing as another park inhabitant. The only criterion used in selecting the subjects was that they appear intelligent enough to understand the procedure, which was a two-person debate format staged by a "roving reporter." Thirty other persons declined to participate when approached.

### General Procedure

The subject was approached by the experimenter, who announced that he was from "Survey Research Associates" and wished to interview him on the issue of discrimination against Negroes in employment. This was an extremely salient issue at the time, since several well-publicized sit-ins protesting discrimination in the building trades had just occurred in New York City, and the "March on Washington" was imminent. The experimenter's credibility as an interviewer was enhanced by the equipment he carried: clip-board, microphone, and tape recorder.

In order to obtain a preliminary indication of the subject's position on the issue, he or she was asked: "What do you think of the recent demonstrations by Negroes against job discrimination; do you favor them or not?" If the subject indicated a generally favorable attitude toward the demonstrations, objecting, if at all, only in cases of property damage and work interference, he was interviewed further. If he had broad objections or was generally opposed to the demonstrations, he was dropped from the experiment. This was done in order to allow the subsequent presentation by the confederate of a uniform set of statements opposing efforts to gain job equality. An equal number of subjects would have been difficult to obtain on both sides of this issue in the chosen locale. Only 11 persons (out of 91 who were asked the initial question) had to be rejected from the experiment because they opposed demonstrations against job discrimination.

Subjects who were accepted were asked to indicate their agreement or disagreement, on a 30-point scale, with the following statement: "The demonstrations against job discrimination, even the peaceful ones, are hurting the Negro's chances for job equality." This was used as the premeasure against which the effect of the discussion with the confederate was evaluated by administering the same statement again at the end of the procedure.

At this point, while the subject was checking his response to the initial statement, the experimenter looked to other people sitting nearby, explaining that he would like to get as many reactions as possible during his survey. He then asked the confederate if he would be willing to express his opinion on the problem of job discrimination. When the confederate indicated his willingness to do so, the same question and statement were administered to him that had been administered to the subject, and he presumably checked a point along the same scale. The scales were printed on 5 × 8 cards, four on each side of the card, eight scales in all. Both "subjects" were encouraged to hold their cards so that the other could not see their responses.

The central part of the procedure consisted of a series of six questions asked by the experimenter of both participants, three in which the subject answered first (1, 3, and 5) and three in which the confederate answered first (2, 4, and 6). These questions covered a broad range of issues involved in the job discrimination problem, e.g., the importance of the problem itself, the role of fair employment laws in helping the Negro, the effectiveness of such laws, their consequences on job conditions, job training, etc. Each time that both participants answered the question, they were asked to check along the scale whether they agreed or disagreed with what the other had said. The confederate had been given a series of prepared statements which he presented throughout the experiment. All of these statements were notably anti-Negro, but they embodied a sufficient assortment of other ideas to permit considerable potential variation in agreement. (For example: "Forced integration in employment will undoubtedly lead to friction on the job, which makes it economically unsound.")

In the final step of the procedure, the subject was asked to respond again to the initial statement (concerning the alleged deleterious effects of antidiscrimination demonstrations), indicating "how you feel now about the issue."

### Experimental Conditions

The basic design was a 2 × 2 × 2 factorial: Insulting vs. Neutral remarks; Opponent leaves vs. Opponent stays; Crowd present vs. No crowd. In addition, there were two "No persuasive intent" control conditions (to be explained below).

To each of these ten conditions, 8 subjects were assigned. Randomization of these assignments was achieved with the aid of a random sequence on a perforated roll in the confederate's pocket. After the experimenter had insured that a particular subject was acceptable, the confederate covertly exposed the next experimental assignment and set himself to behave accordingly. (Except for the "No persuasive intent" condition, it was not necessary for the confederate to signal the experimenter about the assignment, but only to carry out his own part at the appropriate time.) It was not feasible to determine the Crowd conditions in this manner, however. Instead, all Crowd present subjects were run on particular randomly determined days and all No crowd subjects on the remaining days.

In the Neutral remarks variation, the confederate simply presented his six prepared statements, each beginning with a neutral comment to the effect that he was interested in the subject's comments, that he had listened carefully, or that he had heard them before. In the Insulting remarks variation he preceded all of his statements with insults to the subject. He had a list of five standard insults from which he could draw the one which seemed the most appropriate for each statement, provided that he used the majority of them for each subject. They were: (1) "That's ridiculous"; (2) "That's just the sort of thing you'd expect to hear in this park"; (3) "That's obviously wrong"; (4) "That's terribly confused"; and (5) "No one really believes that." In practice, he used all five insults for all subjects, for it was found that they were general enough that they could be said in a natural way almost regardless of what the subject had said.

In the Opponent leaves variation, the confederate delivered a plausible excuse and rushed off immediately following the subject's reply to his sixth statement. In the Opponent stays variation, he delivered the same excuse, but did not leave until after both he and the subject had checked their final attitude scales.

In the Crowd present variation, the "crowd" was actually a group of from 3 to 5 persons (usually 4: 2 men, 2 women) who were also confederates of the experimenter. They were instructed both in how to approach the interview (they either came up singly or in pairs, stopping 15 feet from the experimenter, enquiring what was happening, and then gathering closer to watch), and in what to say in response to the confederate's statements. They had a standard list of comments to make about his statements. (1) "Oh, no!"; (2) "That's absurd"; (3) "I disagree"; and (4) "tut-tut-tut." In practice these tended to be the main comments, although occasionally a similar one was added. To avoid direct social reinforcement of the real subject's statements, the crowd assumed an air of silent attentiveness when the subject was speaking.

For purposes of assessing attitude change due solely to the content of the confederate's six statements as distinct from the effects of the confederate as persuasive communicator, the No persuasive intent variation was added, for which a slightly different procedure was used. When the confederate was initially asked if he would be willing to express his opinions on the issue of job discrimination, he indicated that he would be willing but that he had not followed the issues very closely and, in fact, had been out of the country during most of the demonstrations and felt he had better not comment. He was then asked if he would consent to play the role of someone (actually several people) who had given opinions—that is, to read a series of statements which the interviewer had collected in the course of his survey. This would allow the interviewer to get the reaction of the other person (the subject). This the confederate consented to do, and proceeded to read the statements without responsibility for them, but in much the same forceful vocal fashion as in the experimental conditions (omitting the preliminary insults or neutral comments). All of the remaining parts of the procedure were the same for the No persuasive intent control variation as for the experimental variations, except that no crowd was ever used. Thus there were but two cells involving this variation: No persuasive intent-Opponent leaves and No persuasive intent—Opponent stays.

## RESULTS

**Agreement with Opponent's Statements** Following each of the confederate's six anti-Negro statements, the subject had rated his agreement or disagreement on a 30-point scale. The greatest disagreement was scored 1 and the greatest agreement 30, with the neutral point between 15 and 16. [Table 7-1] displays the mean agreement scores for each condition, averaged first over the six statements and then over the 8 subjects. A separate statement-by-statement analysis reveals nothing not contained in the summary analysis.

At the time the ratings were made, the Opponent leaves vs. Opponent stays variation had not yet been introduced. Thus no systematic differences in mean agreement can accrue to that variable, and the essential facts are revealed more clearly when [Table 7-1] is collapsed into five cells rather than ten. When the

[TABLE 7-1] **Agreement with the opponent's statements**

| Conditions | No crowd | Crowd present |
|---|---|---|
| Insulting remarks | | |
| Opponent leaves | 7.56 (7.41)[a] | 4.21 (4.56) |
| Opponent stays | 7.25 | 4.92 |
| Neutral remarks | | |
| Opponent leaves | 16.04 (16.03) | 9.73 (8.17) |
| Opponent stays | 16.02 | 6.60 |
| No persuasive intent | | |
| Opponent leaves | 10.71 (11.31) | |
| Opponent stays | 11.92 | |

[a]Figures in parentheses represent averages over the two "Opponent" conditions. Each such mean is based upon $N = 16$.

No persuasive intent condition is temporarily set aside and the other four cells are subjected to a two-way analysis of variance, the statistical outcome is as shown in [Table 7-2].

The strong main effect of Insulting remarks can be interpreted as evidence of the effective "take" of the insult manipulation. Much more disagreement with the confederate's brief speeches occurred when these incorporated insults, and it therefore seems safe to infer that this experimental variation succeeded in offending the target subjects. The strong main effect on agreement due to the Crowd variation may be taken to suggest that the crowd performs a supportive function. When there is a crowd present to register disapproval of the confederate's remarks, the subject tends to disagree more strongly in his ratings of those remarks. Whether the social support provided by the crowd is of the specific sort contemplated by the "imagined supporter" hypothesis, however, cannot be judged from the agreement data.

The significant interaction between Remarks and Crowd manipulations on agreement ratings probably indicates nothing more fundamental than inequality of intervals on the graphic rating scale. The means in the several cells fall at such widely separated places along the scale that differential differences between means are not interpretable.

It is interesting that the mean agreement for the Neutral remarks-No crowd cell lies on the agreement side of the scale, although barely so. Apparently,

[TABLE 7-2] **Analysis of variance of agreement data**

| Source | *df* | *MS* | *F* |
|---|---|---|---|
| Remarks (R) | 1 | 598.21 | 26.47** |
| Crowd (C) | 1 | 458.67 | 20.30** |
| R × C | 1 | 100.84 | 4.46* |
| Within cell | 60 | 22.60 | |

*$p < .05$
**$p < .01$

subjects lacking social support did not typically feel so deeply about the attitude issue as to reject the mediocre opposition arguments when these were presented earnestly and politely. For the No persuasive intent cell, with the arguments simply read without personal responsibility for them, the mean agreement score of 11.31 is significantly below ($p < .05$ by the Tukey Test) the mean of 16.03 for the Neutral remarks-No crowd cell, but not quite significantly higher than the mean of 7.41 for the Insulting remarks-No crowd cell.

**Boomerang Effects** Agreements with the interview topic statement, "The demonstrations against job discrimination, even the peaceful ones, are hurting the Negro's chances for job equality," were also scored on a scale from 1 to 30. Higher scores were assigned to the agreement (i.e., anti sit-in) side, and then the after-discussion scores were subtracted from the before-discussion scores. A negative change score thus indicates a boomerang effect, with the subject becoming more opposed to the anti sit-in, anti fair-employment position advocated by the confederate. [Table 7-3] displays the mean change scores in the ten experimental conditions.

As predicted, the average persuasive effect was consistently negative in the Insulting remarks conditions. A (one-tailed) $t$ test of the differences between the average effect (−1.81) in the four experimental cells involving insults and in the two No persuasive intent control cells (+.44) yields a statistically significant result ($t = 1.79$, $p < .05$). The average effect in the four Insulting remarks cells is significantly different also from zero ($t = 2.49$, $p < .05$), i.e., a reliable group boomerang effect occurred. Out of 32 insulted subjects 15 displayed attitude change in the negative direction, 13 no change, and 4 in the positive direction.

The picture of the results becomes less sharp when

[TABLE 7-3] **Attitude-change scores**

| Conditions | No crowd | Crowd | Mean[a] |
|---|---|---|---|
| Insulting remarks | | | −1.81 |
| Opponent leaves | −1.25 | −1.75 | |
| Opponent stays | −3.12 | −1.12 | |
| Neutral remarks | | | −1.19 |
| Opponent leaves | −1.00 | −2.00 | |
| Opponent stays | .00 | −1.75 | |
| No persuasive intent | | | +.44 |
| Opponent leaves | .38 | – | |
| Opponent stays | .50 | – | |

[a]Each cell mean based on $N = 8$. Within-cell mean square = 16.86.

the four Neutral remarks conditions are also considered. In three of the four cells, the average attitude change was negative. The average effect (−1.19) in the four experimental cells without insults is not significantly different either from the control cells ($t = 1.24$) or from the base-line of zero ($t = 1.44$), nor is it significantly less negative than the average effect of −1.81 in the Insulting remarks cells.

Neither experimental variation conjectured to be crucial to the boomerang effect yielded significant main effects or interactions. The Crowd present variation, supposed to provide "imagined supporters" and thus a larger boomerang effect for the victim of insults, instead produced (nonsignificantly) less boomerang than the No crowd variation for Insulting remarks and (nonsignificantly) more boomerang for Neutral remarks. The Opponent leaves variation, supposed to undercut the possibility of social retribution and thus to reduce the boomerang effect for the victim of insulting remarks, did produce a (nonsignificant) lessening in the No crowd variation, but not in the Crowd present variation.

## DISCUSSION

We have demonstrated the primary effect hypothesized at the outset; namely, that personal insults during intended persuasion produce a boomerang effect. We regard this demonstration as more convincing by virtue of its occurrence in the "field" than a corresponding laboratory demonstration would have been.

It should not be supposed, however, that our procedural innovations were easy to effect. A complicated scenario was involved, with deft performances required by the experimenter, the confederate, and the crowd. There was no indication that any of our subjects regarded the "debate" as suspicious or unnatural; yet it was certainly a novel experience calling forth a variety of reactions from the subjects and a number of necessary adjustments by the experimental players. Thus there was inevitably considerable variation in how well the procedure "came off." Additional sources of within-cell variation were age, sex, and personality differences among subjects, and hour-by-hour variations in the surrounding park environment.[4]

The pattern of results among the several experimental cells bears explanation even in the absence of statistical reliability for various differences. In particular, the Crowd present variation produced unexpected results. The "imagined supporter" hypothesis requires that a boomerang effect occur only when the subject is insulted. However, with a crowd present, there was at least as much boomerang effect under Neutral remarks as under Insulting remarks. Informal observations made by the experimenter perhaps explain why this was so. The subjects in the Crowd present variation appeared more relaxed and self-confident. After a brief initial period of nervous attentiveness to the crowd's reactions,[5] subjects appeared reassured by the crowd's hostility to the opponent and began to "play to the crowd," basking in the presumption of right-mindedness. They did not even seem to care very much when they were being insulted, adopting a patronizing tone toward the outnumbered and presumably desperate opponent. In effect, this behavior may be interpreted as social conformity in which the subject takes his cues from the crowd. The crowd disagrees with the opponent's remarks, and hence subjects disagree significantly more in their ratings of those remarks than do subjects in the No crowd condition. The crowd makes it obvious that the opponent's point of view is odious, and thus subjects show a slight tendency toward negative attitude change irrespective of the other experimental variations (a test of the mean change of −1.65 in the Crowd conditions against zero change yields $t = 2.26$; were this not a post hoc comparison, 5% level of significance would be claimed). These outcomes are obverse to those observed by Kelley and Woodruff (1956) in an experiment on the persuasive effects of applause. In their study, applause by an audience enhanced susceptibility to the persuasive communication. Here, opprobrium expressed by a "crowd" enhanced rejection of the persuasive communication. However, the crowd in our experiment did not seem to function as a spur to the rehearsal of an extreme attitude position solely by the victim of insult, as postulated in the "imagined supporter" hypothesis. At this point it is not clear whether this hypothesis is a poor one or whether the chosen experimental manipulations were inadequate to test it.

The evidence in favor of the "social equity" line of explanation is no more than minimal. If in [Table 7-3]

[4] The park is notorious for its Greenwich Village "types" and its sometimes noisy atmosphere. (The police had once unsuccessfully attempted to ban folk-singing there, following complaints from some of the more staid sitters, strollers, and neighborhood residents.) The only extremely unusual incident interfering with our experiment occurred during a pilot run, when a psychotic woman seized the experimenter's microphone and began "broadcasting." However, there were a variety of small distractions during the regular runs, including an occasional real spectator or two.

[5] In a pilot experiment, we had employed a "crowd" instructed to remain completely silent throughout the discussion. We found that subjects became quite tense during this procedure. Most subjects seem both to desire and to expect some kind of feedback from the crowd.

attention is confined to the No crowd cells (on the grounds that the presence of the crowd induces conformity effects overriding all else), one notes that the Opponent stays vs. Opponent leaves variation at least operates in the appropriate direction. When the subject is insulted, the boomerang effect tends to be stronger when the opponent stays than when he leaves, although the difference is not significant.

In his study of a boomerang effect, Cohen (1962) discussed a "bargaining" explanation of his outcome. A person might move his attitude position farther away from that of a resistant or hostile opponent in anticipation of future interaction in which a tough "bargaining position" might prove useful. Cohen tried to rule out this possibility by making clear to his subjects that they were very unlikely to encounter the opponent again. In the present study, the same implication was quite obvious. The opponent was a total stranger who had announced his intention even in the Opponent stays condition to hurry off immediately at the conclusion of the procedure, presumably to vanish forever in the vast anonymity of New York City. In neither study was there an experimental variation offering the prospect of further interaction with the opponent. If the boomerang effect is envisioned as a kind of unthinking "tit-for-tat" maneuver to redress a violation of social equity, it is not obvious that the expectation of further interaction with the opponent would at all increase the effect. On the other hand, if a more self-conscious effort at social bargaining is involved, then an Opponent comes back variation might have produced an even stronger boomerang effect for us. Anticipating that further research is necessary, we feel it important to note that the different shadings of interpretation of the boomerang mechanism are further complicated by the unknown effects of the presence of the experimenter. To the extent that the subject orients his final responses in terms of the perceived demands of the experimenter, the influence of the opponent's parting behavior is attenuated.

One of the many other empirical issues left open is the question of the permanence of negative attitude change following personal insult. One might suspect that the effect is so closely tied to a particular social situation that any attitude change would soon decay if the situation were not reinvoked.[6] Even were this the case, however, it would still be possible to understand the dynamics whereby a social controversy could escalate out of control through rapid successive cycles of insult and return insult. Any social mechanism that tended to reinstitute personal affronts would presumably also tend to sustain abnormal extremity of attitude positions on both sides of the controversy. However, our experimental situation, although field-based, was not directly designed to investigate long-range escalation of controversy. Thus we have succeeded only in isolating one small piece of a much larger and more interesting picture.

---

[6] In a later experiment, we repeated the insult manipulation in a field setting that did not permit assessment of the effects until three weeks later. University students fulfilling an unpopular physical-education obligation were interviewed individually in a gymnasium office by the experimenter, who posed as an advanced physical-education student from a nearby teachers' college. In the Insulting Remarks condition, subjects were ridiculed for neglecting their physical condition and for their overly casual attitudes toward physical fitness. As a precaution against the arousal of suspicion that the interview was part of an experiment, no measures of any kind were obtained during this session. Instead, a questionnaire was mailed three weeks later as part of a regular University Health procedure for keeping in touch with student attitudes.

The insults produced a negative mean change on attitudes toward physical fitness programs, but this mean change was small and not significantly different from zero or from the mean change in the control group. Evidently, whatever boomerang effect may have been produced during the interview was not of sufficient permanence to be strongly manifest three weeks later.

## REFERENCES


**ABELSON, R. P.** Mathematical models of the distribution of attitudes under controversy. In N. Frederiksen and H. Gulliksen (Eds.), *Contributions to mathematical psychology.* New York: Holt, Rinehart, and Winston, 1964. Pp. 142-160.

**ADAMS, J. S.** Inequity in social exchange. In L. Berkowitz (Ed.), *Advances in experimental social psychology.* Vol. 2. New York: Academic Press, 1965. Pp. 267-297.

**ARONSON, E., AND CARLSMITH, J. M.** Experimentation in social psychology. In G. Lindzey and E. Aronson (Eds.), *Handbook of social psychology.* Vol. 1. Cambridge: Addison-Wesley, 1967. In press.

**BERSCHEID, ELLEN.** Opinion change and communicator-communicatee similarity and dissimilarity. *Journal of Personality and Social Psychology,* 1966, **4**, 670-680.

**COHEN, A. R.** A dissonance analysis of the boomerang effect. *Journal of Personality,* 1962, **30**, 75-88.

**COHEN, A. R.** *Attitude change and social influence.* New York: Basic Books, 1964.

**COLEMAN, J. S.** *Community conflict.* Glencoe, Illinois: Free Press, 1957.

**HOMANS, G.** *Social behavior: its elementary forms.* New York: Harcourt, Brace, and World, 1961.

**HOVLAND, C. I.** Reconciling conflicting results derived from experimental and survey studies of attitude change. *American Psychologist,* 1959, **14**, 8-17.

**HOVLAND, C. I., JANIS, I. L., AND KELLEY, H. H.** *Communication and persuasion.* New Haven: Yale University Press, 1953.

**KELLEY, H. H., AND VOLKHART, E. H.** The resistance to change of group-anchored attitudes. *American Sociological Review,* 1952, **17**, 453-465.

**KELLEY, H. H., AND WOODRUFF, C. L.** Members' reactions to apparent group approval of a counternorm communication. *Journal of Abnormal and Social Psychology,* 1956, **52**, 67-74.

**MCGUIRE, W. J.** Attitudes and opinions. *Annual Review of Psychology,* 1966, **17**, 475-514.

**MANN, L.** The effects of emotional role playing on smoking attitudes and habits. Unpublished doctoral dissertation, Yale University, 1965.

**WEISS, W., AND FINE, B. J.** The effect of induced aggressiveness on opinion change. *Journal of Abnormal and Social Psychology,* 1956, **52**, 109-114.

# DEFAMING AND AGREEING WITH THE COMMUNICATOR AS A FUNCTION OF EMOTIONAL AROUSAL, COMMUNICATION EXTREMITY, AND EVALUATIVE SET*

NORMAN MILLER
*University of California***

BURTON H. LEVY
*Yale University*

Irrelevant prior insult, set to evaluate the communicator (versus give own opinion), and extremity of the position advocated in a communication were factorially manipulated by each of 11 experimenters creating a 2 x 2 x 3 x 11 design. Posing as "on the street reporters," experimenters polled 264 overweight middle-aged women in shopping plazas to obtain "after only" measurements of defamation of the communicator and agreement with the communication. Insult did not produce the effects predicted by equating irrelevant emotional arousal with involvement. Though it increased defamation it also increased persuasion. This covariation of persuasion and defamation is noteworthy. The effects of extremity depended on the insult condition; in the absence of insult greater extremity produced less persuasion and more defamation. Evaluative set (which has been labeled "distraction" in other studies) increased defamation and reduced persuasion. This finding directly contradicts previous theoretical and empirical results for "distraction."

In our daily lives we commonly encounter opinions that differ from our own. Attempts to adjust discrepant viewpoints by persuasive argument often ensue. Though consistent restraint is often difficult, experience teaches us to avoid angering the other person if we wish to persuade him of our own ultimate wisdom. Once we get emotionally involved in a position we seem to become hopelessly intractible in the face of persuasive attempts. As our antagonist displays this same pattern of response, our respective positions paradoxically diverge in response to mutual persuasive attempts to produce agreement. These pedestrian observations are represented in Sherif and Hovland's treatment of attitude change by the notion of issue involvement. They argue that involvement curtails attitude change by broadening a person's "latitude of rejection"—the band or bands of positions surrounding his own which he judges to be intolerable or unacceptable. Involvement is a global concept and while it may indeed have several components,[1] emotional arousal would seem to be the component most particularly important in producing the restricted latitudes of acceptance that supposedly mediate reduced persuasion.

**Emotional Arousal** This observation, that the person who has been emotionally aroused about his position on an issue will resist persuasive efforts, seems almost too commonplace to doubt. Thus, the following experiment asks a more subtle question. Can emotional arousal *per se* produce the resistance that is so familiar in our daily lives? In other words, when the emotional reaction is not directly tied to the cognitive elements under attack but is instead irrelevant to them, will we still find resistance to persuasion? One way to arouse a person emotionally is to insult him about a personal attribute which he clearly possesses, for which he is clearly responsible, and which the culture uniformly judges as offensive. Conceivably, the effects of such emotional arousal may generalize to a communication which is temporally contiguous to the insult. To the extent that an emotional state generalizes from the instigating content area to other content areas, it should restrict

*This experiment was supported by National Science Foundation Grants GS-428 to Yale University, and GS-1000 to University of California, Riverside. We wish to thank David P. Hansen, H. Robert Harrison, Marc Janes, Jr., Herbert Lee, Mark Korsten, J. S. McCullough, Jimmy Mitchell, Edward Mulligan, F. Bradford Niebling, Charles Poverman, B. Schumaker, Scott G. Thompson, and Allan Wakefield for aid in conducting this experiment, James McMartin for computational help, and Barry E. Collins and Paul Rosenblatt for criticizing a first draft. A version of this paper was presented at E.P.A., April, 1965.

**Now at the University of Minnesota.

[1] Norman Miller, "Involvement and Dogmatism as Inhibitors of Attitude Change," *Journal of Experimental Social Psychology*, 1 (May, 1965), pp. 121-132.

attitude change on an irrelevant issue. Thus, insulting over-weight women for their obesity might restrict agreement with an unrelated communication advocating a reduction in the salaries of elementary teachers.

It is of course possible that emotional arousal only inhibits opinion change when the arousal is directly tied to the cognitive components of an attitude that is under attack. In other words, relevant and irrelevant emotional arousal may invoke completely different mechanisms. There are, in fact, two sources of support for the competing hypothesis that irrelevant emotional arousal will *enhance* rather than restrict persuasion. For instance, if the communication has a hostile, aggressive orientation, increased opinion change is predicted by the frustration aggression hypothesis, and more specifically, from the prior results of Weiss and Fine.[2] They found that after arousing aggression by insulting the subjects, an aggressively oriented communication produced more attitude change. In other words, if agreement with the communication as well as derogation of the source, is instrumental in the respondent's expression of aggression, insult should lead to more change *and* more derogation. Furthermore, Schachter and Singer's[3] finding that artificially induced emotional arousal increased influencibility, also suggests that irrelevant arousal will facilitate attitude change. Thus, while changing one's opinion and defaming the source of persuasive attempts are readily thought of as alternative or incompatible responses to a persuasive argument, these findings argue for the independence of defamation and attitude change under some circumstances. They suggest that a negative relation between these two response measures requires the "right" conditions.

**Extremity**[4] Research relating opinion change to the discrepancy between the positions of the respondent and the communicator has yielded conflicting outcomes. While some studies obtain more change with a larger discrepancy, others find exactly the opposite.[5] Aronson, Turner, and Carlsmith,[6] in a formulation based on dissonance theory, stress the role of credibility to account for the conflicting effects of discrepancy. Discrepancy produces dissonance, but attitude change is only one of several responses for coping with dissonance. If attitude change is the dissonance reducing technique chosen, then large discrepancy should indeed produce substantial change. However, Aronson *et al.* qualify this relation by specifying that attitude change increases directly with discrepancy only when the communicator is highly credible. They argue that defaming the communicator and changing one's opinion are alternative responses to a discrepant communication and as either discrepancy increases or credibility decreases, defamation replaces opinion change as the preferred response to the communication. They suggest that in those studies in which greater discrepancy produced less opinion change, the communicator had low credibility. While their own data do show credibility effects, discrepancy did not produce the predicted effect on derogation.

In an alternate formulation, Sherif and Hovland[7] attempt to reconcile the conflicting effects of discrepancy by pointing to differences in involvement. They argue that whereas greater discrepancy produces more opinion change when involvement is low, under high involvement opinion change is curvilinearly related to discrepancy. When a person is highly involved in an issue, a vastly discrepant communication is rejected and its distance from the respondent's own position is exaggerated, thereby curtailing opinion change. While they do not specifically mention derogation of the source as mediating the decreased persuasion found when both discrepancy and involvement are high, this mechanism seems implicit in their formulation too. Rejection of the source as incredible, as too extreme and therefore worthy of defamation, would seem to be a concomitant of what Sherif and Hovland describe as placing the communication outside one's "latitude of acceptance." In other words, for a given degree of discrepancy, the person deeply involved in an issue is more likely to derogate the source and

[2] Walter Weiss and Bernard J. Fine, "The Effect of Induced Aggressiveness on Opinion Change," *Journal of Abnormal and Social Psychology,* 52 (January, 1956), pp. 109-114.

[3] Stanley Schachter and Jerome E. Singer, "Cognitive, Social, and Physiological Determinants of Emotional State," *Psychological Review,* 69 (September, 1962), pp. 379-399.

[4] In a more precise theory of attitude change it might be important to differentiate between the effects of manipulating extremity and discrepancy. Whereas in everyday life, as well as in most attitude change studies, they are typically confounded, this need not be the case. Since the present study uses an after-only design, strictly speaking it is inappropriate to use the term *discrepancy.* However, with random assignment of subjects to conditions it is hard to imagine that discrepancy was not in fact highly correlated with extremity.

[5] For references supporting the two opposite findings see Elliot Aronson, Judith A. Turner, and J. Merrill Carlsmith, "Communicator Credibility and Communication Discrepancy as Determinants of Opinion Change," *Journal of Abnormal and Social Psychology,* 67 (July, 1963), pp. 31-36.

[6] Aronson, Turner, and Carlsmith, *op. cit.*

[7] Muzafer Sherif and Carl I. Hovland, *Social Judgment,* New Haven: Yale University Press, 1961.

retain his initial attitude. Thus, under substantial discrepancy, low communicator credibility is a by-product of high involvement and mediates the ineffectiveness of persuasive attempts.[8]

As argued above, a negative correlation between agreeing with the communicator and defaming him, as well as an interaction of both responses with discrepancy, is compatible with both dissonance and social judgment theories of attitude change. Nevertheless, there is probably little reason to suspect that an inverse relation between persuasion and defamation of the source should hold for all levels of discrepancy. Whereas the most favorable evaluations of the source are found when minimal change is advocated, maximal persuasion clearly requires advocacy of more than the most minimal amount of change. In other words, persuasion is probably a curvilinear function of discrepancy. The present study further explores the relation between these three variables. Whatever the effect of discrepancy on attitude change, the two response measures should be inversely related for discrepancy levels ranging from moderate to high.

**Evaluative Set** If opinion change and source derogation are indeed alternative responses to persuasive attempts, any condition increasing one response should decrease the other. In other words, a variety of manipulations besides discrepancy should produce the predicted inverse relation. One such variable is a subject's expectations regarding the response which he will have to make in the particular situation. In most experimental studies of attitude change the subject is asked to display his own position after hearing a communication on the topic. Sometimes, either explicitly or implicitly, he is even told in advance that this is what he will be asked to do. Under these circumstances there may be subtle pressure to accept the view advocated by the communication, provided, of course, that there has been no public commitment to his initial position. People tend to adjust their views to a position for which there is social support. The subject may look for cues indicating the "right" position and the communication provides at least one source of cues for the normative position. Thus, the respondent's knowledge that his opinion will be measured may incline him toward accepting the communication. As a consequence, any subsequent evaluation of the source would tend to be favorable.

If instead, the subject is told that he will be asked to judge or evaluate the communicator, he is thereby cast in the role of an expert. He can more comfortably take a critical stance. In this instance, he may more readily view his own stand as correct, as the objective criterion against which the communicator is to be judged. Under these circumstances, if he were subsequently asked to give his own views on the issue, there should be little opinion change.

While this line of argument may be appealing, precisely the opposite effects are suggested by prior studies.[9] These studies suggest that focusing the respondent's attention on evaluating the personality of the communicator serves as a distraction which interferes with active attempts to defend against the arguments of the communication. Unable to muster combative arguments, the respondent more readily accepts the communication.

**Summary** In summary, this experiment was designed to relate both evaluation of the source of a communication and agreement with its content to three variables: (a) the presence or absence of an insult which occurred prior to the presentation of the communication and was irrelevant to its contents; (b) the discrepancy between the positions of the communication and respondent; and (c) the response which was stressed as being of primary concern and which was measured first–evaluation of the source (communicator) or expression of own opinion.

## METHOD

**Design** The basic experiment was a 3 X 2 X 2 factorial design with "after-only" measurements. The design had the following characteristics: (a) The subjects were unaware they were in an experiment. (b) They read one of three communications which contained identical content except for differences in the extremity of the proposed solutions. (c) Before exposure to the communication, half were told they would be asked to evaluate the communicator but no mention was made about giving their own opinion on the issue. For the other half, evaluation was not mentioned; instead, their attention was focused on stating their own opinion on the issue after reading

[8] Unfortunately, Sherif and Hovland do not experimentally manipulate involvement in their own research; instead, they point to probable differences in involvement between various studies, or in the case of their own research, between natural groups within a single study.

[9] Jane Allyn and Leon Festinger, "The Effectiveness of Unanticipated Persuasive Communication," *Journal of Abnormal and Social Psychology,* 62 (January, 1961), pp. 35-40; and Leon Festinger and Nathan Maccoby, "On Resistance to Persuasive Communication," *Journal of Abnormal and Social Psychology,* 68 (April, 1964), 359-366.

the communication. (d) Half of the subjects were insulted before reading the communication. The insult was inadvertent and irrelevant to the crucial communication and could not be readily blamed on the interviewer. (e) After reading the communication, all subjects responded verbally to three sets of items. One set of eight evaluated the communicator, a second set of five elicited the subject's own opinion on the topic, and a third set of five measured agreement with the content of the communication. Depending on whether evaluation or own opinion had been initially stressed, the evaluation items came first or last. Thus, order of measures was confounded with instructed set. (f) To minimize curtailment of defamation, the credibility or status of the communicator was deliberately left somewhat ambiguous. Nevertheless, it was clear from the communication that she had a facile command of the language and was equal to or above the subject status. (g) The basic experiment was replicated twice by each of 11 experimenters.

**Subjects** The subjects were 264 volunteer women recruited at shopping plazas in the greater New Haven area. The women each experimenter approached were judged to be approximately age 30 and slightly overweight. One third refused to participate.

**Procedure** Each of 11 experimenters ran two replications of the basic 3 x 2 x 2 design. Each of the 22 replications used a different random sequence of the 12 conditions. Experimenters posed as a representative of a local radio station who was interviewing people on the street for the program "The People's Opinion." After obtaining agreement to be interviewed, and assuring anonymity if desired, the experimenter asked the subject for her name and phone number. Then he asked her to read the statement on "today's topic," supposedly obtained in a studio interview with another woman. Under the conditions stressing evaluation of the source, she was told that she would be asked what she thought about the woman who holds these views; what kind of person is she? Under the conditions stressing her own opinion, the interviewer said he would ask her whether she agreed with what the woman said; what were her own opinions on the topic? Then, without looking at it, he took the communication from his briefcase and handed it to her. For those in the insult condition, the communication presented at this stage was a 250-word statement insulting overweight women for their lack of will power, sloppiness, laziness, rationalization, low self-esteem, ugliness, embarrassment to others, selfishness, and psychological maladjustment. Those in the non-insult condition also "inadvertently" received an irrelevant communication, but theirs was innocuous; it simply gave pro and con statements about movies and argued that they were here to stay. When the subject handed the communication back, the interviewer looked at it, professed regret for having given yesterday's topic by mistake, and after rummaging through his briefcase again he selected the appropriate communication. Reminding her again of the kind of questions he would ask (evaluation or own opinion depending on the experimental condition) he handed her the appropriate communication.

The crucial second communication was on teachers' salaries. It, too, was 250 words in length and depicted public elementary school education as poor due primarily to the presence of low standards and poor teachers. It argued that reducing salaries would eliminate poor teachers and attract those with a real dedication to effective teaching. The communication contained one of three solutions which differed in extremity; "lowering salaries a bit," "cutting salaries in half," and "eliminating salaries." In all three versions of the communication, the recommended solution was embedded at the start, the middle, and the end.

After reading the crucial communication, all women were given a card with seven Likert-type responses to use in answering the items. In conclusion, subjects were asked whether they preferred to remain anonymous, whether the first communication was upsetting, and if so, whether it was the content or the interviewer's error which upset her. The interview was terminated after explaining that scheduling problems sometimes made it impossible to broadcast a report of every interview, but that if her interview were to be used, she would be phoned in advance. Then she was thanked and dismissed.

**Experimenters** The 11 experimenters were male sophomore undergraduates comprising an honors' section of an introductory psychology course. Before interviewing, they all practiced their role. In view of recent evidence on intrusions of experimenter bias and error into data,[10] consideration of such problems

[10] For example, Frank J. McGuigan, "The Experimenter: A Neglected Stimulus Object," *Psychological Bulletin,* 60 (July, 1963), pp. 421-428, and Robert Rosenthal, "On the Social Psychology of the Psychological Experiment: The Experimenter's Hypothesis as an Unidentified Determinant of Experimental Results," *American Scientist,* 51 (June, 1963), pp. 268-283.

is warranted for the present experiment. While they may well have had expectations concerning the effect of the independent variables, there was no foundation for unidirectional expectations among them. In addition, a variety of precautions were taken to further insure the validity of the data.[11]

**Response Measures** The responses to the individual opinion and evaluation items were summed to produce three basic response measures for each subject. (a) A defamation score was based on the summed evaluation items after reversing scores on the favorable traits. Individually, these items asked subjects to evaluate whether the source was reasonable, knowledgeable, fair, nice, extreme, intelligent, a crackpot, and practical. (b) The second score was based on agreement with items specifically related to the communication's recommendation about salaries: eliminate salaries completely, cut them in half, reduce them a little, leave them alone, raise them. (c) The third score was based on agreement with the items concerned with the supporting arguments of the communication: elementary teachers are overpaid, lowering salaries would improve education, teachers' standards are too low, many teachers have the wrong attitude about teaching, it wouldn't be difficult to get teachers if salaries were reduced. An 11 x 3 x 2 x 2 analysis of variance was performed on each of these three major response measures.[12] In treating experimenter as a random variable and creating a mixed model design, the interactions with experimenter were used as error terms.[13]

## RESULTS

**Defamation** Analysis of variance of the defamation scores gave main effects for extremity, evaluative set, and insult. Greater communication extremity produced more defamation of the source ($F = 3.86$; $df = 2,20$; $p < .05$). Instructions stressing evaluation produced more defamation ($F = 8.74$; $df = 1,10$; $p < .02$). Insult produced greater defamation ($F = 6.06$; $df = 1,10$; $p < .05$). (See [Table 7-4] for means.) These results accurately summarize analysis of variance outcomes computed separately for each of the individual items comprising the defamation scale. For the eight single items, the direction of difference between the means for the three variables was identical with that obtained with the summed scores in 22 of the 24 instances. The two exceptions occurred for the traits "nice person" and "intelligent." On both, the mean derogation was slightly greater under moderate extremity than under high extremity.[14]

**Persuasion**

*Agreement with the supporting arguments in the communication*[15] In the analysis of the summed items on agreement with the supporting content of the communication, insult gave a main effect (see [Table 7-4] for means). The insulted women agreed *more*

[11] (a) The experimenters were told in advance the sources of experimenter differences. The problems created by experimenter error were discussed along with the issue of scientific integrity. (b) It was not absolutely compulsory that all class members collect data. Thus, one member who tried it and found it too painful was given alternative work on data analysis. (c) They were instructed to collect subjects' name and phone number, presumably so that a followup study could be made at a later point in time. These were obtained in large measure, although a few refused to disclose either their names or phones. Furthermore, they were instructed to comment on each interview, ostensibly so that subanalyses could be performed. All but one experimenter complied. (d) It was made clear that the analysis would allow detection of the difference between the results obtained by the different experimenters. (e) In general, class morale was high and they found the data collection process interesting though time consuming. There was no evidence indicating lack of conscientious data collection.

[12] While an 11 x 3 x 2 x 2 analysis of variance was also performed on each of the individual items, these will not be presented in detail. For all analyses reported, p values are two-tailed.

[13] We would like to be able to think that the reported effects would be obtained by any group of male experimenters. Therefore, this appears to be an appropriate conservative procedure in that only those effects which show up over the variability among experimenters' outcomes are considered significant. In another sense, however, a fixed model is more appropriate because we know that our experimenters are not in fact a random sample of experimenters. If a fixed model had been used, *every* reported result including those which do not quite attain customary two-tailed significance levels, would be highly significant ($p < .001$).

[14] While there was no main effect for experimenter, there were several higher order interactions with experimenter: experimenter, extremity, and insult; experimenter, extremity and evaluative set; and the four-way interaction were all significant ($p < .005$).

[15] As indicated, the items on agreement were separated into one cluster on agreement with the suggested solution and another on agreement with the supporting arguments. While this seemed appropriate on *a priori* grounds and gained further support from differences in outcome for the two sets, an analysis of variance performed on a single index of agreement composed of the total score on both sets of items was essentially consistent with the results presented for the analysis of agreement with the supporting arguments.

with the statements taken from the communication ($F = 17.10$; $df = 1,10$; $p < .0005$). In analyses of variance on the five individual items, insult yielded differences in the same direction for all five items and three of the differences were significant. While the effect of evaluative set did not attain significance ($F = 2.98$; $df = 1,10$; $.10 < p < .15$), the difference was, as expected, in the direction of greater disagreement with the content when evaluation had been stressed. Furthermore, this direction of difference was confirmed on four of the five items comprising the composite measure of agreement with content.

In treating experimenter as a random factor, the mean square for the interaction between experimenter and extremity is the appropriate error term for evaluating extremity. However, since the experimenter X extremity interaction was highly significant ($F = 3.78$; $df = 20,132$; $p < .0005$), it is perhaps not too surprising that no main effect was found for extremity.[16] If instead, the effect of extremity is evaluated against within-group error (fixed model) a significant interaction between extremity and insult is obtained ($F = 3.79$; $df = 2,132$; $p < .025$). Closer inspection (see [Figure 7-1]) shows that for the insulted women, greatest agreement was obtained under moderate extremity whereas for the non-insulted women agreement decreased as a function of extremity.[17]

*Agreement with the solution proposed by the communication* In an analysis of the five summed items on subjects' own opinion about teachers' salaries, none of the three major variables had a significant effect (see [Table 7-4] for means).[18] However, the F of 4.66 ($df = 1,10$) for evaluative set versus own opinion set approached the F of 4.96 which is significant at the 5 per cent level. When measurement of own opinion had been stressed, subjects' own opinion about teachers' salaries was closer to the solution advocated by the communication. This same direction of effect was obtained with the other opinion measure (agreement with supporting arguments). Furthermore, this result is consistent with the outcome of less defamation of the source under this condition. Both the main effect for experimenter and the interaction between experimenter and extremity were significant (experimenter: $F = 4.45$; $df = 10,132$; $p < .005$; experimenter X extremity: $F = 2.94$; $df = 20,132$; $p < .0005$).[19]

**Respondent Reports on "Upset"** The final set of questions dealt with the extent of upset produced by giving the wrong communication first. Those who received the insulting communication more frequently reported being upset ($p < .01$). However, the vast majority of respondents reported no upset. When contrasted with the highly significant effect of insult

[16] Three-way interactions were obtained among experimenter, extremity, and insult, and experimenter, extremity, and evaluative set ($p < .005$).

[17] Greatest variability among experimenters occurred under moderate discrepancy with some obtaining least agreement under this condition. Furthermore, the pattern of means in [Figure 7-1] (which ignores experimenters) was not consistently replicated in analyses performed on the individual items.

[18] These results stand in contrast to the outcome for "agreement with supporting arguments." This difference in outcome for the two measures of agreement is noteworthy and comes into focus more clearly when considered in conjunction with the recent examinations of the laboratory experimental situation as a social situation in its own right. The growing concern with the subtle ways in which the experimenter's interaction with his subjects in the laboratory creates compliance or resistance is reflected in Orne's discussions of "demand characteristics," McGuigan's *Psychological Bulletin* article on the experimenter, the recent attention to social desirability and acquiescence response sets (Marlowe and Crowne; Edwards; Jackson and Messick), Rosenthal's recent empirical work on subject-experimenter interaction, Zimbardo's notion of "response involvement" as contrasted with "issue involvement," Rosenberg's recent discussion of "evaluation apprehension" and others. The use of direct measures of opinion (attitude) in laboratory studies increases the likelihood of distorted outcomes in that the direction of effect produced by the experimenter-subject interaction—whether resistance or compliance—can readily be implemented. The subject knows how to respond in order to produce a given effect. In general the major concern in laboratory experiments has been distortion in the direction of compliance or agreement, particularly when subjects are volunteers. This may well be one of the significant sources of the well noted difference between laboratory studies of attitude change (which almost always show attitude change) and naturalistic or field studies (which typically show little or no attitude change). In other words, there may be little reason to be surprised if direct attitude measures show greater sensitivity in the lab than in the field. Interestingly, if one picks out the most indirect item among the "direct" items (those items measuring agreement with the conclusion) namely, the one item which reversed the direction of wording, it did yield significant effects consistent with the outcome on the items tapping agreement with the supporting arguments. It is concern over this problem that has led to the advocation of indirect measures of attitude. But who is to say which are intrinsically the "real" measures or "better" measures of attitude? We can only judge this by the extent to which a measurement technique yields theoretically meaningful outcomes.

[19] The interactions among experimenter, extremity and insult, and experimenter, extremity, and evaluative set were also significant ($p < .005$ for both).

[TABLE 7-4] **Mean defamation and opinion scores**

| Variable | Mean defamation | Mean attitude: Solution | Mean attitude: Supporting arguments |
|---|---|---|---|
| Communication extremity: | | | |
| Low | 4.33 | 5.75 | 4.95 |
| Medium | 4.79 | 5.73 | 4.91 |
| High | 4.89 | 5.78 | 5.21 |
| Insult: | | | |
| Present | 4.81 | 5.72 | 4.89 |
| Absent | 4.54 | 5.79 | 5.17 |
| Set and response measured first: | | | |
| Evaluation | 4.84 | 5.85 | 5.08 |
| Opinion | 4.52 | 5.66 | 4.97 |

NOTE: The seven response categories ranged from "very definitely yes" through "I don't know" to "very definitely not." The higher the score the greater the defamation of the communicator and the less agreement with the communication.

on opinion and defamation this relatively pervasive denial is noteworthy.[20]

## DISCUSSION

**Extremity** The results show that the greater the extremity of the communication, the more harshly the source was denigrated. Likewise, there was least agreement with the supporting arguments of the communication when it was extreme. For the uninsulted women, the relation between defamation and persuasion shows an orderly inverse relation over the three levels of discrepancy (see [Figure 7-1]). This outcome is in accord with the dissonance theory expectations of Aronson *et al.* for conditions where the communicator's status or credibility is low. Objectively, however, even though it was not explicitly identified, the communicator's status could not readily be perceived as lower than the respondant's. On the other hand, the effect of extremity cannot be handled by social judgment theory unless even the low-extremity communication was substantially discrepant from the normative pre-experimental position of the respondents. For social judgment theory if too little change had been advocated, persuasion would not have been maximal under low extremity. The generally low level of agreement (28 per cent of maximum) and fairly high

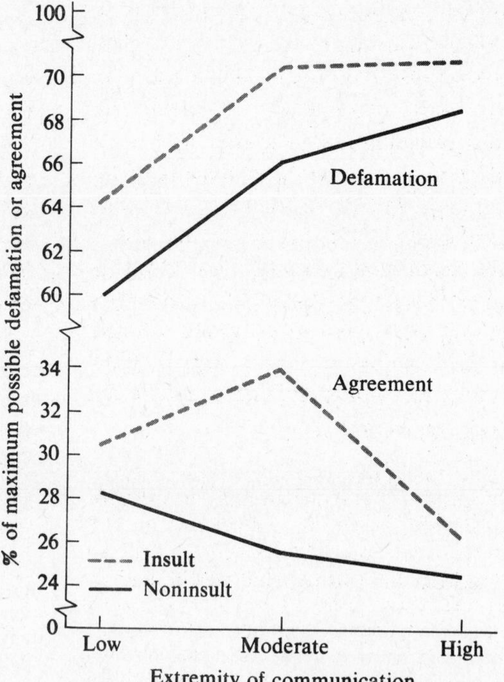


[FIGURE 7-1] Defamation of the communicator and agreement with the supporting arguments of the communication as a function of communication extremity and insult. NOTE: The dependent measures (means) are expressed in terms of the percentage of maximum defamation (or agreement) possible on the seven point response dimension.

[20] Taking this apparent equanimity at face value seems unwarranted. The question only allowed for a yes or no response. Dichotomous response categories cannot provide much sensitivity, particularly when viewed in terms of an experimental setting which probably implicitly pushed respondents toward the "no" category. The public nature of the interview, the likelihood that the respondent perceived the question as an attempt by the interviewer to seek reassurance about his earlier blunder, and the effects of pride and face-saving tendencies would all lead toward denying upset. Among the 18 insulted women who did say they were upset, 15 specified that it was the communication content which upset them, rather than the interviewer's mistake. (The fact that the other three were all subjects of a single interviewer suggests the possibility of a coding error.)

level of defamation (60 per cent of maximum) suggests that this may have been the case. Even after they had been exposed to the persuasive communication, less than 3 per cent of the subjects endorsed a position as extreme as the low-extremity position.

**Insult** The effect of insult on the relation between defamation and agreement is particularly interesting (see [Figure 7-1]). Insult not only increased defamation, but also increased agreement. Furthermore, both defamation and persuasion increase from low to moderate extremity. These results, which show that under some circumstances defamation and agreement can co-vary, are obviously opposite to what is expected if derogation and opinion change are inversely related.[21] In this instance there are several interpretations of the effect. One interpretation emphasizes displacement of hostility. Both derogation and acceptance of communication content can be considered as symptoms of a single response, the diffuse expression of hostility after insult. Defaming the source expresses hostility toward the communicator. Agreeing with the communication content which suggests that teachers are incompetent, have wrong motives, and are overpaid, expresses hostility toward teachers. When the communication urges more extreme action (cutting salaries in half versus lowering them a little), there is still greater agreement with supporting arguments of the communication, even though the increased extremity also increases defamation.[22] However, in the case of the highly extreme solution (eliminating salaries altogether) agreement drops drastically. This suggestion may be so radical that even the insulted women, hostile though they may be, cannot accept it. Note, however, that insulted women still agree more in this condition than the uninsulted women.

An alternative interpretation does not invoke hostility displacement but instead is based on the effects of guilt and lowered self-esteem. Reminding women who are overweight that their condition is disgusting and that the fault is their own might well arouse strong feelings of guilt and self-dissatisfaction. In other words, the insult treatment might have experimentally lowered self-esteem. Low self-esteem has been shown to be related to high persuasibility.[23] Thus, the greater agreement found after insult may be mediated by self-esteem effects. It is less clear, however, what effects this interpretation would predict for defamation. Consistent with the present outcome, however, and supported elsewhere as well,[24] is the interpretation that those who rate themselves unfavorably likewise rate others unfavorably. In the present instance, while the lower self-evaluation may only be temporary, its effects would spread to influence the respondents' more general view of the world. Thus, they denigrate the communicator. According to this interpretation, had they been asked to rate themselves, they would have shown self-denigration as well.

A third possible interpretation of the greater acceptance of the communication after insult points to the extreme and abusive language of the insulting communication. Instead of or in addition to arousing hostility, the insulting communication may have served as an extreme anchor. Containing strong, abusive language, expressed in a highly dogmatic style, it is conceivable that on a dimension of extremity it was even more extreme than the most extreme communication on teachers' salaries. Thus, contrasted against the communication on obesity, the teachers' salaries communications could more readily be judged as tame and reasonable, and thereby produce more agreement. On the other hand, the respondents in the non-insult condition first received a very reasonable, mild, unemotional, two-sided speech on the relative merits of movies and T.V. In juxtaposition to this communication, the extremity of the teachers' salaries communications may have been enhanced. In other words, for the insulted women the extremity of the communications may have been very slight, slight and

---

[21] Examination of within-cell correlations confirms this direction of difference under insult. It is important to note, however, that even under insult there is still the expected inverse relation between the two response measures. In the absence of insult the average (Fisher $z$ transformation) within cell correlation between amount of agreement with supporting arguments and amount of defamation of the communicator was –.48. Under insult, the relation is weaker but still negative ($r = -.36$). Both of these correlations are significantly different from zero but not different from each other.

[22] Yet, even here, where most relative agreement occurs, actual agreement is really absent. The mean response lies approximately halfway between the response alternatives of "I don't know" and "Probably not." In other words, though more hostile toward teachers, the insulted women under moderate extremity still tend to be on the favorable side of the dimension in that they tend to disagree with the communication's negative statements about teachers.

[23] Irving L. Janis and Carl I. Hovland, *Personality and Persuasibility,* New Haven: Yale University Press, 1959; and Norman Miller and Philip G. Zimbardo, "Involvement and Attitude Change," paper read at E.P.A. meeting, April, 1964.

[24] Donald T. Campbell, Norman Miller, Jacob Lubetsky, and Elliot J. O'Connell, "Varieties of Projection in Trait Attribution," *Psychological Monographs,* 78, No. 15 (whole No. 592), 1964.

moderate, while for the non-insulted women the extremity of the same communications was moderate, great, and very great. This argument would readily handle the difference in the opinion agreement data under insult and non-insult. Since the communications are more extreme under non-insult, agreement negatively accelerates as a function of extremity, whereas under insult extremity has a curvilinear effect. One problem with this contrast explanation is that on the defamation item on which the respondents were asked to rate the "extremity" of the communicator, the insulted women rated her as *more* rather than less extreme. In addition, contrast effects would not explain the effect of insult on defamation. Thus, other mechanisms would have to be invoked. Besides the previously suggested "dynamic" effects on personality such as displacement of aggression or lowered self-esteem, the language of the insulting communication may be responsible for the defamation data too. Being abusive and extreme, it may have induced negativism by creating a set toward or providing social support for using derogatory language.

The final choice among these rival explanations must be deferred. Though it is likely that they all have explanatory value, further experimentation will decide. However, one aspect of the insult data is clear. The greater acceptance of the communication content after insult would hardly be expected if insult invokes some of the supposed components of involvement. High involvement restricts attitude change.[25] Thus these data provide no support for social judgment theory, but at the same time, they do not refute it. It is possible that the insult did not produce any emotional arousal, or that emotional arousal is not in fact a component of involvement. A more likely interpretation, however, is that in order to obtain "involvement effects," emotional arousal must be more specifically tied to the relevant cognitive components. In other words, one must not simply be aroused–one must be aroused about one's own stand on an issue. Perhaps, too, any kind of emotional arousal won't do; the specific emotion of anger may be required.

**Evaluative Set** The effect of evaluative set is instructive. When evaluation was measured first, defamation was harsher and agreement slighter. The evaluation instructions of the present experiment correspond directly to the distraction manipulations of Allyn and Festinger and Freedman and Sears, yet the *decreased* agreement found under evaluative set clearly contradicts the previous "distraction" studies.[26] How can the conflicting outcomes be reconciled? The strongest "distraction effect" was found in the Festinger and Maccoby study. There, distraction was manipulated by presenting subjects with an irrelevant movie while they were attending to an auditory presentation of the crucial materials. This manipulation can alternatively be viewed as "high effort." In fact, the authors present anecdotal evidence in which subjects report difficulty in attending to the content of the crucial communication. The greater persuasion produced under this condition is consonant with other studies on the effects of effort.[27] In the experiments of Allyn and Festinger and Freedman and Sears the manipulation has probably also been mislabeled. In the so-called distraction condition of these studies, the instructions request the subject to attend to the personality of the source. In other words, the subject's attention is focused on the credibility of the source of the communication. In both of those studies the source was clearly an extremely high prestige person, an expert on the topic. By focusing on these communicator cues, defaming the source is curtailed. With defamation eliminated as an alternative, opinion change is the dissonance reducing alternative. In the present study, however, the source was much more comparable to the respondent in prestige. Focusing attention on this fact makes defamation a viable alternative to opinion change. Thus, the conflicting outcomes can be resolved in terms of the differences in communicator prestige. Were distraction *per se* the determinant of the outcome, the present study should yield the same outcome as the Allyn and Festinger and Freedman and Sears studies. The prestige interpretation is not only compatible with the internal

[25] Muzafer Sherif and Carl I. Hovland, *op. cit.;* and Norman Miller, *op. cit.*

[26] Jane Allyn and Leon Festinger, *op. cit.;* Leon Festinger and Nathan Maccoby, *op. cit.;* and Jonathan L. Freedman and David O. Sears, "Warning, Distraction and Resistance to Influence," *Journal of Personality and Social Psychology,* 1 (March, 1965), pp. 262-266.

[27] Philip G. Zimbardo, "The Effect of Effort and Improvisation on Self-Persuasion Produced by Role-Playing," *Journal of Experimental Social Psychology,* 1 (May, 1965), pp. 103-120.

results of the individual studies but also handles the inconsistency between studies.[28]

The outcome for evaluative set also emphasizes the importance of considering the interaction between response measures. Of course, in the present instance, it is impossible to extricate the effects of order of measurement *per se* from the experimental instructions which emphasized one or the other of the two major response dimensions. Nevertheless, the results imply that in an experimental design where one group differs from another not just in terms of level of an experimental treatment, but also in the presence or absence of measurements on an additional response dimension, the results become uninterpretable. In other words, the results emphasize the reactivity of measurements.[29] This reactivity of measuring instruments to the materials and other instruments among which they are embedded has been strikingly demonstrated in a recent study by Levy.[30]

**Experimenter Effects** The pervasive higher order interactions between experimenter and other variables are particularly interesting in view of the highly restricted nature of the experimenters' interactions with the respondents. In addition to the fact that the script was uniform and memorized by each experimenter, the role of the experimenter was deliberately designed to be as minimal as possible. Thus, the communications were all read by the respondent from printed sheets; the insult was not from the experimenter, but rather, from a third party; the response measures were all uniform among experimenters and read to the respondent. But obviously such precautions did not succeed in making experimenters alike. A vast array of other factors were necessarily correlated with the difference in experimenters. Experimenters collected their data at different shopping plazas, on different days, and at different times of day. They may also have differed in the type of woman they generally approached. Further, there were undoubtedly differences in their styles of delivering the script and multifold other differences. In view of the fact that experimenter characteristics interact with other experimental manipulations, particularly when precautions were taken to minimize the potency of such differences, we must seriously consider the interpretability of that vast array of social psychological experiments where results may be specific to the particular experimenter of the study. For instance, the experimenter interactions of the present study pose an alternative interpretation for contradictory effects of discrepancy which pervade the literature. They may simply reflect experimenter differences. Inspection of the curves for individual experimenters shows every type of outcome obtained in the previous literature on discrepancy and persuasion (as well as a new one—least persuasion under moderate discrepancy).

[28] Of course, innumerable other differences between the present study and the Allyn and Festinger and Freedman and Sears studies can be invoked to account for the discrepant outcomes. For instance, internal analysis shows that the subjects with extreme opinions were those who changed substantially under the evaluation condition (Allyn and Festinger, 1961). Perhaps most of the respondents in the present experiment occupied moderate positions. In consonance with the direction of effect in the present study, the moderates in the Allyn and Festinger experiment actually showed a slight boomerang effect under the evaluative instructions and positive change under the "own opinion" orientation. Other potentially relevant differences between the studies include the type of respondent, awareness of an "experiment," response involvement of the respondent, etc.

[29] Donald T. Campbell, "Factors Relevant to the Validity of Experiments in the Social Settings," *Psychological Bulletin,* 54 (July, 1957), pp. 297-312.

[30] Burton H. Levy, "Opinion Change as a Function of Personality-Oriented Communications," unpublished paper, Yale University, 1966.

# A FIELD EXPERIMENT ON FEAR AROUSAL WITH DATA ON THE VALIDITY OF QUESTIONNAIRE MEASURES[1]

HOWARD LEVENTHAL AND PATRICIA NILES
*Yale University and John Slade Ely Center*

It is generally acknowledged that information alone is insufficient to change attitudes or to influence behavior. Some form of motivation or arousal seems to be necessary for change to occur (Cohen, 1957; Klapper, 1960; Rosenberg, 1956). Among studies on the effects of arousal on attitudes those using fear-arousing materials seem to indicate that producing relatively high levels of anxiety interferes with attitude change (Goldstein, 1959; Haefner, 1956; Janis & Feshbach, 1953, 1954). It has been suggested that the interference is produced by defensive reactions, such as denial of vulnerability to the threat, which create resistance to persuasion while they reduce the tension generated by the communication (Janis & Feshbach, 1953).

An important assumption underlying this explanation is that denial reactions occurred because the rehearsal of the communicator's recommendations was unsuccessful in reducing the fear drive (Hovland, Janis, & Kelley, 1953; Janis & Feshbach, 1953). Therefore, finding reduced persuasion with high fear communications does not indicate a general superiority of minimal fear appeals. In fact, it is possible that fear facilitates acceptance of immediate actions because the recommendation can be instantly fear reducing (Janis & Feshbach, 1953).

The first aim of the present study was to investigate whether fear arousal would have different effects upon two recommendations differing in ease and immediacy of execution. The fear manipulation was based on the issue of lung cancer. Two different recommendations could be made about the issue: to stop smoking and to take a chest X ray. Taking an X ray is a fairly simple action, and since the study was conducted in a field setting with an X-ray unit nearby, the recommendation could be carried out at no cost and with little inconvenience. In contrast, stopping smoking requires the expenditure of considerable effort over a long period of time.

The second aim of the study was to investigate the effects of fear-arousing communications on actual behavior and, at the same time, to examine the relationship between stated intention (attitudes) and behavior. Questionnaires were used to assess intentions to be X-rayed following each communication. In addition, a complete list of users of the X-ray unit was obtained so that effects of fear on action and the predictive power of the intention question could be determined. Since few barriers to action existed in the setting and the intention measure was taken close to the time for action, a high correspondence was expected between intention to act and action (Campbell, Converse, Miller, & Stokes, 1960).

The present experiment attempts to overcome one frequent and serious criticism of attitude experiments (McNemar, 1946), namely, the absence of behavioral measures. It departs from many other attitude-change experiments in that it was conducted in a natural setting and used a nonstudent population including a wide range of ages, occupational roles, educational levels, and socioeconomic statuses.

## METHOD

**Design** Eighteen groups of 15 to 40 *S*s were run in an after-only design with all measures obtained following the experimental treatments. The groups were assigned to three treatment conditions. Two of these used emotion-provoking movies while the third served as a control and did not see an arousal film. Identical recommendations were given on smoking (by pamphlet) and taking chest X rays (verbal and pamphlet) in all treatments. Important changes in the procedure are reported in the relevant parts of the results section.

[1] Collection and analysis of the present data were supported mainly by grant CH 00077-02 from the U.S.P.H.S. to the senior author, and in part by funds from the Yale Communication and Attitude Change Program under a grant from the Rockefeller Foundation. The authors would like to thank Mrs. Dorothy Noyes Sproul and Mr. Ira L. Nichols of the John Slade Ely Center and Dr. Hans Abeles and Mr. Abe Brown of the New York City Health Department for their co-operation. Special thanks go to Mr. Charles L. Baldwin of the New York State Medical Society and Director of the New York Health Exposition for making the study possible.

We are also indebted to Professor Irving Janis for his encouragement and for supplying the communication used in the study.

**Experimental Setting** The study was conducted at the New York City Health Exposition held during August of 1961 at the New York Coliseum. The Exposition was reasonably well attended and was opened by the governor of the state and the mayor of the city. Numerous films and exhibits on health practices were shown and free diagnostic tests were given for tuberculosis, diabetes, and glaucoma. Thus, for a nominal admission ($.90), the exhibition offered $75.00 to $100.00 worth of diagnostic tests and an air-conditioned afternoon in the midst of a sweltering city.

The experimental sessions were held in a small theater, seating approximately 50 people. Signs advertising the program were placed at the main entrance to the Coliseum, in various corridors, and at the entrance to the experimental theater. Six *E*s kept close control over the sessions.

The senior investigator delivered a short talk to the audience which pointed out that: (*1*) the research group was from Yale University and was collaborating ". . . with other public health organizations in helping them test public reactions to health programs," (*2*) the study was testing public reactions to three separate health programs on smoking and lung cancer, (*3*) the programs were prepared by the "National Biological Research Society in Washington, D.C.," a group of scientists and physicians deeply involved in improving public health standards, (*4*) the particular program that the audience would see was determined by chance, (*5*) one of the programs included a ". . . sequence where the camera is focused at the site of a lung operation," and (*6*) "Since there are some people who prefer not to expose themselves to this kind of material, please feel free to leave now, or at any time during the program."[2] After a brief pause the program was announced and the experimenter concluded by stressing the importance of each person participating ". . . in only one of the program tests."

*Fear arousal* Different portions of the motion picture "One in Twenty Thousand" (in sound and color), produced for the American Temperance Society, were used as the fear-arousing communication in the experimental film treatments. The film credits, title, and producer were not shown. The motion picture presents the story of a young family man whose chain smoking led to lung cancer and ultimate removal of his left lung. For the Mild arousal condition only the first portion of the film was shown. This portrayed, in order: (*1*) the victim's discovery of his condition, (*2*) his trip to New Orleans to the Ochsner Clinic, (*3*) his interview with Dr. Ochsner in which the latter gives his strong opinion that lung cancer is probably caused by cigarette smoking, (*4*) very brief footage showing tumors on rabbits induced in the laboratory by cigarette tars, (*5*) the patient's preparation for surgery in which an intern substantiates Dr. Ochsner's opinions, and (*6*) a dramatized version of the trip to the operating room.

The High-arousal condition included the six sequences mentioned above. However, it also showed a 10-minute section of scenes from the operation in full color. The camera, focused on the chest, showed the initial incision, the separation of the ribs, the removal of a black and diseased lung, and open cavity and beating heart, and the closure of the chest. The redness of blood and flesh was present throughout this period. A few *S*s (5 or 6) were so distraught that they left during the sequence. Many looked away from the screen; some cried out; and most appeared deeply shaken at the close. No portion of the movie was shown in the control or Low condition.

*Recommendation* A recommendation to take a chest X ray was delivered by the experimenter immediately after the movies in the experimental film groups or after the statement that there would be no film in the Low (control) condition. In affirming the need for a chest X ray the speaker stated that ". . . a chest X ray is the only way of detecting the presence of lung cancer," and that ". . . the National Biological Research Society recommends that each of you who has not had an X ray, make use of the unit." In addition, the *E* pointed directly at the X-ray unit which was down the corridor from the theatre. The unit was clearly visible to all *S*s since the curtains making up one side of the theatre were opened during the announcement. Since the X-ray unit was very well advertised and was in a common area with the other test units (between the theatre and the Coliseum entrance) it was very unlikely that anyone in the audience had not noticed its location or known of its presence.

Following the recommendation, the audience was given the booklet, "To Smoke or Not to Smoke." It presented a summary of statistical and experimental

[2] Very few people left, under 15 from all groups, and those who were asked why they left gave many reasons; from being nonsmokers, to unwillingness to see the surgery and unwillingness to be in an experiment.

evidence linking smoking to cancer and death,[3] and repeated the X-ray recommendation stating that "... a heavy smoker (one who smokes a pack or more per day) should have a chest X ray at least twice a year." The tenor of the booklet is well summarized by its conclusion that, "The evidence appears to establish beyond reasonable doubt that cigarette smoking is a causative factor in the rapidly increasing incidence of cancer of the lung." It went on to state that "... in general, those who smoke less are those who live longer."

Questionnaires were handed out as *S*s completed the booklet.

**Questionnaire Measures** To accommodate a voluntary audience from many walks of life, the questionnaire was brief and simple. The items used included: (*1*) two measures of fear arousal, (*2*) questions on the reliability of the source of the program, The National Biological Research Society, and of two other sources of medical information, (*3*) a measure of acceptance of the theme that smoking caused lung cancer, (*4*) a question on intention to reduce or stop smoking, and (*5*) a question on the desire to take an X ray.

[3]It appears to the investigators that the study sample is probably representative of the Coliseum audience. Most of the visitors were looking about for interesting exhibits as there was not very much to see at the Fair. A few asked about the program but relatively few decided not to attend, and these usually because they were nonsmokers.

In addition, questions were asked which would serve as checks on randomness of assignment to conditions and to permit divisions of the sample for analysis. These included age of respondent, number of cigarettes smoked per day, and time since last X ray if the respondent reported having taken one within the last year.

The items will be presented and discussed in the results section.

**Behavior Measures** Names and addresses of all persons obtaining chest X rays were recorded at a mobile chest X-ray unit and were compared to similar information on the postcommunication questionnaire to ascertain which experimental *S*s actually obtained chest X rays.

## RESULTS

**Checks on Manipulation** The data were treated by analysis of variance using unweighted means (Walker & Lev, 1953). The *N*s in each case are the total number of *S*s who answered the question.

[Table 7-5] presents the findings for the measures of fear arousal and communicator credibility. It is clear that both film groups reported more tension than the Low control ($p < .01$) and that the High group exposed to the extreme surgical sequence reported significantly greater tension than the Mild ($p < .025$).

Viewing the films also increased the judged reliability of the program sponsor, the differences between

**[TABLE 7-5] Reported fear and ratings of communicator credibility**

| | Reported fear | | | |
|---|---|---|---|---|
| | High film | Mild film | Low control | |
| Smokers | 4.43 | 3.53 | 2.18 | |
| *N* | (61) | (64) | (11) | $F_{rows} = 3.80, p < .10$ |
| Nonsmokers | 4.07 | 2.96 | 1.00 | |
| *N* | (114) | (140) | (23) | |
| | <---$t = 2.27$---> $p < .025$ (High vs. Mild) | <---$t = 3.74$---> $p < .01$ (Mild vs. Low) | | |

| | Source credibility | | |
|---|---|---|---|
| | High film | Mild film | Low control |
| Smokers | 3.53 | 3.52 | 3.25 |
| *N* | a(53) | (56) | (12) |
| Nonsmokers | 3.61 | 3.58 | 3.21 |
| *N* | (103) | (117) | (19) |
| | | <---$t = 2.92$---> $p < .01$ (Mild vs. Low) | |
| | <------$t = 3.10$------> $p < .01$ (High vs. Low) | | |

the Low control and both the High and Mild conditions being highly significant ($p < .01$). For two irrelevant sources of medical information there were changes in judged reliability. Since the experimental film groups differ from the Low control on judged reliability of source as well as reported anxiety, increased attitudinal or behavioral compliance for High and Mild relative to the Low control can be due to either of these variables. Decreases in compliance for High and Mild relative to Low could hardly be due to enhanced credibility and credibility should not confound any differences between the High- and Mild-film treatments.

There were only slight differences between smokers and nonsmokers for the fear items. Smokers reported somewhat greater anxiety than did nonsmokers ($F = 3.80$; $df$ 1/404; $p < .07$).

### Attitude Measures

*Smoking* When asked if "heavy cigarette smoking (more than one pack per day) increases a normal person's chance of developing cancer?" nonsmokers agreed more strongly than smokers ([Table 7-6]; $p < .01$). *S*s in the experimental film treatments tended to be more certain than the Low control *S*s that smoking is the cause of lung cancer ($F = 3.75$; $df$ 2/398; $p < .05$). Therefore, as fear and credibility increase, the greater becomes the belief that smoking causes lung cancer. Since the great majority of *S*s agreed that smoking causes lung cancer, there was a ceiling effect for this item which was probably responsible for the lack of a significant $t$ between the High- and Mild-film treatments.

The means in [Table 7-6] show that smokers in the experimental film groups reported less desire to stop smoking than smokers in the control group. ("At the present time, how much inclination or desire do you have to decrease the number of cigarettes you smoke each day?"–Low vs. High, $t = 1.94$; $p < .07$; Low vs. Mild, $t = 2.36$; $p < .025$). Responses for nonsmokers ("At the present time, how strong a desire do you have to continue being a nonsmoker?") show no significant trends. If one combines the group means, the over-all result is significantly less desire to

**[TABLE 7-6] Attitudes and intentions for smoking and X-ray taking**

| | Belief that smoking causes cancer | | | |
|---|---|---|---|---|
| | High film | Mild film | Low control | |
| Smokers | 2.52 | 2.26 | 1.85 | $F_{rows} = 19.88$; $df$ 1/397; |
| *N* | (59) | (63) | (13) | $p < .01$ |
| Nonsmokers | 2.67 | 2.69 | 2.65 | |
| *N* | (110) | (136) | (23) | |
| | <---$t = 1.43$---> n.s. (High vs. Mild) | <---$t = 2.33$---> $p < .025$ (Mild vs. Low) | | |

| | Intention to stop smoking or stay a nonsmoker | | |
|---|---|---|---|
| | High film | Mild film | Low control |
| Smokers | 2.40 | 2.24 | 3.15 |
| *N* | (62) | (58) | (13) |
| | | <---$t = 2.36$---> $p < .025$ (Mild vs. Low) | |
| | <------$t = 1.94$------> $p < .10$ (High vs. Low) | | |
| Nonsmokers | 2.64 | 2.70 | 3.13 |
| *N* | (115) | (136) | (23) |

| | Intention to take x rays | | | |
|---|---|---|---|---|
| | High film | Mild film | Low control | |
| Smokers | 2.86 | 2.45 | 2.60 | $F_{rows} = 4.30$; $df$ 1/165; |
| *N* | (22) | (22) | (5) | $p < .05$ |
| Nonsmokers | 2.24 | 2.10 | 1.67 | |
| *N* | (46) | (67) | (9) | |

follow the recommendation in the High- and Mild-film groups (High vs. Low, $t = 2.26$; $p < .025$; Mild vs. Low, $t = 2.45$; $p < .025$). Thus, while the film groups find the source to be more credible and express more conviction in the relationship between smoking and cancer, they appear less willing to follow the recommendation to avoid cigarette smoking than the Low control. Despite the marked difference between the High- and Mild-fear stimuli and the accompanying differences in reported fear between these groups, there is no difference between them in reported desire to avoid smoking.

*Desire to take an X ray.* An examination of the means for desire to get an X ray ["At the present time, how much inclination or desire do you have to obtain a chest X ray? (There is a chest X-ray unit here at the Health Exposition where an X ray may be obtained free of charge.)"] shows some increase in desire going from Low control to the High-fear treatment but the differences are not significant. Thus, there is no indication that fear level affects desire to take an X ray. The data did not change on another analysis which included those *S*s who had had an X ray within the last six months. Smokers, however, reported stronger intentions to be X-rayed than did nonsmokers ($F = 4.30$; *df* 1/165; $p < .05$).

**Correlational Data** The treatment effects do not appear to be consistent with a single interpretation. As we go from the Low control to the High-fear group we find: (*1*) increased fear, (*2*) increased communicator credibility, (*3*) increased belief that smoking causes cancer, (*4*) decreased desire to stop smoking, and (*5*) no change in reported desire for an X ray. Though raising the fear level of the films has opposite effects for avoiding smoking (decrease) and X-ray taking intentions (slight increase) as predicted, the increases in X-ray taking intentions do not approach significance. Moreover, the significant decrease in desire to avoid smoking occurs in a contrast between the Low control with the Mild- and High-fear groups. Although this comparison confounds fear with credibility, the direction of the difference for the measure of desire to stop smoking is opposite to that which credibility could be expected to produce. But fear level does not appear to consistently facilitate or depress either long (smoking) or short (X ray) range action intentions as there are no differences between the High- and Mild-film groups, despite the fact that the level of fear was significantly greater in the former. Of course, if the fear level in the Mild condition exceeded the threshold for denial reactions it would be impossible to obtain a further decrease in desire to stop smoking going from Mild to High fear. But the level of reported fear in the Mild condition does not seem high enough to exceed a denial threshold. Moreover, the means show increased acceptance of the belief that smoking causes cancer. Thus, the hypothesis that increases in the fearfulness of the stimulus lead to increases in denial reactions does not appear to be supported by the treatment effects. A final possibility is that the significance levels for the contrast of Low vs. High and Mild for smoking are chance occurrences. The Low control group is not large, and the differences may be fortuitous.

To resolve the ambiguities due to the confounding of variables and the possibility of an inverse relationship between acceptance of the smoking and X-ray recommendations, the decision was made to take advantage of the considerable individual differences within conditions to examine the correlations between the response measures.

The correlations between reported fear and each of the major attitude measures, (*1*) smoking causes cancer, (*2*) desire to smoke, (*3*) desire for X ray, and (*4*) source credibility, are reported in [Table 7-7]. For smokers, the correlations between reported fear and desire to avoid smoking are significant in both the High- and Mild-fear conditions ($r_{High} = .40$; $r_{Mild} = .47$; $p < .01$), the greater the fear the greater the desire to stop smoking. For smokers, desire to take an X ray is also positively correlated with reported fear in both the High- and Mild-fear treatments. In the High-fear condition the correlation is significant using eligible *S*s, those indicating no X ray in the last six months ($r = .42$; $p < .05$), but is not significant when *S*s having had an X ray in the last six months ($r = .20$) are included. For the Mild-fear condition the correlation misses significance for eligibles only ($r = .34$), and is significant using all *S*s ($r = .47$, $p < .01$).

For smokers, then, both action measures are significantly and positively correlated with reported fear; the greater the reported fear, the greater the reported desire to act. On the other hand, neither the belief that smoking causes cancer nor the judged credibility of the communicator are significantly correlated with reported fear.

Since nonsmokers believe smoking causes cancer, and since they have no desire to smoke, one would not expect these factors to relate to reported fear, and they do not. However, for nonsmokers in the High-fear condition there are significant correlations between reported fear and the desire for X rays (eligibles $r = .41$; $p < .01$) and for fear and credibility

[TABLE 7-7] **Within-treatment correlations of reported fear and communicator credibility ratings with other response measures**

| | A. Reported fear | | | |
|---|---|---|---|---|
| | High fear | | Mild fear | |
| Variable | Smokers | Non-smokers | Smokers | Non-smokers |
| Smoking causes cancer | −.10 (62) | .11 (116) | .00 (62) | .15 (132) |
| Desire not to smoke | .40** (62) | .01 (112) | .47** (57) | .07 (130) |
| Desire X ray (eligible *S*s) | .42* (24) | .41** (46) | .34 (22) | .09 (65) |
| All *S*s (except those in last week)[a] | .20 (38) | .37** (64) | .47** (31) | .29** (92) |
| Credibility of source | .09 (56) | .30** (105) | .11 (54) | .05 (114) |

| | B. Credibility of source | | | |
|---|---|---|---|---|
| | High fear | | Mild fear | |
| Variable | Smokers | Non-smokers | Smokers | Non-smokers |
| Smoking causes cancer | .15 (55) | .34** (104) | .08 (55) | .28** (113) |
| Desire to stop smoking | .06 (54) | −.10 (103) | .31* (51) | .05 (111) |
| Desire X ray (eligible *S*s) | .43 (20) | .25 (42) | .27 (17) | .07 (55) |
| All *S*s (except those in last week)[a] | .24 (32) | .31* (61) | .16 (25) | −.03 (78) |

*$p < .05$.
**$p < .01$.
[a]*S*s having an X ray in the last week (nearly all of these were at the Coliseum) are excluded as are *S*s in two groups who knew the X-ray machine was closed prior to completing the questionnaire.

($r = .30$; $p < .01$). Thus, within the most intense fear treatment two significant relationships with reported anxiety appear for nonsmokers.

On the other hand, it can be seen from Part B of [Table 7-7] that ratings of source credibility produce fewer significant correlations with the intention factors. For eligible smokers in the High-fear treatment there are near significant correlations between credibility rating and desire for an X ray (eligibles $r = .43$; $n = 20$). For smokers in the Mild-fear treatment the only significant correlation is between credibility and the desire to stop smoking ($r = .31$; $p < .05$).

For nonsmokers there are significant correlations between source credibility and belief that smoking causes cancer ($r_{High} = .34$; $r_{Mild} = .28$; $p < .01$) and between credibility and desire for X rays ($r_{High} = .31$; $p < .05$). But credibility appears most strongly related to the nonaction attitude measures for nonsmokers. Since fear and credibility are unrelated except for nonsmokers in the High-fear treatment, it seems reasonable to conclude that action intentions are principally and independently related to self-reports of fear.

Finally, [Table 7-8] shows that for smokers, relatively high and significant correlations exist between desire to avoid smoking and desire to take an X ray. The data suggest, therefore, that in general there is no inverse relationship between desire for an X ray and desire to avoid smoking. Both desires are positively related to reported fear as well as to one another. However, because of the significant correlation in the High-fear treatment between the belief that smoking causes cancer and the desire to take an X ray, and the absence of a correlation between the belief that smoking causes cancer and the desire to avoid smoking, it appears that the High-fear treatment motivated some smokers to take an X ray solely to detect and treat cancer rather than to attempt to prevent it by giving up smoking. The similar correlation between the belief that smoking causes cancer and the desire for X rays among nonsmokers in the High-fear condition is probably due to the fact that fear was related to credibility for this group. The absence of these relationships in the Mild-fear condition suggests that the High-fear treatment had powerful added effects on these *S*s.

**Action and Attitudes** To determine the ability of attitude scales to predict X-ray taking behavior, it was necessary to exclude four groups of *S*s for whom X rays were not available due to a failure of the unit during the late afternoon and evening on the second day of data collection. In addition, since the recommendation to take an X ray was only for those *S*s who had not had an X ray within the last six months, *S*s who had had an X ray within that period were excluded. Before removing these cases, a check was made to see if these *S*s were less likely to take an X ray after the program. Of the people who reported having an X ray in the last six months (excluding those who had just taken one at the Coliseum) 12.5 per cent took an X ray after seeing the program. Of those who had not had an X ray within the last six months 43.1 per cent took an X ray following the program. The significant difference between these proportions (chi-square = 19.52; *df* 1, $p < .01$) shows

[TABLE 7-8] **Relationships between attitude and action measures for smokers and nonsmokers**

| | Smokers | | | |
|---|---|---|---|---|
| | High fear | | Mild fear | |
| | Desire to avoid smoking | Desire to take x ray (eligible *S*s) | Desire to avoid smoking | Desire to take x ray (eligible *S*s) |
| Smoking causes cancer | −.04 (62) | .43* (24) | −.18 (58) | −.08 (22) |
| Desire to avoid smoking | | .46* (24) | | .55* (20) |

| | Nonsmokers | | | |
|---|---|---|---|---|
| | High fear | | Mild fear | |
| | Desire to avoid smoking | Desire to take x ray (eligible *S*s) | Desire to avoid smoking | Desire to take x ray (eligible *S*s) |
| Smoking causes cancer | .07 (112) | .52** (44) | .13 (133) | −.10 (65) |
| Desire to avoid smoking | | .14 (42) | | −.04 (67) |

*$p < .05$.
**$p < .01$.

that the recommendation was followed by those to whom it was specifically directed, and the analysis of X-ray behavior will be confined to these *S*s.

To determine the validity of the questionnaire measure on which the analyses in the previous section are based, a tally was made of the correspondence between the stated desire to take an X ray and X-ray taking. [Table 7-9] shows a clear relationship between behavior and intention. Seventy-five per cent of those who indicated a very strong desire to have an X ray took an X ray. Of those who had a fairly strong, moderate, or slight desire, 41 percent took X rays and only 5 per cent of those who reported no desire were X-rayed. It is clear that the greater the expressed desire, the more likely one is to take X rays (chi-square = 32.00; *df* 2; $p < .001$). Therefore, the questionnaire measure of intention seems to be a valid predictor of action at least in the present situation where the response is readily and easily available to all *S*s.

**Behavior and Fear Arousal** Since action was related to expressed intention to act, the same relationships can be expected between the treatment effects and action as those reported between the treatments and intentions. A count of the eligible *S*s taking X rays showed that 45 per cent (36/80) of the High-, 44 per cent (28/64) of the Mild-, and 31 per cent (5/16) of the Low-control *S*s took chest X rays. As no difference exists between the groups viewing the film (High and Medium fear) they were combined and compared to the Low-fear conditions. The difference between the two proportions, High and Medium (44.44 per cent) vs. Low (31.25 per cent), is not significant (C.R. = 1.003, $p < .16$ one tailed).

[TABLE 7-9] **Relation between expressed intention to take an X ray and X-ray taking**

| Desire to take x ray | Percentage taking an x ray | Total *N* |
|---|---|---|
| Very strong desire | 75.0 per cent | 48 |
| Fairly strong, moderate, and slight desire† | 41.7 per cent | 84 |
| No desire | 4.6 per cent | 22 |
| | $\chi^2 = 32.00; df = 2; p < .001$ | |

†Percentages for each of the subject categories are as follows: fairly strong = 50 per cent; moderate = 47 per cent; and slight = 24 per cent.

Because of the relatively small number of cases, smokers and nonsmokers were combined. However, as smokers expressed stronger intentions to take X rays than nonsmokers it could be that the absence of a treatment difference for action is due to the fact that different numbers of eligible smokers appear in the different treatment conditions. A test of the distribution of smokers and nonsmokers in the three conditions did not approach significance (chi-square = .841; *df* 2). In addition, while the proportion of smokers (47 per cent) who took X rays is slightly greater than the proportion of nonsmokers (42 per cent), the difference is not significant (chi-square = .165; *df* 1). There is also no indication that the proportion of X rays among smokers increased relative to that for nonsmokers with increases in fear arousal.

Since the difference in X-ray taking between the film and Low-control condition was not significant, we have no evidence indicating whether the fearful movies produced more or less X-ray taking than might be expected with no exposure to the impressive communications. Unfortunately, the small number of eligible *S*s remaining in the Low control makes the first contrast equivocal. Because it is of interest to know if people exposed to the credible though frightening films are more likely to take an X ray than a comparison group equally well informed of the presence of the X-ray unit but unexposed to the communications, the proportion of eligible *S*s in our sample who took an X ray prior to the experiment was computed and compared to the proportion of *S*s taking X rays after exposure to the films.[4] The data showed that 25 per cent of the eligible *S*s in the sample had an X ray before the communication. The difference between this base-line proportion and the proportion of eligible *S*s taking X rays in the High and Mild experimental groups is significant (chi-square = 14.89; *df* 2; $p < .01$). While the findings show an increased rate of X-ray taking following exposure, this contrast confounds fear arousal with recommendations to act. Therefore, at best, the data merely suggest an increase in action as one moves from no exposure (25 per cent) to recommendations (31 per cent) to recommendations plus arousal (44 per cent).

[4] All *S*s undoubtedly knew about the X-ray unit before the experiment as it was well advertised, located in the most heavily trafficked area of the Coliseum and most participants in the study were likely to pass it on the way to the theater. Estimating the baseline from the sample ensures that the baseline involves *S*s who were equally interested in the study.

**Takers and Nontakers** Finally, analyses were run comparing X-ray takers to nontakers for reported fear and credibility ratings. As can be seen from [Table 7-10], X-ray takers tended to have stronger desires to stop smoking ($F = 3.83$; *df* 1/30; $p < 10$) and to report greater fear ($F = 3.44$; *df* 1/123; $p < .10$). There were no significant differences for the credibility ratings. Thus, the impressive fear-arousing movies increased X-ray taking relative to a base line and X-ray takers tended to report more fear than nontakers.

## DISCUSSION

The results of the present study pose a number of problems, some of which are the result of the limitations of a design contrived to fit a field setting, and others of which are products of the phenomena under study. For example, it is undoubtedly the case that the film/no-film division is responsible for the confounding of fear and credibility, because the film is a more impressive and "credible" communication. However, while increased belief that smoking causes cancer was associated with higher levels of fear and of credibility, there were no corresponding increments in desire to take an X ray and the treatment means decreased in the High- and Mild-fear conditions for desire to avoid smoking. Thus, while the data do not indicate that a more frightening film was a more effective mass persuader, only the decrease in desire to stop smoking suggests a process of denial in response to a fear-arousing message, as hypothesized by Janis and Feshbach (1953). While it would not make sense to attribute the reduced desire to avoid smoking

**[TABLE 7-10] Comparison of X-ray takers with nontakers on reported fear and other attitude measures**

| Variable | Takers[a] | Non-takers | $F$ | $p$ |
|---|---|---|---|---|
| Fear index | 4.10[b] (60) | 3.30 (67) | 3.44 | .10 |
| Source credibility | 3.62 (56) | 3.44 (65) | 1.6 | n.s. |
| Desire to avoid smoking (smokers only) | 2.64 (17) | 1.58 (17) | 3.83 | .10 |
| Belief that smoking causes cancer | 2.56 (59) | 2.56 (71) | | |

[a] Cases were taken only from the High and Mild film treatments.

[b] Analyses were performed on means for takers versus nontakers by High and Mild fear. Because no new effects appeared the averaged means are reported instead of the 2 × 2 tables.

to increased credibility, it is likewise difficult to attribute it to denial subsequent to fear arousal, as there were no differences between the High- and Mild-film groups on this measure despite the marked difference between them in level of fear.

Making use of the individual differences in reports of fear and action intentions gives a somewhat different picture of the effects of emotional arousal. The more tension and fear reported, particularly for smokers, for whom the communication is relevant, the stronger is the desire to stop smoking and to take a chest X ray. The correlational data point to considerable independence between reported fear and judgments of communicator credibility, and credibility is less frequently and less significantly related to the action factors for smokers than is reported fear. Credibility seems to have had a bigger impact on the responses of nonsmokers, particularly in influencing the belief that smoking causes cancer. Reported fear is associated with more variance in the action measures.

These findings raise a very puzzling question with regard to the fear measures. These indexes appear to be valid in that they reliably differentiate the Low, Mild, and High conditions. But, while the fear measures differentiate between the High and Mild conditions, there are no associated differences between the conditions on the other dependent variables, despite the fact that, within each condition, the fear measures are regularly related to action intention. While such an outcome may indeed seem paradoxical, it is clearly possible mathematically, as the correlations are concerned with variance around a group mean while the analysis of variance is concerned with variance of group means about some population value.

Psychologically this is more puzzling. Could there be two different types of fear, e.g., that produced by the treatment effect and that involved in the individual differences in self-reports? Since the treatment effects are based upon changes in individual reports for a group of *S*s, the same responses are obviously sensitive to both factors. What this disparity seems to suggest is that the effects of the treatments are not constant for all *S*s within a group. For example, in their earlier work, Janis and Feshbach (1953) reported that increases in level of fear produced decreases in compliance to recommendations to brush teeth carefully, but this effect occurred only for those *S*s who were reported to be high in neurotic anxiety (Janis & Feshbach, 1954). *S*s who were low on this dispositional factor showed absolutely no changes across treatments and may not have been motivated by the High-fear message.

Although dispositional measures were not used in the present experiment, it seems very reasonable to assume that a good number of the *S*s attending the Health Exposition would score high in neurotic anxiety and feelings of susceptibility to disease. Radloff (1963) has compared visitors to a health exhibit with visitors to the Smithsonian Institute and found that visitors to the exhibit manifested more concern with illness and stronger feelings of vulnerability to disease, particularly among the majority who did not possess a higher education. Since it has been shown that people who feel vulnerable to disease are more likely to take preventive health actions (Leventhal, 1960; Hochbaum, 1958) this group may experience little or no increase in motivation to act when threatened. In fact, if these *S*s are also high in anxiety, as Radloff (1963) indicates, one might expect them to be less inclined to accept recommendations when threatened. These *S*s may deny the threat, as Janis and Feshbach (1953) assert, or they may see the fearful message as verifying the inevitable and feel a sense of fright and helplessness. On the other hand, *S*s who do not feel vulnerable to disease should become increasingly alarmed and willing to act when frightened. With an interaction between treatment and subject variables, the presence of a main effect will depend upon the size of the group of *S*s for whom fear inhibits acceptance relative to that group of *S*s for whom fear increases acceptance.[5]

Of course, other alternatives exist. It may be that the differences between these findings and those of Janis and Feshbach are related to differences in the issue, i.e., the severity of the threat, and its familiarity. Whatever variables are responsible for the differences between these studies, unlike the Janis and Feshbach study (1953) where fear was never found to be positively related to acceptance, the present study strongly suggests that the amount of fear a person reports is directly related to attitude change and also related to taking recommended actions. While it is also suggested that the relationship of fear to acceptance varies depending upon subject dispositions, the evidence does not seem to indicate that, in the current situation, increasing the fearfulness of the treat-

[5] These hypotheses were tested in the experiment to be reported by Patricia Niles (1964).

ments resulted in denial of the threat.[6] Why then was reported fear directly related to action? One possible reason for this concerns the degree to which the communicator's recommendation appeared to be effective! With the considerable propaganda on smoking and cancer and impressive medical authorities offering X rays, the actions recommended for dealing with lung cancer may seem more effective than the preventive toothbrushing Janis and Feshbach recommended for preventing dental disease. Toothbrushing may just have seemed a feeble and inadequate protective device to ward off the rotted teeth and bloody gums seen in the impressive High-fear communication used by these investigators.[7] Thus, a clear separation must be maintained between denial or refusal to accept information relating to the reality of the threat, and the means of coping with it (Leventhal, 1960, 1961).

The final point of interest is the reassuring finding that the measures of action intention proved their ability to predict subsequent behavior. While this indication of a high degree of validity for a questionnaire measure is gratifying, it must be accepted with important qualifications. In the present setting the action could be taken soon if not immediately after completion of the questionnaires, and there were relatively few barriers to action; the response was free, took little time, and did not require a complex conceptualization of the situation. Moreover, there was little time or opportunity for new attitude change to occur. Official countercommunicators were not represented at the Exposition. In addition, informal countercommunicators were absent in the case of those attending the Exposition alone, while for those attending with others there was relatively little time for group pressure to operate. In fact, since many were exposed to the films together, the group might no longer contain a majority of people with opinions contrary to the communicator's. In this case, group pressure might favor the retention of change. In less favorable situations action should not be expected to relate so simply to intention. There is still much to be learned regarding the relationship of attitude and actions. Other studies in progress indicate that in situations more complex than the present, action and attitudes may be influenced by different factors.

## SUMMARY

Recommendations to have chest X-ray films taken and to stop smoking were presented to audiences attending the New York City Health Exposition. Materials which aroused three different levels of fear were presented along with the recommendations to test how level of fear affected the acceptance of the communications. The fear-arousing materials consisted of a motion picture and a booklet, both on smoking and lung cancer. To create three intensities of fear, varying amounts of the motion picture were used with different groups of *S*s. Some people saw the motion picture with a sequence, in color, depicting the removal of a patient's left lung (High-fear condition). Other groups saw the movie without the surgical sequence (Medium fear) and no movie was used in the other condition (Low-fear control). The booklet on the relationship between smoking and lung cancer was used with all *S*s.

The results indicate that people who viewed the motion pictures (High- and Medium-fear conditions) were more positive toward the sponsors of the program and were more convinced of the relationship between smoking and lung cancer. However, smokers in the High- and Medium-fear conditions expressed less desire to stop smoking than did those in the Low-fear control. There were no treatment effects for intentions to take X rays.

Correlations within conditions showed significant positive relationships of reported fear with (*1*) intentions to stop smoking and (*2*) intentions to take a chest X ray. The latter correlation was stronger for smokers than nonsmokers. Ratings of source credibility were unrelated to reported fear and infrequently

[6] Another possibility suggested by the correlations is that *S*s reporting higher levels of fear denied the possibility of lung cancer by accepting the recommendations. High fear was correlated with acceptance but uncorrelated with seeing smoking as the cause of cancer. More stress would be placed on this pattern if there were no ceiling effect for the "smoking causes cancer" question. It should also be clear that we do not reject the possibility that some *S*s denied the threat. The fact that some *S*s reported little fear in the presence of the frightening film is circumstantial though not sufficient evidence for denial.

[7] It is interesting to note that Janis and Feshbach (1953) found increased persuasion from a countercommunication for anxious *S*s who were initially exposed to the fear-arousing materials. Rather than supporting a denial hypothesis, this result seems to support Janis' (1958) later hypothesis that highly anxious people are less capable of reassurance and remain at a high level of tension. This could make them continually open to persuasion. Radloff (1959) also reports that for his anxious *S*s the reassuring aspects of the cancer exhibit only had a temporary effect in ameliorating *S*s' anxiety.

related to intentions. In addition, intentions to take X rays and to stop smoking were positively related. Thus, the correlational evidence is consistent with the hypothesis that fear facilitates rather than interferes with the acceptance of recommendations. It was suggested that the apparent inconsistency between the treatment effect for smoking and the correlation is due either to individual differences in reaction to threat, or to the fact that the treatment effect is an artifact of the small size of the Low-fear–no-film control group.

The relationship between the attitude measure of intention to be X-rayed and taking an X ray was positive and highly significant. The ease, and immediacy of action and several factors minimizing the likelihood of countercommunications were suggested to account for this finding. In addition, a higher proportion of the *S*s exposed to the fear-arousing movies took X rays than in a noncommunication base-line control. X-ray takers reported more fear than nontakers.

## REFERENCES

**CAMPBELL, A., CONVERSE, P. E., MILLER, W. E., & STOKES, D. E.** *The American voter.* New York: John Wiley, 1960.

**COHEN, A. R.** Need for cognition and order of communication as determinants of opinion change. In Hovland, C. (Ed.), *Order of presentation.* Published for the Institute of Human Relations. New Haven, Conn.: Yale Univer. Press, 1957.

**GOLDSTEIN, M.** The relationship between coping and avoiding behavior and response to fear-arousing propaganda. *J. abnorm. soc. Psychol.,* 1959, **58**, 247-252.

**HAEFNER, D. P.** Some effects of guilt-arousing and fear-arousing persuasive communications on opinion change. *Amer. Psychologist,* 1956, **11**, 359 (Abstract).

**HOCHBAUM, G. M.** *Public participation in medical screening programs: a socio-psychological study.* Public Health Service Publication No. 572. Washington, D.C.: Superintendent of Documents, Government Printing Office, 1958.

**HOVLAND, C. I., JANIS, I. L., & KELLEY, H. H.** *Communication and persuasion.* New Haven, Conn.: Yale Univer. Press, 1953.

**JANIS, I. L.** *Psychological stress.* New York: John Wiley, 1958.

**JANIS, I. L., & FESHBACH, S.** Effects of fear-arousing communications. *J. abnorm. soc. Psychol.,* 1953, **48**, 78-92.

**JANIS, I. L., & FESHBACH, S.** Personality differences associated with responsiveness to fear-arousing communications. *J. Pers.,* 1954, **23**, 154-166.

**KLAPPER, J. T.** *The effects of mass communications.* Glencoe, Ill.: The Free Press, 1960.

**LEVENTHAL, H.** Development of model for behavior in face of health threats. Paper read at A.P.A., Chicago, 1960.

**LEVENTHAL, H.** Health education-attitude and behavioral change. In Moss, B. R., Southwarth, W. H., & Reichert, J. L. (Eds.), *Health education.* Washington, D.C.: National Education Association of the United States, 1961.

**LEVENTHAL, H., ROSENSTOCK, I. M., HOCHBAUM, G. M., & CARRIGER, BARBARA K.** *The impact of the 1957 epidemic of influenza upon the general population in two cities.* Washington, D.C.: U.S. Dept. of Health, Ed. and Welfare, 1960.

**MCNEMAR, Q.** Opinion-attitude methodology. *Psychol. Bull.,* 1946, **43**, 289-374.

**NILES, PATRICIA.** Two personality measures associated with responsiveness to fear-arousing communications. Unpublished doctoral dissertation, Yale University, 1964.

**RADLOFF, R.** An evaluation of the exhibit 'Man Against Cancer.' Personal communication, 1963.

**ROSENBERG, M. J.** Cognitive structure and attitudinal effect. *J. abnorm. soc. Psychol.,* 1956, **53**, 367-372.

**WALKER, HELEN M., & LEV, J.** *Statistical inference.* New York: Holt, 1953.

# THE POWER OF DISSONANCE TECHNIQUES TO CHANGE ATTITUDES*

EWART E. SMITH

New and unusual foods provide an opportunity for experimenting with attitude change. Here is a report of experiments conducted with Army personnel to test the effectiveness of dissonance in inducing changes in attitude.

Ewart E. Smith has been engaged in military research for a number of years on questions involving group problem solving, acceptance of new leadership, survival training, and related subjects. He is currently Research Scientist on the staff of the Los Angeles Division of the Matrix Corporation.

The Army Quartermaster recently presented the Matrix Corporation with the problem of determining the best methods for changing attitudes in military organizations. To find out, we undertook a series of experiments to evaluate the relative power of several techniques. The first objective of this research program was to select from the theory and experimental data on attitude change those techniques which might be applicable to changing consumer attitudes in military organizations. To be selected, potential techniques had to be (1) consistent with the culture and practices of the Armed Forces, (2) powerful enough to produce results of practical as well as theoretical and statistical significance, and (3) applicable to large numbers of personnel simultaneously even when the majority attitude might be one of opposition to the intended change. The next objective was to compare empirically the relative power of these selected attitude change techniques with each other and with methods traditional in the Armed Forces. Finally, we hoped to develop methods for applying these techniques in field situations.

## APPROACH

**Dissonance Theory** A large body of theory and research in the last few years in the area of attitude change has been based on the notion that man strives to be consistent.[1] This consistency concept was first developed by Heider, who discussed it in terms of a concept of balance.[2] Later work was done in this area by Osgood and Tannenbaum, working with the congruity principle.[3] Festinger, however, with his development of the concept of cognitive dissonance, has provided us with the best statement of the theory for use in the area of attitude change, where he has stimulated considerable research.[4] Festinger states that two elements of knowledge "... are in dissonant relation if, considering these two alone, the obverse of one element would follow from the other." Dissonance, according to Festinger, has drive characteristics which will motivate the person to reduce the dissonance and achieve consonance.

A number of interesting hypotheses have been developed from the dissonance principle and subjected to experimental test.[5] Of particular relevance

*This paper reports research undertaken in cooperation with the Quartermaster Food and Container Institute for the Armed Forces, QM Research and Engineering Command, U.S. Army, and has been assigned number 2148 in the series of papers approved for publication. The views or conclusions contained in this report are those of the author. They are not to be construed as necessarily reflecting the views or endorsement of the Department of Defense.

[1] The theory and research in this area is thoroughly covered in the special edition on attitude change of *Public Opinion Quarterly,* Vol. 24, No. 2, 1960.

[2] F. Heider, "Attitudes and Cognitive Organization," *Journal of Psychology,* Vol. 21, 1946, pp. 107-112.

[3] C. E. Osgood and P. H. Tannenbaum, "The Principle of Congruity in the Prediction of Attitude Change," *Psychological Review,* Vol. 62, 1955, pp. 42-55.

[4] L. Festinger, *A Theory of Cognitive Dissonance,* Evanston, Ill., Row, Peterson, 1957.

[5] J. W. Brehm, "Increasing Cognitive Dissonance by a *Fait Accompli,*" *Journal of Abnormal and Social Psychology,* Vol. 58, 1959, pp. 379-382. J. W. Brehm and A. R. Cohen, "Choice and Chance Relative Deprivation as Determinants of Cognitive Dissonance," *Journal of Abnormal and Social Psychology,* Vol. 58, 1959, pp. 383-387. A. R. Cohen, J. W. Brehm, and W. H. Fleming, "Attitude Change and Justification for Compliance," *Journal of Abnormal and Social Psychology,* Vol. 56, 1958, pp. 276-278. A. R. Cohen, H. I. Terry, and C. B. Jones, "Attitudinal Effects of Choice in Exposure to Counterpropaganda," *Journal of Abnormal and Social Psychology,* Vol. 58, 1959, pp. 388-391. L. Festinger and J. H. Carlsmith, "Cognitive Consequences of Forced Compliance," *Journal of Abnormal and Social Psychology,* Vol. 58, 1959, pp. 203-210. J. M. Rabbie, J. W. Brehm, and A. R. Cohen, "Verbalization and Reaction to Cognitive Dissonance," *Journal of Personality,* Vol. 27, 1959, pp. 407-417.

to the present investigation is the deducation from the dissonance principle that, if a person makes a statement or engages in behavior which is contrary to an attitude that he holds, he will experience dissonance. Furthermore, if other means of reducing the dissonance are not available to the individual he will be motivated to change his attitude. An example is the "sweet lemon" reaction of the executive who is induced to transfer from New York to a section of the country he does not like, and who immediately begins to "dislike" New York and to say that he is looking forward to living in Podunk.

Dissonance theory was selected for possible application to changing food attitudes because it is consistent with, in fact requires, an authority figure acting as the influencing agent who has some control of rewards and punishments. This requirement is obviously compatible with military situations, whereas many of the most common techniques using group discussion, such as those used by Lewin in his famous food studies, are not.[6] In fact, recent research by Kipnis has shown that Lewinian group-centered attitude change techniques permit the group to take an even more negative position than they previously held just as easily as a more positive attitude, depending on the averaging of the prior individual attitudes that occurs during the group discussion.[7]

Another advantage of dissonance techniques is that the theory predicts that they will be more powerful the more difficult the attitude problem: dissonance theory states that the more negative the original attitude, the greater will be the dissonance between the original attitude and the induced positive behavior and hence the greater the attitude change.

A third reason for selecting dissonance techniques was the prior work of Brehm, in which he demonstrated increased liking on the part of school children for their most disliked vegetable through the use of a dissonance technique, that is, inducing the subjects to eat the vegetable by offering them a positive reward.[8]

Zimbardo has suggested that, using dissonance techniques, a negative communicator may be a more effective influencing agent than a positive communicator.[9] This is predicted because there would probably be less justification (in the mind of the subject) for conforming to the wishes of a negative communicator, hence more dissonance when inconsistent behavior was induced, and thus more attitude change.

Previous research has generally indicated that those with opinions most discrepant from the position advocated by the communicator change them the most (see Zimbardo for references and discussion). These results are consistent with the theory, because the greater the divergence of opinion the greater the dissonance. We wanted to investigate this phenomenon, since the use of those with the most negative attitudes as subjects for attempts to change attitudes should increase the power of dissonance techniques, and such a selection would have obvious practical advantages in an applied situation.

**Leader Influence** The use of a group leader to present positively the reasons for the needed attitude change and to request that the group consider the change and try out the new behavior was included as one of the attitude change techniques. Leader influence techniques are currently the major method for producing attitude change in the Armed Forces and have been supported by previous research by Scollon and by Torrance and Mason.[10] We could thus compare with current practices the effects of the newer attitude change techniques being tested, and in this sense leader influence functioned as a control condition throughout the research program.

## THE GRASSHOPPER EXPERIMENT[11]

**Method** Army reservists undergoing evening training, mostly young privates with a sprinkling of NCO's, were told that they were to be the subjects of an experiment to determine the reactions of the men in

[6] K. Lewin, "Forces behind Food Habits and Methods of Change," *Bulletin of the National Research Council,* Vol. 108, 1943, pp. 35-65.

[7] D. Kipnis, "The Effects of Leadership Style and Leadership Power upon the Inducement of an Attitude Change," *Journal of Abnormal and Social Psychology,* Vol. 57, 1958, pp. 173-180.

[8] Brehm, *op. cit.*

[9] P. G. Zimbardo, "Involvement and Communication Discrepancy as Determinants of Opinion Conformity," *Journal of Abnormal and Social Psychology,* Vol. 60, 1960, pp. 86-94.

[10] R. W. Scollon, *The Relative Effectiveness of Several Film Variables in Modifying Attitudes: A Study of the Application of Films for Influencing the Acceptability of Foods,* Naval Training Device Center, Port Washington, N.Y., Technical Report NAVTRADEVCEN 269-7-60, printed document. E.P. Torrance and R. Mason, "Psychologic and Sociologic Aspects of Survival Ration Acceptability," *American Journal of Clinical Nutrition,* Vol. 5, 1957, pp. 176-179.

[11] Detailed descriptions of the three experiments, data presentation, and statistical analyses are contained in a report to the Quartermaster, copies of which can be received upon request from: Los Angeles Division, The Matrix Corporation, 14827 Ventura Blvd., Sherman Oaks, Calif.

the Armed Forces to unusual foods that they might have to eat in an emergency. Ten groups of about ten men each were served fried Japanese grasshoppers in open cans. Because most Americans dislike the idea of insects as food, the grasshoppers were seen as a severe test of techniques for changing attitudes toward food. There were four experimental conditions:

1. Dissonance, positive communicator. The experimenter was friendly, warm, and permissive throughout the experiment. He paid 50 cents to each man who would eat one grasshopper.

2. Dissonance, negative communicator. The experimenter was formal, cool, and official in manner throughout the experiment. He paid 50 cents to each man who would eat one grasshopper.

3. Leader influence. A sergeant with several years' experience, who had been selected on the advice of the officers as being highly respected by the men, gave the men a talk in his own words on why they should learn to eat survival foods such as grasshoppers. The sergeant concluded his talk by eating a grasshopper.

4. Control (no influence attempt, rationale). The men were presented with the grasshoppers and told the reason for eating them. There was no attempt to influence the men to eat them.

**Results** All subjects rated the experimenter on a seven-point scale on the item "The instructor was friendly and courteous," to determine whether the experimental manipulation to produce positive and negative communicators was effective. A mean rating of less than 4 would have indicated a negative perception. The mean (average) rating of the experimenter was 6.85 in the first condition and 6.40 in the second, with a critical ratio on the mean difference of 3.31†[12] (the other mean ratings are 6.48 for the third condition and 6.65 for the fourth condition). These results indicate that the positive and negative communicator manipulation did produce a differential perception of the experimenter on the part of the subjects, but it should be noted that this is a relative difference only and that the experimenter was seen positively in both conditions.

As the main objective of the research was to determine the most effective methods for changing consumer attitudes, the analysis started with the difference between the subjects' rating of the grasshoppers on a hedonic scale before and after the various attitude change techniques were tried out. These data are presented in [Table 7-11]. The hedonic scale, widely used in food research, is a 9-point rating scale ranging from "dislike extremely" to "like extremely."[13] It is scored by giving a value of 9 to "like extremely," a value of 8 to "like very much," etc., to a score of 1 for "dislike extremely." The two conditions which produced statistically significant attitude change were the dissonance technique with a negative communicator (condition 2), which produced a mean attitude change on the hedonic scale of 2.50, and the control (no influence attempt) condition (4), which produced a mean attitude change of 1.82. Condition 2 was significantly better than condition 1 ($t$ = 2.84†) or condition 3 ($t$ = 3.24†). Condition 4 also was significantly better than condition 1 ($t$ = 2.12*) or condition 3 ($t$ = 2.59*).[14]

These results support the hypothesis that a negative communicator (at least in relative terms) will

[TABLE 7-11] **Mean change in rating of grasshoppers on hedonic scale**

| Condition | $n$ | Mean change |
|---|---|---|
| 1. Dissonance, positive communicator: | | |
| Subjects accepting inducement | 19 | 0.63[a] |
| All subjects | 20 | 0.60 |
| 2. Dissonance, negative communicator: | | |
| Subjects accepting inducement | 10 | 2.50[a] |
| All subjects | 20 | 1.25 |
| 3. Leader influence: | | |
| All subjects | 19 | 0.37[a] |
| Refusing grasshoppers | 2 | |
| 4. No influence: | | |
| All subjects | 17 | 1.82[a] |
| Refusing grasshoppers | 2 | |

[a] $F$-test on mean change scores is 3.99†.

[12] Statistical significance at the .05 level has been indicated by an asterisk, at the .01 level or better by a dagger.

[13] D. R. Peryam and F. J. Pilgrim, "Hedonic Scale Method of Measuring Food Preferences," *Food Technology*, Vol. 12, 1957, pp. 9-14.

[14] It will be noted that the subjects who refused to eat the experimental food in the dissonance conditions were eliminated from the analysis, because they did not undergo the experimental manipulation, but were included in the other conditions, because they were subjected to the appropriate experimental variable. As this differential elimination of subjects raises the question of favoring the dissonance conditions in the analysis, the data have also been analyzed eliminating those who refused the grasshoppers from all conditions. This additional analysis produces significance levels identical to or higher than those given in the text.

enhance dissonance and produce greater attitude change than a more positively perceived communicator. The subjects in the dissonance, negative communicator condition changed their attitudes toward grasshoppers as a food two and a half steps on the 9-point hedonic scale, or from slightly more negative than the dislike moderately step to a little on the positive side of the neutral point of the scale. The failure of the dissonance, positive communicator technique (mean attitude change of only 0.63) can be ascribed to insufficient dissonance; the subjects in this condition were motivated both by the proffered reward of 50 cents and by their desire to please the more positively perceived experimenter. It follows from dissonance theory that the greater the size of the inducement, the less the dissonance and the less the attitude change. This interpretation is supported by the fact that nineteen of the twenty men in the positive communicator condition agreed to eat a grasshopper, whereas only ten of the men in the negative communicator groups did so. This difference in the number agreeing to accept the inducement and eat a grasshopper is statistically significant (chi square of 10.16†).

The leader influence condition was relatively ineffective, in spite of the seemingly effective presentation made by the sergeant. The subjects in the leader influence condition ate more grasshoppers than did the subjects in other conditions (chi square of 8.02†), apparently believing that it was consistent with the sergeant's role for them to behave as he recommended, but they did not feel it was necessary to agree with him. This result should not be surprising and suggests that the leader influence technique is an effective way of obtaining desired behavior while the leader is present but may not be the best method to change attitudes so that individuals will behave differently when the leader is no longer there.

The most interesting result was produced by the control condition. This was a no influence attempt condition in which it was expected that there would not be any significant change. Apparently, our subjects, like everyone else in our culture, have been subjected to so many attempts to change their attitudes that they responded favorably to a situation in which they were exposed to a new attitude with no pressure placed on them to accept it. They were told, in effect, "This is a learning situation: do what you will with it." Under these circumstances they approached the unusual food open-mindedly and were persuaded, in many cases, by the logic of this situation, that is, the need for soldiers to be prepared to accept survival foods. These results are consistent with some research done by Torrance.[15]

As noted in footnote 14, the results we have so far discussed on the dissonance techniques concern only those subjects who met the design requirements for these conditions by agreeing to eat a grasshopper for a 50 cent inducement. It is interesting to note that if the data on the subjects who did not qualify are included (see [Table 7-11]), the change score mean for the positive communicator condition is 0.60 and for the negative communicator condition is 1.25. We now find that the negative communicator condition is still superior to the positive communicator and leader influence conditions but is second to the control condition in effectiveness. If we analyze these new data, the only statistically significant differences are the control condition versus the dissonance, positive communicator condition ($t$ = 2.20*) and versus the leader influence condition ($t$ = 2.59*). These data reveal a serious limitation in dissonance techniques in so far as practical application is concerned. Although it is standard practice to eliminate from data analysis those subjects who do not in fact receive the experimental induction, and although this methodology is quite appropriate for determining the validity of dissonance as a theoretical concept, the elimination of those who did not accept the inducement is quite another matter when considering dissonance techniques as useful methods in an applied situation. If we wish to use dissonance techniques to change the attitudes of consumers, we must usually deal with the entire population and cannot discard from our analysis those who will not accept a given inducement. Thus, for evaluation as an applied technique, it would seem appropriate to consider the mean attitude change for the dissonance, negative communicator condition as 1.25, which includes the subjects who refused the inducement, rather than the 2.50 mean attitude change obtained on the 50 per cent of the subjects who did accept the inducement. Of course, it is possible to increase the size of the inducement to the point where all or nearly all the subjects will accept the inducement and therefore be subject to dissonance. However, the greater the inducement used to obtain the inconsistent behavior, the weaker the dissonance becomes and the less attitude change will be obtained, as was shown in the results on the dissonance, positive communicator technique.

---

[15] E. P. Torrance, "An Experimental Evaluation of 'No-Pressure' Influence," *Journal of Applied Psychology,* Vol. 43, 1959, pp. 109-113.

Additional information was obtained by dividing our sample into a high group who were initially more favorable to the grasshoppers and a low group who were initially more negative, as measured by the prehedonic scale. Analysis of these two groups indicated that the low, or most negative, group had a mean attitude change of 2.08, compared to a mean attitude change of 0.18 for the high, or more positive, group. The critical ratio on this mean difference is 5.64†. Apparently those who are originally most negative are most susceptible to attitude change techniques and, in fact, are the only ones likely to show appreciable change.

## THE IRRADIATED MEAT EXPERIMENT

**Method** The subjects in this experiment—primarily privates with a sprinkling of NCO's and one second lieutenant—were attending Army reserve meetings. Eight groups of about ten men each were served sandwiches made from white bread, all-beef bologna, and margarine. Half the sandwiches had green toothpicks in them and were described as plain bologna sandwiches, and half had red toothpicks and were described as irradiated bologna sandwiches. All the meat was the same and none of it was irradiated. There were four experimental conditions:

1. Dissonance. The experimenter paid 50 cents to each subject who would eat one irradiated meat sandwich.

2. Leader influence. The groups' sergeant gave a talk on why the men should sample and learn to like irradiated meat.

3. No influence attempt, rationale. The experimenter read the following statement:

> The reason for irradiating meat is so that it can be stored and kept good to eat without refrigerating it or canning it. Irradiated meat is one of the new foods the Army is experimenting with because it will keep in the field. The Army wants to know how the men feel about new, different, or unusual foods, like irradiated meat, because the new Army will consist of smaller, more mobile units than we had in past wars. These new units will be more on their own, and will move faster and more often than they did before. They won't have a lot of support personnel and big field kitchens, as this would slow them down. This means that the Army will have to learn to eat new foods in the field, foods that are easy to carry and easy to keep without refrigeration, like irradiated meats, if they want to survive. Tonight you can try one of these new foods if you want to.

4. Control (no influence attempt). There was no manipulation or attempt to change attitudes.

**Results** The most successful technique in this experiment was condition 3, the no influence attempt with a rationale, which produced a mean attitude change of 2.05 on the 9-point hedonic scale. An analysis of the mean change scores, presented in [Table 7-12], indicated that the no influence attempt with a rationale was significantly better than the dissonance technique ($t$ = 2.21*) or the leader influence technique ($t$ = 2.28*). These results support the findings in the grasshopper experiment on the effectiveness of the no influence attempt technique. It will be recalled that in the grasshopper experiment a reason for eating grasshoppers was given to all conditions, including the no influence attempt condition. We see again that no influence attempt with a rationale is an effective attitude change technique. The marked improvement in attitude with this technique is certainly large enough to have practical value. It also has the advantage, unlike dissonance, of being applicable to the total group rather than only to those who will respond to an inducement. The no influence attempt without a rationale produced a mean attitude change of 1.74, which is less than that obtained when the rationale was added but is a significant difference ($t$ = 3.21†).

The disappointment in this experiment is the failure of the dissonance technique relative to the no influence attempt technique. Although the dissonance technique produced a mean attitude change of 0.90, which is statistically significant ($t$ = 2.20*), it was much less effective than the no influence attempt techniques, both with and without a rationale. The data suggest that the relative failure of the dissonance technique in this experiment was due to the same factor that produced the failure of the dissonance,

**[TABLE 7-12] Mean change in rating of irradiated meat on hedonic scale**

| Condition | $n$ | Mean change[a] |
|---|---|---|
| 1. Dissonance: | | |
| All subjects | 20 | 0.90 |
| Refusing irradiated meat sandwich | 0 | |
| 2. Leader influence: | | |
| All subjects | 18 | 0.83 |
| Refusing irradiated meat sandwich | 4 | |
| 3. No influence, rationale: | | |
| All subjects | 20 | 2.05 |
| Refusing irradiated meat sandwich | 0 | |
| 4. No influence: | | |
| All subjects | 23 | 1.74 |
| Refusing irradiated meat sandwich | 0 | |

[a] $F$-test on mean change scores is 2.74*.

positive communicator technique in the grasshopper experiment. The attitudes toward irradiated meat sandwiches, as indicated by the pre-ratings on the hedonic scale, were not as negative as toward the grasshoppers. Consequently, the 50-cent reward for eating an irradiated meat sandwich was a larger inducement (relative to the resistance) than was the 50-cent reward in the grasshopper experiment. Since the inducement was relatively stronger, the subjects must have experienced a feeling of greater justification and less choice in eating an irradiated meat sandwich than they did in eating a grasshopper, and consequently felt less need to change their attitudes. This reasoning, which follows from dissonance theory, is borne out by the fact that every subject in the dissonance condition accepted the 50-cent inducement to eat an irradiated sandwich, whereas in the grasshopper experiment in the successful dissonance, negative communicator condition, only half ate a grasshopper.

This failure of the dissonance technique to produce a substantial degree of attitude change when the inducement used to produce the inconsistent behavior was sufficiently powerful that the entire population participated is clear-cut evidence of the problems in successful application of dissonance techniques. If a small, barely-over-the-threshold, inducement is used so that the subjects will experience high phenomenological choice and low justification for their inconsistent behavior, a large percentage of the recipients will not participate. If, on the other hand, the inducement is sufficiently large to cause everyone to participate, many will feel low choice and high justification for their inconsistent behavior and the amount of attitude change will not be impressive. This clearly supports the interpretation in the grasshopper experiment that dissonance techniques are a powerful means of producing attitude change if it is not necessary to produce change in the entire population. However, if the success of the technique is to be judged on the basis of the average attitude change of the entire population, then the no direct influence attempt technique with a rationale is superior to the dissonance techniques that have been used in these two experiments.

Although the leader influence condition produced the smallest amount of attitude change in this experiment, it is statistically significant ($t = 2.70^*$).

When the subjects were divided according to their pre-experimental attitudes toward eating irradiated meat, it was found that the mean attitude change for the low, or more negative, group was 3.10 compared to a mean attitude change for the originally more positive group of 0.89. The critical ratio on this mean difference is 5.01†, which again indicates that those whose attitudes are originally most negative are most susceptible to attitude change.

## THE INSTANT COFFEE EXPERIMENT

**Method** The subjects—primarily privates with a sprinkling of NCO's—were Army reservists attending Sunday meetings. There were six groups of about ten men each. Instant coffee was purchased at a retail food market and emptied into a large glass jar bearing a label indicating that it was a Quartermaster item. There were three experimental conditions:

1. Dissonance, one small inducement. The experimenter passed out to each subject sheets with the following information:

QM PROMOTION INFORMATION

**I have tasted the Quartermaster's new instant coffee and like it better than regular coffee. I think it is excellent coffee, and I think the Quartermaster should use it instead of regular coffee for the whole Army.**

Signed ______

Army Unit ______

The experimenter explained that these were testimonials that the Quartermaster would like to have the men sign so they could be used as ammunition in getting the Army to use instant coffee. The experimenter paid 25 cents to every man who signed one of the statements.

2. Dissonance, two inducements. The same sheets were handed out for the men to sign, but after all those who would sign for 25 cents had done so, the experimenter offered and paid 50 cents to the remaining men if they would now sign for the higher reward. After the new testimonials had been handed in, the experimenter paid an additional 25 cents to those who had signed first.

3. Leader influence. A sergeant who had been suggested by the unit commander as most able to persuade the men to change their attitudes gave a brief talk on why they should learn to use and accept instant coffee.

**Results** The primary data used in the analysis, as in the other experiments, were the differences between the subjects' ratings of instant coffee before and after the various attitude change techniques. These change scores are presented in [Table 7-13]. Only one subject (in the leader influence condition) refused to drink a cup of coffee. Significant attitude change was produced by the dissonance, one small inducement condition, with a mean attitude change of 1.92, and by the dissonance, two inducements (small accepted) condition, with a mean attitude change of 2.14. Both these conditions produced significantly greater changes in attitude than did the leader influence condition, with *t*-tests of 2.96† and 2.37* respectively. These results again indicate the power of dissonance techniques for changing food attitudes. However, the primary objective of this experiment was to evaluate the effectiveness of the two-step inducement in increasing the number of subjects participating, and therefore susceptible to dissonance, without weakening the amount of dissonance experienced by increasing the size of the inducement. The use of the two-step inducement to increase the number of subjects participating and therefore susceptible to dissonance did cause an additional 23 per cent of the subjects to participate. However, their mean attitude change was only 1.67, which was not statistically significant, although greater than the mean attitude change of 0.47 obtained in the leader influence condition.

Dividing the subjects according to their original attitudes toward instant coffee into a more positive and a less positive group again demonstrated that significantly greater attitude change occurred in the originally most negative group, with a mean attitude change of 2.44 for the negative group and 0.97 for the positive group, and a critical ratio on the mean difference of 2.96†.

Data were also obtained on how much pressure the subjects felt was placed on them to change their attitudes toward instant coffee. These data reveal that the subjects who were finally induced to sign the testimonial by the 50-cent reward after initially refusing the 25-cent reward felt the greatest pressure. The felt pressure in this condition was significantly greater than that in most of the other conditions. The high degree of pressure experienced by the subjects finally induced by the higher reward to sign the statement

**[TABLE 7-13] Mean change in rating of instant coffee on hedonic scale**

| Condition | $n$ | Mean change[a] |
|---|---|---|
| 1. Dissonance, one small inducement | 24 | 1.92 |
| 2a. Dissonance, two inducements (small accepted) | 7 | 2.14 |
| 2b. Dissonance, two inducements (large accepted) | 3 | 1.67 |
| 3. Leader influence | 19 | 0.47 |

[a]$F$-test on mean change scores is 3.56*.

suggests that the degree of choice felt may have been rather low. The subjects may have perceived that the inducement would be increased in size until they were in effect forced to accept it. This feeling of increasing pressure to force acceptance would account for the failure of the two-step inducement to produce sufficient dissonance, and suggests that the multiple-level inducement technique cannot readily be used to increase the range of dissonance techniques.

## CONCLUSIONS

**Cognitive Dissonance Techniques** This research has demonstrated that dissonance is a powerful method for changing food attitudes. The negative communicator variation produced a change from quite negative to slightly positive toward the use of grasshoppers as a food. Dissonance techniques have the further advantage of being easily imposed upon a group from the outside by an authoritarian figure who has some control over rewards and punishments. In fact, it was seen in the grasshopper experiment that the technique is most powerful when used by a figure perceived relatively negatively by the target population.

A disadvantage of dissonance attitude change techniques is their complexity. In order to use dissonance techniques it is first necessary to determine what behavior on the part of those whose attitudes are to be changed would be inconsistent with their attitudes. It is then necessary to determine what inducement can be used to cause the subjects to engage in the inconsistent behavior and the exact level of inducement which is just barely sufficient to produce the inconsistent behavior. If the size of the inducement necessary for producing the inconsistent behavior is overestimated, as in the "irradiated" meat experiment, insufficient dissonance will be produced and there will not be a significant amount of attitude change. An even more serious disadvantage, which is related to the level-of-inducement problem, is that the technique does not include the entire target population. Thus we saw in the grasshopper experiment that although the dissonance technique utilizing the negative communicator variation produced extremely marked attitude change, it did this in only half the target population. If the size of the inducement is increased in order to cause a larger percentage of the subjects to engage in the dissonance-producing behavior, the inducement then becomes too large, in the case of many subjects, for dissonance to be produced (because they feel high justification or low choice) and insufficient attitude change is produced.

On the basis of this research, dissonance techniques can be recommended for changing attitudes about food, or almost any attitude for which inconsistent behavior can be induced. However, it would be necessary to use highly skilled individuals, and preferably communicators perceived in a negative manner by the population concerned. Dissonance techniques cannot be recommended at the present time in instances where it is necessary or desirable to change the attitudes of all individuals but rather would be useful where it is necessary to produce marked attitude change in some.

**Low-pressure Techniques** The low-pressure techniques discovered accidentally in the grasshopper experiment and cross-validated in the "irradiated meat" experiment are consistent with earlier research by Torrance[16] in which he found no-pressure and no-influence techniques to be effective. Presenting the subjects with a new food and permitting them to sample it without any attempt to pressure or influence them proved to be effective, and was even more effective if a rationale for trying and learning to accept the new food was included. This technique of exposure to a new food with a rationale but without any pressure has much to recommend it. It is consistent with democratic process and is therefore unlikely to produce negative side effects. It is a simple and easy technique to use, unlike dissonance, and does not require highly skilled personnel or pre-determination of behavior thresholds as do dissonance techniques. And, unlike dissonance techniques, it is applicable to the entire target population. Consequently, the no-pressure technique in combination with a rationale is recommended for changing attitudes where (1) it is important to reach large and entire populations, (2) highly skilled personnel are not available to apply attitude change techniques, and (3) acceptance of the new attitude can be shown to be to the advantage of the subjects involved.

**Attitude Change Targets** All three experiments produced results consistent with other research indicating that those subjects whose attitudes are originally most negative are the most susceptible to attitude change. In fact, the data have consistently shown that little if any attitude change is produced on the part of those subjects originally most positive toward the item used. Consequently, if it is not possible or feasible to apply attitude change techniques to an entire population, it is recommended that those subjects who are known to be most resistant be singled out for application of these techniques.

[16] *Ibid.*

# THE LOST-LETTER TECHNIQUE

STANLEY MILGRAM
*The City University of New York*

Throughout the summer and fall of 1967, the Communists staged a series of strikes, terrorist attacks and civil disorders in the British Crown Colony of Hong Kong. The aim was to apply pressure to the British and, some experts said, to dislodge them. The political sympathies of the 4,000,000 people in Hong Kong, an active, vibrant city precariously perched on Red China's doorstep, were largely unknown. Harrison Salisbury of the New York *Times* noted that pictures of Chiang Kai-shek were displayed in shop windows of the overseas Chinese merchants, but wondered whether portraits of Mao-Tse-tung hung in the back rooms. What exactly were the political loyalties of the overseas Chinese?

In 1967, the populace of Hong Kong stood firm. Despite the disorder, they did not join the Communist cause. The outcome was an unexpected relief to many Westerners, but it came as no surprise to our small research team. A few months earlier, we had obtained evidence that the majority of Chinese in Hong Kong favored Taiwan over Peking, and that they would act on their political loyalties.

The evidence consisted of several hundred letters, identical in content but differently addressed. They constituted the most recent application of an experimental method for assessing community orientations toward political institutions: the Lost-Letter Technique.

We shall return to the study in Hong Kong, but first, let me tell you how a lost-letter study is conducted—and why.

At the root, the technique is a simple one. An investigator distributes—drops—throughout a city a large number of letters, addressed and stamped but unposted. A person who comes across one of these "lost" letters on the street must decide what to do: mail it? disregard it? destroy it?

There is a widespread feeling among people that one *ought* to mail such a letter. This behavior is so widely acknowledged as proper that an item on the Wechsler Adult Intelligence Scale is based on it. This feeling also prevails in Chinese-speaking communities. In some circumstances, however—as when the letter is addressed to an organization the finder thinks highly objectionable—he may *not* mail it. Thus, by varying the addresses on the letters and calculating the proportion returned for each address, one can measure sentiment toward an organization.

The technique gets around certain problems inherent in the survey interview—the usual method of assessing attitudes. When a research team wants to test public sentiment on a social issue, it ordinarily chooses a representative group of persons from the community, and questions them. The methods for selecting a representative sample have been worked out in very careful fashion, and are so effective that a sample of only 1,200 persons can be used to predict national trends with great accuracy. But it remains true that once the person is selected for questioning, the information must come through a structured conversation. The resulting measurements measure only what the person *says.* This exclusive focus on verbal accounts, though of great utility, seems an unwise fixation in any scientific social psychology. It ought to be possible to measure *deeds* on a large scale and in a way that permits experimental variation.

In the lost-letter method, the respondent is not asked to speak; instead he is presented with a chance to act in regard to an object with political and social attributes. The basic premise of the technique is that his action will tell us something of how he relates to that object. By mailing the lost letter, he aids the organization in question; by disregarding or destroying the letter he hinders it. And he has defined his relationship toward the organization by the quality of his actions.

People confronted with interviews and questionnaires know they are in a special situation. They know that they have been chosen for study and that their behavior will be scrutinized. As Milton Rosenberg of the University of Chicago has shown, their concern with the way their responses will be evaluated can have a strong effect on what they say.

This problem is particularly acute in research concerning politically sensitive issues. A Chinese merchant in Kowloon is unlikely to tell an interviewer that he is willing to take actions to advance the fortunes of Peking.

Several years ago, in my graduate research seminar at Yale, I, along with Leon Mann and Susan Harter,

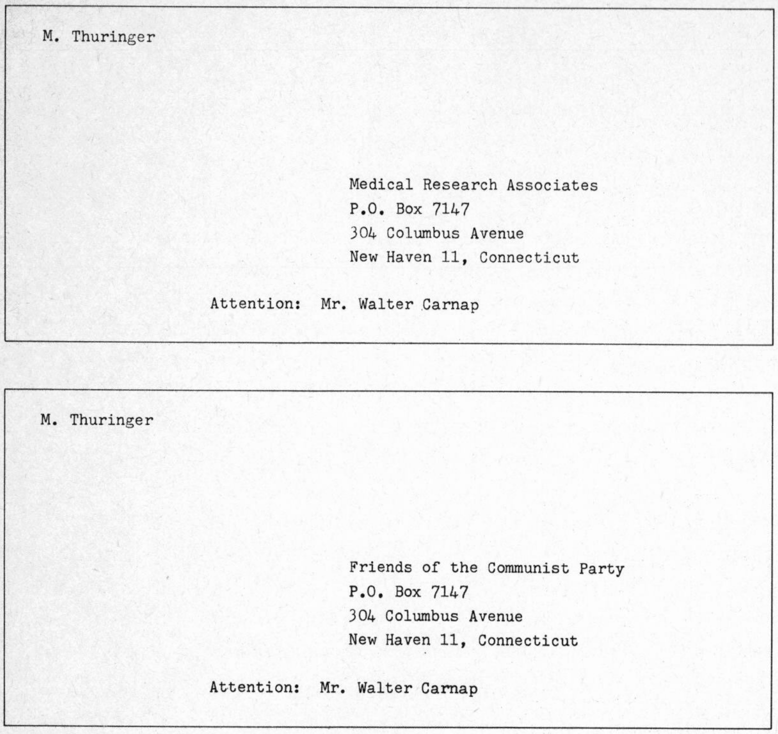

M. Thuringer

Medical Research Associates
P.O. Box 7147
304 Columbus Avenue
New Haven 11, Connecticut

Attention: Mr. Walter Carnap

M. Thuringer

Friends of the Communist Party
P.O. Box 7147
304 Columbus Avenue
New Haven 11, Connecticut

Attention: Mr. Walter Carnap

[FIGURE 7-2] How envelopes were addressed.

developed a technique that avoided these problems—one that would measure attitudes without people's knowledge, through their actions instead of their words. The lost-letter technique was one solution. Lost letters have been used to inflame a populace and to study personal honesty, but we were interested in using the returns as a clue to how people felt and—more important—how they would act toward different political organizations. The information we gained would be sociological, not psychological. We would not know about the individuals who returned the letters, but we would have a return rate specific to each organization, and thus useful for certain purposes. The nature of the procedure guaranteed the anonymity of those who took part.

## NAZIS AND COMMUNISTS

The first study, carried out in New Haven, was intended not to tell us something new about the world, but to show whether the technique would work at all. Members of the seminar addressed 100 envelopes each to two organizations that would doubtless prove unpopular with New Havenites, *Friends of the Nazi Party* and *Friends of the Communist Party.* As a control, we addressed 100 more to an organization about which we expected people to feel positively, *Medical Research Associates,* and 100 to a private person, *Mr. Walter Carnap.* [See Figure 7-2.]

The envelopes, all addressed to the same post-office box in New Haven, contained identical letters. The letter was straightforward but, we felt, could interact suggestively with each address. [See Figure 7-3.]

We distributed the letters in 10 preselected districts in New Haven—on sidewalks, in outdoor phone booths, in shops, and under automobile windshield wipers (with a penciled note saying "found near car"). Each letter had been unobtrusively coded for placement and section of city and, in a final bit of cloak-and-daggersmanship, each envelope was sealed in a way that would show us later whether or not it had been opened. Then we waited. In a few days the letters came in, and as we had predicted—in unequal numbers. Whereas 72 per cent of the Medical Research letters and 71 per cent of the personal letters came back, just one-quarter of the Nazi and Communist letters were returned. [See Table 7-14.]

A considerable number of the envelopes had been

4/3/63

Dear Walter,

Just a note to tell you that the plans have been changed. The speaker can't be in New Haven in time for next week's meeting, so bring the two reels of film instead. My guess is the film will have a very good effect on the group, particularly the new members. I'll try to get a few recent acquaintances to show up.

Grace and I are flying to Chicago as usual, but we'll be back in time for the meeting. Regards from my brother, and keep up the good work.

Best,

Max

[FIGURE 7-3] Letter for all seasons. The wording of lost letter in New Haven test is ambiguous enough to be addressed to Friends of the Communist Party or to Medical Research Associates.

opened: 40 per cent of the Communist letters, 32 per cent of the Nazi ones, and 25 per cent of the Medical-Research letters. Apparently people were more reluctant to tamper with a personal letter, for Mr. Carnap's mail came through 90 per cent intact. The least returned letters were also the most opened. The trend held not only from letter to letter, but from location to location.

The initial results and the discrepant return rates showed that the basic premise of the technique held up: the probability of lost letters being returned depends on the political and social attributes of the organization to which they are addressed. Having established this, we could then apply the lost-letter technique to other circumstances where the answers were hard to obtain by conventional means.

**[TABLE 7-14]**

| Address | Placement | | | | |
|---|---|---|---|---|---|
| | Shops | Cars | Streets | Phone booths | Per cent return |
| Medical Research Associates | 23 | 19 | 18 | 12 | 72 |
| Personal letter | 21 | 21 | 16 | 13 | 71 |
| Friends of the Communist Party | 6 | 9 | 6 | 4 | 25 |
| Friends of the Nazi Party | 7 | 6 | 6 | 6 | 25 |
| Total | 57 | 55 | 46 | 35 | 48 |

In the realm of imagination the lost-letter technique seemed like a lazy man's social psychology, consisting of nothing more than dropping envelopes here and there, and waiting for the returns. But in actual practice, the physical distribution of letters to predesignated locations is a difficult and exhausting chore. Aching feet were common. We tried distributing the letters from a moving car, but this had to be done in darkness. The envelopes tended not to fall where we meant them to; also, as often as not, they landed wrong-side up.

Later, we tried an air drop over Worcester, Massachusetts (after requesting and receiving an official exemption from the city's littering ordinances). This did not work well either. Many letters, of course, came to rest on rooftops, in trees and in ponds. Worse still, many were swept directly into the aileron structure of the Piper Colt, endangering not only the results but the safety of the plane, pilot and distributor. In the end, we never did find a substitute for legwork.

To facilitate the research, some legal spadework seemed useful. We obtained permission of the Post Office Department to use the names of fictitious organizations. And a week before the New Haven study began, I told the F.B.I. of our work, hoping to save our Government the expense of pursuing an illusory conspiracy. The agent I spoke with seemed appreciative and even offered to let me know how many reports his office received from the citizenry. As things turned out, however, when I phoned again, the agent said he had forgotten my earlier call. Half the force, he hinted, was out on the case. The number of reports that had come in was now classified and unavailable to me.

## ON RACE

The New Haven study showed that the technique could work. We next wanted to see if it could be applied to a current social issue. In 1963, tensions over racial integration in the Southern states were at a peak. Newspaper headlines reported dramatic confrontations at motels and restaurants. A Yale graduate student, Mr. Taketo Murata, drove south from New Haven with a batch of letters addressed to pro-civil rights groups and anti-civil rights groups. He dispersed them in black and in white neighborhoods in North Carolina tobacco towns. Inside, as before, was the same letter. The returns showed a neat reversal across neighborhoods. In black neighborhoods, the pro-civil rights letters were returned in greater numbers, while from Caucasian residential areas the "Council for White Neighborhoods" came in more strongly. Thus the technique seemed applicable to a real social issue and was also responsive to a demographic variable. Mann and Murata repeated the study in a Connecticut industrial town, where the results, though tending in the same direction, were less clear, reflecting the more moderate sentiments on racial integration in the North at that time. The growth of militant Northern civil rights activity in the past six years could conceivably lead to stronger differentials in response. In general the more divisive a society, the more likely the differences in return rates of letters relevant to social issues. In an extreme case, when a country has polarized into hostile camps, neither side will mail any letters for the other.

**[TABLE 7-15]**

| | Johnson | Goldwater |
|---|---|---|
| Committee to Elect | 25 | 9 |
| Committee to Defeat | 13 | 27 |

## AN ELECTION

The technique had one serious shortcoming: we had no objective evidence of its validity. True, the Medical-Research letters had come in more strongly than the political-extremist letters, and the civil-rights letters reflected the neighborhoods in which they were dropped in a way that made sense, but we needed an exact criterion against which the results could be assessed. The 1964 Presidential election provided the opportunity. Working closely with Dr. Rhea Diamond, I distributed the following letters in several election wards of Boston: Committee to Elect Goldwater, Committee to Defeat Goldwater, Committee to Elect Johnson, and Committee to Defeat Johnson.

The results were summarized by the *Harvard Crimson* a few days before the election: "SOC REL FINDS PRO-LBJ BOSTONIANS WON'T MAIL LETTERS TO ELECT BARRY." And the historical record shows that the lost-letter technique correctly predicted the outcome of the election in each of the wards. But, although the technique identified the trend, it badly underestimated the strength of Johnson support. Overall, it gave Johnson a scant 10 per cent lead over Goldwater when the actual lead in these wards was closer to 60 per cent. This suggests that *the difference in return rates of letters will always be weaker than the extent of actual difference of community opinion.* Even if a person plans to vote for Johnson he may still be a good enough fellow to mail a pro-Goldwater letter. And some letters are always picked up and mailed by children, illiterates and street-cleaners. There is a good deal of unwanted variance in the returns.

In this election study the letters placed under car windshields provided the best results. [See Table 7-15.]

Thirty-seven letters for each one of the four committees were dropped. There seem to be two reasons for the superior predictive power of windshield letters. First, it is more likely that adults, and therefore voters, will encounter them. Second, a letter found on a car windshield, as opposed to one found on the street, seems more in one's personal possession and is more likely to be disposed of according to personal whim.

## MAO VS. CHIANG

The lost-letter technique really showed us things we already knew, or soon would know. It was not so much that the technique confirmed the *events* as the fact that *events* confirmed the technique. Could the lost-letter technique be applied to a situation where the answers were not clearly known and would be difficult to get? The situation of the 17 million overseas Chinese provided an interesting case in point. How would they respond to an extension of Red Chinese power? Were they pro-Mao or pro-Nationalist? These are questions difficult to investigate with ordinary survey methods, but perhaps they would yield to the lost-letter technique. I wanted to disperse throughout Hong Kong, Singapore and Bangkok letters addressed as follows: Committee for the Taiwan Government, Committee for the Peking Government, Committee to Overthrow Mao Tse-Tung, Committee to Overthrow Chiang Kai-shek and (replacing Medical Research Associates) Committee to Encourage Education.

Almost at once problems arose. Riots between the Malays and the Chinese began in Singapore just before our experimenter arrived. And in spite of written consent from the Malaysian Government, he was put back onto the plane almost as soon as he arrived at the airport. We postponed the Singapore study. The following year our experimenter in Hong Kong, a journalist from that city who had offered to distribute the letters and had been paid in advance, disappeared. After many months a Chinese colleague of mine reached him by telephone. The would-be experimenter said that in China research takes a *very long time.* In truth, he had absconded with the research funds. I decided to go to Hong Kong myself, stopping only in Tokyo to confer with Robert Frager, who was to assist me in this study. Informants warned us that distributing "overthrow" letters in the Crown Colony would be unwise.

In the end we used all five addresses in Bangkok and Singapore but only the pro-Mao, pro-Chiang and Education letters in Hong Kong. The letters themselves were a Chinese equivalent of the straightforward earlier letter. [See Figure 7-4.] All were addressed to a post-office box in Tokyo, where many political organizations are located. One serious problem was the possibility of post-office interference in the mailing of the letters. Even if the letters were returned to our Tokyo headquarters in unequal numbers, how could we be certain that post-office policy was not producing the result? Perhaps postal officials systematically removed pro-Communist letters while sorting mail. We therefore introduced an experimental control by personally dropping several coded letters of each type directly into mailboxes served by various post offices in each city. The controls arrived in Tokyo intact, assuring us that differences in response rates were not due to postal policies but to the different response of the man in the street to the political attributes of the letters.

We employed groups of Chinese students as distributors. The students prepared written reports, some of which captured the ambiance of the Chinese study. Typical is this one:

"This is the first job which I think most embarrassing for I have to drop 100 letters on streets and roads

Executive Secretary Shiu Sang:

We have previously arranged for a gathering of our friends sometime next month for the exchange of views. But I'm afraid that the plan has to be revised, since the central figure will not be able to be present in time. Will you please, therefore, bring with you the two reels of film to the meeting for the purpose of showing. I'm confident that these will be highly useful to our members, particularly those new members. I am also trying to get as many new acquaintances as possible to come.

I shall be going to Japan next week for the purpose of handling some routine official business, and shall be back as soon as it is through in order to be present at the meeting.

May I remind you to continue with your greatest effort for our common cause so as to ensure its accomplishment.

Best regards. All the brothers ask me to say "Hello" to you.

Your younger brother,

Ping Kai

**[FIGURE 7-4] Translation from the Chinese. The letter, addressed to a Chinese name as common as John Smith is to the U.S.A., reads [as shown].**

as I walk along in Kowloon side. The Colony is always crowded and the pedestrians seem to stare at me when I have the intention of dropping a letter which has been addressed and stamped. In order to carry out my job efficiently I went to several bus stops and knelt down, pretending to deal with my shoes. By doing so I left the letter on the road as I stood up and proceeded on my way.

"The dropping of letters became difficult as I came to Kowloon Isai Village, the re-settlement. Here the dwellers are very mixed. There are people even on the staircase which is dirty and moisty. However the letters must be dropped and so I just dropped the letters on the sidewalk casually and carefully. If some people stare at me, I just gave them a smile . . . It is a delight for me to observe in some areas where I have dropped the letters, the letters disappeared (as I came back the second time). Obviously they have been picked up by somebody else."

We found that substantially more pro-Chiang than pro-Mao letters were picked up and mailed. The returns were consistent, and taken together, the findings from the three cities showed a statistically significant pro-Taiwan feeling on the part of the overseas Chinese.

While I would hardly offer the superior return rate of pro-Chiang letters as definitive proof of the sentiment of overseas Chinese toward Peking and Taiwan, it is certainly evidence worth feeding into the total equation of political assessment. And it makes sense too. In Hong Kong, thousands of residents are political escapees from mainland China; and in Bangkok and Singapore many are engaged in small family businesses and would be hurt seriously by an extension of Communist power and influence.

Other investigators now have used the lost-letter technique to study attitudes toward Vietnam, and the McCarthy-Johnson primary in Wisconsin, with varying results. While the technique seems to reflect gross differences of opinion, it fails to reflect the subtle differences that are more typical of social disagreement. Yet when the study starts with an interesting idea, interesting results sometimes follow. For example, William and Melissa Bowerman, graduate students at Harvard, distributed anti-Nazi letters in Munich, and found a depression in the return of anti-Nazi letters in specific neighborhoods of that city. Thus, they pinpointed the areas of strongest neo-Nazi sentiment.

Some advice to persons who wish to employ the lost-letter technique:

1. In order to get significant differences between control and experimental letters, they must be distributed in sufficiently large numbers. No fewer than 100 and preferably as many as 200 letters should be assigned to each cell of the experimental design. There is much uncontrolled variance and it can only be transcended by using large numbers.

2. The lost-letter technique is not very good for subtle issues, or in connection with issues that do not arouse very strong feelings. It only works for issues in which there is clear-cut polarization, and which arouse a high level of emotional involvement.

3. There is no simple way to estimate population parameters from the differential response rates. On the whole, the procedure should not be used where sample survey technique is equally convenient or applicable, but primarily when the respondents' knowledge that he is involved in a study seriously distorts his response.

# WALLACE SUPPORTERS AND ADHERENCE TO "LAW AND ORDER"[1]

LAWRENCE S. WRIGHTSMAN
*George Peabody College for Teachers*

Cars bearing Davidson County, Tennessee, license plates were observed in public parking lots between the period of November 1 to November 5, 1968, in order to determine if they possessed (*a*) a county auto tax sticker, costing $15 and required as of November 1, or (*b*) a bumper sticker supporting any of the three major presidential candidates. Cars without a presidential sticker, parked adjacent to the above cars, served as controls. The results were as follows: 74.8% of 361 Wallace cars displayed the tax sticker; 86.5% of 304 Nixon cars; 86.5% of 178 Humphrey cars; and 81.25% of 843 controls. Differences in percentages were statistically significant. It was concluded that Wallace supporters less frequently obeyed this law. Possible reasons for this were explored; differences in voters' socioeconomic status and observers' candidate preferences do not appear to be explanations.

During the 1968 presidential election campaign, the issue of "law and order" was a salient one. Though it was often unclear as to just what surplus meanings were attached to this provocative phrase, it was more strongly advanced as a campaign issue by George Wallace than by the other two major candidates. The present study was generated by a curiosity as to whether supporters of Wallace were, in fact, more law abiding than were supporters of the other candidates. A second reason for doing the study was that locally, a convenient opportunity to measure obedience of law occurred just at the time of the election.

Obedience to the law is a variable, which if measured by a self-report questionnaire or interviews, is clearly classifiable as a "reactive" one (Webb, Campbell, Schwartz, & Sechrest, 1966); that is, a respondent's response might well be colored or altered by his considerations of social desirability, his needs to appear law abiding, etc. Therefore, a behavioral "unobtrusive measure" of law obedience was sought—one which could be assessed without having to ask the subject anything at all.

An excellent unobtrusive measure of obeying one law manifested itself in Nashville and Davidson County, Tennessee, during the pre-election period. Earlier in the fall of 1968 the Metropolitan Council of Nashville-Davidson County (a consolidated government) passed a law requiring all motor vehicles in Davidson County to display a new automobile tax sticker, effective November 1, 1968. The sticker (henceforth to be called "the Metro sticker") went on sale by mail and at the County Courthouse early in October, at a price of $15 per vehicle. It was announced early in October that failure to possess a Metro sticker after November 1 was illegal and subject to a $50 fine. (In actuality, on Thursday, October 31, it was announced that two days of grace—till midnight Saturday, November 2—would be given because of the long lines waiting to buy the sticker.) Abetted by an influential local newspaper, a great deal of public sentiment developed against the sticker, not only because it was an added tax, but also because the present municipal administration had campaigned against an earlier tax sticker established by the previous administration. Shortly after the present administration took office it terminated requirement of the then-current $10 sticker, only to institute its higher priced one in 1968 (6 years later). However, despite grumbling, many Davidson Countians bought the sticker and slapped it on their car's windshield.

Thus, presence of the Metro sticker on the car served as an operational definition of obeying the law. (It is recognized that this refers to obeyance of only one specific law.) Support of a presidential candidate was assessed by observing the car's bumpers and back window to determine the presence of a

[1]This study was completed as a project by the Psychology 270 class at Peabody College during the fall semester, 1968. The students and the instructor (and assorted spouses) served as the observer-recorders. This study was completed without the expenditure of any funds from the federal government or private foundations; the only cost to Peabody College was for the typing and duplication of this report. The author wishes to thank the following for their useful comments on an earlier draft of this report: G. W. Baxter, F. C. Noble, Anne Smead Fay, P. Schoggen, Laura Weinstein, and M. Buhl. Portions of this paper were presented at the Midwestern Psychological Association convention, Chicago, May 9, 1969.

political sticker. The following classification was used:

| *Sticker* | *Tabulated as:* |
|---|---|
| "Nixon-Agnew," "Nixon," or "Vote Republican" | – Nixon supporter |
| "Humphrey-Muskie," "Humphrey," or "Vote Democratic" | – Humphrey supporter |
| "Wallace-LeMay," or "Wallace" | –Wallace supporter |

Cars bearing stickers for other political candidates (McCarthy, local congressional candidates, Snoopy, etc.) were *not* counted as political supporters *or* as controls. Cars with *no* political bumper stickers of any kind were used as controls. Many of the owners of these cars obviously had political preferences, too, but we feel it is defensible to assume their allegiance to and identification with a candidate was less strong than those displaying bumper stickers. There is a problem in the comparability of the strength of allegiance of Wallace supporters versus those of the other two candidates. During much of the campaign, Wallace stickers were not given away free in this area, but rather were sold for $.50 or $1; in the last week of the campaign they were given away. Humphrey and Nixon stickers were generally available for the asking, although donations were accepted. Thus it is probable that the average Wallace bumper-sticker car reflected its owner's stronger allegiance than did cars belonging to supporters of the other two candidates. The extent of difference, if any, is impossible to assess.

## METHOD

Cars were observed during the period from 1 P.M. Friday, November 1, through 6 P.M. Tuesday, November 5 (Election Day). Only cars parked in specified parking areas were used (shopping centers, church parking areas, college campus lots, and parking areas for large companies).

Observer-recorders were instructed to survey a parking lot until they found a car with a presidential bumper sticker. If the car bore a Davidson County tag (Tennessee license plates include the name of the county), the following was recorded: type of presidential sticker, license plate number, presence or absence of Metro sticker, and make and age of car. For the latter a crude designation of "new" (post-1964) or "old" (1964 or pre-1964) was used. Then the observer-recorders were instructed to go to the left of the presidential bumper-sticker car and find a "control car" without any bumper sticker. Usually the adjacent car qualified by being from Davidson County and possessing no political bumper sticker. The information about presence or absence of Metro sticker, license plate, and make and year were recorded for this car, also. Thus, after surveying a given area, the recorder would have a list of $x$ number of cars with presidential stickers and the same number without. The recording of the controls was carried out in order to have a comparison on "nonsupporters" (or at least less committed supporters) *who came from the same socioeconomic backgrounds* as the political supporters. It was assumed that if two cars were adjacent in the same lot (church, shopping center, etc.) they came from relatively similar or homogeneous socioeconomic backgrounds.

A total of 46 parking areas were surveyed; these included 14 shopping centers, 13 church and synagogue parking areas, 6 college campuses, 2 voting areas, and 11 lots for large factories and businesses.[2] Coverage of the different predominantly white areas of the county was good, ranging from upper class to lower class. Only one predominantly Negro area was surveyed–the parking lots in the Fisk University area.

Observer-recorders usually worked singly, although some, working in pairs, checked each other. It should be recognized that the possibility of recording errors motivated by experimenter expectation (Rosenthal, 1966) exist in this study; that is, after recording the presence of a particular bumper sticker a solitary observer could fail to see a Metro tax sticker that was actually there. Several precautions were taken, however. Observers were instructed to walk to the front of the car, observe the presence or absence of the Metro sticker, record, and observe again. The fact that there were supporters of all three major candidates among the 26 observers is also of relevance to possible recording bias. The tabulation of presidential preferences of the observer-recorders was as follows: Humphrey, 15; Nixon, 8; Wallace, 1; none, 2. An analysis of recording results by observers' presidential preferences will be reported in the Discussion section.

## RESULTS

[Table 7-16] presents the results of this study. It is estimated that approximately 180,000 cars are registered in Davidson County. A total number of 1,686 cars were observed and recorded in this study. Of these, 304 had Nixon (or Republican) bumper stickers, 178 had Humphrey (or Democratic) stickers, and 361 had Wallace Stickers.[3] The remaining 843 cars,

---

[2]An analysis by days indicated that fewer cars had Metro stickers on the first 3 days than on Monday and Tuesday, but this difference had no effect on the candidate differences.

[3]These percentages are as follows: Nixon, 36%; Humphrey, 21%; Wallace, 43%. The unofficial vote in Davidson County on November 5 was the following: Nixon, 44,228, or 32.4%; Humphrey, 44,739, or 32.79%; Wallace, 47,464, or 34.79%. However, these totals include the Negro votes (approximately 15%) and the Negro areas of the county were only minimally included in our survey. The predominantly Negro precincts voted strongly for Humphrey (examples: Pearl High School precinct, Humphrey, 1,025; Nixon, 17; Wallace, 0; and Hadley Park precinct, Humphrey, 1,235; Nixon, 23; Wallace, 2). If the all-Negro and predominantly Negro boxes are removed from the voting total, the results are as follows: Nixon, 43,117, or 35.05%; Humphrey, 33,350, or 27.10%; Wallace, 46,562, or 37.84%. These latter percentages are closer to those of the bumper sticker sample.

**[TABLE 7-16] Numbers and percentages of cars bearing Metro tax sticker**

| No. cars | Groups | With tax sticker | | Without tax sticker | |
|---|---|---|---|---|---|
| | | *n* | % | *n* | % |
| 304 | Nixon | 263 | 86.51 | 41 | 13.49 |
| 304 | Nixon controls | 245 | 80.59 | 59 | 19.41 |
| 178 | Humphrey | 154 | 86.52 | 24 | 13.48 |
| 178 | Humphrey controls | 137 | 76.97 | 41 | 23.03 |
| 361 | Wallace | 270 | 74.79 | 91 | 25.21 |
| 361 | Wallace controls | 303 | 83.93 | 58 | 16.07 |
| 843 | Political-sticker | 687 | 81.49 | 156 | 18.51 |
| 843 | Controls | 685 | 81.26 | 158 | 18.74 |

NOTE.—Tests of statistical significance for the difference in two proportions (Walker & Lev, 1953, p. 76): Wallace versus Wallace controls: $z = -5.31$, $p < .0001$; Nixon versus Nixon controls: $z = 1.97$, $p < .05$ (two-tailed); Humphrey versus Humphrey controls: $z = 2.33$, $p < .02$ (two-tailed); Wallace versus Humphrey controls: $z = -3.12$, $p < .001$ (two-tailed); Wallace versus Nixon controls: $z = -3.77$, $p < .0001$ (two-tailed).

without presidential stickers, served as controls.

As [Table 7-16] indicates, 86.5% of the cars of Nixon supporters displayed the Metro sticker, compared with 80.6% of their adjacent controls. The probability of this difference occurring by chance was $p < .05$ (two-tailed test). The percentage of Humphrey cars with the Metro sticker was 86.5%, the same as the Nixon percentage. As was the case with the Nixon cars, the percentage was significantly greater ($p < .02$) than the percentage for the controls (which for the Humphrey controls was 77.0%).

Of the 361 Wallace cars, 270 or 74.8% had the Metro sticker. This percentage is significantly lower ($p < .0001$) than the percentage (83.9%) for the Wallace controls, and is also significantly lower than the percentage for Nixon cars ($p < .0001$) and Humphrey cars ($p < .001$).

It thus appears clear that committed supporters of Wallace were less frequently law abiding than were other groups, including committed supporters of other candidates or others who were not demonstrably committed to any candidate. This difference is even more impressive when one considers that some of the control cars (no bumper stickers) were no doubt Wallace supporters, too; that is, the "control" group possesses some—albeit less committed—experimentals.

It is interesting to note that the percentages of political-supporters cars and control cars having the Metro stickers were almost exactly the same—81.49% and 81.26%, respectively. This is a difference of only 2 cars out of 843.

## DISCUSSION

This section of the paper will deal with possible causes of the less frequent law obeyance by Wallace supporters. Several possible explanations, such as defiance of authority and a rejection of the actions of bureaucrats, are not testable by our data. It may be that Wallace supporters are more often characterized by these feelings, but the investigators did not interview any of the owners of cars in the sample and cannot say. Several car owners told the recorders that they had purchased Metro stickers but were carrying them on their person rather than placing them on their car's windshield. They were waiting for the police to stop them, they said, so that they could show the police they were law abiding. There were not enough cases of this interesting (possibly passive-aggressive) behavior, however, to relate it to presidential preference.

Another possible reason that fewer Wallace supporters displayed a Metro sticker is that they are poorer and are less able to pay the $15. Perhaps Wallace supporters are law abiding except when it costs money. The Gallup Poll (1968) and other polls have shown that a relatively greater percentage of Wallace supporters came from the lower socioeconomic class. Therefore it is important to determine whether a social class difference existed between Wallace supporters and their controls. To determine this, the age distribution of Wallace cars was compared with that of the Wallace controls. A total of 208 of the 361 Wallace cars were classified as "new" or "recent" (1964 or later), compared with 231 of the Wallace controls. These percentages—57.6% versus 64.0%—are not significantly different ($z = 1.83$, $p < .10$) although in the direction of a greater number of Wallace supporters having older cars. The Wallace supporters do less often have newer cars than do the Nixon supporters (74.3%) or the Humphrey supporters (74.7%). (These percentages are amplified in [Table 7-17].)

Of more direct relevance to the issue of age of car (as a measure of socioeconomic status) and presence of a Metro sticker is the fact that the percentage of *old* Wallace cars with the Metro sticker—74.5%, or 114 of 153 cars—is almost identical with the percentage of *new* Wallace cars with the sticker—75.0% or 156 of 208. Apparently lower socioeconomic-level does not serve as an explanation of the candidate-supporter differences in law obeyance.

Could the differences in sticker percentages be a function of observer-recorder bias? Might observers who are pro-Humphrey, for example, fail to "see" the

[TABLE 7-17] **Presence of Metro sticker in new and old cars**

| Group | Sticker present | % | Sticker absent | % | Total | % |
|---|---|---|---|---|---|---|
| Nixon supporters | | | | | | |
| New | 195 | 86.28 | 31 | 13.72 | 226 | 74.34 |
| Old | 68 | 87.18 | 10 | 12.82 | 78 | 25.66 |
| Total | 263 | 86.51 | 41 | 13.49 | 304 | 100.00 |
| Nixon controls | | | | | | |
| New | 181 | 80.08 | 45 | 19.91 | 226 | 74.34 |
| Old | 64 | 82.05 | 14 | 17.95 | 78 | 25.66 |
| Total | 245 | 80.59 | 59 | 19.41 | 304 | 100.00 |
| Humphrey supporters | | | | | | |
| New | 119 | 89.47 | 14 | 10.53 | 133 | 74.72 |
| Old | 35 | 77.78 | 10 | 22.22 | 45 | 25.28 |
| Total | 154 | 86.52 | 24 | 13.48 | 178 | 100.00 |
| Humphrey controls | | | | | | |
| New | 98 | 83.05 | 20 | 16.95 | 118 | 66.29 |
| Old | 39 | 65.00 | 21 | 35.00 | 60 | 33.71 |
| Total | 137 | 76.97 | 41 | 23.03 | 178 | 100.00 |
| Wallace supporters | | | | | | |
| New | 156 | 75.00 | 52 | 25.00 | 208 | 57.62 |
| Old | 114 | 74.50 | 39 | 25.49 | 153 | 42.38 |
| Total | 270 | 74.79 | 91 | 25.21 | 361 | 100.00 |
| Wallace controls | | | | | | |
| New | 200 | 86.58 | 31 | 13.42 | 231 | 63.99 |
| Old | 103 | 79.23 | 27 | 20.77 | 130 | 36.01 |
| Total | 303 | 83.93 | 58 | 16.07 | 361 | 100.00 |

Metro tax sticker when it was on a pro-Nixon or pro-Wallace car? [Table 7-18] presents data relevant to this question, as it shows the number and percentage of each type of car bearing the Metro tax sticker, separated by presidential preference of the observer-recorder. For example, when tabulating Nixon cars, the 15 pro-Humphrey observers reported that 88.39% of the Nixon cars had the Metro sticker, compared to a report by the 8 pro-Nixon observers of 82.79% of *their* Nixon cars possessing the Metro sticker. [Table 7-18] reports these percentages for each of six types of cars (Nixon, Humphrey, and Wallace cars and controls for each); chi-squares were computed and in none of the six sets were the observed frequencies different from the expected. It may be concluded that in observing cars allied with a particular candidate, the observer's presidential preference was unrelated to the percentage of cars he reported bearing the Metro tax sticker.

The data in [Table 7-18] may be studied in another way. One may ask: Do Humphrey supporters report a greater percentage of law-abiding cars for their candidate? [Table 7-18] indicates that pro-Humphrey observers reported that 88.18% of the Humphrey cars had a Metro sticker, 88.39% of the Nixon cars did, and 77.84% of the Wallace cars did. Pro-Nixon observers reported that 82.79% of the Nixon cars, 85.19% of Humphrey cars, and 70.63% of the Wallace cars had a Metro sticker. Thus both pro-Humphrey and pro-Nixon observers reported a slightly higher percentage for another candidate than for their own. The lone observer who was pro-Wallace reported higher percentages of Nixon and Humphrey cars having the tax sticker (100%) than the Wallace cars (75%, or 3 of 4).

Although the data of [Table 7-18] are not a conclusive test of the possible effects of observer bias, there is nothing in the table which indicates that the observer's presidential preference influenced his recording.

Further evidence for candidate-supporter differences emerges from an independent study by John McCarthy[4] of law-breaking also done in Nashville in the fall of 1968. He stationed observers at a Nashville intersection with a stop sign and recorded the percentage and types of cars failing to stop. A significantly higher percentage of cars with Wallace bumper stickers failed to stop.

It seems that while Wallace has advocated "law and order," his supporters, in their own behavior, subscribe to it to a less frequent degree than do other citizens.

[4] J. McCarthy. Personal communication, December 2, 1968.

[TABLE 7-18] **Numbers and percentages of cars bearing Metro tax sticker, separated by presidential preference of observer-recorder**

| No. Observers | Observers' preference | Possess Metro tax sticker? | | | | | | | |
|---|---|---|---|---|---|---|---|---|---|
| | | Nixon cars | | | | Control cars (Nixon) | | | |
| | | Yes | % | No | % | Yes | % | No | % |
| 15 | Humphrey | 137 | 88.39 | 18 | 11.61 | 133 | 85.81 | 22 | 14.19 |
| 8 | Nixon | 101 | 82.79 | 21 | 17.21 | 90 | 73.77 | 32 | 26.23 |
| 1 | Wallace | 14 | 100.00 | 0 | 0.00 | 11 | 78.57 | 3 | 21.43 |
| 2 | None | 11 | 84.62 | 2 | 15.38 | 11 | 84.62 | 2 | 15.38 |
| Total | | 263 | 86.51 | 41 | 13.49 | 245 | 80.59 | 59 | 19.41 |
| | | Humphrey cars | | | | Control cars (Humphrey) | | | |
| 15 | Humphrey | 97 | 88.18 | 13 | 11.82 | 88 | 80.00 | 22 | 20.00 |
| 8 | Nixon | 46 | 85.19 | 8 | 14.81 | 40 | 74.07 | 14 | 25.92 |
| 1 | Wallace | 5 | 100.00 | 0 | 0.00 | 3 | 60.00 | 2 | 40.00 |
| 2 | None | 6 | 66.67 | 3 | 33.33 | 6 | 66.67 | 3 | 33.33 |
| Total | | 154 | 86.52 | 24 | 13.48 | 137 | 76.97 | 41 | 23.03 |
| | | Wallace cars | | | | Control cars (Wallace) | | | |
| 15 | Humphrey | 144 | 77.84 | 41 | 22.16 | 162 | 87.57 | 23 | 12.43 |
| 8 | Nixon | 101 | 70.63 | 42 | 29.37 | 112 | 78.32 | 31 | 21.68 |
| 1 | Wallace | 3 | 75.00 | 1 | 25.00 | 3 | 75.00 | 1 | 25.00 |
| 2 | None | 22 | 75.86 | 7 | 24.14 | 26 | 89.66 | 3 | 10.34 |
| Total | | 270 | 74.74 | 91 | 25.21 | 303 | 83.93 | 58 | 16.07 |

NOTE.—Chi-square for the differences; Nixon cars: $\chi^2 = 4.11$, $p < .25$; Nixon controls: $\chi^2 = 6.47$, $p < .10$; Humphrey cars: $\chi^2 = 5.27$, $p < .25$; Humphrey controls: $\chi^2 = 2.18$, $p > .50$; Wallace cars: $\chi^2 = 2.24$, $p < .50$; Wallace controls: $\chi^2 = 6.08$, $p < .25$.

## REFERENCES

**GALLUP, G.** Voting profile in 1968. *Nashville Tennessean,* December 8, 1968, 5B.

**ROSENTHAL, R.** *Experimenter effects in behavioral research.* New York: Appleton-Century-Crofts, 1966.

**WALKER, H., & LEV, J.** *Statistical inference.* New York: Holt, Rinehart & Winston, 1953.

**WEBB, E. J., CAMPBELL, D. T., SCHWARTZ, R. D., & SECHREST, L.** *Unobtrusive measures: Nonreactive research in the social sciences.* Chicago: Rand McNally, 1966.

# CHAPTER EIGHT

# CONSUMER BEHAVIOR

This chapter contains articles which deal with the testing of social-psychological theories in the real world. McGuire (1967) has promulgated theory testing in natural environments as the answer to the schism between pure laboratory research and action-oriented research. He feels there will be more "applied fall-out" from theoretical research in applied settings than in laboratory settings (p. 130). And, although Ring (1967, p. 115) quotes McGuire as saying, "We are not here to turn out consumer goods," much of the world *is* concerned with precisely this, a fact which is reflected in the research done in natural settings presented in this chapter.

The first article, by Doob, Carlsmith, Freedman, Landauer, and Tom, is a good example of the "applied fall-out" resulting from research such as that McGuire describes. In addition to an interesting test of a theory, there are multiple replications within one experiment. Unfortunately, not many laboratory experiments are replicated even once. Further research should be done to determine how adaptation level theory and dissonance theory operate on the effect of initial selling price.

Brock's article (page 264) also attempts to determine how dissonance theory can account for buying behavior. Brock also checked on experimenter bias, which can exist in the field, too.

Regan and Brehm's article (page 269) is concerned with what we consider an offshoot of dissonance theory. That is, dissonance theory deals with the motivation which arises once an individual *willingly* reduces his freedom; reactance theory deals with the motivation which arises from someone else's having reduced one's freedom. The notion of reactance is also related to the articles by Abelson and Miller and by Miller and Levy in Chapter 7: when someone insults you for maintaining your position, your "freedom" to hold that position may be threatened. The resultant reactance motivation to regain his freedom causes an individual to remain in his position with a vengeance, that is, to become even more extreme. Regan and Brehm also note the relationship of reactance motivation to "personal insult", and Wicklund and Brehm (1968) demonstrate the relationship between the "boomerang effect" and reactance theory.

The article by Nisbett and Kanouse (page 275), although slightly reactive (e.g., asking a fat man when he last ate), provides us with good reasons for using behavioral field measures and is a good demonstration of how sophisticated statistical techniques can glean relatively simple data. McGuire (1967) has also advocated the greater use of statistical advances to "tease out the causal derivates among covariantes in situations where we do not have the resources to manipulate one of the factors (p. 134)."

McGuire (1967, p. 134) has also asked for more use of unobtrusive measures. These are ingeniously used in the study by Goldman, Jaffa, and Schachter (page 280). It is interesting that this article also specifies the importance of nonobvious predictions. Ring (1967) denigrates these as part of the "fun and games" approach to social psychology; i.e., "Never make an obvious prediction (p. 117)." In addition, Goldman et al. deal with alternative explanations, but, more interestingly, they point out that they can think of no alternative explanation for their entire body of data. This is a strong argument, too often ignored.

## REFERENCES

**McGUIRE, W. J.** Some impending reorientations in social psychology. *Journal of Experimental Social Psychology*, 1967, **3**, 124-139.

**RING, K.** Experimental social psychology: some sober questions about some frivolous values. *Journal of Experimental Social Psychology*, 1967, 3, 113-123.

**WICKLUND, R. A., & BREHM, J. W.** Attitude change as a function of felt competence and threat to attitudinal freedom. *Journal of Experimental Social Psychology*, 1968, **1**, 64-75.

# THE EFFECT OF INITIAL SELLING PRICE ON SUBSEQUENT SALES[1]

ANTHONY N. DOOB,[2] J. MERRILL CARLSMITH,
JONATHAN L. FREEDMAN, THOMAS K. LANDAUER,[3]
AND SOLENG TOM, JR.
*Stanford University*

Five field experiments investigated the effect of initial selling price on subsequent sales of common household products. Matched pairs of discount houses sold the same product at either a discounted price or the regular price for a short period of time. The prices were then made the same for all stores. The results were consistent with the prediction from dissonance theory that subsequent sales would be higher where the initial price was high.

The "introductory low price offer" is a common technique used by marketers. A new product is offered at a low price for a short period of time, and the price is subsequently raised to its normal level. Since the goal naturally is to maximize final sales of the product, the assumption behind this technique is that it will accomplish this goal. An economic model based entirely on supply and demand would of course predict that the eventual sales would not be affected by the initial price. The lower price would be expected to attract many marginal buyers and produce greater sales; but as soon as the price is raised, these buyers should drop out of the market. The hope of the marketer, however, is that some of these marginal buyers will learn to like the product enough so that they will continue to purchase it even at the higher price.

Unfortunately for the marketer, this may be a vain hope. There are various psychological reasons why we might expect the introductory low price to have an opposite effect from that which the marketers intend, such that the introductory low price would reduce rather than increase eventual sales. Since this technique is so widespread, it provides an unusual opportunity to investigate the applicability of social psychology in a natural setting, and to compare the marketer's predictions with that of social psychology.

The most interesting analysis of this situation is based on the theory of cognitive dissonance (Festinger, 1957). One of the clearest deductions from the theory is that the more effort in any form a person exerts to attain a goal, the more dissonance is aroused if the goal is less valuable than expected. The individual reduces this dissonance by increasing his liking for the goal; therefore the greater the effort, the more he should like the goal. This prediction has received some substantiation in laboratory experimentation (e.g., Aronson & Mills, 1959; Gerard & Mathewson, 1966). Its applicability to the marketing situation is straightforward: the theory predicts that the higher the price a person initially pays for a product, the more he will come to like it. Presumably this greater liking will produce "brand loyalty" in the form of repeat purchases. Thus, when the initial price is high, a higher *proportion* of buyers should continue to purchase the product than when the initial price is low. Accordingly, although the introductory price will initially attract more customers, we may expect the sales curves for the two conditions to cross at some later point, and the higher brand loyalty, induced by the dissonance involved in paying a high price, to manifest itself in higher final sales in that condition.

Five experiments were performed to demonstrate that introducing a new brand of a product at a low price for a short time and then raising it to the normal selling price leads to lower sales in the long run than introducing the product at its normal selling price. The general design of all the experiments was to introduce the new brand at a low price in one set of stores and, after the price is raised to the normal selling price, compare sales with matched stores where the product was introduced at the normal selling price and held there throughout the course of the experiment.

All of the experiments that are to be reported here were done in a chain of discount houses. All

[1] This study was supported in part by NSF Grants to Carlsmith and to Freedman.
The authors are grateful to management and personnel of the discount chain for their cooperation in this research.

[2] Now at University of Toronto.

[3] Now at Bell Telephone Laboratories, Murray Hill, New Jersey.

sales figures have been multiplied by a constant in order to maintain confidentiality.

This chain of discount houses differs from most others in a number of important ways. They do not advertise much, and what advertising they do does not include prices on specific items. Price changes occur very seldom in these stores and are usually not advertised. In most cases, prices are lowered because an item is overstocked, and unless the customer remembers the regular selling price, he has no way of knowing that the price is lower than usual. Management in most of these stores is under direct control of the central office. When the manager receives orders from the central office, he has little or no power to change them.

The chain sells a large number of "house brands" at prices lower than the equivalent name brands. These house brands have the same registered trade mark, and constitute a brand which customers can easily identify with the store. Generally, the quality of the house brand item is as high as the equivalent name brand, the differences usually being in characteristics which do not directly affect the usefulness of the item (e.g., mouthwash bottles are not as attractive as those of the name brand; the average grain size of powered detergent is larger than that of the name brand which is chemically equivalent).

The products used in the studies reported here were house brands. All were being introduced into the stores at the time when the study was being run. The particular products used and the price differential were both determined by management.

## EXPERIMENT I: MOUTHWASH

**Method** Twelve pairs of discount houses, matched on gross sales, were randomly assigned to one of two experimental conditions. In one store of each pair, the house brand of mouthwash was introduced at $.25 per quart bottle. The price was held at this level for nine days (two weekends and the intervening days), and then the price was brought up to $.39 for all stores. In the other store, it was introduced at its normal selling price of $.39.

None of the managers had any reason to believe that the price of mouthwash at his store was not the same as in all other stores in the chain. No one was given any special instructions beyond the place in the store where the item was to be sold and its selling price. The location was essentially identical for all stores. In stores where mouthwash was introduced at the low price, the manager received a memo at the end of the first week instructing him to change the price to $.39 after that weekend.

**Results** Sales were recorded by the sundries buyer as he replenished stock. At the end of each week, these figures were sent to the central office and then relayed to the experimenters. Average sales for the 12 matched stores in each condition are shown in [Figure 8-1]. It is estimated that at least two weeks had to pass before customers would return to buy more mouthwash, and, therefore, one would not expect there to be any difference between the height of the curves until the third week. In fact, the curves cross at this point, and, after this point, it is clear that the stores where the initial selling price was high were selling more mouthwash than stores where the initial price was low. This is true in spite of the fact that more mouthwash was sold the first week in stores where the price was low. Unfortunately, for a variety of reasons, the authors were not able to collect continuous data. They were able, however, to check sales 19 weeks after the price change, and clearly the difference still existed. When sales for Weeks 3, 4, 5, and 20 are combined, sales of mouthwash were higher in the store where the initial selling price was high in ten of the twelve pairs of stores ($p = .02$).

Sales in the two sets of stores during Weeks 3, 4, 5, and 20 (pooled) were also compared by use of a $t$ test, resulting in a $t$ of 2.11 ($df = 11$, $p < .10$). Thus, stores where the initial selling price was low sold less mouthwash than did stores where the initial selling price was the same as the final selling price.

**Replications** The same experiment was repeated four times, using different products. The procedures were very similar in all cases. In each experiment, the stores were rematched and randomly assigned, independent of all other replications.

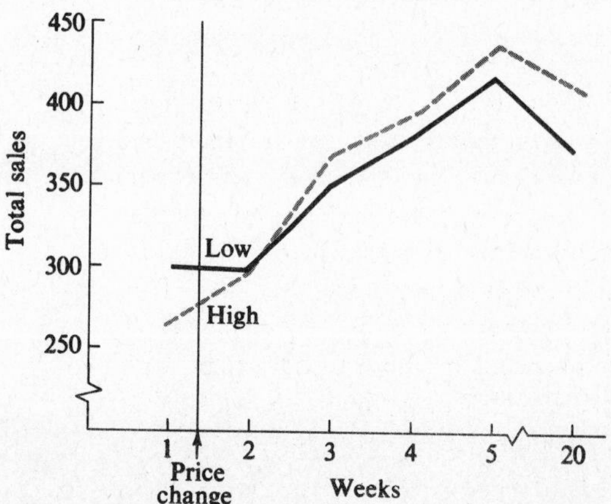


[FIGURE 8-1] Mouthwash sales.

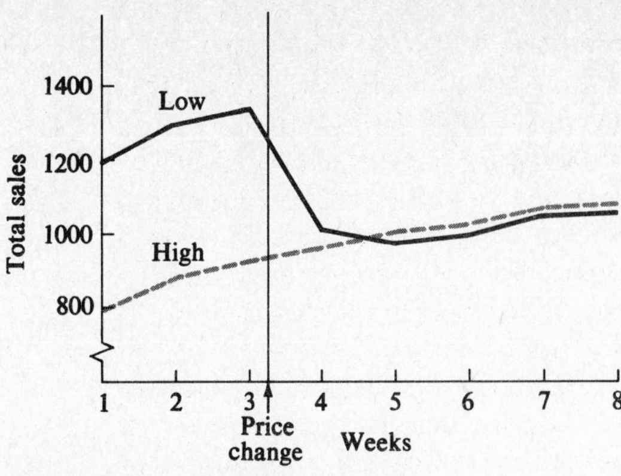


[FIGURE 8-2] Toothpaste sales.

## EXPERIMENT II: TOOTHPASTE

Six pairs of stores were matched on the basis of sundries sales and randomly assigned to conditions in which the selling price for the first three weeks was either \$.41 or \$.49 for a "family size" tube of toothpaste. After three weeks, the price in all stores was set at \$.49. The results are presented in [Figure 8-2]. When the sales for the last four weeks are combined as in the previous experiment, four of the six pairs show differences in the predicted direction ($p$ = .34). When the more sensitive $t$ test is done on the data from these four weeks, the $t$ is 2.26 ($df = 5, p < .10$).

## EXPERIMENT III: ALUMINUM FOIL

Seven pairs of stores were matched on the basis of grocery sales and randomly assigned to conditions in which the selling price for the first three weeks was either \$.59 or \$.64 for a 75-foot roll of foil. After three weeks, the price in all stores was set at \$.64. The results are presented in [Figure 8-3]. For Weeks 5 through 8 combined, all seven pairs ($p$ = .01) show differences in the predicted direction ($t = 5.09, df = 6, p < .005$).

## EXPERIMENT IV: LIGHT BULBS

Eight pairs of stores were matched on the basis of hardware sales and randomly assigned to conditions in which selling price for the first week was either \$.26 or \$.32 for a package of light bulbs. After one week, the price was brought up to \$.32 in all stores. The results are presented in [Figure 8-4]. For Weeks 3 and 4 combined, six of the eight pairs ($p$ = .15) show differences in the predicted direction ($t$ = .837, $df$ = 7). Although this difference is not significant, it might be noted in [Figure 8-4] that there was the predicted reversal, even though initial sales were almost 50% higher at the low price.

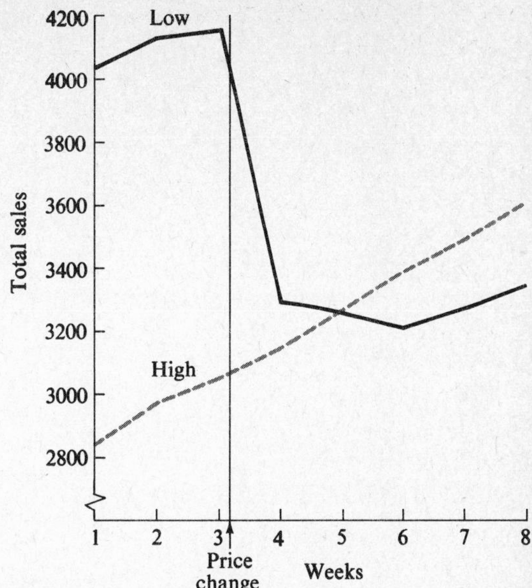


[FIGURE 8-3] Aluminum foil sales.

## EXPERIMENT V: COOKIES

Eight pairs of stores were matched on the basis of grocery sales and randomly assigned to conditions in which the selling price for the first two weeks was \$.24 or \$.29 for a large bag of cookies. After two weeks, the price was at \$.29 for all stores. The results are presented in [Figure 8-5]. For Weeks 4

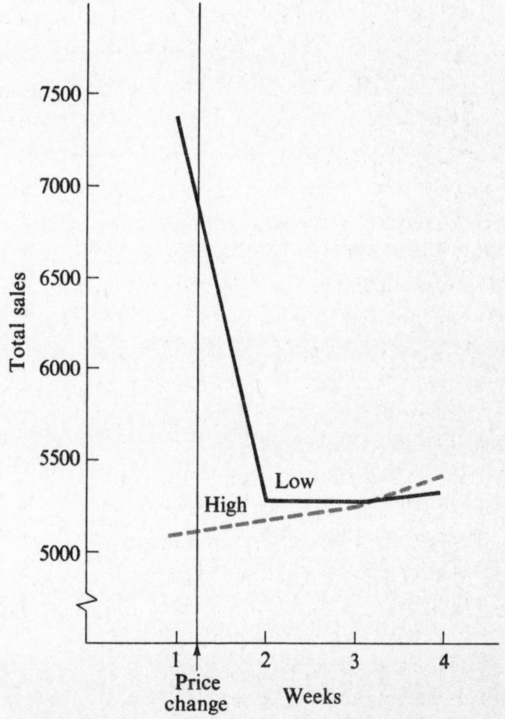


[FIGURE 8-4] Light bulb sales.

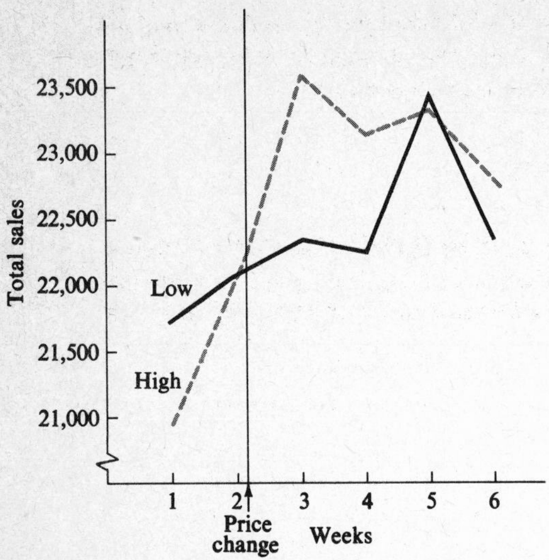


[FIGURE 8-5] Cookie sales.

through 6 combined, six of the eight pairs show differences in the predicted direction ($t = .625, df = 7$).

## RESULTS

When the results of all five experiments are combined into one test of the hypothesis, a $z$ of 3.63 ($p < .0002$) is obtained. Clearly, so far as this has been tested, the practice of introducing a product at a low price is not a good strategy for this chain of stores to use.

## DISCUSSION

These studies indicate that introducing products at a lower than usual price is harmful to final sales. It was earlier argued that one possible reason for this is the lower proportion of buyers who return to a product when the initial price is lower than the normal price. Whether or not this causes eventual sales actually to be lower when the initial price is low is not critical to the argument. If, for example, there is an extremely large difference in initial sales, even a lower proportion of returning buyers may produce an advantage for the initial low price. Similarly, if the product has some special feature which would be expected to produce loyalty merely from exposure, it would be beneficial to maximize initial sales by the use of low introductory offers. In the experiments reported here, neither of these possibilities seems to have been present. For the range of prices studied, even a 50% increase in sales due to the lower price was not enough to overcome the increased consumer loyalty engendered by the higher price. Because of the presence of other identical brands, differing only in price, exposure alone was not enough to produce loyalty.

Whether or not eventual sales are actually lower when the initial price is low is not critical to the argument. From a theoretical point of view, the only essential comparison is the relative proportion of repurchases in the two conditions. A stringent method of showing that this proportion is higher when the initial price is high is to demonstrate that the absolute volume of eventual sales is greater for the high-price condition, even though initial sales are lower. For the products and prices studied here, this was true.

There are at least two alternative explanations of this result. The first is that in the low-initial-price stores, the market is glutted after the first few weeks, and it takes a long time for there to be any need to repurchase the product. This might be a partial explanation of the difference between the conditions, but seems implausible as a total explanation. For all the products except light bulbs the length of time that the sales curves were followed exceeded by a goodly margin the marketer's estimate of the normal time until repurchase. Indeed, with mouthwash, for which the repurchase period is about two weeks, the difference between conditions is still present 19 weeks after the price switch. Customers might have stocked up by buying more than their usual supply of a product, but pricing practices of this chain of stores makes this unlikely. These stores have rarely used low introductory price offers and they were not advertised as such for the products studied. Buyers therefore had no reason to believe that the "low price" was a special price and accordingly little reason to stock up on the product. Thus, although one cannot entirely rule out this "glutting the market" explanation, it is not convincing.

A second and more interesting alternative is in terms of what might be called the customers' adaptation level regarding the particular product. When mouthwash is put on sale at $.25, customers who buy it at that price or notice what the price is may tend to think of the product in terms of $.25. They say to themselves that this is a $.25 bottle of mouthwash. When, in subsequent weeks, the price increases to $.39, these customers will tend to see it as overpriced, and are not inclined to buy it at this much higher price. Therefore, sales drop off considerably. In the $.39 steady condition, initial sales are lower, but there is no reason for them to drop off due to this effect. Therefore, introducing it at the ultimate price results in greater sales in the long run than does introducing it at the low price. This explanation fits the data as nicely as does the one in terms of cognitive dissonance. In many ways, they are quite similar and are difficult to distinguish experimentally.

It should be noted that the adaptation level and dissonance explanations are by no means mutually exclusive. It is entirely possible that both mechanisms are operating to some extent. In any case, the basic result stands—the introduction of a product at a low price tended to decrease subsequent sales, and this effect lasted for at least 20 weeks.

## REFERENCES

**ARONSON, E., & MILLS, J.** The effect of severity of initiation on liking for a group. *Journal of Abnormal and Social Psychology*, 1959, **59**, 177-181.

**FESTINGER, L.** *A Theory of Cognitive Dissonance*. Stanford, Calif.: Stanford University Press, 1957.

**GERARD, H. B., & MATHEWSON, G. C.** The effects of severity of initiation on liking for a group: a replication. *Journal of Experimental Social Psychology*, 1966, **2**, 278-287.

# COMMUNICATOR-RECIPIENT SIMILARITY AND DECISION CHANGE[1]

TIMOTHY C. BROCK[2]
*Ohio State University*

A field experiment in the paint department of a large retail store supported the hypothesis: a recipient's behavior with respect to an object is modifiable by the communicator's appeal to the extent that the recipient perceives that he and the communicator have a similar relationship to the object. A salesman, who reported his own magnitude of paint consumption as similar or dissimilar to the purchaser's, attempted to induce the purchaser (N = 88) to switch to a different price level. The findings were ordered to theories of identification (Stotland) and social comparison (Festinger).

The recipient's perception of his similarity to a communicator or model has been hypothesized to account for change toward the communicator (Back, 1951; Leventhal & Perloe, 1962), attraction to the communicator (Byrne, 1961; Byrne & Wong, 1962; Gerard & Greenbaum, 1962), for adoption of the model's preferences (Stotland, Zander, & Natsoulas, 1961), ability level (Burnstein, Stotland, & Zander, 1961; Stotland & Dunn, 1962; Stotland & Hillmer, 1962), and "anxiety" (Stotland & Dunn, 1963). These studies, which can be fitted within the framework of Stotland's cognitive theory of identification or Festinger's (1954) theory of social comparison processes, do not yet sum to a set of principles shown to yield clear predictions of behavioral change in real-life situations. This shortcoming was noticed when an attempt was made, with the management of a department store, to learn more about the effects of interpersonal influence on consumer behavior.

Management assigned special value to informal, word-of-mouth endorsement (Katz & Lazarsfeld, 1955) of a product and sought means of improving interpersonal, rather than media, promotion. It was proposed that a communicator, who is perceived to be thoroughly experienced with a product, will be more likely to influence the recipient than a less experienced communicator. Perceived expertise of the communicator was considered crucial in face-to-face contexts. To illustrate, management believed that a person about to buy a Chevrolet would be less influenced by a neighbor's approbation of his car (a Ford, say) than an equally enthusiastic endorsement by the owner of a fleet of Fords. The first hypothesis was: the more experience a communicator is perceived to have had with an object, the more likely it is that the recipient's behavior with respect to the object will be modified by the communicator's influence attempts.

The second hypothesis followed the aforementioned research on communicator-recipient similarity: to the extent that the recipient perceives that he and the communicator share an attribute, that is, have a similar relationship to an object, to that extent is the recipient's behavior with respect to the object likely to be modified by the communicator's influence attempts. The two forces, perceived communicator expertise and perceived communicator similarity, were pitted against one another by conducting a field experiment in which the communicator, for half the recipients, was perceived as similar but inexperienced while for the other half, he was perceived as dissimilar but experienced.

## METHOD

In the paint department of a large retail store,[3] salesmen attempted to induce paint purchasers to change to a different price level. There were two independent variables: the similarity of the salesman and customer with respect to the salesman's prior magnitude of paint consumption; the direction of the advocated change in price level, upward or downward. The dependent variable was whether

[1] A portion of the data was collected while the writer was at the University of Pittsburgh. The comments of Leroy Wolins are gratefully acknowledged.

[2] Report completed while the author was at Iowa State University.

[3] The experiment was conducted during a 5-month period in the paint department of a retail store in an Eastern city. The store is a unit in an international chain with annual sales volume greater than one billion dollars. A *sine qua non* for conducting the experiment was preservation of anonymity for the store and its permanent staff in any public report. The writer is indebted to the manager for his unusual accessibility and enlightened contribution to the execution of the research. Thanks are due J. Blackwood and D. Koenigsberg for their skill and objectivity in collecting the data.

or not the paint purchaser changed his decision concerning price level after an influence attempt by the salesman.

## Procedure

The role of experimenter-communicator was taken by two part-time salesmen. The experimenter selected customers or subject-recipients for inclusion in the experiment, attempted to modify the subject's price decision, and recorded whether or not the influence attempt was successful. Selected subjects were randomly assigned to a similar or dissimilar condition and to a higher or lower condition, resulting in a 2 X 2 design. Influence attempts were restricted to paint purchases, particularly the kinds and prices given in [Table 8-1]. In the higher condition, the experimenter advocated buying paint at prices in Column 3 rather than Column 2 in [Table 8-1]. In the lower condition, the experimenter advocated purchases at prices in Column 1 if the subject had chosen a price in Column 2, or in Column 2 if the subject selected a price in Column 3. In the similar condition, the experimenter emphasized that the magnitude of his own consumption was the same as the amount being purchased by the subject; in the dissimilar condition the experimenter reported his own magnitude of consumption to be 20 times that of the subject's prospective purchase.[4]

The treatments were administered after the subject indicated he wished to purchase *X* units at a given price and had proceeded with the experimenter to the cash register to "ring up" the sale. At this point, the experimenter delivered himself of the following well-practiced appeal. Alternative terms for the dissimilar and higher conditions appeared in brackets.

Listen, I just thought, I wonder if I can give you some advice. I'm going to college right now and working here part-time as a salesman to meet my expenses. Two weeks ago I bought *X* [20 *X*] gallons of *a* to help my dad on some work like your *b* that we were doing. It costs a little less [more] and [but] it turned out beautifully. I also got a little of the *c* you want to buy, and, honestly, it didn't work out as well at all. There just was no comparison. Those *X* [20 *X*] gallons at *a* have proved out terrifically for us in every way. [Pause] On the basis of my experience with *X* [20*X*] gallons at *a*, I can really recommend your changing to the *a* if you want to. I certainly would if I were you.

The italicized *a* above refers to the type of paint at the advocated price; *b* refers to details of the experimenter's "job," described so as to seem akin to the subject's and, in the dissimilar condition, to require the use of much paint; and *c* refers to the subject's initial selection of paint and price level. In an actual appeal to a subject who decided to buy floor paint at $6.98 per gallon, the variations were: *a*, "the 4.98 paint" or simply "4.98"; *b*, "porches and basement too [in some duplexes]"; *c*, "6.98." The material in brackets would have been omitted in the similar condition.

In addition to noting whether or not the influence attempt was successful, the experimenter recorded the original price, the advocated price, whether the sale was cash or charge, estimated the subject's age, and noted any contaminating factors.

[4]The multiple of 20 was chosen because the experimenters' experience in the paint department led them to believe such a magnitude would be perceived by the typical paint purchaser as plausible but at the same time very different from his own acquisition of a gallon or two.

[TABLE 8-1] Paints and price per gallon in dollars

| Type of paint | 1 | 2 | 3 |
|---|---|---|---|
| Latex | 2.97 | 5.59 | 6.90 |
| House (outside) | | 5.89 | 6.98 |
| Floor | | 4.98 | 6.69 |
| Semigloss | 3.98 | 6.59 | 7.98 |

## Communicator Standardization and Ratings of Appeals

The experimenters appeared before the writer's students (class *N*s = 25 and 18) who rated their appeals using Likert scales with anchors labeled "none at all" and "to a very high degree." The experimenters were rated for warmth, expertness, believableness, speaking effectiveness, and the likelihood that "this salesman would make me change my mind." In addition, the raters were asked to reproduce the appeals in writing. The raters were told that the experimenters were sales trainees and the ratings would not affect the trainee's position and salary but would be important in deciding what kind of sales job he was given. The experimenters spoke in a balanced order before the two classes. The rating forms asked the raters to imagine they had just bought "some paint" at a specified price level: in this fashion half of each class was given a higher, and half, a lower treatment. The dissimilar experimenter reported his prior consumption as 20 gallons; the similar experimenter, as 1 gallon. Detailed description of the communicator's "job" and devaluation of the recipient's price were omitted. There were only three statistically reliable ($p < .05$, two-tailed) outcomes: one of the experimenters was rated higher than the other in "warmth"; the dissimilar communicator was rated higher in expertness, defined for the rater as "knows what he is talking about"; and female raters gave higher ratings.

Both experimenters knew the hypotheses but their preferences, prior to the experiment, did not agree. The experimenters returned data cards to the writer biweekly and they were not informed about the results during the course of the data collection. Since they were employed in the paint department anyway, the experimenters felt they might enliven a humdrum selling task by sometimes making it a meaningful scientific activity. The experimenters received no additional remuneration or inducements of any kind. One of the experimenters had taken advanced psychology courses; the other, a chemistry major, had taken only an introductory psychology course. The experimenters did not collect data at the same time.

### Selection of Subjects

A small proportion of the purchasers entering the paint department during the period of the experiment was selected as subjects. No attempt was made to collect data when: neither experimenter was on duty; the paint department or store was very crowded; there was a sale in the store, in the paint department, or in adjacent departments; remodeling was being done in the paint or adjacent departments; the sales help in the paint department was below full strength. A purchaser was excluded as a subject if: the purchaser was female or was accompanied by other persons; the purchaser was completing a project and returning for more supplies; the purchaser was not exclusively interested in the products listed in [Table 8-1]; the desired color was not available at the price level to be advocated by the experimenter; special color mixing was necessary; the purchaser did not appear to make a choice or decision concerning price but seemed to the experimenter to have had a definite price in mind before entering the paint department. The purchaser was excluded if he forced the experimenter to give information that was favorable or unfavorable to a certain price level prior to the influence attempt or in addition to the influence attempt. For example, if a purchaser wanted to know why the $6.90 Latex cost more than the $5.59 Latex the experimenter would first say "probably different chemicals in them." In many instances this ambiguous reply was insufficient and the experimenter had to endorse or evaluate the paints. A purchaser was excluded if his price decision did not permit the experimenter to apply the higher (or lower) treatment which had been randomly determined beforehand. When the experimenter was interrupted and not allowed to complete his influence attempt, the purchaser's data were omitted. Finally, the experimenters excluded purchasers who seemed disturbed (as reported by the experimenters) by words on the paint can label, such as "enamel." In sum, the subject obviously made a price decision, the surround was normal and tranquil, only the products in [Table 8-1] were involved, and the experimenter was able to apply the treatments in standardized fashion. Data collection was terminated when the experimenters completed their period of employment at the store. At this time 88 subjects had been run, 22 in each of the four conditions, higher or lower, similar or dissimilar.

## RESULTS AND DISCUSSION

Before evaluating the hypotheses it was necessary to ascertain whether bias was introduced by excluding purchasers who did not make a decision about price,

**[TABLE 8-2] Number of paint purchasers who changed decision in relation to direction of influence attempt and similarity of communicator's consumption**

| Direction of influence attempt | Similar | Dissimilar | Total |
|---|---|---|---|
| To a lower price level | 16 (73%) | 10 (45%) | 26 (59%) |
| To a higher price level | 12 (55%) | 7 (32%) | 19 (43%) |
| | 28 (64%)[a] | 17 (39%)[a] | |

Note.—Cell $N = 22$ purchasers.
[a]Chi-square, $p < .05$.

forced the experimenter to enlarge on the content of his influence attempt, elicited supplemental evaluation from the experimenter, or interrupted and prevented the experimenter from completing his appeal. If purchasers in these categories were disproportionately represented in the four cells of the design, the test of the hypotheses could be impugned. Appropriate analysis of the data revealed no relationship between the independent classifications (higher versus lower, similar versus dissimilar) and the frequency of subjects who made no real price decision, who forced enlargement or endorsement, or who interrupted the experimenter. All exact test and chi-square $p$ values were greater than .25.[5]

The same pattern of outcomes was obtained for both experimenters, for cash and charge purchases, and for purchasers estimated to be over and under 40 years of age. The combined results, shown in [Table 8-2], favored the second hypothesis. The dissimilar communicator, although presumably perceived as more knowledgeable, was less effective than the communicator whose paint consumption was the same as the purchaser's ($p < .05$). There was an expected tendency for downward influence attempts to encounter less resistance than upward advocacy.

Note that half of the 88 subjects changed in response to the influence attempt. No base line was available for evaluating this overall frequency of change; it could be attributed to an inherent instability of price decisions or to the elaborate screening of subjects. In any case, recent research has empha-

[5]The exclusion of subjects might still have biased the outcome if, for some reason, the excluded types of subjects were more modifiable by a dissimilar than by a similar communicator. No rationale for this possibility could be constructed, however, and, in any event, the population, to which inferences were allowable, was defined as paint purchasers given the present treatment, nothing more and nothing less.

sized postdecision phenomena other than decision revocation (Brehm & Cohen, 1962).

The findings add clarity to the literature in that previous attempts to demonstrate before-after change, as a function of identification with a model, yielded ambiguous results (Burnstein et al., 1961; Leventhal & Perloe, 1962). The present test of the perceived similarity hypothesis was considered stringent because the expertise effect, to the extent that it was operative, worked against confirmation of the hypothesis. Also opposing confirmation was the presumed reluctance of purchasers in the higher condition to spend more money than they had initially decided upon. The present results increased understanding of why a face-to-face encounter may be more effective in modifying a recipient than the importunities of mass-media communicators (Katz & Lazarsfeld, 1955); the recipient changes toward the position of a communicator to the extent he perceives that he shares with the communicator an attribute pertinent to the dimension along which change is advocated. An interesting problem for subsequent research is whether real-life behavior can be modified as readily when the similarity attribute is *irrelevant* to the change dimension.

Subsequent research must also deal with a possible alternative explanation for the present findings. Perhaps the decisive factor in producing the observed differences was not the similarity of the "*X* gallon" communicator but the dissimilarity of the "20 *X* gallon" communicator. The subject may have rejected the dissimilar communicator because his experience seemed irrelevant; or the subject may have resented the experimenter's "showing off" how much paint he used or disbelieved the experimenter's figure and regarded it simply as a sales ploy. If these processes were operative, it would affect the interpretation that similarity is a sufficiently powerful factor to overcome the effects of expertness. Although pretesting of the communicators showed no differences in their believableness, and the dissimilar communicator was rated higher in expertness, future replications should include a control group in which the appeal to change is unaccompanied by inductions of either similarity or expertness.

The cognitive theory of identification (Stotland et al., 1961) fits the present results, but it does not specify the likely motivational factors as well as the more dynamical theory of social comparison processes (Festinger, 1954). In terms of Festinger's theory, the purchaser wanted to evaluate the correctness of his price decision and, in the absence of nonsocial means of evaluation, would be sensitive to the judgment of other persons. The salesman, of course, provided the wanted standard but when he was perceived as noncomparable on the relevant issue of paint consumption, the purchaser was neither attracted to him nor motivated to reduce discrepancy between the chosen and advocated price levels.

Kelman's (1962) presentation of hypotheses dealing with action and attitude change provided a third theoretical view. Kelman reasoned that gradients of approach or avoidance based on "identification" are steeper than those based on "internalization." Hence, when the purchaser's approach toward another price level was based on identification with the communicator, this sufficed to overcome avoidance based on internalized values such as "spend no more than necessary" and/or "take no advice from inexperienced persons." The relationship between communicator-recipient similarity and modification of the recipient requires further research in which an attempt is made to sort out *contrasting* predictions from theoretical formulations such as the three here examined.

Finally, the present study showed that contemporary theories in social psychology are not necessarily inadequate to "study the powerful forces which affect people in the real social world [Katz & Stotland, 1959, p. 467]." With some noteworthy exceptions (Hovland, 1961; Schachter, Willerman, Festinger, & Hyman, 1961), the problem may lie rather in the understandable reluctance of experimenters to forego the comfort, convenience, and methodological refinement of the laboratory.

## REFERENCES

**BACK, K.** The exertion of influence through social communication. *Journal of Abnormal and Social Psychology*, 1951, **46**, 9-24.

**BREHM, J. W., & COHEN, A. R.** *Explorations in cognitive dissonance*. New York: Wiley, 1962.

**BURNSTEIN, E., STOTLAND, E., & ZANDER, A.** Similarity to a model and self-evaluation. *Journal of Abnormal and Social Psychology*, 1961, **62**, 257-264.

**BYRNE, D.** Interpersonal attraction and attitude similarity. *Journal of Abnormal and Social Psychology*, 1961, **62**, 713-715.

**BYRNE, D., & WONG, T. J.** Racial prejudice, interpersonal attraction, and assumed dissimilarity of attitudes. *Journal of Abnormal and Social Psychology*, 1962, **65**, 246-253.

**FESTINGER, L.** A theory of social comparison processes. *Human Relations*, 1954, **7**, 117-140.

**GERARD, H. B., & GREENBAUM, C. W.** Attitudes toward an agent of uncertainty reduction. *Journal of Personality*, 1962, **30**, 485-495.

**HOVLAND, C. I.** Two new social science research units in industrial settings. *American Psychologist*, 1961, **16**, 87-91.

**KATZ, D., & STOTLAND, E.** A preliminary statement to a theory of attitude structure and change. In S. Koch (Ed.), *Psychology: A study of a science*. Vol. 3. *Formulations of the person and the social context*. New York: McGraw-Hill, 1959. Pp. 423-475.

**KATZ, E., & LAZARSFELD, P. F.** *Personal influence.* Glencoe, Ill.: Free Press, 1955.

**KELMAN, H. C.** The induction of action and attitude change. In G. Nielson (Ed.), *Proceedings of the XIVth International Congress of Applied Psychology*. Vol. 2. *Personality research*. Copenhagen: Munksgaard, 1962. Pp. 81-110.

**LEVENTHAL, H., & PERLOE, S. I.** A relationship between self-esteem and persuasibility. *Journal of Abnormal and Social Psychology*, 1962, **64**, 385-388.

**SCHACHTER, S., WILLERMAN, B., FESTINGER, L., & HYMAN, R.** Emotional disruption and industrial productivity. *Journal of Applied Psychology*, 1961, **45**, 201-213.

**STOTLAND, E., & DUNN, R. E.** Identification, "oppositeness," authoritarianism, self-esteem, and birth order. *Psychological Monographs*, 1962, **76**(9, Whole No. 528).

**STOTLAND, E., & DUNN, R. E.** Empathy, self-esteem, and birth order. *Journal of Abnormal and Social Psychology*, 1963, **66**, 532-540.

**STOTLAND, E., & HILLMER, M. L., JR.** Identification, authoritarian defensiveness, and self-esteem. *Journal of Abnormal and Social Psychology*, 1962, **64**, 334-342.

**STOTLAND, E., ZANDER, A., & NATSOULAS, T.** Generalization of interpersonal similarity. *Journal of Abnormal and Social Psychology*, 1961, **62**, 250-256.

# COMPLIANCE IN BUYING AS A FUNCTION OF INDUCEMENTS THAT THREATEN FREEDOM[1]

JUDITH WEINER REGAN
*Wells College*

JACK W. BREHM
*Duke University*

The induction of behavior or behavioral change has been and remains one of the central problems in psychology. Primary attention has been given to understanding the mechanisms, such as conditioning, and the emotional and motivational processes that tend to produce specified behaviors. More recently, however, increased attention has been given to another class of factors that logically would affect the success of behavioral inducement—those mechanisms, emotions, and motivations that act against inducing forces. Arousal of fear (Janis & Feshback, 1953), forewarning of a persuasive communication (Allyn & Festinger, 1961), and inoculation against persuasive attacks (McGuire, 1964) are some of the relevant processes that have been studied. Another factor that may play a part in resistance to behavioral induction is threat to the target person's freedom, and the experiment to be reported here was designed to examine this possibility.

The basic proposition (Brehm, 1966) is that when a person feels free to engage or not engage in a given behavior, elimination or threat of elimination of that freedom will arouse in him a state of "psychological reactance," a motivational state directed toward restoration of freedom. The more important the freedom is to the individual, the more reactance he will experience when that freedom is threatened or eliminated. Given some degree of importance for the freedom, the greater the threat to it, the greater will be the magnitude of reactance experienced. Since reactance impels the individual to attempt to restore his freedom, and since one way to restore freedom would be to engage in the threatened behavior, we may expect that where engaging in the behavior is possible, there will be some tendency to do so when reactance is aroused.

When a person feels free *not* to engage in some specified behavior $X$, any threat to this freedom will arouse reactance and a consequent tendency to avoid engaging in behavior $X$. What constitutes a threat, conceptually, is any kind of force on the individual to engage in behavior $X$. Thus, telling the individual to do $X$ (social pressure), threatening him with punishment if he does not do $X$ (coercion), or offering him an incentive for doing $X$ (reward) would all qualify theoretically as threats to his freedom not to do $X$. Thus, the greater the social pressure, coercion, or reward for doing $X$, the more reactance the individual should experience and the greater would be his motivation to avoid doing $X$.

When inducing forces threaten behavioral freedom, prediction of the outcome (that is, whether or not the person will comply) is difficult because, theoretically, the individual's behavior is determined by two opposing forces, the inducing force and the reactance, and the magnitude of the second is directly proportional to the magnitude of the first. What can be predicted is that inducing forces will produce less tendency to comply when they threaten behavioral freedom than when they do not, that the decrease in tendency to comply will be directly proportional to the importance of the freedom threatened, and that it is possible for the tendency to comply to decrease as the inducing force increases.

A variety of laboratory experiments have lent support to the proposition that inducing forces can arouse reactance and a consequent decrement in tendency to comply. Brehm and Sensenig (1966), for example, gave high school students the impression that a peer was trying to tell them which of two approximately equally attractive alternatives they should choose and found there was less compliance with the peer's recommendation than in a condition in which subjects simply learned what the preference of the peer was. More recently, Jones (1970) found that the tendency to comply with a request for help was a direct func-

[1] This is a specially prepared adaptation of a report by Judith Weiner and J. W. Brehm that appeared in Brehm (1966). This work was carried out while Miss Weiner held an undergraduate fellowship in the National Science Foundation's Undergraduate Science Education Program (G-22736), and it was also supported by National Science Foundation Grant G-23928 to Jack W. Brehm. The authors wish to express their great appreciation to the district and local personnel in the supermarket chain in which this experiment was conducted.

tion of the requester's need for help when subjects did not feel free to refuse, but was an inverse function of the requester's need for help when subjects did feel free to refuse. This experiment also showed that the tendency to comply decreased when there was the possibility that the requester would ask for help on future projects as well–that is, when the request for present help implied threats to future freedom to refuse.

The project to be reported here was an attempt to examine the reactance effects of inducing forces in a field-experimental setting. We thought that buying behavior would be a typical example, for a person normally feels free to choose what to buy, but is often subjected to inducing forces that could arouse reactance. Strong inducing forces may then be relatively ineffective in producing the purchases intended, because of the large amount of reactance aroused. Specifically, we decided to look at buying behavior in a supermarket, and as 'behavior X' we chose the buying of a king-size loaf of the supermarket's brand of sandwich bread. We assumed the average buyer would feel free not to buy this particular item, and that this freedom would have some importance to him.

Two forms of inducing force were used, verbal and monetary, with a variation in the strength of each. The general plan was to give each shopper a card on which there was a verbal inducement to buy bread *X*, along with some money. The verbal inducement either asked the shopper to try bread *X* or stated that the shopper would buy bread *X*. The money attached to the card was either the price of the bread or the price of the bread plus ten cents. Thus a shopper could receive either of four kinds of cards: a low-force verbal appeal with low or high monetary incentive, or a high-force verbal appeal with low or high monetary incentive.

The hypotheses were: (1) instructing the shopper that he is going to buy bread *X* produces less compliance than asking him to buy bread *X*; and (2) giving the shopper more money than is necessary to buy bread *X* produces less compliance than giving him just enough money to buy it.

## METHOD

The study was conducted in a supermarket in a shopping center. On Monday and Tuesday[2] of one week premeasures were drawn and the procedure was practiced. On the following Monday and Tuesday shoppers were randomly assigned to one of the two verbal-inducement conditions and received either the price of the item or more than the price of the item. On these days from 8:30, when the store opened, until approximately 12:30, when the noon lull began, a customer entering the store received a printed card requesting him to buy a specified type of bread and containing money for its purchase. On each day bread-buying was observed and approximately one-fourth of the shoppers were interviewed after they left the store.

**Verbal inducement** Some cards contained a statement ("low pressure") designed to encourage the customer to purchase the bread without greatly threatening his perceived choice to refuse. It read, "Today, regardless of whether or not you planned to buy bread or what kind you planned to buy, please try . . . [brand name] sandwich bread, king-size loaf, 25¢." Other cards contained the statement ("high pressure") designed to restrict freedom. It was identical to the low-pressure card except that it substituted "you are going to buy" for the words "please try."

**Monetary inducement** The advocated product was a 25-cent loaf of bread. On Monday each card contained a quarter attached below the verbal inducement. On Tuesday each card contained a quarter and a dime. There appeared at the bottom of all cards the sentence, "You need not retain this card," in order to assure the customer that he could actually pocket the money and would not have to turn it in at the checkout counter.

**Assignment to experimental conditions** Shopping baskets bore on each side an inconspicuous but easily discernable marking of either red or green tape. The baskets were alternated and were kept in alternating order by a male assistant. Those customers who happened to select green-marked baskets were given low-pressure cards as they passed the dispensary point, and those who selected baskets with red markings received high-pressure cards.

**Card distribution** The experimenter was dressed casually and carried a brown folder containing the cards. She was at all times pleasant and friendly. She wished the customer good morning and offered him the card. When there was any ambiguity about whether or not to give a card, she asked the customer if he was shopping, or in instances of couples or groups entering together, she asked if they were shopping

[2] Observations were also made on Wednesday but the experimental procedures carried out on the following Wednesday were of an exploratory nature and will not be reported here.

singly or together. The constituents of a group shopping together were given identical cards; however, only the data of the first group member were used. Two standard replies were used by the experimenter to answer questions about the card: "The card is for you; please keep the card," or "I really don't know. I was just hired to give a card to every customer, and I really don't know any more than what's on the card." If questioned about it, she explained that the sentence, "You need not retain the card," meant "You need not show the card to any store personnel."

**Observation**[3] Two female observers were stationed at the checkout counters where they, while obvious to customers who had completed their shopping, were not conspicuous to incoming patrons. They wore street clothes and each carried a clipboard. Each was responsible for two check-out lanes and whenever possible they observed each other's lanes to provide some estimate of accuracy. For each transaction, the two observers recorded on a prepared form whether or not the customer had a basket and, if so, its tape color, the amount of each of the several kinds of bread bought, the sex, race, and approximate age of the customer, and his total expenditure.

A third female observer, who was stationed with the experimenter, was responsible for assigning customers without baskets alternately to conditions, and for keeping track of any exceptions to the standard procedure.

At the end of each day's operations, the cash-register tape for each check-out lane was procured as a check against the records of all cash transactions by the observers.

**Interview** A male interviewer was stationed outside the store near the exit. He made his selection of interviewees by rotating between the checkout lanes in operation and taking the first customer whose total sales he could positively identify. He generally could not identify the experimental condition of the shopper at the time of interviewing. After the customer left the store, the interviewer first asked him if he had received a card and upon an affirmative reply proceeded with the interview. He used an interview schedule but allowed himself some flexibility in order to glean as much information as possible.

The interview began with very general questions about what was going on in the store, and gradually focused on the specific operations of the experiment. The intention was to find out how much customers were aware of the observation and the connection between it and the bread promotion, and then to find out how customers reacted to the verbal and monetary inducements. Evidence from the interviews will be presented later, but it may be noted here that customers did not connect the bread promotion and the observation, and generally did not realize there was a check to see whether or not they had bought bread and what kind they had bought.

**Compilation of raw data** Cash-register tapes were checked against the records of the observers, common observations were matched, and disagreements were reconciled by assuming that they were cases of omission. Customers returning or refusing cards were placed in a special category. When a group of shoppers came through a checkout lane, only the first was used as a subject. One subject who the interviewer discovered could not read was deleted. Those shoppers who might recognize any of the study personnel or their affiliation with Duke University were deleted.

[Table 8-3] shows the remaining number of usable subjects.

## RESULTS

The observations made it possible to classify each shopper along the following dimensions: sex, race (white or Negro), and amount of purchases. However, sex of shoppers was the only categorization to produce a detectable effect and is the only one retained in the following presentation of results.

A shopper's behavior could be categorized into one of four classes: bought bread *X* (the specified item); bought bread *X* plus other bread; bought other bread; bought no bread. Since, if a person bought bread *X and* some other bread as well, it might mean he was complying or that he was resisting compliance, people who fell into this category were eliminated

**[TABLE 8-3] Number of usable subjects in each condition**

| | Premeasure (week 1) | Low pressure (week 2) | High pressure (week 2) |
|---|---|---|---|
| Females | | | |
| Monday | 61 | 41 | 40 |
| Tuesday | 68 | 32 | 34 |
| Males | | | |
| Monday | 19 | 8 | 15 |
| Tuesday | 27 | 20 | 9 |

[3] The help of our observers, Mary Lee Brehm, Caryl Anderson, and the late Kathryn Formica, and our male assistant, Norman Staples, Jr., is gratefully acknowledged.

from the final analysis. There were 16 such people scattered throughout the various conditions and their inclusion would have no effect on the conclusions one might draw.

The index of primary interest is the extent to which shoppers bought bread *X*. An estimate of the normal proportion of shoppers buying bread *X* is available from the pre-experimental observation on corresponding days. Looking first at female shoppers, in [Table 8-4] it may be seen that 23.6 percent on Monday, and 17.9 percent on Tuesday, bought bread *X*. There is a very slight decrease in the proportion buying the critical loaf from Monday to Tuesday, but the difference is nowhere near statistical reliability ($\chi^2 = .59$). On the following Monday, when just the price of the bread was given with the verbal inducement, it was expected that the low-pressure request to buy bread *X* would increase the proportion buying it, whereas the high-pressure insistence that one was going to buy *X* would produce relatively less compliance, perhaps even below-normal buying of *X*. The outcome, as seen in [Table 8-4], shows that female shoppers exposed to the low-pressure inducement were much more likely than normal to buy bread *X*, exactly 70 percent of them doing so. However, although the high-pressure inducement also produced a large proportion buying *X* (51.3 percent), it did not produce as much compliance as the low-pressure approach. While the difference between the low- and high-pressure conditions might fairly easily have occurred by chance ($.10 < p < .15$), it nevertheless lends some support to our expectations that the stronger verbal inducement would arouse reactance and result in less compliance.

On Tuesday, an additional dime was added to the card in order to put more pressure on customers to buy bread *X*, with the expectation that the additional pressure would result in less compliance. [Table 8-4] shows that this expectation is supported strongly in the low-pressure condition, where compliance drops from Monday's 70 percent to Tuesday's 40 percent, and is supported weakly in the high-pressure condition, where compliance drops from 51.3 percent to 40 percent. This decrease is reliable in the low-pressure condition ($p < .05$), nowhere nearly reliable in the high-pressure condition, and reliable in the two conditions combined ($p < .05$). Hence, as expected, the additional dime tends to *decrease* compliance among female shoppers.

The effects of the verbal and monetary inducements on male shoppers was quite different from that on the females. As may be seen in [Table 8-5], the verbal appeal had a rather large effect, with the high-pressure form producing more compliance than the low-pressure form. On the other hand, the amount of the monetary incentive seems to have had no effect at all. While this different reaction of the males was not predicted, it is not difficult to understand in terms of our previous analysis. Males, we may assume, are less knowledgeable and discriminating about the products in a grocery store. It should be true, then, that the importance of the freedom to select one item rather than another would be less for males than for females. Thus, inducements to buy a given item would be less likely to threaten an important freedom for males, and males would therefore experience less reactance and would be more likely to comply.

The interview data add some support to the reactance interpretation of this study. For example, although few interviewees expressed strong annoyance about either the verbal inducement or the money, there was a tendency, among those who did not buy bread *X*, for those in the high-pressure condition to report more annoyance with both the verbal message and money than those in the low-pressure condition. In addition, while the most frequent view was that

**[TABLE 8-4] Compliance (buying bread *X*) among female shoppers**

| | Monday | | Tuesday | |
|---|---|---|---|---|
| | *N* | % | *N* | % |
| Control (normal buying) | 55 | 23.6 | 67 | 17.9 |
| | With 25¢ | | With 35¢ | |
| | *N* | % | *N* | % |
| Experimental | | | | |
| Low pressure | 40 | 70.0 | 30 | 40.0 |
| High pressure | 39 | 51.3 | 30 | 40.0 |

**[TABLE 8-5] Compliance among male shoppers**

| | Monday | | Tuesday | |
|---|---|---|---|---|
| | *N* | % | *N* | % |
| Control (normal buying) | 18 | 16.7 | 27 | 11.1 |
| | With 25¢ | | With 35¢ | |
| | *N* | % | *N* | % |
| Experimental | | | | |
| Low pressure | 8 | 37.5 | 20 | 45.0 |
| High pressure | 15 | 73.3 | 9 | 77.8 |

"it is just another advertising scheme," and nothing to get excited about, three of the interviewed shoppers said outright that they did not like to be told what to buy. This, it should be recalled, is despite the fact that customers were given the money with which to buy the bread.

## DISCUSSION

The results indicate that monetary, and probably verbal, inducements may produce less compliance as their strength increases. Our interpretation of this effect is that increases in the magnitude of an inducing force increase the perceived threat to the individual's freedom not to perform the behavior. To the extent that the freedom not to perform the behavior has some importance for the individual, the more threat he perceives, the more reactance he will experience, and, consequently, the more he will be motivated to restore his freedom not to comply. By not complying, the individual restores his freedom.

While the present results can be interpreted in terms of other factors such as 'personal insult,' 'being treated like a child,' etc., an interpretation in terms of psychological reactance is supported by the interview data and by other research on reactance theory. The interviews revealed little or no evidence that participants felt insulted or belittled, and laboratory experiments (Brehm & Cole, 1966; Sensenig & Brehm, 1968) have shown that dramatic reactance effects can occur with little or no apparent derogation of the person who threatens freedom.

It seems reasonable to suppose that inducing forces can be applied in ways that would minimize the arousal of negative interpretations and emotional reactions. Justifications for the intended inducement can indicate that the inductee is to benefit or that there will be some general benefit with which the inductee can sympathize. But while such justifications can increase the motivation to comply, they do not reduce the threat to the freedom of the target person to refuse to comply and so they do not eliminate the arousal of reactance. Hence, even the most skillfully applied and highly justified inducing force can theoretically create reactance and the consequent resistance against compliance.

From the point of view of reactance theory, the crucial determinant of resistance to compliance is not so much the character of the inducing force or the way in which it is applied, but rather the importance of the freedom that the inducing force threatens. Furthermore, the importance of the freedom to choose between two alternatives should be a direct function of how competent the person feels to make the relevant judgment about which is better. This point has been supported in an experiment by Wicklund and Brehm (1968), in which it was found that a person who is to make a judgment about which of two candidates for a job is better, and who receives a message from a peer stating that one candidate is unquestionably better, tends to make an opposing (boomerang) judgment *but only to the extent he has previously been led to believe that he has high competence to make this kind of judgment*. The same point seems to be illustrated by the differential responses of males and females in the present experiment. It is plausible to assume that females feel relatively competent to judge items in a supermarket, and that they would therefore value the freedom to select or reject particular items. Males, on the other hand, may feel relatively less competent to judge items and would not put much value on being free to select or reject particular ones; in addition, males who have been sent shopping by their wives may feel they have no freedom of selection or rejection. Thus, the females experience more reactance than do the males when pressured by the verbal and monetary inducing forces to buy a particular item.

The fundamental theoretical point is that any inducing force, no matter how benign, how well-intended, how well justified, will create its own countermotivational force (reactance) when it threatens or eliminates any of a person's freedoms. While there are many areas of behavior having to do, for example, with one's job, with social custom, etc., in which people tend to feel they have little or no freedom, there remains a wide variety of behaviors about which people do tend to feel free. Furthermore, the very need to use an inducing force to obtain a particular behavior frequently implies that the target person has freedom not to perform that behavior and to that extent the force guarantees the arousal of reactance. It would seem that the occurrence of reactance in response to inducing forces should be relatively frequent, and, with just that frequency, the effectiveness of inducing forces should be diminished.

In summary, the present view is that a particular behavior may be obtained by the application of an inducing force, but that the effectiveness of the inducement will depend in part on the individual's feeling that he is not free to refuse or his feeling that there is little value in the freedom to refuse. When the individual feels free not to engage in the particular behavior and this freedom is of high importance to him, the application of an inducing force may produce so much reactance that the individual will stand firmly against engaging in the behavior. Thus, to obtain the specified behavior where freedom not to engage in it is important, the individual's motivation to engage in the behavior must be increased without simultaneously increasing the threat to his freedom. Whether or not there is some way to accomplish this is not yet clear.

## REFERENCES


**ALLYN, JANE, & FESTINGER, L.** The effectiveness of unanticipated persuasive communications. *Journal of Abnormal and Social Psychology*, 1961, **62**, 35-40.

**BREHM, J. W.** *A theory of psychological reactance*. New York: Academic Press, 1966.

**BREHM, J. W., & COLE, ANN H.** Effect of a favor which reduces freedom. *Journal of Personality and Social Psychology*, 1966, **3**, 420-426.

**BREHM, J. W., & SENSENIG, J.** Social influence as a function of attempted and implied usurpation of choice. *Journal of Personality and Social Psychology*, 1966, **4**, 703-707.

**JANIS, I. R., & FESHBACK, S.** Effects of fear-arousing communications. *Journal of Abnormal and Social Psychology*, 1953, **48**, 78-92.

**JONES, R. A.** Volunteering to help: the effects of choice, dependence, and anticipated dependence. *Journal of Personality and Social Psychology*, 1970, **14**, 121-129.

**McGUIRE, W. J.** Inducing resistance to persuasion. In L. Berkowitz (Ed.), *Advances in experimental social psychology*, Vol. 1. New York: Academic Press, 1964.

**SENSENIG, J., & BREHM, J. W.** Attitude change from an implied threat to attitudinal freedom. *Journal of Personality and Social Psychology*, 1968, **8**, 324-330.

**WICKLUND, R. A., & BREHM, J. W.** Attitude change as a function of felt competence and threat to attitudinal freedom. *Journal of Experimental Social Psychology*, 1968, **4**, 64-75.

# OBESITY, FOOD DEPRIVATION, AND SUPERMARKET SHOPPING BEHAVIOR[1]

RICHARD E. NISBETT
*Yale University*

DAVID E. KANOUSE
*University of California, Los Angeles*

It was predicted that food deprivation would increase the attractiveness of food for individuals of normal weight, but would not increase its attractiveness for overweight individuals. Grocery shopping in a supermarket was observed. As predicted, normal individuals bought more food if they were deprived than they did if they had recently eaten. Overweight individuals actually bought more food if they had recently eaten than they did if deprived. Shopping time was also measured, and it was found that normal individuals shopped more slowly than overweight individuals if deprived and more rapidly if they had recently eaten.

Several recent studies by Schachter and his colleagues have demonstrated that the types of stimuli which motivate eating for the obese individual differ from those which motivate eating for the individual of normal weight. For the most part, overweight individuals are quite responsive to a variety of environment- and food-related cues which have nothing to do with the satisfaction of nutritional needs. Overweight individuals eat more when persuaded by a rigged clock to believe that it is mealtime (Schachter & Gross, 1968); they eat more when food cues are immediate and palpable than when they are remote and weak (Nisbett, 1968b); and they are extremely responsive to taste (Nisbett, 1968a). At the same time, the overweight are less responsive than normal individuals to bodily cues which vary with nutritional state and which signal hunger and satiety. Food deprivation does not increase the overweight individual's intake; and fear, which is known to decrease gastric motility and stimulate blood sugar release, does not decrease intake (Schachter, Goldman, & Gordon, 1968). The state of food deprivation is apparently not aversive to the obese; they are more willing to fast for religious purposes than are normal individuals and are less discomfited by their abstinence (Goldman, Jaffa, & Schachter, 1968). Moreover, it appears that the obese do not label as "hunger" either the sensation of gastric motility (Stunkard & Koch, 1964) or the state of food deprivation (Nisbett, 1968a). This evidence has been summarized by Schachter (1967) in the form of two generalizations: (*a*) Overweight individuals are highly responsive to "external" cues, that is, to cues inherent in food or the environment. (*b*) Overweight individuals are quite unresponsive to "internal," physiological cues of hunger and satiety.

The proposition that the overweight are unresponsive to internal state is supported only by self-report data and by evidence about actual consummatory behavior. Although consummatory data probably constitute the single most convincing type of evidence, it would be desirable to have behavioral evidence of a nonconsummatory type as well. The process of eating obviously alters the internal state of the organism and may affect a variety of external cues also. Thus, the measurement of the dependent variable contaminates the independent variable. The interpretive problems inherent in consummatory measures have prompted the use of instrumental and other nonconsummatory dependent variables in most work with animals which employs deprivation as an independent variable. It would add to our confidence if data were available for food-related but nonconsummatory behavior.

Most people would agree that one of the dramatic subjective changes occurring with deprivation is the heightened attractiveness which food takes on. The sight, smell, and taste of food have a compelling quality for the individual in a state of food deprivation which is altogether lacking in the satiated state. A behavioral measure of the attractiveness of food would be of considerable value in testing the hypothesis that the overweight are unresponsive to internal state. One would expect such a measure to indicate

[1] This research was supported by Grant GS1684 from the National Science Foundation. We wish to thank Mr. Jack Bernstein of Pegnataro's Super Food Markets of New Haven for his kind cooperation. Michael Storms provided valuable criticism of an earlier draft.

that while deprivation increases the attractiveness of food for the normal individual, it does not increase the attractiveness of food for the overweight.

Intuitively it seems that behavior in the supermarket should reflect the differential attractiveness of food due to deprivation. For most people who shop on an empty stomach, supermarket aisles are lined with temptations. Imagination readily places potatoes and onions around roasts and transforms pancake mix into a steaming, buttered stack. An egg and milk run can turn out to cost considerable money and time. When one has recently eaten, on the other hand, roasts are examined with an efficient, dispassionate eye, and pancake mix is just pancake mix. The trip may be less enjoyable, but escape with budget and schedule intact is more likely.

It seems, then, that normal individuals will spend increasing amounts of time and money in the supermarket as their state of food deprivation increases. If overweight individuals are insensitive to internal cues, the time and money they spend should not increase with increasing deprivation.[2]

## METHOD

Data were collected in a New Haven supermarket from 9:00 a.m. to 6:00 p.m. on a single day. The population which the supermarket serves is predominantly working class, and the largest single group in the ethnically diverse community is Italian-American. Eighty-one percent of the sample were female, and the median estimated age was 46.

After customers had selected carts, which were tagged with identifying numbers, they were approached by an interviewer. The interview took about 45 seconds to conduct, and went as follows:

> Hello, I'm conducting a survey and I wonder if I could ask a couple of quick questions.
> How many people do you shop for?
> How many times a week do you ordinarily shop?
> How much do you expect to spend in the store today?
> When did you last have something to eat?

During the questioning, interviewers recorded the sex of the subjects, made judgments about their weight and age, and noted their shopping cart numbers and the time.

Observers were posted at the check-out lanes to record totals from the cash registers. The observers also recorded shopping cart numbers, as complete a description of the subjects as time permitted, and the time when the total was rung on the register.

Because it was not possible to interview and observe all shoppers, some problems of matching entry and exit data arose. As a check to ensure that there were entry and exit data for a single shopper, rather than one shopper's entry data and another's exit data, cases were discarded under the following circumstances: if interviewer and observer did not agree on the sex of the subject or on age within 15 years, or if the subject's prediction of his bill and the total on the cash register did not agree within 15 dollars.

The criterion of overweight employed was necessarily a subjective one, since it was not possible to weigh or measure the subjects. A subject was classified as overweight if, in the opinion of the interviewer, he would look better if he lost 15 pounds or so. This standard resulted in the classification of a slight majority of the subjects—149 out of 283—as overweight. While this may seem to be a large proportion of overweight individuals, the demographic characteristics of the population would suggest that by any standards the frequency of overweight should be high (Goldblatt, Moore, & Stunkard, 1965).

## RESULTS

It was anticipated that food deprivation would increase the attractiveness of food for normal individuals. If so, food deprivation should prompt normal individuals to buy more items on impulse. This should result in larger and larger grocery bills for the normal shopper as the time since his last meal increases. The authors did not anticipate that food deprivation would increase the attractiveness of food for overweight individuals. They should show no tendency to buy more items on impulse when deprived of food, and the size of their grocery bills was not expected to increase with increasing food deprivation. [Figure 8-6] presents the average total on the cash register as a function of the number of hours of food deprivation at the time of the interview. It may be seen that, for normal subjects, there is a decidedly positive relationship between deprivation and the amount of food purchased. The most deprived normal subjects spent 43% more money than the least deprived normal subjects. The linear component of the curve for normal subjects is

[2] Scotch (1967), in a discussion of Schachter's work which the authors discovered shortly after completing the study described below, has observed both types of supermarket behavior in the same individual, namely himself. He reports that at a time when he was slender, the size of his grocery bill was highly related to his deprivation state. The correlation disappeared, however, during a period when he was gaining weight.

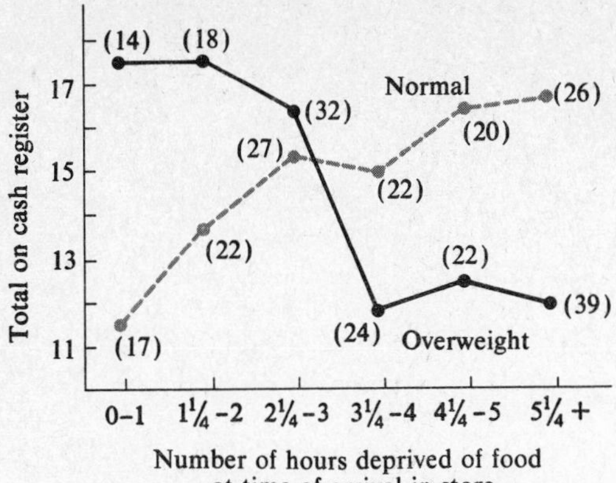


[FIGURE 8-6] Total on cash register as a function of degree of food deprivation. Numbers in parentheses denote $n$.

significant at the .05 level ($F$ = 4.30, $df$ = 1/128).[3] The relationship for overweight subjects has precisely the opposite form—increased deprivation is associated with decreased purchase (linear $F$ = 8.66, $df$ = 1/143, $p < .01$). Although more deprived subjects were by and large late afternoon shoppers, the relationships portrayed in [Figure 8-6] are in no way dependent upon an association between time of day and deprivation state. The interaction between weight and deprivation is present at all times of the day—early morning, late morning, early afternoon, and late afternoon.

These data were in accord with the authors' anticipations. Normal individuals buy more and more food as their state of deprivation increases, while overweight subjects do not. However, it cannot be ascertained that the trends in [Figure 8-6] are due to impulse buying until there is further information. It certainly seems likely that the increase in purchases observed for normal subjects is due to increased impulse buying, but it seems less likely that the decrease observed for overweight subjects is due to decreased impulse buying. It was anticipated that the attractiveness of food for overweight individuals would be unaffected by deprivation, and it would be puzzling to discover that food has less appeal for the overweight individual who is deprived than for the one who has just eaten.

It is possible to examine the extent to which the curves in [Figure 8-6] reflect impulse buying by performing an analysis of the shopping intentions of the subjects. Shopping intention data are available in the form of the estimates of their bills which shoppers gave to the interviewer. If the increase in [Figure 8-6] observed for normal subjects is due to increased impulse buying as suspected, then normal subjects show a tendency to "overshoot" their estimates—buy more than they intended—as their state of deprivation increases. [Figure 8-7] presents subjects' shopping intentions as a function of the number of hours they had been deprived of food. It may be seen that there is no relationship between deprivation and the size of the estimate for normal subjects (linear $F < 1$, $df$ = 1/128). Though it appears that the very most deprived subjects gave larger estimates than other subjects, this group differs only marginally from the others. A contrast of this very deprived group with all others yields an $F$ of 3.17 ($df$ = 1/128, $.05 < p < .10$). Otherwise, it is apparent from [Figure 8-7] that there is no consistent relationship between deprivation and the estimates given by normal subjects. This strongly suggests that the progressive increase in the amount they actually purchased was due to a greater and greater tendency to overshoot their estimates as their state of deprivation increased. A covariance analysis of the purchase data, with estimate of bill as the covariate, corroborates this assumption. Such an analysis yields a prediction of the total based on the estimate. It is then possible to examine deviations from the predicted total as a function of deprivation. As anticipated, the total purchased by normal subjects is more and more likely to overshoot the estimate-derived prediction as deprivation state increases (linear $F$ = 9.55, $df$ = 1/127, $p < .01$).[4] The conclusion is then justified that for normal subjects, the positive relationship between deprivation and purchase was due to a tendency to buy more food on impulse when deprived.

In distinct contrast, a similar analysis indicates that impulse buying was not a factor in the negative relationship between deprivation and purchase which was observed for overweight subjects. It is apparent

[3] All $p$ values reported are based on two-tailed tests.

[4] The nonlinear term of the analysis of covariance is also significant, due to a tendency of the most deprived group to overshoot their estimates less (actually undershoot) than other deprived subjects. It is not clear whether this should be regarded as evidence that the relationship between deprivation and impulse buying is curvilinear for normal subjects. As shown in [Figures 8-6 and 8-7], the most deprived group bought more food than any of the other groups, but they also intended to buy more. It may be that extreme hunger makes the supermarket's wares more attractive to normal subjects even before they enter the store. In other words, the very hungry normal individual may do some of his impulse buying outside of the store, fantasizing about the foods he will soon see and adding them to his mental shopping list.

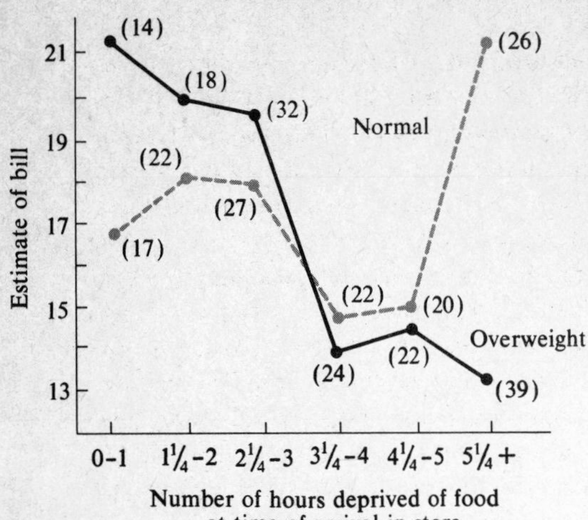


[FIGURE 8-7] Estimate of bill as a function of food deprivation. Numbers in parentheses denote *n*.

from [Figure 8-7] that there is a pronounced negative relationship between deprivation and estimated bill for overweight subjects (linear $F = 10.32$, $df = 1/143$, $p < .001$). The decrease observed in [Figure 8-7] parallels almost exactly that observed in [Figure 8-6]. This suggests that the drop in the amount purchased does not reflect impulse buying but rather the intentions with which the overweight subjects entered the store. The analysis of covariance corroborates this. For overweight subjects, there is no relationship between deprivation and the degree to which the total overshoots the estimate (linear $F < 1$). Deprivation, then, apparently has no effect on the reactions of overweight subjects to the food they see in the store. Their shopping behavior reflects their intentions when they are deprived as much as it does when they have recently eaten. However, the fact that overweight subjects *plan* to buy more food if they have recently eaten than they do when deprived must be explained. Perhaps, for the overweight individual, eating is a stimulus for grocery shopping. Upon finishing a meal, the overweight individual may in effect say to himself, "My but that was good. I think I'll go and buy some more." This notion will be considered later.

The second hypothesis is that normal individuals spend more time shopping when deprived and that overweight individuals do not. Of course this is probably the case for absolute shopping times, since normal subjects bought more food when deprived and overweight subjects bought less. The interesting question to ask is whether normal subjects spend more time per dollar when deprived. That is, normal subjects might be expected to shop in a brisk and

[TABLE 8-6] **Minutes spent shopping, corrected for amount purchased, as a function of weight and deprivation state.**

| Deprivation state | Weight | |
|---|---|---|
| | Normal | Overweight |
| Low | 29.53<br>(73) | 32.31<br>(67) |
| High | 31.26<br>(61) | 27.34<br>(82) |

NOTE.—Numbers in parentheses denote *n*.

efficient way when satiated and to linger when deprived. [Table 8-6] presents mean shopping time as a function of weight and deprivation state. The shopping times in the table take into account the amount which subjects actually purchased. They are adjusted by the results of a covariance analysis for the regression of time on amount purchased and are thus a measure of time controlling for amount purchased. Comparing first the less deprived subjects, it may be seen that the overweight subjects shop more slowly. The difference in shopping time between overweight and normal subjects is almost three minutes greater than would be predicted on the basis of the amounts which the two groups purchased. In contrast, among more deprived subjects, it is the normal subjects who shop slowly. The difference between overweight and normal subjects is almost four minutes greater than would be predicted. The interaction between weight and deprivation, covarying amount purchased, is significant at the .05 level ($F = 4.84$, $df = 1/278$). Normal subjects are thus more likely than overweight subjects to shop slowly when deprived. It should be noted, however, that the difference between more and less deprived normal subjects is not significant by itself, and that these data on time are considerably weaker than the data on amount purchased.

## DISCUSSION

To summarize, it was found that:

1. Individuals of normal weight bought more groceries as their state of deprivation increased, whereas overweight individuals bought fewer groceries.
2. The increase in amount purchased by normal subjects was apparently due to increased impulse buying. They were inclined to overshoot their estimated bills when deprived.
3. The decrease in amount purchased by overweight subjects was merely a reflection of a decrease in purchase intentions. The decrease in amount actually purchased paralleled almost exactly the decrease in size of the estimated bill.

4. Deprived normal subjects were more likely to shop slowly than deprived overweight subjects.

These results are thoroughly consistent with the hypothesis that deprivation does not increase the attractiveness of food for overweight individuals. In one respect, however, the results deviated from the anticipations. Overweight individuals intended to buy, and actually did buy, more food if they had recently eaten than if they were deprived. This finding suggests that for the overweight, the process of eating may actually trigger a concern with food. This notion would be consistent with the characterization of the overweight proposed by Schachter (1967). If the overweight individual lacks responsiveness to internal state, eating would not decrease the attractiveness of food, and the external cues associated with eating might serve to arouse still greater interest in food.

There is reason to hesitate, however, before putting a "triggering" interpretation on the behavior of overweight subjects in the present study. Such an interpretation would seem to require that overweight individuals be more likely to shop after eating a meal than normal subjects, and this is not the case. Overweight subjects were, on the average, more deprived at the time they shopped than normal subjects. Whether this represents a bias on the part of overweight individuals in favor of shopping when deprived is not clear. In order to reach this conclusion, the deprivation state of a comparable group of nonshoppers must be known. In any case, the most direct implication of the "triggering" notion is that overweight individuals should be more likely to shop after eating a meal, and there is no evidence that this is true. It is the authors' guess that eating sometimes triggers a desire in the overweight individual to buy orgiastically: "My but that was good; instead of picking up odds and ends, I think I'll do the week's shopping." This interpretation has the virtue of being consistent with both theory and data, but it has a somewhat hollow, *post hoc* ring.

Whatever the reason for the tendency of overweight subjects to plan larger purchases after eating a meal, the present data indicate that deprivation does not increase the attractiveness of food for the overweight. The impulse buying of overweight individuals is quite unrelated to their deprivation state. The results are therefore in accord with previous data indicating that the state of deprivation is not labeled as hunger by the overweight and does not increase the amount which they eat. The self-report and consummatory evidence indicating that the overweight are unresponsive to internal state is thus supported by nonconsummatory data of considerable intuitive appeal.

An examination of nonconsummatory variables of a physiological nature might be of value in determining the precise locus of the obese individual's insensitivity. Two promising candidates for such an investigation are salivation and heart rate. Salivation in response to food stimuli increases with increasing deprivation. (At least it does for dogs.) If the overweight fail utterly to experience deprivation as hunger, they cannot be expected to salivate differentially to food stimuli as a function of deprivation. Buckhout and Grace (1966) have recently demonstrated that the heart rate of long-deprived human subjects is higher when food cues are present than when they are absent. Again, it is suspected that this relationship would not hold for the overweight.

## REFERENCES


**BUCKHOUT, R., & GRACE, T.** The effect of food deprivation and expectancy on heart rate. *Psychonomic Science*, 1966, **6**, 153-154.

**GOLDBLATT, R. G., MOORE, M. E., & STUNKARD, A. J.** Social factors in obesity. *Journal of the American Medical Association*, 1965, **192**, 1039-1044.

**GOLDMAN, R., JAFFA, M., & SCHACHTER, S.** Yom Kippur, Air France, dormitory food, and the eating behavior of obese and normal persons. *Journal of Personality and Social Psychology*, 1968, **10**, 117-123.

**NISBETT, R. E.** Taste, deprivation, and weight determinants of eating behavior. *Journal of Personality and Social Psychology*, 1968, **10**, 107-116. (a)

**NISBETT, R. E.** Determinants of food intake in obesity. *Science*, 1968, **159**, 1254-1255. (b)

**SCHACHTER, S.** Cognitive effects on bodily functioning: Studies of obesity and eating. In D. Glass (Ed.), *Neurophysiology and Emotion*. New York: Rockefeller University and The Russell Sage Foundation, 1967, pp. 117-144.

**SCHACHTER, S., GOLDMAN, R., & GORDON, A.** Effects of food deprivation and fear on eating behavior. *Journal of Personality and Social Psychology*, 1968, **10**, 91-97.

**SCHACHTER, S., & GROSS, L.** Eating and the manipulation of time. *Journal of Personality and Social Psychology*, 1968, **10**, 98-106.

**SCOTCH, N. A.** Inside every fat man. In D. Glass (Ed.), *Neurophysiology and Emotion*. New York: Rockefeller University and The Russell Sage Foundation, 1967, pp. 155-160.

**STUNKARD, A. J., & KOCH, C.** The interpretation of gastric motility. I. Apparent bias in the reports of hunger by obese persons. *Archives of General Psychiatry*, 1964, **11**, 74-82.

# YOM KIPPUR, AIR FRANCE, DORMITORY FOOD, AND THE EATING BEHAVIOR OF OBESE AND NORMAL PERSONS[1]

RONALD GOLDMAN, MELVYN JAFFA,
AND STANLEY SCHACHTER
*Columbia University*

3 field studies, designed to test the generalizability of experimental findings on the eating behavior of obese and normal *S*s, are presented. These studies examine the relationship of weight deviation to fasting on Yom Kippur, toleration of institutional food, and adjustment to time-zone changes. Conforming to laboratory-generated expectations, fat Jews prove to be more likely to fast on Yom Kippur, fat students to be more intolerant of dormitory food, and fat fliers to more easily adjust to time-zone changes than do their normal counterparts.

The results of recent studies of the eating behavior of obese and normal subjects indicate that: (*a*) Physiological correlates of food deprivation such as gastric motility and hypoglycemia are directly related to eating and to the reported experience of hunger in normal-size subjects but unrelated in obese subjects (Schachter, Goldman, & Gordon, 1968; Stunkard & Koch, 1964); and (*b*) external or nonvisceral cues such as smell, taste, the sight of other people eating, the passage of time, etc., stimulate eating behavior in obese subjects to a greater extent than in normal subjects (Nisbett, 1968; Schachter & Gross, 1968). This paper will examine implications of these relationships in a variety of non-laboratory settings–specifically, religious fasting, tolerance of institutional food, and the effects of time-zone changes on eating behavior.

## WHO FASTS ON YOM KIPPUR?

Evidence indicates that for obese subjects the impulse to eat is triggered by an external, food-relevant cue. In contrast, the impulse to eat for normal individuals appears to be stimulated by the set of physiological cues consequent on food deprivation. Assuming that blocking this impulse by doing without food is an irritating or painful state, it should follow that in circumstances where food-relevant external cues are sparse, or, where the individual can successfully distract himself from such external cues, the obese person should have a considerably easier time fasting or doing without food than should normal size persons. The Schachter and Gross (1968) findings that the obese rarely eat breakfast or, on weekends, lunch can be construed as consistent with this expectation.

In order to test directly this expectation and some of its corollaries the relationship of overweight to fasting on Yom Kippur was studied. Yom Kippur, the Jewish Day of Atonement, is the most sacred of Jewish holy days and the only one for which fasting is commanded by Biblical Law. The traditional Jew begins his fast on the evening of Yom Kippur and does without food or water for 24 hours. Except when sleeping, he spends virtually all of his time in prayer in a synagogue, a physical environment notoriously barren of graven images, let alone food-related cues; a ritual conducted in Aramaic and Hebrew whose chief direct reference to food is passing mention of a scapegoat. Almost certainly informal conversations within the synagogue at this time must to some degree be concerned with the fast; but the ritual proper and the physical surroundings are virtually devoid of food-relevant cues.

Among contemporary Jews, observance of Yom Kippur ranges from those who meticulously adhere to every detail described to those who are only vaguely aware that there is such a day. Between these extremes lies every variation of token or partial observance–people who will spend only an hour or two in synagogue, Jews who do without regular meals but sneak half a sandwich and a sip of celery tonic, and so on.

Given this characterization of Yom Kippur, if these speculations about obesity and fasting are correct, it should follow among Jews for whom the day has any meaning that (*a*) Fat Jews will be more likely to fast than normally built Jews; (*b*) the difficulty of fasting will, for obese Jews, depend upon the abundance of food-related cues in their immediate environment, while for normal Jews these two variables will be unrelated. Thus it should be anticipated that fat, fasting Jews who spend a great deal of time in synagogue will suffer less from fasting than fat, fasting

[1] These studies were supported by National Science Foundation Grant GS732. Our thanks are due to Sidney Morgenbesser and Stanley Engelstein for advice about Yom Kippur.

Jews who spend little time in synagogue and there will be no such relationship for normal, fasting Jews. Plausibly, there will be far fewer food-related cues in the synagogue than on the street or at home. The likelihood, therefore, that the impulse to eat will be triggered is greater out of synagogue than in. For normal Jews, this distinction is of less importance. In or out of synagogue, stomach pangs are still stomach pangs.

In order to test these expectations, a few days after Yom Kippur, 1965, a questionnaire was administered to all of the students in several classes in introductory social science and psychology at the City University of New York and at New York University. The questionnaire was anonymous and designed to learn from Jewish respondents their sex, height, and weight, whether or not they had fasted on Yom Kippur, how unpleasant they had found the fast, and a variety of other information relevant to how religious they were and their experiences during Yom Kippur.

Since these hypotheses are irrelevant to Jews who are totally irreligious and only dimly aware of the holiday and its proscriptions, our sample for analysis is limited to those Jews who gave some indication of being religious. The criterion is simple and derives from answers to the question, "Approximately how many times have you been to synagogue in the last year?" Any Jew who had been to synagogue at least once during the past year, for some reason other than a wedding or a bar mitzvah, was considered a religious Jew. Of a total of 748 questionnaires, 456 were from Jewish respondents (247 men, 209 women). Of these, 296 respondents (160 men, 136 women) are, by this criterion, religious Jews.[2]

The basic data on obesity and fasting are presented in [Table 8-7]. Whether or not a subject fasted was determined by his answer to the question, "Did you attempt to fast last Wednesday for the Yom Kippur holiday?" Anyone who answered "Yes" is classified as a faster. The Metropolitan Life Insurance Company (1959) norms for height and weight were used to calculate weight deviations. Subjects were classified as obese if their weight deviations fell among the top 20% of all subjects of their own sex, a cutoff point used in the three studies described in this paper. In this sample, any male who was 15.4% overweight or more is classified as obese. For females, a 20% cutoff point includes girls who, from their answers to the questions about weight and height, are as little as 4.8% overweight. Despite the fact that one would hardly consider a woman, truly of this slight weight deviation, as obese, we have, for consistency's sake, employed the 20% cutoff point for both males and females in all of the studies described in this paper. Not wishing to debate the pros and cons of this procedure we note simply that in the two studies in this paper involving females, employing a higher cutoff point for females tends to strengthen the main effects.

**[TABLE 8-7] Obesity and fasting on Yom Kippur**

| | Obese Jews | Normal Jews |
|---|---|---|
| Fasters | 49 | 163 |
| Non-fasters | 10 | 74 |

NOTE.—$\chi^2 = 4.74, p < .05$.

The data in [Table 8-7] are clearly consistent with expectations. Among fat religious Jews 83.1% fasted on Yom Kippur. In comparison, 68.8% of normal Jews fasted. Obesity does play a part in determining who fasts on Yom Kippur.[3]

Let us examine next the impact of those factors presumed to differentially affect the difficulty of fasting for normal and obese subjects. In keeping with our general scheme, we have assumed that the presence or absence of food-relevant cues directly affects the ease with which an obese person fasts and has less impact on a normal person. If one accepts our characterization of the synagogue on Yom Kippur as devoid of food-related cues, it should be anticipated that for obese fasters answers to the question

[2] Included in this group of religious Jews are 25 respondents who had not been to synagogue during the past year but who had fasted on Yom Kippur. In puzzling over just how to classify such respondents, it seemed to us that undertaking the Yom Kippur fast was, at least, as good an indication of religiousness as attending synagogue once or twice during the year. These non-synagogue-going fasters, are, then, classified as religious. It should be noted, however, that the main effects of the study (and the statistical levels of confidence involved) remain much the same whether or not this subgroup is treated as religious.

[3] There is a tendency for obese respondents to be slightly more religious than normal subjects, that is, to attend synagogue slightly more during the year. Though this is a nonsignificant difference, it is troubling, for obviously the more religious are more likely to fast. In order to check on this alternative interpretation, the proportion of fasters among obese and normal respondents of various degrees of religiosity (as measured by the amount of synagogue going) was compared. At every point of comparison from slightly religious (one or two visits to synagogue) to extremely religious (20 or more visits), the obese are more likely to fast.

"For how many hours did you attend religious services this Yom Kippur?" will be negatively related to ratings of fasting unpleasantness as measured by a scale headed, "Insofar as you did fast this Yom Kippur, how unpleasant an experience was it?" The more hours in synagogue, the less exposure to food-relevant cues and the less unpleasant should fasting be for the externally controlled obese person. For the normal faster, attuned to his viscera, there should be little relationship.

The data are consistent with these expectations. For the obese, the correlation between hours in synagogue and unpleasantness is −.50. For normals, the correlation is only −.18. Testing the difference between these correlations, $z = 2.19$, which is significant at the .03 level. For the obese the more time in synagogue the less of an ordeal is fasting; for normals, hours in synagogue has little to do with the difficulty of the fast.

## WHO EATS DORMITORY FOODS

The taste or quality of food can be considered an external determinant of eating behavior. As such, food quality should have more of an effect on obese than on nonobese eaters. In an experiment designed to test this hypothesis Nisbett (1968) found that when the available food was generally rated as good, obese subjects ate more than did normals, who ate more than did skinny subjects. When the food was considered bad, this trend tended to reverse with skinny subjects eating more than either normal or obese subjects. Generalizing from these findings, it seems reasonable to assume that taste will not only have an effect on how much fat, as compared with normal, subjects eat, but on where they eat. It seems a plausible guess that the obese will be more drawn to good restaurants and more repelled by bad ones than will normal subjects.

At Columbia, students have the option of eating in the university dining halls or in any of the swarm of more or less exotic restaurants and delicatessens that surround this metropolitan campus. It is probably small surprise to the reader to learn that typical campus opinion of dormitory food is unfavorable. Student-conducted surveys document widespread dissatisfaction with the university dining halls, enumerating complaints about cold food, poor service, stale desserts, etc., etc. (University Dormitory Council, 1964).

If an undergraduate elects to eat in a dormitory dining hall, he may if he chooses join a prepay food plan at the beginning of the school year. For $500 he purchases a meal contract which entitles him to a weekly meal ticket worth $16.25 with which he can pay for food at the university dining hall or snack bar. Anytime after November 1, the student may cancel his food contract by paying a penalty of $15, and the remainder of his money is refunded. If general campus opinion of dormitory food is at all realistically based, those for whom taste or food quality is most important should be most likely to discontinue their food contracts. Obese students should be more likely to drop out of the food plan than normal students.

**[TABLE 8-8] Relationship of obesity to renewing meal contracts**

| | Obese | Normal |
|---|---|---|
| Dropped meal contract | 32 | 100 |
| Renewed meal contract | 5 | 49 |

NOTE.—$\chi^2 = 5.40, p < .05$.

The sample for this study is the entire body of freshmen entering Columbia in 1965 who signed up for the food plan on first entering the college. There were 698 students in this freshman class, 211 of whom signed food contracts. This sample is limited to freshmen first because they constitute the bulk of meal-plan subscribers and second because the noncommuters among them are required to live in dormitories during their entire first academic year. Thus, their decision to leave the plan could not be affected by moving out of the dormitories as it could for upperclassmen. All freshmen fraternity pledges (five obese and 16 normal students) are also eliminated from the sample, for pledges automatically, and without penalty, switch to eating at their fraternity houses when they pledge.

Weight deviations were computed from records in the Dean of Students' office using the Metropolitan Life Insurance Company (1959) norms.[4] As in the other studies in this report, the top 20% of the weight-deviation distribution is classified as obese. For this sample, this includes all students who were 11.3% overweight or more.

The basic data are presented in [Table 8-8] where it can be seen that expectancies are confirmed. Some 86.5% of fat freshmen let their contracts expire as

[4]For 25 of the 211 freshmen who signed food contracts, the existing records were incomplete or unavailable so that it was impossible to determine weight deviation. [Table 8-8] includes the 186 cases for whom the data are complete.

compared with the 67.1% of normal students who dropped out of the meal plan. Obesity does, to some extent, predict who chooses to subsist on institutional food.

## ADJUSTING TO TIME ZONE CHANGES

There are occasions when there is a marked discrepancy or opposition between external cues relevant to eating and the internal, physiological correlates of food deprivation or satiation, for example, being served a gorgeous dessert after consumption of a mammoth meal or confronted with some nauseating, rudely prepared concoction after a period of starvation. Our line of thought leads to the expectation that the obese will be relatively more affected by the external cue than will the normal subject, that is, he will eat more of the dessert and less of the mess. Studies by Hashim and Van Itallie (1965) and Nisbett (1968) do, in good part, support these expectations.

A more subtle instance of this opposition of cues is represented by the Schachter and Gross (1968) study in which, by means of doctored clocks, subjects were manipulated into believing that the time was later or earlier than the true time. If we assume that the intensity of gastric motility, etc., is a function of true time (i.e., hours since last meal), then this clock manipulation can create circumstances in which external and internal cues are, to some degree, in opposition. For example, a subject may be under the clock-produced impression that it is after his usual dinner time while in actuality it is before this time. In such circumstances, Schachter and Gross found that the manipulated external cue almost entirely determined how much obese subjects ate and did not similarly affect normal subjects.

Long-distance East-West travel creates a state which is, in a way, a real life analogue of this time-manipulation experiment. Given time-zone changes, the traveler, biologically more than ready to eat, may arrive at his destination at a local time still hours away from routine eating times and from the barrage of food-related external cues invariably synchronized with culturally routinized meal times. A jet flight leaving Paris at 12:00 noon requires 8 hours to reach New York, where on arrival the local time is 2:00 P.M. If the passenger has eaten an early lunch on the plane and no dinner, he is, on arrival, physiologically more than ready for a full meal but still 4 or 5 hours away from local dinner hours. Whatever mode he chooses of coping with his situation, eating a full meal on arrival, snacking, or putting off a meal until local dinner time, his situation is for a time an uncomfortable one, characterized by a marked discrepancy between his physiological state and locally acceptable eating hours and he must, in short order, adjust to an entirely new eating schedule. A prediction is by no means unequivocal, but from the variety of facts already presented it seems an intuitively sound guess that the obese will have an easier time in this situation than will normal travelers.

Thanks to the good offices of the Medical Department of Air France we have had access to data which to some extent permit evaluation of this hypothesis. Concerned with medical and psychological effects of time-zone changes, Air France studied a sample of flight crew members assigned to transatlantic routes (Lavernhe, Lafontaine, & Laplane, 1965). The subjects of this inquiry were 194 male and 42 female personnel regularly flying the Paris-New York and Paris-Montreal routes. On the East to West journey these flights are scheduled to leave Paris roughly around noon, French time, fly for approximately 8 hours, and land in North America sometime in the early afternoon, Eastern time. Flight crew members eat lunch shortly after takeoff and, being occupied with landing preparations and servicing passenger needs, are not served another meal during the flight. They land in North America some 7 hours after their last meal at a time that is generally past the local lunch hour and well before local dinner time.

The Air France study was *not* directly concerned with reports of hunger or eating behavior, but the investigators systematically noted all individuals who volunteered that they "suffered from the discordance between their physiological state and meal time in America."[5] This coding appears to apply chiefly to fliers who complain about the fact that they either do without food or make do with a snack until local dinner time.

The basic data are presented in [Figure 8-8] which plots the proportion of complainers at each quintile of the weight-deviation distribution of this group of flying personnel. Because of the stringent physical requirements involved in air crew selection there are, of course, relatively few really obese people in this sample. Despite this fact, it is evident that there is a consistent relation between the extent of weight deviation and the likelihood of spontaneously mentioning difficulties in adjusting to the discrepancy between physiological state and local meal times. The

[5] J. Lavernhe and E. Lafontaine, personal communication, 1966.

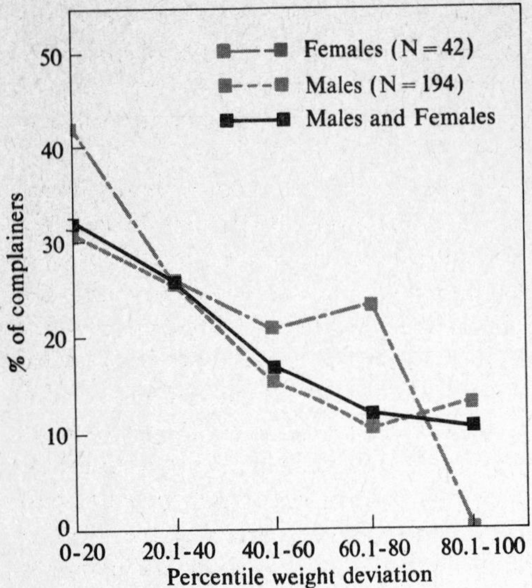


**Range of weight deviation:**

**Males** (−20.7% to −9.2%) (−9.1% to −3.4%) (−3.1% to +1.7%) (+1.9% to +9.0%) (+9.8% to +29.2%)

**Females** (−21.5% to −12.5%)(−10.7% to 7.5%)(−6.9% to −4.1%) (−3.8% to +0.5%) (+0.6% to +11.4%)

**[FIGURE 8-8] The relationship of weight deviation to complaining about the effects of time-zone changes on eating.**

more overweight the French flier, the less likely he is to be troubled by this discrepancy. The linear nature of the relationship is consistent with the results of Nisbett's (1966) experiment. Comparing groups of extremely skinny, fat, and normal subjects, Nisbett demonstrated that the impact of the external cue, taste, on eating behavior was a direct function of the degree of overweight.

Testing the significance of the differences in these data by the procedure employed in the two previous studies, we find $\chi^2 = 2.93$ ($p < .10$) for the heaviest quintile of French fliers compared with the remainder of the sample. If we compare all of those flying personnel who are overweight (.1% to 29.9% overweight) with all of those who are not overweight (0% to 21.5% underweight) the data distribute as in [Table 8-9],

**[TABLE 8-9] Relationship of weight deviation to complaining about the effects of time-zone changes on eating behavior**

| Subjects who: | Subjects who are: | |
|---|---|---|
| | Overweight | Not overweight |
| Complain | 12 | 34 |
| Don't complain | 89 | 101 |

NOTE—$\chi^2 = 6.52, p < .02$.

where it can be seen that 11.9% of the overweight complain as compared with 25.2% of the nonoverweight ($\chi^2 = 6.52, p < .02$). Apparently fatter, flying Frenchmen are less likely to be troubled by the effects of time changes on eating.

## DISCUSSION

From these three studies we know the following facts: (*a*) Fat Jews are more likely to fast on Yom Kippur than normal Jews; (*b*) for fat, fasting Jews there is an inverse relationship between the "unpleasantness" of fasting and the number of hours spent in synagogue on Yom Kippur. There is no such relationship for normally built Jews who fast; (*c*) fat freshmen are more likely to drop university meal plan contracts than are normal freshmen; (*d*) fatter French fliers are less likely to be troubled by the effects of time-zone changes on eating routine than are thinner French fliers.

We have chosen to interpret these facts in terms of a conceptual scheme involving assumptions about the relationship between weight deviation and the relative potency of external and internal stimulants to eating. These three studies were designed to test specific implications of this schema in appropriate field settings. As with any field research, alternative explanations of these findings are legion and, within the context of any specific study, impossible to overrule. Except for the most obvious alternatives, we have chosen to avoid the tedium of listing and feebly feuding with more or less plausible alternative interpretations—a procedure whose chief virtue would be the demonstration that we are aware of our interpretive problems even if we can do nothing about them.

There is, however, one alternative interpretation cogent not only to the present studies but to some of the findings in our various laboratory experiments. Two of these field studies, Yom Kippur and Air France, are concerned with some aspect of fasting behavior and the ease with which the obese can do without food[6]—a finding deriving from and related to the laboratory demonstration that manipulated food deprivation has no effect on the eating of the obese. Rather than the interpretation we have elected, which rests on the assumption that the obese do not label the physiological correlates of food deprivation as hunger, one could suggest that the obese are, after all, overweight, that they have large stores of body fat and, within the time limits of these studies, that they actually do not experience such states as gastric motility and hypoglycemia. Though a plausible hypothesis, the available evidence suggests that for gastric motility, at least, the hypothesis is not correct. The Stunkard and Koch (1964) study of gastric contractions and self-reports of hunger was in essence conducted under fasting conditions. Subjects ate their regular dinners, ate no breakfast, and at 9:00 A.M. came to the laboratory where, having swallowed a gastric balloon, they remained for 4 hours. During this period the extent of gastric motility was much the same for obese and normal subjects. The obese simply did not coordinate the statement, "I feel hungry" with periods of gastric motility while normal subjects did.[7]

One final point in defense of our general schema. It is the case that nonobvious derivations do plausibly follow from this formulation of the interrelationships of external and internal determinants of eating behavior. For example, the negative correlation between hours in synagogue and the unpleasantness of fasting for the obese and the lack of such correlation for normal subjects must follow from this set of ideas and we can conceive of no alternative conceptualization of this entire body of data which would lead to this prediction. In any case, whatever the eventual interpretation of the three studies, if one permutes these facts, the implications are unassailable: fasting, fat, French freshmen fly farther for fine food.

[6] Other investigators who have noted this phenomenon in various contexts are Brown and Pulsifer (1965) and Duncan, Jinson, Fraser, and Christori (1962).

[7] One final datum from our own studies also suggests that this alternative interpretation is incorrect. If it is correct that the intensity of the physiological correlates of food deprivation is, within time limits, less for the obese than for normal subjects it should follow that, under any conditions, obese subjects will find it easier to fast. The data on the relation of hours in synagogue to self-ratings of fasting difficulty in the Yom Kippur study indicate, however, that this is not the case. Obese subjects who spend most of the day in synagogue (8 or more hours) do suffer considerably less from fasting than do normal subjects who spend the same amount of time in synagogue. However, among those who spend little time in synagogue (2 hours or less), the obese report more difficulty with the fast than do normals. It would appear that the obese have an easier time doing without food than do normals in the absence of external, food-relevant cues but a more difficult time in the presence of such cues.

## REFERENCES

**BROWN, J. D., & PULSIFER, D. H.** Outpatient starvation in normal and obese subjects. *Aerospace Medicine*, March 1965, 267-269.

**DUNCAN, G., JINSON, W., FRASER, R., & CHRISTORI, F.** Correction and control of intractable obesity. *Journal of the American Medical Association*, 1962, **181**, 309-312.

**HASHIM, S. A., & VAN ITALLIE, T. B.** Studies on normal and obese subjects with a monitored food dispensing device. *Annals of the New York Academy of Sciences*, 1965, **131**, 654-661.

**LAVERNHE, J., LAFONTAINE, E., & LAPLANE, R.** An investigation on the subjective effects of time changes on flying staff in civil aviation. Air France Medical Department paper delivered before the Aerospace Medical Association, April, 1965. (Mimeo)

**METROPOLITAN LIFE INSURANCE COMPANY.** New weight standards for men and women. *Statistical Bulletin*, 1959, **40**, 1-4.

**NISBETT, R. E.** Taste, deprivation, and weight determinants of eating behavior. *Journal of Personality and Social Psychology*, 1968, **10**, 107-116.

**SCHACHTER, S., GOLDMAN, R., & GORDON, A.** The effects of fear, food deprivation, and obesity on eating. *Journal of Personality and Social Psychology*, 1968, **10**, 91-97.

**SCHACHTER, S., & GROSS, L.** Manipulated time and eating behavior. *Journal of Personality and Social Psychology*, 1968, **10**, 98-106.

**STUNKARD, A., & KOCH, C.** The interpretation of gastric motility: I. Apparent bias in the report of hunger by obese persons. *Archives of General Psychiatry*, 1964, **11**, 74-82.

**UNIVERSITY DORMITORY COUNCIL.** Report on food services at Columbia University *Columbia Spectator*, March 9, 1964, p. 1.

# CHAPTER NINE

# METHODS IN SEARCH OF MORE DATA

As is true of many books of readings, this final chapter is a potpourri of interesting studies which defy categorization. Hence, there is no conclusion, but rather an open-ended set of studies. By intention or by accident, it is probably good to leave the reader with new ideas and questions which give a truer picture of the present state of field research. Although some of the research in this book goes back as far as 1927, about 70 percent of it has been published in the last four years. Our search for studies between 1927 and the mid-1960's has not been fruitful. It appears that research in natural settings has only recently begun to be done by large numbers of psychologists. Thus, it is appropriate for the last chapter of this book to point the way to future research.

The first study in this chapter was done by Stanley Milgram. It investigates the meaning behind the statement, "It's a small world, isn't it?" It seems to be a common occurrence to meet somebody in a place far from home and find out that he knows your next-door neighbor. Milgram phrased the problem as "Starting with any two people in the world, what is the probability that they will know each other?" Milgram then provides a rather ingenious method by which to answer this question.

While Milgram reports on the results of his research and some interesting sidelights, we feel that his method has great potential for answering questions about social structure and paths of communication. Milgram mentions that his techniques can be used to measure such things as cross cultural and ethnic differences in communication patterns. It is also interesting to note that the average number of intermediaries needed to link any two randomly chosen persons in the United States is not intuitively obvious. However, Milgram does explain this gap in common sense.

The next paper in this chapter is a short study by Carney Landis. It is interesting from a number of viewpoints. First is the simple way in which the data were collected. Landis, in studying conversational content in public places, recorded the content of the conversation between two people and the sex of the persons who were conversing. All the equipment that was needed were sharp ears and a pencil and paper. Using this simple technique, Landis found interesting differences in the content of the conversation as the sex and nationality of the speakers varied. Landis points out that the differences he found in the types of conversations between Londoners and New Yorkers are an indictment against the standardization of intelligence tests "on one race, national group, or cultural group . . . even when the two groups speak the same language." Today, this does not seem to be a startling conclusion, since there is a great deal of controversy over the use of intelligence tests on members of minority groups. However, historically this paper was far ahead of its time, as it was published in 1927.

Landis also has interesting data on how men in England and the United States treat women in a conversation. In England, men adapt their conversation to the women's interests, while in the United States, the women adapt to the men's. It would be interesting, in this time of changing sex role expectations, to find out if these results still apply. This technique can be used to study racial and ethnic differences in conversation and should give some indication as to the relationship between persons. With modern recording devices and more sophisticated content analyses, we should be able to use this technique to study many aspects of social behavior.

It should be noted that Landis's technique raises new ethical issues. In previous chapters we were concerned with the issue of affecting the behavior of others without their consent or awareness. Landis's research introduces a related issue—invasion of privacy. Although there was no attempt to manipulate the subjects' behavior (i.e., this was an observational study), their right to have private discussions in public places had been violated. With modern recording devices, conversations in private places can also be monitored.

The ethical issues raised by Landis's technique and the techniques used in other studies in this book will not be resolved easily. To some critics this collection of studies may represent the extension of "psychological deceit" from an academic to a general setting. If field studies become prevalent, will people be able to distinguish between reality and a field experiment in social psychology? The authors believe that the merits of the unobtrusive field approach to understanding social behavior outweigh its negative aspects. However, we should recognize that methods which allow us to deal with significant issues and to cause changes in others' behavior may raise significant ethical questions.

Instead of eavesdropping on people, McEvoy, Chesler, and Schmuck chose to analyze the letters written to the editor of a national magazine. McEvoy et al. analyzed 435 letters sampled from 2,254 persons protesting the appearance of what they considered to be communist literature. The writer of one of the letters described the article in the following way: "To me it was brazen, and the most anti-Christ article I have ever read." The authors are able to draw some interesting conclusions about the kind of people who write such letters. It would be interesting to compare the characteristics of these far-right writers with far-left writers. That is, are all extremists similar? Like Landis's technique, this method can be applied to a variety of situations.

In the next study, by Kohn and Williams, the authors chose not to eavesdrop nor read, but to involve themselves actively in real-life situations. These authors believe that in order to study social change, one must study "unpatterned situations." These are situations in which the way people are supposed to act is not clearly spelled out. It is these situations, which lack clear definition, that should tell us most about intergroup relations.

Kohn and Williams explore one area of intergroup relations that is still subject to lack of definition. They observed how blacks and whites behave when they confront each other in an unpatterned situation. The authors present a vivid description, from different points of view, of what took place when a black couple entered a working-class tavern which the researchers had reason to believe was discriminatory. In reading this, it is interesting to observe how individuals try to decide what behavior is appropriate for this unusual situation. While the authors do not present any data on how people's definitions arise, it should be noted that there is similarity between this research and that of Schachter and Singer (1962). The research by Schachter and Singer was concerned with how people "label" their emotions. These authors found that a state of physiological arousal, induced by an injection of epinephrine, was interpreted on the basis of the behavior of the others present. That is, when a confederate acted happy, the subject reported feeling happy. However, when the confederate reported feeling angry, the subject also reported feeling angry. An unpatterned situation should also provide a great deal of emotional arousal because of its uncertainty. This arousal should lead the person to seek out cognitive cues that would explain his feelings. These cues may, as in the study by Schachter and Singer, come from the behavior of others.

Another interesting aspect of the authors' findings concerns what occurs when two participants confront each other with opposing definitions of the situation. As reported in a footnote, the authors found that in no case did such a confrontation lead to either person's changing his definition. They only observed a stronger commitment to their original positions. This observation is related to Abelson and Miller's article in Chapter 7. They found that more extreme commitments will occur when insults start to be traded.

Kohn and Williams point the way to the study of certain real-life situations that have importance because the behavior is not socially prescribed. Study of behavior in these situations should allow us to discover how situations like these become defined. Although Kohn and Williams present only a description of what occurs in these situations, it is possible to develop specific measuring instruments that would give a more precise indication of the conflict and how it is resolved. Not only could a more precise dependent variable be developed, but certainly we can experimentally vary other factors. For example, are males and females treated differently in various situations? Is the manner in which a person creates an unpatterned situation important, e.g., demanding versus passive?

The paper by Shor (page 319) also examines unpatterned situations. Specifically, Shor is concerned with the normative expectations of automobile driving. This is a behavior which, at first glance, we would expect to be clearly defined because of the legal regulations and its routine nature. However, the situation is rather unpatterned when one first learns to drive and when drivers with different expectations confront one another.

Shor provides a model of what could happen when a driver from Boston, Massachusetts, with his competitive norms, encounters a driver from Lawrence, Kansas, with his more courteous norms. As pointed out in the introduction to the articles on social status, driving behavior has not received a great deal of study. With Shor's model we should be able to provide descriptive data on just what norms exist in different sections of the country and try to predict what behavior would occur based on these norms.

The last article in this chapter also deals with transportation. We have been concerned with this topic in previous chapters dealing with helping behavior, collective behavior, and racial prejudice. In their article, Davis and Levine do not present any empirical data about public transportation, nor is there a model or theory present. Instead, they offer us a number of observations of what occurs on public transportation. For example, the authors discuss the limits of diversions found on public transportation. They point out that on elevators there is nothing to read. On the other hand, subways do provide a variety of visual stimuli. Another aspect of public transportation includes the image one has of it—safe, dirty, slow, or crowded. With respect to this last characteristic, Bickman has preliminary evidence that, in contrast with the evidence found by Sommer and Becker and by Felipe and Sommer (Chapter 6), there is no indication that there is personal space in a subway. That is, subjects did not react when someone intruded upon their territory, even when the train was not crowded. It may be that people do not form concepts of personal space or territory on public vehicles because of the short amount of time spent on them.

## REFERENCES

**SCHACHTER, S., & SINGER, J. E.** Cognitive, social, and physiological determinants of emotional state. *Psychological Review*, 1962, **69**, 379-399.

# THE SMALL-WORLD PROBLEM

STANLEY MILGRAM
*The City University of New York*

> Fred Jones of Peoria, sitting in a sidewalk cafe in Tunis, and needing a light for his cigarette, asks the man at the next table for a match. They fall into conversation; the stranger is an Englishman who, it turns out, spent several months in Detroit studying the operation of an interchangeable-bottlecap-factory. "I know it's a foolish question," says Jones, "but did you ever by any chance run into a fellow named Ben Arkadian? He's an old friend of mine, manages a chain of supermarkets in Detroit . . ."
>
> "Arkadian, Arkadian," the Englishman mutters. "Why, upon my soul, I believe I do! Small chap, very energetic, raised merry hell with the factory over a shipment of defective bottlecaps."
>
> "No kidding!" Jones exclaims in amazement.
>
> "Good lord, it's a small world, isn't it?"

Almost all of us have had the experience of encountering someone far from home, who, to our surprise, turns out to share a mutual acquaintance with us. This kind of experience occurs with sufficient frequency so that our language even provides a cliché to be uttered at the appropriate moment of recognizing mutual acquaintances. We say, "My it's a small world."

The simplest way of formulating the small-world problem is: Starting with any two people in the world, what is the probability that they will know each other? A somewhat more sophisticated formulation, however, takes account of the fact that while persons X and Z may not know each other directly, they may share a mutual acquaintance—that is, a person who knows both of them. One can then think of an acquaintance chain with X knowing Y and Y knowing Z. Moreover, one can imagine circumstances in which X is linked to Z not by a single link, but by a series of links, X-*a*-*b*-*c*-*d* . . . *y*-Z. That is to say, person X knows person *a* who in turn knows person *b*, who knows *c* . . . who knows *y*, who knows Z.

Therefore, another question one may ask is: Given any two people in the world, person X and person Z, how many intermediate acquaintance links are needed before X and Z are connected?

Concern with the small-world problem is not new, nor is it limited to social psychologists like myself. Historians, political scientists, and communication specialists share an interest in the problem. Jane Jacobs, who is concerned with city planning, describes an acquaintance chain in terms of a children's game:

> When my sister and I first came to New York from a small city, we used to amuse ourselves with a game we called Messages. I suppose we were trying, in a dim way, to get a grip on the great, bewildering world into which we had come from our cocoon. The idea was to pick two wildly dissimilar individuals—say a head hunter in the Solomon Islands and a cobbler in Rock Island, Illinois—and assume that one had to get a message to the other by word of mouth; then we would each silently figure out a plausible, or at least possible, chain of persons through which the message could go. The one who could make the shortest plausible chain of messengers won. The head hunter would speak to the head man of his village who would speak to the trader who came to buy copra, who would speak to the Australian patrol officer when he came through, who would tell the man who was next slated to go to Melbourne on leave, etc. Down at the other end, the cobbler would hear from his priest, who got it from the mayor, who got it from a state senator, who got it from the governor, etc. We soon had these close-to-home messengers down to a routine for almost everybody we could conjure up . . .

The importance of the problem does not lie in these entertaining aspects, but in the fact that it brings under discussion a certain mathematical structure in society, a structure that often plays a part, whether recognized or not, in many discussions of history, sociology, and other disciplines. For example, Henri Pirenne and George Duby, important historians, make the point that in the Dark Ages communication broke down between cities of western Europe. They became isolated and simply did not have contact with each other. The network of acquaintances of individuals became constricted. The disintegration of society was expressed in the growing isolation of communities, and the infrequent contact with those living outside a person's immediate place of residence.

There are two general philosophical views of the

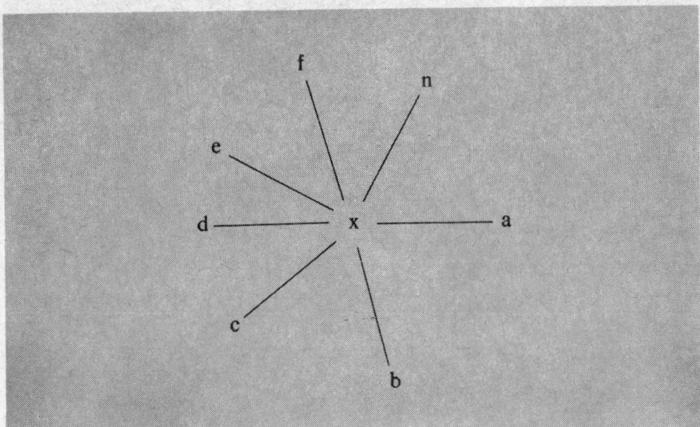


[FIGURE 9-1] Acquaintances of x, a . . . n.

small-world problem. One view holds that any two people in the world, no matter how remote from each other, can be linked in terms of intermediate acquaintances, and that the number of such intermediate links is relatively small. This view sees acquaintances in terms of an infinitely intersecting arrangement that permits movement from any social group to another through a series of connecting links.

The second view holds that there are unbridgeable gaps between various groups and that therefore, given any two people in the world, they will never link up because people have circles of acquaintances which do not necessarily intersect. A message will circulate in a particular group of acquaintances, but may never be able to make the jump to another circle. This view sees the world in terms of concentric circles of acquaintances, each within its own orbit.

## THE UNDERLYING STRUCTURE

Sometimes it is useful to visualize the abstract properties of a scientific problem before studying it in detail; that is, we construct a model of the main features of the phenomenon as we understand them. Let us represent all the people in the United States by a number of points. Each point represents a person, while lines connecting two points show that the two persons are acquainted. [See Figure 9-1.] Each person has a certain number of first-hand acquaintances, which we shall represent by the letters *a*, *b*, *c*, . . . *n*. Each acquaintance in turn has his own acquaintances, connected to still other points. The exact number of lines radiating from any point depends on the size of a person's circle of acquaintances. The entire structure takes on the form of a complex network of 200 million points, with complicated connections between them. [See Figure 9-2.] One way of restating the small-world problem in these terms is this: Given any two of these points chosen at random from this universe of 200 million points, through how many intermediate points would we pass before the chosen points could be connected by the shortest possible path?

## RESEARCH AT M.I.T.

There are many ways to go about the study of the small-world problem, and I shall soon present my own approach to it. But first, let us consider the important contributions of a group of workers at The Massachusetts Institute of Technology, under the leadership of Ithiel de Sola Pool. Working closely with Manfred Kochen of IBM, Pool decided to build a theoretical model of the small-world, a model which closely parallels the idea of points and lines shown. However, unlike my own model, which is purely pictorial, Pool and Kochen translate their thinking into strict mathematical terms.

To build such a model they needed certain information. First, they had to know how many acquaintances the average man has. Surprisingly, though this is a very basic question, no reliable answers could be found in the social science literature. So the information had to be obtained, a task which Michael Gurevitch, then a graduate student at M.I.T., undertook. Gurevitch asked a variety of men and women to keep a record of all the persons they came in contact with in the course of 100 days. It turned out that on the average these people recorded names of roughly 500 persons, so that this figure could be used as the basis of the theoretical model. Now, if every person knows 500 other people, what are the chances that any two people will know each other? Making a set of rather simple assumptions, it turns out that there is only about one chance in 200,000 that any two Americans chosen at random will know each other.

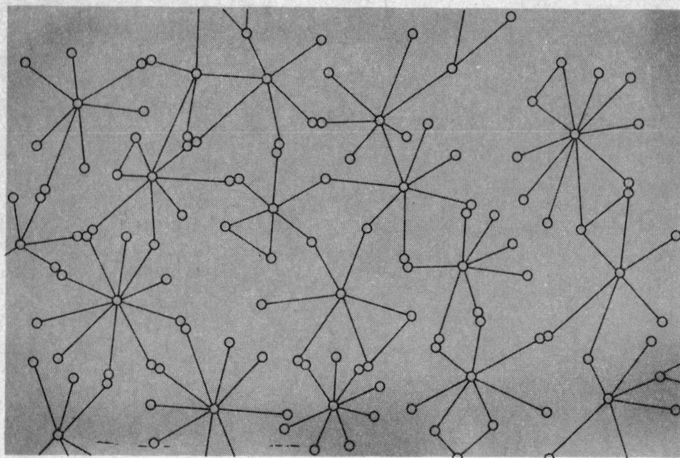

[FIGURE 9-2] Network of acquaintances.

However, when you ask the chances of their having a mutual acquaintance, the odds drop sharply. And quite amazingly, there is better than a 50-50 chance that any two people can be linked up with two intermediate acquaintances. Or at least, that is what the Pool-Kochen theory indicates.

Of course, the investigators were aware that even if a man has 500 acquaintances, there may be a lot of inbreeding. That is, many of the 500 friends of my friend may be actually among the people I know anyway, so that they do not really contribute to a widening net of acquaintances; the acquaintances of X simply feed back into his own circle and fail to bring any new contacts into it. [See Figure 9-3.] It is a fairly straightforward job to check up on the amount of inbreeding if one uses only one or two circles of acquaintances, but it becomes almost impossible when the acquaintance chain stretches far and wide. So many people are involved that a count just isn't practical.

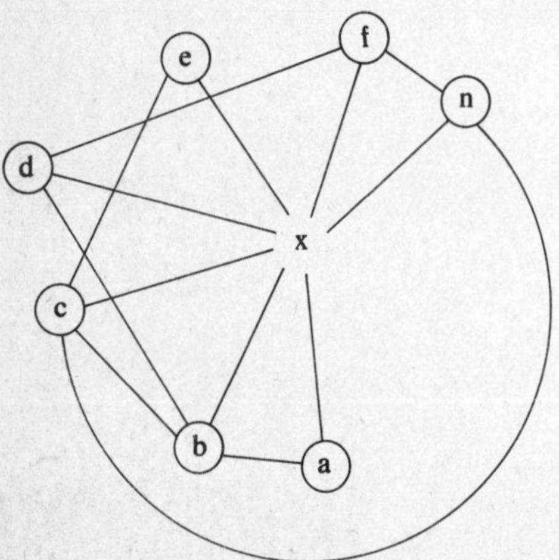


[FIGURE 9-3] Inbreeding.

So the big obstacle one runs up against is the problem of social structure. Though poor people always have acquaintances, it would probably turn out that they tend to be among other poor people, and that the rich speak mostly to the rich. It is exceedingly difficult to assess the impact of social structure on a model of this sort. If you could think of the American population as simply 200 million points, each with 500 random connections, the model would work. But the contours of social structure make this a perilous assumption, for society is not built on random connections among persons but tends to be fragmented into social classes and cliques.

## A HARVARD APPROACH

The Pool and Kochen mathematical model was interesting from a theoretical standpoint, but I wondered whether the problem might not be solved by a more direct experimental approach. The Laboratory of Social Relations at Harvard gave me $680 to prove that it could. I set out to find an experimental method whereby it would be possible to trace a line of acquaintances linking any two persons chosen at random.

Let us assume for the moment that the actual process of establishing the linkages between two persons runs only one way: from person A to person Z. Let us call person A the *starting* person, since he will initiate the process, and person Z the *target* person, since he is the person to be reached. All that would be necessary, therefore, would be to choose a starting person at random from the 200 million people who live in the United States, and then randomly choose a target person.

This is how the study was carried out. The general idea was to obtain a sample of men and women from all walks of life. Each of these persons would be given the name and address of the same target person, a person chosen at random, who lives somewhere in the United States. Each of the participants would be asked to move a message toward the target person, using only a chain of friends and acquaintances. Each person would be asked to transmit the message to the friend or acquaintance who he thought would be most likely to know the target person. Messages could move only to persons who knew each other on a first-name basis.

As a crude beginning, we thought it best to draw our starting persons from a distant city, so we chose Wichita, Kansas for our first study and Omaha, Nebraska for our second. (From Cambridge, these cities seem vaguely 'out there,' on the Great Plains or somewhere.) To obtain our sample, letters of solicitation were sent to residents in these cities asking them to participate in a study of social contact in American society. The target person in our first study lived in Cambridge and was the wife of a divinity school student. In the second study, carried out in collaboration with Jeffrey Travers, the target person was a stockbroker who worked in Boston and lived in Sharon, Massachusetts. To keep matters straight, I will refer to the first study as the Kansas Study, and the second as the Nebraska Study. These terms indicate merely where the starting persons were drawn from.

Each person who volunteered to serve as a starting person was sent a folder containing a document [see Figure 9-4] which served as the main tool of the investigation. Briefly, the document contains:

1. The name of the target person as well as certain information about him. This orients the participants toward a specific individual.
2. A set of rules for reaching the target person. Perhaps the most important rule is: *"If you do not know the target person on a personal basis, do not try to contact him directly. Instead, mail this folder . . . to a personal acquaintance who is more likely than you to know the target person . . . it must be someone you know on a first-name basis."* This rule sets the document into motion, moving it from one participant to the next, until it is sent to someone who knows the target person.
3. A roster on which each person in the chain writes his name. This tells the person who receives the folder exactly who sent it to him. The roster also has another practical effect; it prevents endless looping of the folder through participants who have already served as links in the chain, because each participant can see exactly what sequence of persons has led up to his own participation.

In addition to the document, the folder contains a stack of 15 business reply, or "tracer" cards. Each person receiving the folder takes out a card, fills it in, returns it to us, and sends the remaining cards along with the document to the next link.

Several other features of the procedure need to be emphasized. First, each participant is supposed to send the folder on to one other person only. Thus the efficiency with which the chain is completed depends in part on the wisdom of his choice in this matter. Second, by means of the tracer card, we have continuous feedback on the progress of each chain. The cards are coded so we know which chain it comes from and which link in the chain has been completed. The card also provides us with relevant sociological characteristics of the senders of the cards. Thus, we know the characteristics of completed, as well as incompleted, chains. Third, the procedure permits experimental variation at many points.

In short, the device possesses some of the features of a chain letter, though it does not pyramid in any way; moreover it is oriented toward a specific target, zeroes in on the target through the cooperation of a sequence of participants, and contains a tracer that allows us to keep track of its progress at all times.

## WOULD IT WORK?

The question that plagued us most in undertaking this study was simply: Would the procedure work? Would any of the chains started in Kansas actually reach our target person in Massachusetts? Part of the excitement of experimental social psychology is that it is all so new we often have no way of knowing whether our techniques will work or simply turn out to be wispy pipe dreams.

The answer came fairly quickly. It will be recalled that our first target person was the wife of a student living in Cambridge. Four days after the folders were sent to a group of starting persons in Kansas, an instructor at the Episcopal Theological Seminary approached our target person on the street. "Alice," he said, thrusting a brown folder toward her, "this is for you." At first she thought he was simply returning a folder that had gone astray and had never gotten out of Cambridge, but when we looked at the roster, we found to our pleased surprise that the document had started with a wheat farmer in Kansas. He had passed it on to an Episcopalian minister in his home town, who sent it to the minister who taught in Cambridge, who gave it to the target person. Altogether the number of intermediate links between starting person and target person amounted to *two!*

COMMUNICATIONS PROJECT

322 EMERSON HALL HARVARD UNIVERSITY CAMBRIDGE, MASSACHUSETTS 02138

We need your help in an unusual scientific study carried out at Harvard University. We are studying the nature of social contact in American society. Could you, as an active American, contact another American citizen regardless of his walk of life? If the name of an American citizen were picked out of a hat, could you get to know that person using only your network of friends and acquaintances? Just how open is our "open society"? To answer these questions, which are very important to our research, we ask for your help.

TARGET PERSON

Name, address, and information about the target person is placed here.

You will notice that this letter has come to you from a friend. He has aided this study by sending this folder on to you. He hopes that you will aid the study by forwarding this folder to someone else. The name of the person who sent you this folder is listed on the Roster at the bottom of this sheet.

In the box to the right you will find the name and address of an American citizen who has agreed to serve as the "target person" in this study. The idea of the study is to transmit this folder to the target person using only a chain of friends and acquaintances.

HOW TO TAKE PART IN THIS STUDY

1 ADD YOUR NAME TO THE ROSTER AT THE BOTTOM OF THIS SHEET, so that the next person who receives this letter will know who it came from.

2 DETACH ONE POSTCARD. FILL IT OUT AND RETURN IT TO HARVARD UNIVERSITY. No stamp is needed. The postcard is very important. It allows us to keep track of the progress of the folder as it moves toward the target person.

3 IF YOU KNOW THE TARGET PERSON ON A PERSONAL BASIS, MAIL THIS FOLDER DIRECTLY TO HIM (HER). Do this only if you have previously met the target person and know each other on a first name basis.

4 IF YOU DO NOT KNOW THE TARGET PERSON ON A PERSONAL BASIS, DO NOT TRY TO CONTACT HIM DIRECTLY. INSTEAD, MAIL THIS FOLDER (POST CARDS AND ALL) TO A PERSONAL ACQUAINTANCE WHO IS MORE LIKELY THAN YOU TO KNOW THE TARGET PERSON. You may send the folder on to a friend, relative, or acquaintance, but it must be someone you know on a first name basis.

Remember, the aim is to move this folder toward the target person using only a chain of friends and acquaintances. On first thought you may feel you do not know anyone who is acquainted with the target person. This is natural, but at least you can start it moving in the right direction! Who among your acquaintances might conceivably move in the same social circles as the target person? The real challenge is to identify among your friends and acquaintances a person who can advance the folder toward the target person. It may take several steps beyond your friend to get to the target person, but what counts most is to start the folder on its way! The person who receives this folder will then repeat the process until the folder is received by the target person. May we ask you to begin!

Every person who participates in this study and returns the post card to us will receive a certificate of appreciation from the Communications Project. All participants are entitled to a report describing the results of the study.

Please transmit this folder within 24 hours. Your help is greatly appreciated.

Yours sincerely,

Stanley Milgram

Stanley Milgram, Ph. D.
Director, Communications Project

ROSTER

1
2
3
4
5
6
7
8
9
10
11
12
13
14
15

SIGN YOUR NAME HERE

PLEASE FILL IN THIS INFORMATION ABOUT YOURSELF

My Name:
My Address:
My Occupation:
Age: Sex: Race:
Spouse's Occupation:
How many people do you know on a first name basis? Give us your best guess:

Please Fill In The Following Infomation About The Person To Whom You Are Sending The Folder.

His (Her) Name:
His (Her) Address:
His Occupation:
Age: Sex: Race:
Nature of His Relationship to you. (Please explain whether he is a friend, acquaintance, relative, etc.)
Why did you select him to receive the passbook?

DETACH ONE POSTCARD.
FILL IT OUT AND RETURN IT TO HARVARD UNIVERSITY.

[FIGURE 9-4] **Document sent to starting person.**

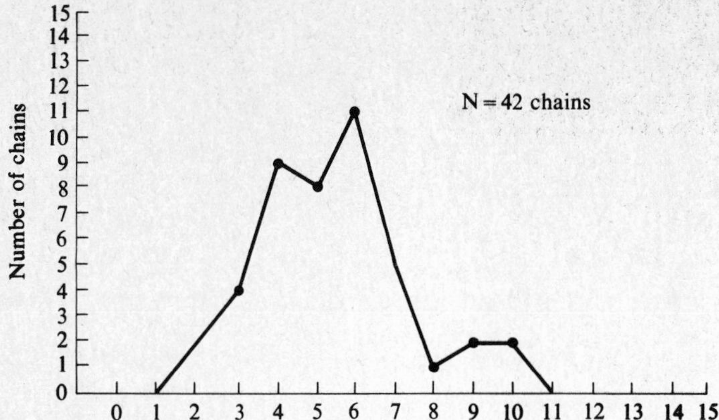


[FIGURE 9-5] Number of intermediaries needs to reach target person. Each chain started in Nebraska and reached a target person in Massachusetts.

## HOW MANY INTERMEDIARIES?

As it turned out, this was one of the shortest chains we were ever to receive, for as more tracers and folders came in, we learned that chains varied from two to 10 intermediate acquaintances, with the median at five. [See Figure 9-5.] A median of five intermediate persons is, in certain ways, impressive, considering the distances traversed. Recently, when I asked an intelligent friend of mine how many steps he thought it would take, he estimated that it would require 100 intermediate persons or more to move from Nebraska to Sharon. Many people make somewhat similar estimates, and are surprised to learn that only five intermediaries will—on the average—suffice. Somehow it does not accord with intuition. Later, I shall try to explain the basis of the discrepancy between intuition and fact.

On a purely theoretical basis, it is reasonable to assume that even fewer links are essential to complete the chains. First, since our participants can send the folder to only one of their 500 possible contacts, it is unlikely that even through careful selections, they will necessarily and at all times, select the contact best able to advance the chain to the target. On the whole they probably make pretty good guesses but surely, from time to time, they overlook some possibilities for short cuts. Thus, the chains obtained in our empirical study are less efficient than those generated theoretically.

Second, by working on a highly rational basis, each intermediary moves the folder toward the target person. That is, a certain amount of information about the target person—his place of employment, place of residence, schooling, and so forth—is given to the starting subject, and it is on the basis of this information alone that he selects the next recipient of the folder. Yet, in real life, we sometimes know a person because we chance to meet him on an ocean liner, or we spend a summer in camp together as teenagers, yet these haphazard bases of acquaintanceship cannot be fully exploited by the participants.

There is one factor, however, that could conceivably have worked in the opposite direction in our experiments, giving us the illusion that the chains are shorter than they really are. There is a certain decay in the number of active chains over each remove, even when they do not drop out because they reach the target person. Of 160 chains that started in Nebraska, 44 were completed and 126 dropped out. These chains die before completion because on each remove a certain proportion of participants simply do not cooperate and fail to send on the folder. Thus, the results we obtained on the distribution of chain lengths occurred within the general drift of a decay curve. It is possible that some of the incompleted chains would have been longer than those that were completed. To account for this possibility, Harrison White of Harvard has constructed a mathematical model to show what the distribution of chain lengths would look like if all chains went through to completion. In terms of this model, there is a transformation of the data, yielding slightly longer chains.

## EXAMINING THE CHAINS

Several features of the chains are worth examining, for they tell us something about the pattern of contact in American society. Consider, for example, the very pronounced tendency in our Kansas Study for females to send the folder on to females, and males to send it on to males. Of the 145 participants involved in the study, we find:

| | | |
|---|---|---|
| Female | → Female | 56 |
| Male | → Male | 58 |
| Female | → Male | 18 |
| Male | → Female | 13 |

Thus participants were three times as likely to send the folder on to someone of the same sex as to someone of the opposite sex. Exactly why this is so is not easy to determine, but it suggests that certain kinds of communication are strongly conditioned by sex roles.

Participants indicated on the reply cards whether they were sending the folder on to a friend, a relative, or an acquaintance. In the Kansas Study, 123 sent the folder to friends and acquaintances, while only 22 sent it to relatives. Cross-cultural comparison would seem useful here. It is quite likely that in societies which possess extended kinship systems, relatives will be more heavily represented in the communication network than is true in the United States. In American society, where extended kinship links are not maintained, acquaintance and friendship links provide the preponderant basis for reaching the target person. I would guess, further, that within certain ethnic groups in the United States, a higher proportion of familial lines would be found in the data. Probably, for example, if the study were limited to persons of Italian extraction, one would get a higher proportion of relatives in the chain. This illustrates, I hope, how the small world technique may usefully illuminate varied aspects of social structure.

[Figure 9-6 shows the kinds of people found in three typical chains from the Nebraska study.]

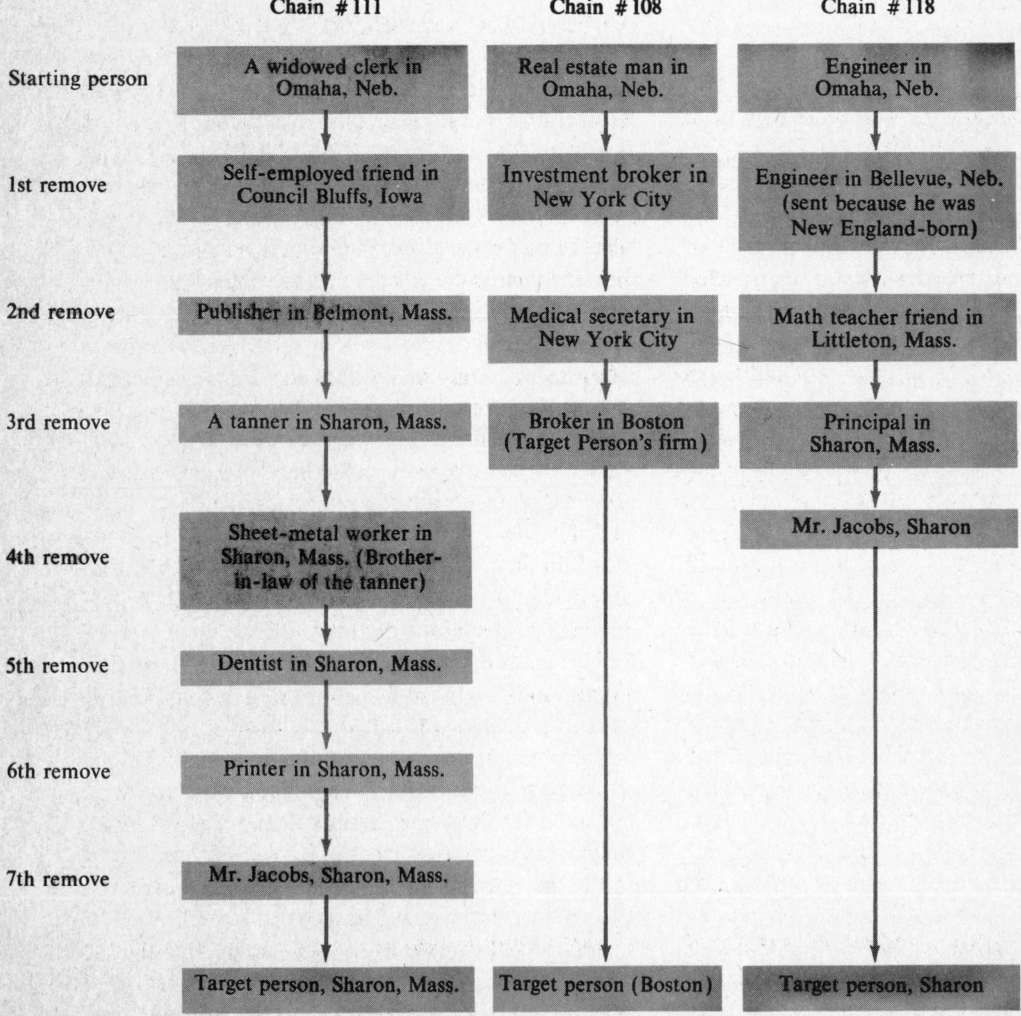


[FIGURE 9-6] Typical chains in the Nebraska study.

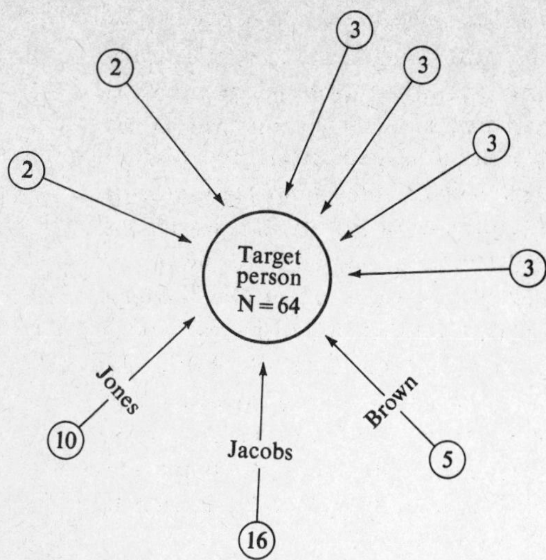


[FIGURE 9-7] Convergence through common channels (includes 42 chains that started in Nebraska and 22 that started in the Boston area).

## COMMON PATHWAYS

Each of us is embedded in a small-world structure. It is not true, however, that each of our acquaintances constitutes an equally important basis of contact with the larger social world. It is obvious that some of our acquaintances are more important than others in establishing contacts with broader social realms; some friends are relatively isolated, while others possess a wide circle of acquaintances, and contact with them brings us into a far-ranging network of additional persons.

Referring to our Nebraska Study, let us consider in detail the pattern of convergence crystallizing around the target person—the stockbroker living in Sharon, Massachusetts, and working in Boston. [See Figure 9-7.] A total of 64 chains reached him. (42 chains originated in Nebraska and 22 chains, from an auxiliary study, originated in the Boston area). Twenty-four of the chains reached him at his place of residence in the small town outside of Boston. Within Sharon, 16 were given to him by Mr. Jacobs, a clothing merchant in town. Thus, the clothing merchant served as the principal point of mediation between the broker and a larger world, a fact which came as a considerable surprise, and even something of a shock for the broker. At his place of work, in a Boston brokerage house, 10 of the chains passed through Mr. Jones, and five through Mr. Brown. Indeed, 48 percent of the chains to reach the broker were moved on to him by three persons: Jacobs, Jones, and Brown. Between Jacobs and Jones there is an interesting division of labor. Jacobs mediates the chains advancing to the broker by virtue of his residence. Jones performs a similar function in the occupational domain, and moves 10 chains enmeshed in the investment-brokerage network to the target person.

More detail thus fills in the picture of the small world. First, we learn that the target person is not surrounded by acquaintance points, each of which is equally likely to feed into an outside contact; rather, there appear to be highly popular channels for the transmission of the chain. Second, there is differentiation among these commonly used channels, so that certain of them provide the chief points of transmission in regard to residential contact, while others have specialized contact possibilities in the occupational domain. For each possible realm of activity in which the target person is involved, there is likely to emerge a sociometric star with specialized contact possibilities.

## GEOGRAPHIC AND SOCIAL MOVEMENT

The geographic movement of the folder from Nebraska to Massachusetts is striking. There is a progressive closing in on the target area as each new person is added to the chain. [See Figure 9-8.] In some cases, however, a chain moves all the way from Nebraska to the very neighborhood in which the target person resides, but then goes round and round, never quite making the necessary contact to complete the chain. Some chains died only a few hundred feet from the target person's house, after a successful journey of 1000 miles. Thus we see that social communication is sometimes restricted less by physical distance than by social distance.

The next step is to see what happens when we change the relationship between the starting person and the target person. That is, if the two are drawn from different class backgrounds, does this then decrease the probability of completing the chain? Does it increase the number of links?

In collaboration with Charles Korte, I am now applying the small-world method to the study of communications between subgroups in American society —Negro and white. We will have both Negro and white starting persons, but only Negro target persons, and try to trace the lines of communication between them. First, we want to ask: In what degree are the racial lines surmounted? Can any sizeable fraction of the communications get through the racial barrier? If the answer is yes, we then want to identify the typical locus of transmission. Does it occur at the neighborhood level, or at the place of work? We are particularly interested in the persons who serve as links between Negro and white groups. In what way

| | |
|---|---|
| 1305 miles | (starting position) |
| 710 miles | first remove |
| 356 miles | second remove |
| 210 miles | third remove |
| 79 miles | fourth remove |
| 44 miles | fifth remove |
| 20 miles | sixth remove |
| Target area | seventh remove |

The chains progress toward the target area with each remove. Figure 9-8 shows the number of miles from the target area with each remove averaged over all chains, completed as well as incompleted. For example, by the sixth remove, the average chain (assuming it is still active) is 20 miles from the target area. The target area is defined as any location less than 20 miles from Boston.

[FIGURE 9-8] Geographic movement from Nebraska to Massachusetts.

do they differ from others in the chain? Do they tend to occupy particular professional categories, such as minister, teacher, and so forth? Is the communication flow between Negroes and whites easier in Northern or in Southern locales? Perhaps some new light can be cast on the structural relationships between Negro and white communities by probing with the small-world method.

## INTUITION AND FACT

As we saw above, many people were surprised to learn that only five intermediaries will, on the average, suffice to link any two randomly chosen individuals, no matter where they happen to live in the United States. We ought to try to explain the discrepancy between intuition and fact.

The first point to remember is that although we deal directly with only five intermediaries, behind each of them stands a much larger group of from 500 to 2500 persons. That is, each participant has an acquaintance pool of 500 to 2500 persons from which he selects the person who, he thinks, is best able to advance the chain. Thus we are dealing only with the end product of a radical screening procedure.

The second thing to remember is that geometric progression is implicit in the search procedure, but nothing is more alien to mathematically untutored intuition than this form of thinking. As youngsters, many of us were asked the question: If you earned a penny a day and the sum were doubled each day, how much would you have earned by the end of a 30-day working period? Most frequently people give answers on the order of $1.87 or $6.45, when in fact the sum is more than $10 million for one 30-day working period, the last day alone yielding $5,368,709.12. Elements of geometric progression with an increase rate far more powerful than mere doubling underlie the small-world search procedure, and thus, with only a few removes, the search extends to an enormous number of persons.

Finally, when we state there are only five intermediate acquaintances, this connotes a closeness between the position of the starting person and the target person. But this is in large measure misleading, a confusion of two entirely different frames of reference. If two persons are five removes apart, they are far apart indeed. Almost anyone in the United States is but a few removes from the President, or from Nelson Rockefeller, but this is true only in terms of a particular mathematical viewpoint and does not, in any practical sense, integrate our lives with that of Nelson Rockefeller. Thus, when we speak of five intermediaries, we are talking about an enormous psychological distance between the starting and target points, a distance which seems small only because we customarily regard "five" as a small manageable quantity. We should think of the two points as being not five persons apart, but "five circles of acquaintances" apart – five "structures" apart. This helps to set it in its proper perspective.

There is a very interesting theorem based on the model of the small world. It states that if two persons from two different populations cannot make contact, then no one within the entire population in which each is embedded can make contact with any person in the other population. In other words, if a particular person, *a*, embedded in population A (which consists of his circle of acquaintances), cannot make contact with a particular person, *b*, embedded in population B, then:

1. No other person in A can make contact with *b*.
2. No other person in A can make contact with any other person in B.
3. In other words, the two sub-populations are completely isolated from each other.

Conceivably, this could happen if one of the populations were on an island never visited by the outside world. In principle, any person in the United States can be contacted by any other in relatively few steps, unless one of them is a complete and total hermit, and then he could not be contacted at all.

In sum, perhaps the most important accomplishment of the research described here is this: Although people have talked about the small-world problem, and have even theorized about it, this study achieved, as far as I know, the first empirically-created chains between persons chosen at random from a major national population.

Although the study started with a specific set of questions arising from the small-world problem, the procedure illuminates a far wider set of topics. It reveals a potential communication structure whose sociological characteristics have yet to be exposed. When we understand the structure of this potential communication net, we shall understand a good deal more about the integration of society in general. While many studies in social science show how the individual is alienated and cut off from the rest of society, this study demonstrates that, in some sense, we are all bound together in a tightly knit social fabric.

# NATIONAL DIFFERENCES IN CONVERSATIONS

CARNEY LANDIS
*Wesleyan University*

Several years ago Moore[1] published a classified tabulation of fragments of conversations overheard on Broadway, New York City. Moore was interested in a demonstration of psychological sex differences, especially differences in "interest" or "drive". He says in part, "The presence of strong personal interests is nowhere more apparent than in the natural trend of easy conversation, when the topics seem to be flowing of themselves. This seems to be especially true at the end of the day, when the mind is comparatively free from the preoccupation of the immediate tasks at hand." This approach to the problem of individual and group differences is, I believe, new and has much to recommend it on logical grounds. The results of Moore's study of sex differences are certainly more in agreement with ordinary experience (common sense) than any differences thus far demonstrated by intelligence tests, association tests or any other of the accepted psychological methods.

M. H. Landis and H. E. Burtt[2] in 1924 used the same method in a study of five hundred fragmentary conversations overheard in Columbus, Ohio. They were interested in three problems: (1) the use of Moore's method in a different locality with a larger number of cases; (2) an analysis of the topic of conversation with regard to the approximate social status of the person speaking; and (3) an examination of the effect of the immediate environment on the topic of conversation. The tabulations indicate marked differences in the interests of business and industrial workers as compared to students. The environment in which the conversation was overheard, *e.g.*, restaurant, theater, etc., had a marked influence on the topic of conversation. However, the same sex differences in conversational topics found by Moore were also found by these writers when their results were grouped in a general table. (See [Table 9-1].) Such results indicate that the method should be a promising one for further application.

The intelligence test has been almost as poor in the demonstration of objection-proof national differences as it has been in the revealing of sex differences. Tests made and standardized on one race, national, or cultural group are never very satisfactory when applied to a different group, even when the two groups compared speak a common language.

In order to make a comparison of national differences in interest as indicated by conversations, the writer collected fragments of conversations overheard in London on Oxford and Regent Streets and their immediate vicinity, during the late afternoon and early evening. Notation was made of the sex of the speaker and of the person spoken to, and of the general topic of conversation when the conversation was easily classified, or the actual words when the topic was unusual. In all, two hundred such fragments were collected. These are summarized in [Table 9-1]. This table gives the comparative percentage frequency of topics for London, New York and Columbus.

There are 74 man to man conversations tabulated in London. These show a remarkably close approximation in their frequency distribution of interest to the American figures. Business does not predominate quite so heavily in London, but otherwise the distribution is practically the same. When Englishman talks to Englishwoman, this study indicates a marked difference from the American's choice of topics. He does not talk "shop" or sport but rather about women, clothes, or himself.

The conversation of Englishwomen (woman to woman, 76 cases) shows a different predominance of interest from that of American women. American women talk predominantly about men and clothing, Englishwomen talk most frequently of other women or of themselves, and show a tendency to converse on a greater variety of topics than do Americans. When Englishwoman talks to Englishman her preference of topics is the same as when she talks with a woman. This limited sample indicates that the Englishman adapts his conversations to the interests of his feminine companion while American studies show that the American woman adapts her conversation to the interests of her masculine companion.

The larger percentages entered in [Table 9-1] opposite "Other Classifications" for London as compared to New York and Columbus seem to indicate a wider range of interests on the part of the Londoner.

[1] Moore, H. T.: 1922, Jour. Abnormal and Soc. Psychol., xvii, 210.

[2] Landis, M. H., and H. E. Burtt: 1924, Jour. Comparative Psychol., iv, 81.

**[TABLE 9-1] Table giving percentage frequency for topics of conversation. Figures for New York are from Moore[1] and those for Columbus from M. H. Landis and H. E. Burtt.[2]**

| Classification | Place | Man to man | Woman to woman | Man to woman | Woman to man |
|---|---|---|---|---|---|
| | London | 35 | 5 | 0 | 8 |
| Money and business | New York | 48 | 3 | 22 | 12 |
| | Columbus | 49 | 12 | 19 | 10 |
| | London | 16 | 0 | 8 | 4 |
| Amusements or sports | New York | 14 | 4 | 25 | 10 |
| | Columbus | 15 | 11 | 25 | 24 |
| | London | 15 | 14 | 12 | 4 |
| Men | New York | 13 | 44 | 13 | 22 |
| | Columbus | 12 | 22 | 11 | 14 |
| | London | 5 | 26 | 20 | 24 |
| Women | New York | 8 | 16 | 10 | 13 |
| | Columbus | 4 | 15 | 5 | 10 |
| | London | 5 | 16 | 16 | 4 |
| Clothing or decoration | New York | 2 | 23 | 3 | 17 |
| | Columbus | 5 | 19 | 7 | 17 |
| | London | 7 | 20 | 16 | 12 |
| Self | New York | – | – | – | – |
| | Columbus | 9 | 15 | 23 | 18 |
| | London | 16 | 18 | 28 | 44 |
| Other classifications | New York | 15 | 10 | 27 | 26 |
| | Columbus | 6 | 6 | 10 | 7 |
| | London | 74 | 76 | 25 | 25 |
| Total number of cases | New York | 80 | 30 | 32 | 32 |
| | Columbus | 195 | 155 | 63 | 87 |

[1] Moore, *op. cit.*
[2] Landis and Burtt, *op. cit.*

Whether this is actually true or not is uncertain since the classification of any material of such a nature is subject to the influence of the personal bias of the classifier.

In so far as conversations offer that which Moore has termed, "very considerable and ineradicable differences in the original capacities of the two sexes for certain types of enthusiasm," the differences found in this study, and the random samplings made in two other communities cannot be well explained as due to chance.

One would not expect great differences in the conversational topics of the Englishman as compared to the American, especially the Londoner and the New Yorker. The commercial and manufacturing environment attracts and holds men of much the same temperament. Even though the Englishwoman favors conversational topics differing from the American favorites, still the predominating topics in either case are those which concern persons rather than things.

## SUMMARY

Fragments of two hundred conversations overheard on the streets of London have been classified according to the sex of the speaker, the person spoken to, and the topic of conversation. The results of this tabulation are compared to previous conversation studies made in New York and in Columbus, Ohio. The comparisons indicate that the same interests are exhibited by the Englishman as by the American when in a man to man conversation but that the Englishman when talking to a feminine companion adapts his conversation to her interests while American women adapt their conversation to the interests of their masculine companions. Englishwomen talk more frequently of other women and of themselves, while American women talk of men and of clothes. There is a greater variety in the conversations on the London streets than in those heard on the American streets. Sex differences in topics of conversation (interests) are as marked in London as in America.

# CONTENT ANALYSIS OF A SUPER PATRIOT PROTEST*

JAMES McEVOY AND MARK CHESLER
*University of Michigan*

RICHARD SCHMUCK
*Temple University*

> "That story in your last issue was the most brazen and infuriating piece of propaganda against God and Country that I have ever read."

This quotation is an example of one of the most significant phenomena of mid-twentieth century America—super patriotism. Variously called extreme conservatism, right-wing extremism, and radical rightism, super patriotism is a manifestation of the ideologies and energies of persons who reject aspects of contemporary American social and political life. Super patriotism is characterized by political conservatism and fervent nationalism, by active participation in conservative social and political organizations, and by the perception of a major and dangerous internal Communist conspiracy operating to influence many areas of American life.[1] Some of the areas of change figuring most prominently as targets of right-wing protest involve international relations, civil rights activity and domestic welfare policies, modernist religious and educational institutions, and community mental health services. In many cases, super patriots view the mass media as channels through which "Communists" brainwash Americans into accepting these changes in American society and therefore through which Americans will eventually be entrapped by Communism.

A short story in a recent issue of a national magazine seemed to some super patriots to be an example of just such usage of the mass media. It depicted the rapid and dramatic takeover of a group of children's minds through the use of rather crude techniques of brainwashing. In a few minutes, a "new teacher" was able to convert her students' beliefs in the authority of their parents, their allegiance to their country, and their faith in God, into faith in and adulation of "Our Leader," a figure with a strong likeness to the "Big Brother" of Orwell's *1984*. Included in the story were incidents depicting the destruction of the American flag, the teaching of atheism, and the encouragement of disrespect for parents.

In the *Bulletin* of the John Birch Society, a publication which presents a monthly program of action for local chapters, this story was presented by Robert Welch, founder and leader of the John Birch Society, as being strikingly anti-religious, un-American, and Communistic; and as a result, several thousand protest letters were received by the author and editors of the magazine. It is not possible to identify all of the letters as the result of the instructions in the *Bulletin*, or as in any sense being written only by members of the John Birch Society; however, the issue to which they were directed and their observed content strongly suggest that much of this sample of writers is exceptionally sensitive to patriotic and nationalistic content in the media to which it is exposed.

The editors of the magazine and the author of the story defended its theme and content as pro-American, claiming that it tried to exemplify the subtlety with which a Communist takeover of the country might be performed. Despite what the authors of this paper, the editors of the magazine, and the author of the story all believed to be the unmistakable anti-Communism of the story, it was, nevertheless, seen by more than two thousand letter writers as subversive or Communistic. It is the nature of these writers' responses to the story and their demographic, sociological, and psychological characteristics that are the subject of this paper.

## METHODS

The total population of letters numbered 2,254. A random number was selected as a starting point and every tenth letter was then drawn for inclusion in the sample. This sample was then coded and a second sample was drawn in the same way and compared with the first. No significant differences were found between these two samples; they were therefore considered to be representative of the population and combined. The entire sample of letters upon which this study is based was 453, or 20 per cent of the

*This research was sponsored by the Office of Research Administration of the University of Michigan, Ann Arbor, Michigan, and administered by the Center for Research on Utilization of Scientific Knowledge, Institute for Social Research.

[1] R. Schmuck and M. Chesler, "Super Patriotism: A Definition and Analysis," *Journal of Social Issues,* **19** *(1963),* pp. 31-50.

population. Content analysis of the letters sampled was employed as the method of study. The following groups of categories were designed for use in the analysis.[2]

Several *demographic* categories were designed to describe data as the census region of the letter's origin and the population of the city of its origin.

Estimates of a very general nature were made about the *social status* of the writers on the basis of coding each letter for the type of writing implement used by its author, the author's occupation, and the quality (imprinted, unimprinted, tablet) of the stationery used by the writer.

The level of *literacy* of each letter was measured by a count of the grammatical, spelling, and syntactical errors occurring in the letter.

Group *salience*, or the nature and frequency of references made to groups or associates, was recorded by several different categories. These included indications of group salience by mentions of families in general or the writer's family, references to secondary groups or voluntary associations such as clubs or lodges, and indications that the writer had discussed or would discuss the story with a group with which he was in some way affiliated. Also recorded were statements about the responses (actual or expected) that these groups had or were expected to have to the story.

The *identity* of the writer was assessed by two categories. One simply recorded whether or not the writer said he was a member of the John Birch Society; the second was the self-expressed identity of the writer, such as "I am a long time reader . . ." or "I am a mother . . . ."

Another category was employed to discriminate between the writers' reactions in terms of *personal* or *general values*. In other words, did the writer see the story as a personal affront, or, rather, did he couch his objections in terms of the story being an attack on such broad general values as patriotism, God, religion, and the like.

Several code categories were devised to measure roughly the *hostility* and affect of each letter. One of these, threats, provided a count of those writers who cancelled or threatened to cancel their subscriptions and those who said they would stop reading or in other ways employ negative sanctions against the magazine.

Another set of categories measured the *mimetic frequency* of each letter. The particular editor to whom the letter was addressed and the number of arguments in the letter which paralleled those in the *Bulletin* were coded. The instructions in the *Bulletin* were broken down into twenty-five separate phrases and the frequency of occurrence of these phrases was recorded for each letter.

Finally, two categories were used to code the letter on the dimensions of *patriotism* and *religiosity* using the frequency of references of these themes as the basis for a scale of relative intensity.

## THE SOCIOLOGICAL AND DEMOGRAPHIC CHARACTERISTICS OF WRITERS OF PROTEST LETTERS

For the most part, letter writing campaigns have been studied by researchers interested in political mail as a reflection of public opinion.[3] But recent studies[4] have focused more on the characteristics of the letter writers themselves. Wartenburg and Thielens's study is especially pertinent here because it analyzed another set of protest letters solicited by Welch in the John Birch Society *Bulletin*. Although that campaign and the one studied here focus on different issues, some demographic comparisons can be made of the characteristics of the writers studied by Wartenburg and Thielens and those studied by McEvoy, Chesler, and Schmuck.

The writers in this study were nearly identical with Wartenburg and Thielens's population in the proportion coming from suburbs of major cities larger than 100,000. However, the letters in this sample indicated a greater proportion of writers from cities ranging in size from 5,000 to 50,000 than we would expect on the basis of the distribution of the national population. The data indicated that relatively few residents of rural areas were among the writers and that at least 80 per cent of this sample is located in urban and suburban centers or small towns as compared with 60 per cent of the national population

[2] For a more complete description of the categories and coding methods, see the monograph *Letters from the Right*, J. McEvoy with R. Schmuck and M. Chesler, Ann Arbor: Center for Research on Utilization of Scientific Knowledge, University of Michigan, 1966.

[3] E. Kefauver and J. Levin, "Letters That Really Count," in Katz *et al.*, *Public Opinion and Propaganda*, New York: Holt, Rinehart & Winston, 1954. See especially L. Sussmann, *Dear FDR: A Study of Political Letter Writing*, Totowa, N.J.: Bedminster Press, 1963.

[4] H. Wartenberg and W. Thielens, *Against the United Nations: A Letter Writing Campaign by the Birch Movement*, New York: Columbia University, 1964, mimeo.

[TABLE 9-2] **Population of writers' home community by per cent of protest writers and national population***

| Size of community | Letters (%) | National population(%)* |
|---|---|---|
| Below 5,000 | 19.2 | 40.2 |
| 5 - 10,000 | 7.1 | 5.5 |
| 10 - 25,000 | 13.5 | 9.8 |
| 25 - 50,000 | 13.2 | 8.3 |
| 50 - 100,000 | 11.0 | 7.7 |
| 100 - 500,000 | 22.5 | 12.5 |
| Above 500,000 | 11.0 | 16.0 |
| Not available | 2.4 | – |
| | 100.0% | 100.0% |

*Based on current urban definition, 1960 census, *Statistical Abstract of the United States*, 1966, p. 15, including both rural and urban population.

[TABLE 9-3] **Percentage, by region, of letter writers and national population**

| Region | National* population (%) | Wartenburg and Thielens (%) | Letters (%) |
|---|---|---|---|
| California | 8.8 | 33 | 30 |
| Other Far West | 6.8 | 9 | 11 |
| South | 30.7 | 29 | 29 |
| North Central | 28.8 | 18 | 19 |
| North East | 24.9 | 11 | 10 |
| Unknown | – | – | 2 |
| | 100.0% | 100% | 100% |

**Statistical Abstract of the United States*, 1966.

residing in these areas. [Table 9-2] summarizes these data.

An early study of letter writing[5] demonstrated that some regions and states, particularly California, had a high rate of political letter writing. For the sample studied here, and that studied by Wartenburg and Thielens, California outranked all other states in this regard. Indeed, in both studies it supplied four times as many letter writers than would be expected on the basis of its population. Moreover, of those letters in our sample from California, over four-fifths were from Southern California, mostly from Orange and Los Angeles counties. Thirty-three per cent of those letters analyzed by Wartenburg and Thielens were from the same state.

[Table 9-3] demonstrates the distribution patterns of our study and Wartenburg and Thielen's study as compared with the national population.

Some other studies of political mail, however, suggest a heavy concentration of writers in the Eastern states, with only 12 per cent coming from the West.[6] An interesting parallel to these sources of super patriots' protest letters is found in the "Western" conservative hegemony which eventually placed Barry Goldwater as the Republican presidential nominee in 1964. That letter writing played an important part in his nomination has been suggested by Converse, Clausen, and Miller.[7] These authors draw on survey interview data to propose that the "reality" basis of the Goldwater Campaign was in part created by a massive letter writing campaign which encouraged the Goldwater camp in its belief that it could win the election. "It is to the world of letter opinion or one like it that the Goldwater campaign, in its original design, was addressed."[8] These same authors discovered that 15 per cent of the adult population had written politically relevant letters, but that the majority of all political letters were written by only 3 per cent of the population. Of those who wrote in 1964, well over 50 per cent favored the candidacy of Goldwater. The kind of letter writing campaign that we have been analyzing here may have been a training ground for those writers who inflated the expectations of the Goldwater camp in the Spring of 1964.

In this analysis an attempt was made to gather data on the socioeconomic status and the occupations of the writers. In comparison with the letter writers studied by Wartenburg and Thielens, these writers were slightly lower in socio-economic status. While only 8 per cent of the letters gave any indication of occupation, there seemed to be an extraordinary number of doctors of medicine and doctors of osteopathy who wrote in protest. After the sampling was completed and the overrepresentation of doctors discovered, all the letters in the population were examined once again in order to extract all doctors from the population. The result was a total of 48 letters or

[5] R. Wyant, "Voting via the Senate Mailbag," *Public Opinion Quarterly*, 5 (1941), pp. 359-382.

[6] Sussmann, *op. cit.*

[7] P. Converse, A. Clausen, and W. Miller, "Electoral Myth and Reality: The 1964 Election," *American Political Science Review*, **59** (1965), pp. 321-336.

[8] *Ibid.*, p. 335. Letter opinion was obtained by analyzing the interviews of persons who indicated that they had written a letter with political relevance to any editor, public official, or the like, determining the frequency of writing, and then comparing these responses with expressed vote preference.

2.13 per cent of our total population being so identified. This represents twenty-one times the number of M.D.'s and D.O.'s in the resident civilian population for the year in which the letters were written.[9]

## STYLISTIC DIMENSIONS OF PROTEST

In this section we review the relevance of variables such as literacy, education, dogmatism, and flexibility of protest for these letter writers. Literacy, and perhaps by inference education, has been related to relative flexibility and openness to differences in conservative populations.[10] In this sample the more literate writers significantly more often asked for an explanation for the appearance of story than did less literate writers ($\chi^2 = 7.92, p < .01$). Asking for an explanation suggests a more open-minded posture toward the story and the media, indicative of greater cognitive flexibility. Literacy was also found to be closely connected with another set of categories which were devised to measure the overall group salience or the generalized indications of group support and consciousness found among our writers. Within these categories, we coded each letter for indications that its writer saw himself as part of a larger group or that he was attempting to elicit real or mythical group support for his feelings toward the magazine. An example of this sort of letter is:

> Dear Editor,
>
> After reading ——————— I asked several friends to do likewise. We all agreed it is a very pro-Communist story.
>
> We are surprised and shocked that the ——————— with its standing should stoop so low.
>
> You have just lost five faithful readers.
>
> Sincerely,

A high level of literacy more often produced letters which *lacked* indications of group salience. That is, the more literate writers did not as frequently try to justify their position with attempts to magnify the effect of their protest by introducing groups who, they claimed, also supported their position. These findings are illustrated in [Table 9-4].

Organized political letter writing campaigns are, according to Kefauver and Levin, destined to the same fate as huge petitions to Congress: "No one reads them. They gather dust in Capitol files until finally carried away. They seldom influence legislation."[11] Therefore, some of the more sophisticated mail campaigns and more sophisticated people might consciously attempt to avoid sponsoring group references in protests such as this one. The pattern of avoiding reference to the sponsoring group is evident in these letters where the John Birch Society, the *Bulletin*, or Robert Welch were mentioned only four times. One of these references was made by a public health physician—one of the few writers who saw the story as anti-Communist—who violently criticized the magazine for its "Birch-like" stories, and went on to denounce it as right-wing. One other reference to Welch in which the story was interpreted as anti-Communist was made by a self-identified member of the John Birch Society who had read both the instructions in the *Bulletin* and the story and had then decided that Welch was wrong. He wrote complimenting the magazine for its anti-Communism. The other two references to Society membership were in protest letters, one of which was a threatening note signed "Birch Chapter XYZ." Two additional letters contained references to membership in a "conservative club."

On the other hand, 38 per cent of the writers used one or more of the assertions contained in the *Bulletin's* commentary and instructions, and 30 per cent used one or more of the phrases taken directly from the *Bulletin*. Occasionally a letter would be simply a word for word copy of the *Bulletin's* statement. More often, however, one or two phrases—particularly those describing the writer's supposed interpretation of and emotional reaction to the story—were integrated into an otherwise original text. Wartenburg and Thielens also found that 29 per cent of their population used verbatim quotations and that "closely parallel" arguments appeared in more than 50 per cent of their letters. Noting the obvious consequences of this sort of copying, they conclude: ". . . some writers were transparently unsuccessful in their efforts to present the appearance of independent thought."[12]

Even though these letters were easily detected as a "campaign," the editors answered every letter personally, trying to explain their interpretation of the story. They also made a brief analysis of the letters, published an editorial report to their readers about the campaign, and allowed these letters to be used

---

[9] A forthcoming report will discuss this group in detail: J. McEvoy, *Medicine and Super Patriotism: An Analysis of Physicians' Protest Letters*, in preparation.

[10] See H. McCloskey, "Conservatism and Personality," *American Political Science Review*, **52** (1958), pp. 27-45; and T. Adorno, E. Frenkel-Brunswick, D. Levinson, and N. Sanford, *The Authoritarian Personality*, New York: Harper, 1950.

[11] Kefauver and Levin, *op. cit.*, pp. 221-226.

[12] Wartenburg and Thielens, *op. cit.*, p. 22.

**[TABLE 9-4] Literacy of letter related to two measures of group salience**

| Literacy | Group salience* | | | | |
|---|---|---|---|---|---|
| | A) Would make contact with others | | B) Cite reactions of others | | |
| | High | Low | High | Low | N |
| High literacy | 25 (11%) | 203 (89%) | 38 (17%) | 190 (83%) | 228 |
| Low literacy | 45 (20%) | 180 (80%) | 61 (27%) | 164 (73%) | 225 |
| N | 70 | 383 | 99 | 354 | 453 |

*$\chi^2$ A = 7.11, $p < .01$; $\chi^2$ B = 7.30, $p < .01$.

for research. The magazine lost, if the writers are to be believed, about 485 readers or subscribers as a direct result of publishing this story. Moreover, 27 per cent of those cancelling stated that they would attempt to get other people to do likewise. These statistics say nothing about the thousands of people who must have seen the *Bulletin* and who may have retaliated in other ways but did not write to the magazine. Nevertheless, economic sanctions were not the major threats of the protest. For every person who wrote to cancel, there are four who simply protested; this, of course, may be in part due to the fact that many writers were not subscribers.

## ADDITIONAL CHARACTERISTICS: THE TRUE BELIEVERS AND RELIGIOSITY

Some of the methods used by elites to control mass behavior are to supply a population susceptible to mobilization with an identity, proffer a set of abstract, de-personalized symbols, and control as much as possible the information which reaches this population. Eric Hoffer's description of the True Believer, whose "rejected self ceases to assert its claim to distinctiveness, and there is nothing to resist the propensity to copy," seems quite relevant here.[13] On a small scale, those writers who relied on the leadership of the John Birch Society for literal formulation of their opinions exemplify these processes. Those persons would be expected to have a high score on *mimetic frequency* in our coding procedure. Indeed, the fact that 30 per cent of this sample was marked by the use of phrasing copied directly from the *Bulletin* indicated to us that a significant number of our writers lacked sufficient autonomy to formulate their own responses and suggested that they might differ in other ways from the remainder of the population. Some examples of their letters follow:

> It must be pseudo-leaders like you who have created the turmoil of today, causing tens of thousands of citizens and taxpayers to begin a tide of protest against our federal lack of resistance to infiltration of the red butchers . . . . This (story) was the most brazen and infuriating piece of propaganda against God and Country that I have ever read.
>
> A writer

> If the ———— story in your last issue was intended to bring all red-blooded Americans up fighting, then you've succeeded.
>
> . . . This (story) was the most brazen and infuriating piece of propaganda against God and Country that I have ever read.
>
> Taken at face value this story makes Communism appear right and beautiful and taken at face value, you deserve the anger and contempt of all who love God and Country.
>
> A writer

On almost all measures, the writers who quoted from the John Birch Society *Bulletin* tended to be slightly lower in their socio-economic status than were those who did not so quote. They were also slightly less literate than writers who did not include quotations from the *Bulletin*'s text. But perhaps more important, the writers who copied from the *Bulletin* more often came from rural areas or small towns than did those who did not quote from it. Of the 137 people who quoted from the *Bulletin*, 34 per cent came from cities of less than 10,000 people. Only 23 per cent of the writers who did not use direct quotations resided in cities of that size. These figures compare with 34 per cent of the national population which live in cities of 10,000 or smaller. Perhaps an

[13] E. Hoffer, *The True Believer*, New York: Mentor, 1963, p. 95.

absence of cross-pressures in the small town environments of these writers may in turn result in more rigid adherence to the ideas of their leaders than would be the case for persons of similar ideology living in larger cities. In these latter areas social and occupational interaction is likely to be more frequently experienced by a given individual.

The rigidity or conformity indicated by the writers' use of quotations from the *Bulletin* was further reflected in their interpretation of, and response to, the story. Each letter was coded on the dimension of personal or general value reaction: whether or not the writer saw the story as threatening to his personal values–e.g., "I do not believe that this story is in good taste and I don't want it in my house"–or to general values he believed to be characteristic of American society–e.g., "Your publishing of this story is wicked. Men have died for liberty and Our Flag. This story is a disgrace to those men." Twenty-eight per cent of those persons responding with personal values conformed to the *Bulletin* text, while 39 per cent of those responding with only general values so conformed ($p < .05$).

The propensity to respond at a general value level can be seen as another indication of the loss of self-relevant values of the True Believer. In this particular regard, however, it must be recognized that the statement in the *Bulletin* was written primarily in abstract or "general value" form, and, as a result, these findings are in some ways confounded due to the nature of the symbols taken over by the writers who quoted from the *Bulletin*. These same limitations apply to the analysis of the ambiguity perceived in the story, that is, whether the story was seen as a clear cut example of the Communist line or not. Nevertheless, it is readily apparent that those writers quoting from the *Bulletin* were far more often willing to accept Welch's conclusions than were those who did not use the *Bulletin* text. This is a further indication of the high degree of conformity characteristic of those writers who quoted from the *Bulletin*; they not only used symbols of their leaders to initiate or reinforce a reaction of their own, but they also apparently internalized the meaning of these symbols as well. This behavior is also a close approximation of the profile of the True Believer's response to the directions of his significant elites, and gives additional support to the application of Hoffer's thesis to this group of writers.

Additionally, those writers who quoted from the *Bulletin* were slightly more likely to threaten the magazine than were those who did not; another element of this picture is the slightly more threatening posture on the dimension of group contact taken by those quoting. They more often said that they could attempt to get others to act against the magazine than did those writers who wrote original letters. They also more often wrote group letters, apparently trying to invoke greater sanctions by making their letters the product of more than one writer.

In conclusion, those writers who quoted from the *Bulletin* are, in some ways, strikingly different from the remainder of our population. The variables apparently most significant are the population of the cities in which they reside, and those which attempted to measure the nature of their response to the story in terms of ambiguity and personal-general value interpretation. As measured by their threat of cancellation and their frequency of group signatures, their protests toward the magazine appear to be more hostile than those writers who did not quote. As we have noted, however, these differences often do not reach an acceptable level of significance and appear only to suggest the possible existence of a relationship.

Religious fundamentalism and super patriotism have been demonstrated to occur together,[14] and rigid adherence to religious doctrine and practice is often a manifestation of the True Believer's impulse toward identification with a cause. In our sample, however, we found that only 7 per cent of the letters received by the magazine were predominantly religious in content. Some examples follow:

> Dear Sir:
>
> I have just read . . . and I am shocked. How could you print such a story, telling the children to believe there is no God? It smacks of Communism.
>
> I am deeply hurt, and raise my voice in protest against such literature being printed in ——————. I am a firm believer in God and have been a teacher in our local Sunday School for over fifty years, teaching little children to believe THERE IS A GOD.
>
> Most Sincerely,

> Dear Sir:
>
> . . . I couldn't believe that you would put such an article (story) before the public's eyes. To me it was brazen, and the most anti-Christ article I have ever read. Do you know, actually know, that God gave us this country? That God only is the One, who not only made

[14] See R. Schmuck and M. Chesler (eds.), *Super Patriots and Radical Rightists: Social Psychological Studies*, in preparation; S. Lipset, *Political Man*, New York: Doubleday, 1960; and D. Danzig, "Radical Right and the Rise of the Fundamentalist Minority," *Commentary*, April, 1962, pp. 291-298.

> a place in our Wonderful Country for a good magazine and He only has brought you forth to success? Why did you do it? Why brainwash people with Communist slants? When on Judgement Day you will be asked "Why sell my people into slavery by printing as you did?" No one can help you then. I know I can't allow such stories in my home and therefore, I can't buy the ———— any more. I wanted you to know why (sic).
>
> Former Subscriber

The thirty-two highly religious letters were extracted from the sample and, like those letters which employed phrases from the *Bulletin*, analyzed and compared with the remaining portion of the sample. As might be expected, this group of writers was different in several respects from the sample as a whole. Indications of group salience in these writers' letters centered mainly on the family. In 38 per cent of the letters some mention of the family occurred, as compared with 18 per cent of the non-religiously oriented group which indicated family group salience. Most often this concern with families was general rather than specific to the writer's own primary group. Very frequently a writer would state that this story was, for example, "sure to help break up more American homes . . . ." Furthermore, he saw the story's result as primarily disintegrative of present social institutions. Thus, a primary group anxiety is characteristic of this group; and it may be the case that their strong religious beliefs are an attempt to increase the solidarity of the family unit of which they are a part.

This concern with certain social institutions is evident in the fact that 56 per cent of these highly religious writers expressed their protests wholly on the grounds that publication of the story was in conflict with most important general and common values of the nation. Finally, the highly religious writers tended to be less punitive than the remainder of the population as expressed in their threats of cancellation of their subscription and the like. Unfortunately, there were too few highly religious letters to permit meaningful statistical analysis along these several dimensions.

These empirical referents of character and attitudes constitute one way of identifying the letter writers. Observations or interviews with these protestors would, of course, shed more light both on their characteristics and the concepts employed here. The limitations of these data also prohibit more diverse theorizing into the social psychological qualities and attributes of the writers. However, the data that are available and have been analyzed here provide an instructive description of one expression of super patriot protest.

# SITUATIONAL PATTERNING IN INTERGROUP RELATIONS*

MELVIN L. KOHN
*National Institute of Mental Health*†

ROBIN M. WILLIAMS, JR.
*Cornell University*

There is now abundant research evidence of situational variability in intergroup behavior: an ever-accumulating body of research demonstrates that allegedly prejudiced persons act in a thoroughly egalitarian manner in situations where that is the socially prescribed mode of behavior, and that allegedly unprejudiced persons discriminate in situations where they feel it is socially appropriate to do so.[1] It is also well known that patterns of "appropriateness" in intergroup behavior have been changing with increasing tempo in recent years. The unthinkable of a short time ago has in many areas of life become the commonplace of today. For a brief period the transition from unthinkable to commonplace arouses extreme emotional fervor; but as the new definition of the situation becomes the socially prescribed, the fervor soon diminishes. What was for the moment an "unpatterned" situation becomes, in Karl Mannheim's terms, "built into the framework of the society."[2]

Unpatterned situations, in which definitions of appropriate conduct are in process of change, occur infrequently, and it is even more infrequent that they occur at the convenience of the research observer. Yet their importance for social change is likely to be great. In the multitude of unambiguous, patterned situations we have the raw material for documenting existing patterns of intergroup behavior. In the relatively rare unpatterned situations, however, we may hope to find important information concerning social change. It appears, for instance, that one of the most basic changes in race relations in the South is the growing uncertainty of all concerned about what is appropriate, "proper" intergroup behavior. This, along with the decreased personal interaction between whites and Negroes (especially middle- and upper-class Negroes), is compounded with the relative impersonality of the new urban South, to create an unprecedented situation in which further changes can occur with a rapidity that would have been thought impossible only a few years ago.

The social scientist who wishes to study the processes by which unpatterned situations come to be defined by their participants is faced with several major problems, not the least of which is the difficulty of finding situations that can be studied systematically. It is not sufficient to create hypothetical situations and to ask people how they think they would behave in them. People's responses to hypothetical situations are patterned in the same way as ordinary opinion-items—for example, they can be ordered into unidimensional scales. But behavior studied in actual intergroup situations has not proven scalable; such behavior encompasses factors idiosyncratic to the particular situation, that cannot be foreseen by the person asked to predict his probable behavior.

Since hypothetical situations are not adequate, and actual unpatterned situations occur but rarely, the research worker is left with little choice but to initiate new situations. The procedure must be covert, for if the participants knew that the situations were created for research purposes, their definitions would be radically altered. Many problems are necessarily created, on both ethical and practical levels: the procedure involves a degree of manipulation; it poses a degree of danger to the participant observers and perhaps to other participants as well; it creates barriers to observation and interviewing. In the absence of preferable alternatives, however, we felt justified

---

*We wish to acknowledge our very considerable debt to our research collaborators, John P. Dean and Robert B. Johnson. John Dean was primarily responsible for inaugurating this research, and both he and Robert Johnson participated actively in the field work.

†Melvin Kohn was at Cornell University at the time this research was carried out. His participation in the research was supported by the Social Science Research Council.

[1] We shall define a situation as a series of interactions, located in space and time, and perceived by the participants as an *event*: in this usage "situation" is a delimiting term, cutting out from the flow of experience a particular series of interpersonal actions which are seen by the participants as a describable event, separable from preceding and succeeding events, constraining the participants to act in particular ways, and having its own unique consequences.

[2] "Although situations are in their very nature dynamic and unique, as soon as they become socialized—that is to say, built into the framework of society—they tend to become standardized to a certain extent. Thus we must distinguish between what is called patterned and unpatterned situations." [Karl Mannheim, *Man and Society in an Age of Reconstruction*, (London: Kegan Paul, Trench, Trubner, and Co., 1940), p. 301.]

in initiating a series of forty-three situations in which we could observe and interview in a reasonably systematic fashion.

These situations were initiated in social contexts that were neither so intimate as automatically to exclude Negro participation, nor so functionally specific as to make acceptance of Negroes unproblematic. In particular, we focused on service establishments, such as restaurants and taverns. In white neighborhoods infrequently visited by Negroes, for example, we found many restaurant and tavern managers who had never faced a situation where it was necessary to decide whether or not to serve Negro patrons. Frequently the manager, when confronted by a Negro customer, was caught in a serious dilemma. On the one hand, it is illegal in the communities studied to refuse to serve Negroes. On the other hand, these establishments are often informal neighborhood social centers, and the managers' fears that their customers would object to the presence of Negroes militate against serving. For the manager who has no already established policy, this can be a highly problematic situation.

Within the restricted area in which it was possible to initiate situations—in public service establishments, voluntary organizations, and the like—we attempted to vary the situational conditions to the maximum degree possible. Even so, it must be recognized that our conclusions are based on studies in a very limited range of social institutions; e.g., we could not initiate new situations in industrial organizations or in schools. Thus we cannot assert that the present findings are directly applicable to institutions outside of the range studied. It seems probable, however, that though the processes by which unpatterned situations arise in these institutions are different from those of the present research, the processes by which they come to be defined by participants are similar.

## PROCEDURE

Before initiating a situation, we attempted to assess the usual patterns of behavior in the particular setting. The formality of our procedure depended on the social context: in formal organizations we were able to attend meetings, and to interview leaders and a sample of the membership; in service establishments we could only visit frequently enough to establish informal relationships with the staff and a few steady customers. Only after we felt we had some basis for predicting their probable reception, did we introduce Negro "stimulus-participants." White observers, located at strategic positions, observed the reactions of the principal participants.

Immediately after the Negroes withdrew from the scene, these "stimulus-participants" recorded the chronological sequence of events, and in addition filled out recording forms that had been designed to elicit their interpretations of the events. The white observers remained behind long enough to observe after-the-fact reactions, and then recorded their observations and interpretations in similar fashion. Thus we were able to secure the definitions held by non-participant observers and by Negro participants, as well as data on the overt behavior that occurred. In most cases we were also able to secure retrospective reports from white participants (organizational leaders, bartenders, customers) by formal interviewing procedures.

As an example of the procedure followed, let us consider one of these situations in some detail. A Negro couple (members of the research staff) entered a working-class tavern that was believed to discriminate. White observers, some of whom had visited the establishment frequently enough to be able to ask questions without arousing undue suspicion, were seated at strategic spots throughout the tavern. The following are the chronological accounts written by one of the Negro "stimulus participants" and one of the white observers:

### The Report of the "Stimulus-Participant"

Entered at 10:15. People looked around, but we strode dauntlessly to table near fire. Most people seemed to look around, notice us, and comment. I needed a match and went to the couple in the first booth. The fellow had a lighter. I asked for a light. He replied eagerly, "Yes sir," and flicked his lighter for me. Testing the afternoon hunch on restrooms, I went to the men's room. As I passed the lady's room, the bartender blocked my way.

*Bartender:* "What did you say?"

*Researcher:* "How do you do. I didn't say anything. I'm looking for the men's room."

*Bartender:* "I'll show you." He leads me to the men's room, stands at the next urinal in a grand rapport gesture, and says confidently, "Now, mind you, I don't have anything against you people. I went to school with you folks and I've got a lot of friends among you. But some of my customers don't like to see you in here. Five or six of them have already complained to me and left. Now I can't have that. I hope you'll understand if I ask you to leave."

*Researcher:* "It's pretty hard to understand. I went to war for these people."

*Bartender:* "Yeah, I went to war too. But some of our people are funny. They don't like to see you in here. So

I'll have to ask you to go." He leaves, and another young Caucasian enters. I am pretty damn upset.

*I:* "I suppose you're one of these fine people who wants me to leave."

*He:* "No, no, everybody's all right with me. What's the matter, you have some trouble?"

*I:* "You're damned tootin!" I go back to the table. Several people are entering and leaving for no apparent connected reason. No one comes to wait on us. Ten minutes later I go to the cigarette machine.

*Bartender* (stops me again)*:* "Say, are you going to leave or are we going to have some trouble? Some of the boys are pretty hot. Now I suggest that you get out of here before something happens. We don't want your kind. Remember, I've told you." I go back to the table. L (the Negro girl) is enthusiastic. The waitress comes near to clean off a table and L calls her three times. Waitress tosses her head and leaves. Band returns from intermission and begins to play. After about five danceless numbers, three couples move out on floor. We go to dance. Here comes bartender again.

*Bartender:* "Now look, I've told you three times. War or no war, now you get out of here. We don't want you. I've got my customers to think of. Come on, get off the floor and get out of here before you have trouble."

I ask him to call the cops if there's trouble, but he demurs and shoves us off dance floor. We leave. Must have been a great side-show to the white customers and observers, but I'm boiling so much I could kill every white face. Decide I'm through with this stunt. As we left, a fellow standing in front of the cigarette machine said, "Hell, we're all Americans. I'm all for you." Bartender was just behind us, shepherding us out, and he stopped and asked, "What did you say?" I didn't hear the rest, but the fellow was evidently championing us in a weak but determined way. Maybe there is some hope for some white folks.

## The Report of One of the White Observers

I arrived to find the bar crowded. D and J (observers) arrived, went through barroom to dancehall, just as I was climbing on a recently-vacated stool at the bar. Proprietor was serving a tray of drinks to blonde waitress. The bartender was standing akimbo at north end of the bar, waiting for electric mixer to finish stirring drink for him. Door opened, Negro researchers walked in, going through barroom and into hallway to dance floor. Blonde looked around at them, staring, then looked back at proprietor with her mouth open.

*Proprietor* (amazed)*:* "Well, how do you like that!"

*Bartender* (turning)*:* "What?"

*Proprietor and Blonde* (simultaneously)*:* "Those two jigs that just walked through here." "Two colored people just went in."

*Bartender* (in surprise)*:* "Where'd they go?"

*Blonde:* "Into the dance hall."

Enter Jane, a second waitress, from kitchen.

*Jane:* "I'm not going in there. What can we do? This never happened before. (To proprietor) "What'll we do? (Anguished) Do I *have* to serve them?"

*Proprietor* (peering through service peephole from bar to dance floor): "Let 'em sit."

*Bartender:* "Yes, stay away from them. I didn't see them. Where'd they go?"

*Blonde:* "They're at the table for six. What are we going to do?"

*Jane:* "I'm not going in there. This is awful."

Proprietor ducks under the lift-up gate at the end of the bar, takes a quick look into dance hall, then back under the gate board to his station behind the bar.

*Proprietor:* "Just let them sit." For the next several minutes, the proprietor inquired anxiously, from time to time, "What are they doing now? Did they go?" Each time he looked more amazed. Said to me, "Never in my time here did we have any of them at the bar." After a wait of perhaps 15 to 18 minutes:

*Proprietor:* "Well, I'm going to see that they leave." He took off apron, started to duck under the bar gate again, then said to bartender: "You better go in and get them out of there. I don't think I should go, because my name's on the license . . . if there's any trouble."

*Schoolteacher* (sitting with husband at the bar): "How can you get them to leave? (then to me) She was an attractive little thing, wasn't she?"

*Proprietor* (again)*:* "I wish they'd go. (Then to blonde waitress) Are any of your customers leaving?"

*Blonde:* "A couple, but I think they were leaving anyway. They'd asked for their check. Others are looking around at them, and they're all talking about it . . . it gives me the creeps to have to walk in there, and know they're staring at me, expecting me to come over and wait on them."

*Jane* (to me): "We never had colored people here. This is the first couple that ever went in there. (Shrugging) I'm just not going in. What a time they picked to come! Saturday night–our busiest time! Why didn't they make it some week night?–there aren't so many people here.

By this time the bartender had taken off his apron, left the barroom, and a few minutes later returned and went directly into the men's room, followed by the Negro researcher.

*Proprietor* (after a minute or so): "Where did the bartender go?"

*Jane:* "In the men's room."

*Teacher:* "They've been in there quite a while."

*Proprietor* (ducking under gate, apron and all): "I'd better see what's going on. He may have a knife." Goes and peers through four inch opening, as he holds the door ajar. Returns. "They're o.k." Bartender returned to bar, researcher to the dance hall.

*Bartender:* "He wanted to give me an argument. Said he was a veteran."

*Proprietor:* "They all have something like that to say, I guess. I want them to get out. What did he say?"

*Bartender:* "He said yes."

*I* (turning to man on stool beside me): "This is some situation, isn't it?"

*Man* (venomously): "It stinks!"

*Blonde* (watching Negroes through doorway): "He's sitting down. It's a good thing the orchestra is having intermission."

*Proprietor:* "Yes, I suppose they'd be dancing."

*Bartender:* "That looks like that Robeson stuff."

*Waitress:* "I can't think of any time I've seen colored people in here."

*Bartender:* "Stay away from them. Don't look at them. Don't let them catch your eye." Waitress departs for dance hall again.

*Youth* (at bar, to proprietor): "Maybe you can get a date." Proprietor snorted, ready to blow his top.

*Teacher:* "He's getting cigarettes."

*Bartender:* "Where is he?"

*Jane:* "At the cigarette machine."

*Bartender* (apron and all, under the bar gate again): "I'll tell him to get going." Went and spoke to researcher, then back to bar. "They'll leave, I think. I told him there were a couple of fellows were going to see about it, if they didn't." Just about this time the orchestra's intermission was over; they returned to the bandstand.

*Proprietor:* "There goes the band. I suppose they'll start to dance now. I wish I'd thought to hold up the orchestra until they got out of here. (To blonde) Watch them now. (To Jane) Jane, get me a sandwich, will you?"

*Teacher:* "You're in a tough spot, aren't you? Are you going to serve them?"

*Proprietor:* "No."

*Bartender:* "We'll have to put them out for causing a disturbance."

*Blonde:* "Four of my couples have left."

*Proprietor:* "That does it! Go in and get them out of there, NOW!"

Bartender went into dancehall, one man followed him, and three or four other men gathered around. The Negro researchers walked out through the bar. Bartender went back behind the bar and the man resumed his seat.

*Proprietor* (who had followed, with his eyes, the Negro girl as she left): "Did you see the cute little smile she had on?"

*Bartender:* "Well, that buck thinks he's tough, I guess. Robeson stuff."

*Customer:* "You could have served them. They got rights!"

*Bartender:* "You want to make something of it? Are you with them?"

*Customer:* "No, I'm not with them. They got a right to have a drink. You all stink."

*Bartender* (threateningly): "Pick up your change and drift. You want to drink with them? Go on down to the C.D. bar. Lots of them there." Man picked up his change and stalked to door, mumbling.

*Proprietor:* "What the hell do you suppose is the matter with him? He's not drunk."

*Teacher:* "Maybe he's one of those people who has Negro friends."

*Another customer:* "In Germany those black bastards got everything they wanted. Excuse me, ma'm. (To teacher) Two or three of them would come along and take a white soldier's girl right away from him. I hate their guts. They want to stay away from me. I just wish you'd told me, I could have thrown them out. . . ."

*Proprietor:* "You can if they come back. You can throw out their whole gang. They've probably gone to get the bunch. I don't think they came in just to get a drink."

*Teacher's husband:* "No, I think they came here deliberately to get served or make trouble. If they dropped in for a drink, they would have left when the bartender talked to him. I think this must be planned somehow."

*Bartender:* "Yeah, Robeson stuff. Spooks! Little Peekskill, they wanted to make out of this place."

*Teacher:* "I feel sorry for them. (To me) She looked like a real nice girl. I have to teach my children tolerance and things like that . . . ."

## DEFINING UNPATTERNED SITUATIONS

In these situations, it appeared that the participants attempted to achieve cognitive clarity by striving to assimilate the situation to their past actual or vicarious experience, that is, to categorize it as one of a type of situation with which they knew how to cope. The process, of course, was rarely as rational or as purposive as this formulation would imply. Yet the behavior manifested in these situations can be interpreted as an attempt to see a socially unstructured situation in terms of one or possibly even of several alternative socially acceptable structures. For example, in the illustration above, the bartender and waitress perceived the situation as one that could be categorized in either of two ways:

1. Here are two Negro out-of-towners who do not realize they are not welcome here.
2. Here are a couple of troublemakers who are trying to create another Peekskill riot here.

The importance of being able to categorize the situation is suggested by their dilemma. If the situation were the first type, they could expect the Negroes to leave when asked politely. If the situation were the second type, they could expect resistance to such a request–the Negroes might cause an immediate disturbance, "come back with their gang," or file suit for violation of the State Civil Rights Statute.

In this example two reasonably clear-cut alternative definitions of the situation were possible. At the extreme, even this degree of structure was missing. Here participants reacted by confusion: either the situation was so totally outside the range of their experience, or it partook of so wide a variety of possible definitions, that these participants were initially unable to see any structure to the situation at all.

It seems useful to distinguish these two possible reactions to an unpatterned situation. In one, the individual is confused about what behavior to expect from others and what is appropriate action to take himself. In the other, he has reasonably definite, but contradictory, expectations of how others will act and how he himself should act. These two types of reaction differ in degree only, and it is difficult to distinguish them in some concrete situations. Nevertheless, the distinction is useful because the probable future actions of the person whose orientation is primarily marked by *confusion* are different from the probable future actions of the person whose orientation is primarily marked by *contradiction*.[3]

In the situations studied, the participants who were primarily *confused* actively sought cues from others' behavior that could be useful in clarifying their own definitions of the situation. Where formal leadership roles existed, other participants turned to the presumed leaders for clarification. Members of organizations almost invariably took their cues from the presiding officers–if the club president greeted a Negro lecturer warmly, the members were likely to listen to his speech attentively. Similarly, waitresses and bartenders studied the reactions of owners and managers for hints as to whether or not service to Negro patrons was in order.

But in the nature of the case it most often happened that the people in leadership positions were themselves confused; for them the situation was not structured enough even to suggest where to turn for clarification. In consequence, action on the part of *any* participant became disproportionately important in determining their definitions. Expressions of discomfiture on the part of *any* customer were taken as an index that "the customers" objected to the presence of Negroes. Direct intervention on the part of a customer almost invariably proved decisive. If any white undertook to act as intermediary for a Negro patron, by ordering a drink for him, or buying him a drink, the bartender served the Negro. Even if the white were a disheveled drunk with a friendliness born of liquor, the bartender was likely to take his action as an index that the customers did not object to his serving Negroes. The possibility that the drunk's attitudes were atypical of the attitudes of other customers was for the moment ignored.

Initial behavioral cues, of course, could be variously interpreted. The cues themselves were often ambiguous, allowing of several alternative interpretations even to similarly-situated persons. Furthermore, some persons seemed to be more sensitive to nuances of behavior than were others, for reasons that did not seem related to their roles in the situation. However, the most important factor in how participants interpreted behavioral cues appeared rather clearly to

[3] We are at the moment concerned only with situations where the individual participants are initially unable to achieve consistent workable definitions of the situation. Situations where two or more participants have *different* definitions of the situation will be considered later. In this latter case each participant has a consistent definition, and the problem is how definitions are *modified*, rather than how unstructured situations become defined.

be their prestige-status in the situation. Negro participants were typically far less secure in these situations than were whites. They were more likely to be sensitive to minimal cues, and to interpret cues as indices of prejudice or lack of prejudice. A casual reference by a white to "you people" was frequently taken by Negro participants as an indication that the white was categorizing them as Negroes, and was therefore prejudiced. The white would have no idea that his statement—often made in the form of a testimonial meant to communicate good will—was so interpreted.

Finally, in some situations there were almost literally no appropriate behavioral cues to guide the confused participant. A white woman who taught a theatrical make-up class was thrown into a flurry of aimless excitement for almost ten minutes when a Negro girl who unexpectedly attended the practice session of her class asked her for an appropriate shade of face powder. She knew which shade would be best, but she had no idea of how to react to having a Negro girl attend the class. The reactions of the other members of the class did not help to resolve her confusion, and there were no other adults present. The consequence was that she persisted in her confusion for several minutes.

These interpretations apply only when the impediment to a satisfactory definition of the situation is confusion or ambiguity. Where the problem is that two alternative definitions are applicable to the situation (i.e., where the problem is one of *contradiction* or *conflict*), different behavioral consequences ensue. Usually, in such situations, it is possible to resolve the conflict by *exempting* the particular situation from all but one definition—in effect, by assigning one definition of the situation a higher priority than that accorded to the others. Two forms of exemption were apparent in the observed situations:

1. A particular *type of event* can be exempted from a more general definition: for example, a restaurant-owner, who in other contexts does not discriminate against Negroes, does discriminate against them in his restaurant because he feels that "business" takes precedence over other values.
2. A particular *individual* can be exempted in a range of situations: for example, a white treats a particular Negro as "different from other Negroes" and therefore acceptable in contexts where other Negroes would be unwelcome. One bar-owner served former high school classmates, although he refused to serve other Negroes.[4]

On occasion, however, neither of the alternative definitions can be avoided—the situation constrains the participants to act on the basis of both definitions simultaneously. For example, at a dinner-meeting tendered to party workers of a major political party, many of the white participants wished to avoid eating with the Negro party-workers, but at the same time did not wish to rebuff them and risk losing Negro votes. Their common mode of behavior was to act in a friendly fashion toward these Negroes, but not to sit at the same tables with them. When all other tables were fully occupied, some of the whites waited for new tables to be set up, rather than sitting at tables already partly occupied by Negroes. This we interpret to be a common mode of behavior by which the whites attempted to act in partial conformity to both definitions of the situation—the definition that this was a solidary group of party members, and the definition that this was an inter-racial situation. They had to eat at tables adjoining the tables at which Negroes were seated, but they did not have to eat with Negroes. Although they rebuffed these Negroes, they did not entirely alienate them. It appears that when an individual is constrained to act on the basis of two or more mutually incompatible definitions of the situation, he will seek a compromise solution by which he deviates as little as possible from the action appropriate to each of these definitions.

Finally, there are situations in which the alternative definitions cannot be reconciled. For example, the dilemma of the bartender who does not know whether or not to serve Negroes and feels: if I serve them, the white customers will object; if I don't, they may create a disturbance. In such a situation, the typical response is withdrawal from the situation, as when the bartender "looks the other way" or the prejudiced club-member leaves upon discovering that the lecturer of the evening is Negro. But withdrawal is not always possible. The bartender may "look the other way" when a Negro patron enters, but he can-

[4] Calling this behavior exemption does not necessarily mean that the bar-owner perceived his action as making an exception of these particular Negroes; he might have seen it simply as serving friends. Nevertheless the *effect* of his action is exemption, whether he consciously perceives it that way or not, because from the observer's point of view he is acting differently from the way he would act toward other Negroes.

not continue to do so when the Negro walks up to the bar directly in front of him. Then the result is usually an inconsistent series of actions, marked by a good deal of wavering. The bartender may begin to serve the Negro quite cordially, then appears to be unwilling to serve the Negro, then once again is quite cordial. If an observer asks him about it, he will be quite frank in stating that he feels impelled first towards one course of behavior, then towards the other. This inconsistent behavior may perseverate for an extraordinarily long time, until the individual is finally able (often for apparently irrelevant reasons) to give one or the other definition a higher priority.

## MODIFICATION OF DEFINITIONS

Although these covertly-initiated situations enabled us to study the processes by which unpatterned situations are initially defined, they did not provide adequate data on the processes by which initial definitions are modified in interaction. The very conditions required for initiating unpatterned situations precluded our continued observation once the single event had transpired. To study the processes of change, it was necessary to find naturally-occurring situations, or series of situations, in which changes of definition were taking place. We wanted to be able to observe a group of people engaged in a continuing series of situations; to interview these people at regular intervals, in order to elicit their interpretations of each situation; and to secure data about their behavior in past situations that might prove useful in interpreting their present behavior. Our procedure was to search for a group that had formed in response to a particular problem in which all were interested. We found the group we sought engaged in a rather dramatic endeavor—a civil rights law suit.

Two Negro men had been refused service in a country tavern, in the presence of Negro waiters. The men left the tavern quietly in spite of the fact that one of the waiters quit his job in protest. Two days later, the wife of one of these men telephoned the president of the local chapter of the National Association for the Advancement of Colored People, who in turn suggested that the men re-visit the tavern in the company of the executive committee of the NAACP chapter.[5] A first visit was, from their point of view, ineffectual: the proprietor was absent, and his son equivocated. A second trip found the proprietor prepared. After protesting his own lack of prejudice, he argued that he could not risk a boycott by white customers. When this argument fell on unresponsive ears—the NAACP president waved a copy of the State Anti-Discrimination Statute in his face—he argued that he didn't care what the law said, he simply was not going to serve Negroes. Then ensued a long debate on whether or not minority groups should insist on service where they were not wanted, ending in an impasse.

The NAACP leaders attempted, without success, to interest the local district attorney in taking court action. Then, with tacit approval by the prospective plaintiffs, they established contact with the state NAACP legal department. Initial plans for court action were made, followed by a delay of several months before the case was tried. The period of quiessence was marked by the plaintiffs' loss of interest in the case.

The weekend preceding the case brought feverish activity on the part of the NAACP lawyer and two members of the executive committee, first in questioning witnesses, and later in detailed "cross-examination" of one waiter who reported that he would testify for the defense. Other members of the executive committee, the second waiter, and another participant-observer were brought in during the last stages of this examination—at a time of open conflict, with the lawyer and NAACP president accusing the dissident waiter of "selling out the race." The incident ended in excited denunciation of the "turncoat" by the waiter who had quit his job in protest against discrimination.

To this point, the plaintiffs had not participated. They, and their wives, joined the group at a meeting that evening, called to plan strategy for the trial. The first order of business was a dramatic account of the afternoon's activities. Then the lawyer interrupted abruptly to ask for his clients' minimum demands. He added that cash settlements generally weren't very high in this type of case. The plaintiffs said nothing. But the president jumped in to aver that "these men aren't in this for cash. They're in it for the principle of the thing!" He paid tribute to "men who have the guts to stick it out." A member of the executive committee spoke about the effects that this case would have on the Negro community generally. Others spoke *for* the plaintiffs. One asked that the men be given a chance to speak for themselves—but he too congratulated them "for having the courage to go through with the case *for the principle of it!*"

[5] Robert B. Johnson, a member of the Cornell research staff, attended these conferences in his role as a member of the NAACP executive committee. Johnson, and others of us who were involved in later situations, filled out detailed research reports after each period of observation.

The lawyer asked the plaintiffs directly: "How do you feel about this?" A long silence. Then one plaintiff answered. He said that he and his friend were fighting for the good of the race. He said that he hoped this action would benefit the Negro community as a whole. He said that he believed in *action* to improve the position of Negroes. He added that he was a poor man.

At once the president exclaimed that he too was a poor man, but that even if it meant losing his job, he would stick it through. There was no further ambiguity about money. The lawyer congratulated the plaintiffs for not seeking monetary retribution, and then asked the group as a whole for a statement of minimal demands. Almost all members of the group spoke up now, including the heretofore-silent plaintiffs and their wives. All agreed to a policy enunciated by the president: the demands were to be a full public apology, together with a statement by the proprietor that he would not discriminate in the future.

Succeeding events need not be described in detail here. The defendant, upon pressure from the judge, settled the case in court on the plaintiffs' terms.

For present purposes, the most striking aspect of this series of events was the radical change in the behavior of the plaintiffs. Their behavior in the discriminatory situation had been passive; upon their return to the community they did nothing to institute action against the bar-owner. Personality studies of the two men, based on detailed life history data, indicate that this passive acceptance of the intergroup relations status-quo was entirely in keeping with their behavior in other situations. In fact, they had but a few weeks before this incident predicted (in response to a questionnaire-interview administered to a cross-section of the Negro community) that in such a situation they would leave the establishment without saying anything, and take no further action. Yet in the course of these situations the positive or negative evaluation of their behavior by a militant group of Negro leaders became important to their own evaluations of their behavior; their self-conceptions changed to those of "race men," or fighters for the good of the Negro community; their definitions of the discriminatory incident and of their own subsequent behavior were enlarged to include an evaluation of how these actions affected other Negroes in the city; and their passive behavior was transformed into militancy.

In broadest outline, this change can be viewed as the consequence of a long series of successive redefinitions of the situations in which they participated. When the bartender refused to serve them, they quickly developed an initial definition on the basis of which they hurriedly left the tavern. Their definition of this original situation held important consequences for their behavior in subsequent situations. Although each of these, too, contained idiosyncratic elements, there was a significant degree of continuity in their definitions of succeeding situations. The plaintiffs did not define each situation anew, solely on the basis of its idiosyncratic elements, but developed their definitions of particular situations from their definitions of preceding situations. It was as if they tried on their previous definitions for fit, modified them to meet the exigencies of the present, then modified them anew as these exigencies changed. Since new elements entered these situations almost continuously, this process never ceased. In the end, a revolution in definition and in behavior had been produced. But seen as a step-by-step process, this "revolution" was never more than a minor change in a preceding definition, with its appropriate behavioral consequences.[6]

The most readily apparent change in the plaintiffs' orientation was their coming to depend upon the NAACP leaders as referents.[7] But why did the NAACP come to play this role?

It would seem that the plaintiffs must have been predisposed, at least to a limited degree, to see the NAACP definition of the situation as legitimate—even if not the only legitimate definition. It seems further that they must have felt constrained to co-operate with the NAACP leaders, provided that this did not entail

[6] On the basis of one case study, we certainly cannot generalize that this is always the process. One observation can, however, be made: in none of the situations studied (either in this series, or in the situations we initiated for our study of unpatterned situations) did direct and overt conflict bring about a change of definition. Wherever two participants with opposing definitions attempted to argue each other into changing their definitions, an impasse resulted. In fact, overt conflict served only to strengthen the participants' commitment to their original positions. Of course, a participant was on occasion forced to accede to another's demands; but this brought no lasting change in definition, merely resentful compliance.

[7] For purposes of analysis and prediction, it is not necessary that the individual actor be aware of the role his referents play in defining the situation. "Reference group" may be used as an intervening variable in situational analysis if this provides a more adequate explanation of behavior than do alternative methods of analysis. (We may posit that an individual acts *as if* he used certain referents in defining the situation.) In the present research, however, this was not necessary: the plaintiffs came to be very much aware of the major role played by the NAACP leaders in their definitions of the situations.

a major commitment of time. Otherwise, the president could not have prevailed on them to participate even to the extent of a discussion with the tavern proprietor. Once they were involved in the NAACP activities, several factors conspired to commit them more and more firmly to the NAACP group: the NAACP leaders could and did shame them by holding out the threat that they would be regarded by the community as "quitters"; at the same time, these leaders were able to argue the logic of their philosophy, and to demonstrate by their own action how their philosophy worked in practice; continued group enterprise brought the emotional satisfactions of group *esprit de corps* and of participation in "something important"; finally the plaintiffs' behavior brought approbation from some other members of the Negro community.

At the same time, other pressures generated by the situations served to bring the plaintiffs' definitions into harmony with that of the NAACP leaders. Perhaps the most important event here was the "cross-examination" of the dissident waiter. The NAACP leaders could not have asked for a more compelling demonstration that the point at issue was a moral principle, with all other considerations irrelevant. A clear dichotomy was drawn between those who "sell out the race" and those who "fight for the race." If the dissident waiter stood as the symbol of selling out, his courageous colleague embodied the virtues of the man of principle. In the face of his sacrifice of his job, who could undertake to do less?

Even then, the plaintiffs were not fully committed. Interviews with the major participants indicate that the men hoped to be able to fight for the race and exact some monetary retribution as well. But this was exactly what the NAACP leaders wished to avoid; they did not want it said that the case was merely a matter of Negroes "trying to con a white man out of his money." It had to be a matter of principle, and principle alone! Here the introduction of new information enabled the plaintiffs to redefine the situation: if cash awards were generally not very high in these cases, it was considerably easier to forego the possibility of a windfall. Even so, foregoing cash was not easy. It took some time for a plaintiff to make the offer, and even then his offer was hardly forthright. His statement did, however, allow of slight reinterpretation; once this occurred, the men were hardly in a position to back-track.

For the plaintiffs, acceptance of the NAACP position brought a change in self-conception: they now thought of themselves as "race men." It also brought a rewriting of history, to bring all past events into line with their present definition. If you ask them now, they will tell you that their orientation has not changed. They are, and always have been, militant. From the very beginning, their one interest has been to fight discrimination. That is why they were so quick to bring the NAACP into the case.

In spite of this, their change in self-conception has not been productive of other militant action. Although they may continue to think of themselves as "race men," and although they may behave like "race men" in any future situation in which they are directly refused service, they have given no evidence that they are likely to carry out the logical implications of the "race man" role and engage in a wider range of interracial activities on behalf of the Negro community. Stated otherwise, it would appear that an individual who uses a particular reference group in defining a particular type of situation will not necessarily use that reference group in defining other types of situations. This is perfectly consistent with the general observation that people do not necessarily behave consistently in different types of situations.

## SUMMARY

We have in this report endeavored to interpret the processes by which participants define unpatterned intergroup situations, and the processes by which definitions are in turn modified over the course of time. We recognize that the research has been conducted within a very limited range of institutional contexts; we further recognize that the social constraints operating within other contexts may be quite different. Nevertheless, we believe it likely that the present interpretation is applicable to situations arising in other social contexts; for that reason, we present this summary in the form of hypotheses amenable to testing in a broad range of institutional contexts.

### 1. Unpatterned Situations

*Ambiguous or confused definitions* When an individual is constrained to act but feels that he cannot predict the consequences of his own or other participants' behavior, his response to the situation will be to seek cues from other participants' behavior that can be used as indices of their definition of the situation. Where he can turn to persons in formal leadership roles, he will do so; but where this is not possible, the behavior of *any* other participant will be utilized as an index of how "other participants" define the situation. Where there are no appropriate behavioral cues available, the confused participant will tend to perseverate in his confusion until new action intervenes to structure the situation.

*Contradiction or conflict of definition* When an individual is constrained to act but feels that two or more distinct definitions (each with its appropriate behavioral imperatives) are applicable to the situation, he will first attempt to resolve the conflict by exemption, i.e., by assigning one definition a higher priority than that accorded to others. (This can be done either by exempting a particular type of event or a particular person from a more general definition.) Where this is not possible, he will attempt to achieve a compromise solution by which he can act in partial conformity to both (or all) definitions of the situation. When even this is not possible, he will seek to withdraw from the situation, unless otherwise constrained. If constrained, he will behave inconsistently, wavering between the two alternative definitions, until new action intervenes to structure the situation.

**2. Modification of Definitions** Direct, overt interpersonal conflict is not likely to change either party's definition of the situation; its principal effect is likely to be the reinforcement of each combatant's values. Major changes of definition are more likely to be the result of a series of minor redefinitions, each dependent upon one or more of the following:

*Changed referents* When an individual's experience in a situation (or in a series of situations) leads to the reinforcement of particular reference groups, or to the internalization of new reference groups, his ideas of how he should act in the situation will be modified to conform to his modified self-conception.

*Expectations of consequences* When an individual's experience in a situation (or in a series of situations) leads to modification of his expectations of the consequences of his behavior, his ideas of how he should act in the situation will be modified to meet his new expectations of these consequences.

Similarly, when an individual's experience in a situation (or in a series of situations) leads to the modification of his expectations of how other participants will behave, his ideas of how he should act in the situation will be modified to meet his new expectations of their behavior.

# SHARED PATTERNS OF NONVERBAL NORMATIVE EXPECTATIONS IN AUTOMOBILE DRIVING[1]

RONALD E. SHOR
*Laboratory of Social Relations, Harvard University; and Brandeis University*

## A. PURPOSE

The multiple spheres of competence which the automobile driver must keep cognitively mobilized while driving may, for descriptive convenience, be classified as four general skills: (a) a working knowledge of legal rules, (b) mechanical control of the vehicle, (c) competence in judging physical interplays of objects in relative motion, and (d) working knowledge of how to interpret the locomotive intentions of other drivers and how to communicate one's intentions in return.

The present brief discussion is limited in scope to the fourth of these general skills—the nonverbal communication of relative intentions—which has heretofore received little attention in the scientific literature on automobile driving. The first three skills have been discussed in detail in many other publications (e.g., 1, 2, 4, 5, 6, 7, 8, 9). The best theoretical treatment of the third general skill has been made using a Lewinian field-analytic point of view by Gibson and Crooks (3); also relevant is the discussion by Van Lennep (10).

## B. MUTUALLY UNDERSTOOD PATTERNS OF EXPECTATIONS

Wherever humans interact in patterned activities, normative conventions develop to serve various social functions. Sometimes social norms are codified into abstruse laws; sometimes they are so embedded in immediate cultural functioning that they remain mostly unverbalized. In automobile driving, mutually understood patterns of social expectations (norms) develop out of the realities of the driving situation. While always in flux, these shared expectations serve as the basis for the nonverbal communication of relative intentions among drivers.

Given a set of mutually understood normative meanings, the slightest movements of a car in relation to the total ongoing driving situation may convey vital information of a driver's intentions, which otherwise would be meaningless. In the specific, concrete driving situation, only a few lines of rational possibility are open, and these are so rigidly overdetermined by the complex interdependency of factors that the slightest cue given at the crucial instant may convey the intentions of a complex chain of events. Usually, however, the cues (signals) are multiple. The following example illustrates concretely how drivers' relative intentions are communicated.

Two drivers, A and B, are approaching each other from opposite directions along a city thoroughfare, both at moderate speed (see [Figure 9-9]). The two cars are about one-half block apart. Driver A is closer to an intervening intersection than is driver B, and driver A wishes to turn

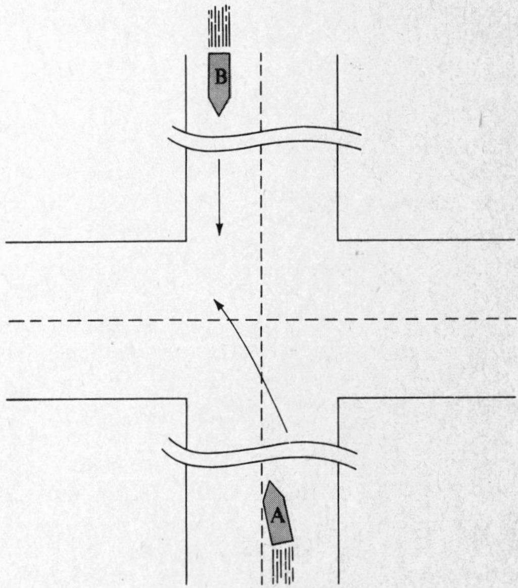


[FIGURE 9-9] Schematic representation of the initial situation in the interplay of how driver A communicates his intention to turn left and how driver B then communicates his consent. (A's veer to the left is deliberately exaggerated in the diagram.)

[1] This work was supported in part by grants from the Institute for Experimental Psychiatry and the Society for the Investigation of Human Ecology. I wish to thank my colleagues, Martin T. Orne, Donald N. O'Connell, Emily Carota Orne, and Esther C. Damaser, for their critical comments and editorial assistance in the preparation of this manuscript.

left at this intersection. To communicate his intention to turn, driver A signals by veering his car slightly to the left. But after the signal is given, driver B maintains his speed and direction so that driver A is not sure whether B will consent to A's proceeding first. Driver A thus slows down a little more than he would merely to make the turn, half-preparing to stop, but not enough to signal B that he definitely will stop. Driver B perceives A's signals of hesitation and, since B is quite willing to let A proceed first, B slows down *just enough* and veers to his left *just enough* to inform A to make his turn. Driver A immediately interprets B's actions, ceases hesitating, and confidently makes his turn as B travels by on A's right.

## C. CONFUSIONS WHEN NORMATIVE EXPECTATIONS ARE NOT SHARED

Different social norms of driving may emerge as dominant in given areas at given times. Confusions result when normative expectations are not shared. Indeed, the functional properties of the driving norms, otherwise taken for granted, are seen most clearly when observed in conflict. The following extended example illustrates the interactions of two partially disparate sets of normative systems.

## D. EXTENDED EXAMPLE OF NORMATIVE SYSTEM INTERACTIONS

In urban, congested Boston, Massachusetts, highly competitive norms of driving behavior have emerged in which every driver is expected to remain acutely aware of the positions and intentions of everyone else. In rural, uncongested Lawrence, Kansas, more leisurely and courteous driving patterns have emerged in which less acute attention need be given to the positions and intentions of other drivers.

The unwritten driving norms in congested Boston require and expect that every driver will take every reasonable advantage for himself. The unwritten driving norms in uncongested Lawrence require and expect that every driver will first show courtesy to others before taking his own advantage. Boston drivers *must* act competitively in order to communicate proper signals of their intentions to other Boston drivers. The mutually understood driving patterns in rural Lawrence, on the other hand, insist on courtesy to others first—since drivers in Lawrence cannot be at all sure that other drivers are fully alert to relative positions and intentions. Both systems work efficiently for their respective traffic conditions. In urban Boston less effort is required in the long run when everyone acts competitively. In rural Lawrence less effort is required in the long run when everyone acts courteously. Although trouble arises for both functional systems when expectations clash, each functional system is

1. The stop-sign situation

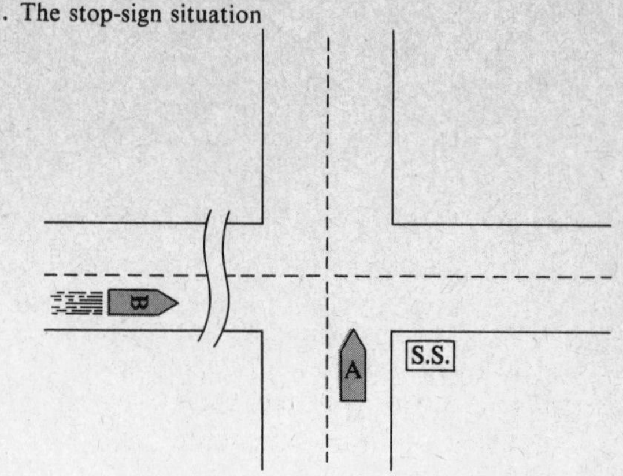


2. The entering heavy traffic situation

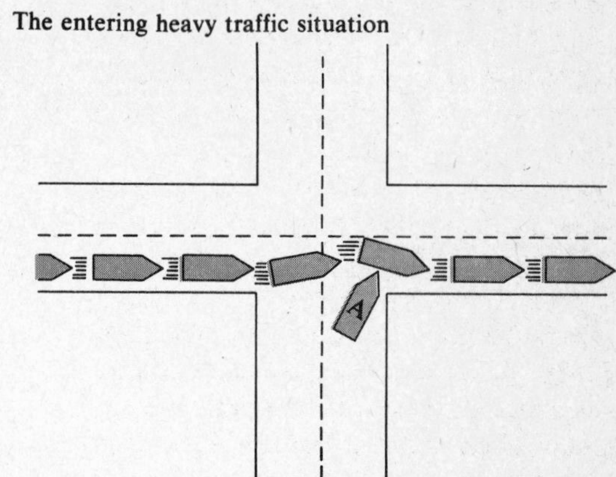


[FIGURE 9-10] Schematic representation of the two illustrative traffic situations.

self-consistent. The Bostonian in Lawrence or the Lawrencian in Boston is a source of confusion because normative expectations are in disarray.

The divergence between the norms in urban Boston and rural Lawrence is illustrated further by tracing the functional consequences of the disparate norms in a few common traffic situations.[2]

The two traffic situations illustrated are I. The Stop-Sign Situation, and II. The Entering Heavy Traffic Situation. These two illustrative traffic situations are schematically represented in [Figure 9-10].

Illustration I.: The Stop-Sign Situation. Driver A has just made a complete stop at a stop-sign preparatory to entering a highway. Driver B is driving along the highway which A wishes to enter. B is rapidly approaching the intersection where A is stopped, but B is still a modest distance away.

---

[2] Many of these relationships would appear, moreover, to lend themselves to rigorous, quantitative field-observation with minimum apparatus such as a stopwatch and a motion-picture camera.

[TABLE 9-5] Fourfold table

| | | Driver B | |
|---|---|---|---|
| | | Bostonian | Lawrencian |
| Driver A | Bostonian | 1 | 3 |
| | Lawrencian | 4 | 2 |

Since both drivers, A and B, may either be Boston or Lawrence drivers, a fourfold table [Table 9-5] depicts the four basic permutations of their interaction in this particular situation. These four permutations are discussed separately below.

1. Both A and B are Boston drivers. If B is far enough away, driver A will immediately try to start moving again and get far enough into the intersection to communicate to B that he, A, has the competitive advantage in the situation and, thus, that B is required to stop. Driver A expects without thinking about it that other (Boston) drivers will expect him to engage in just this kind of competitive maneuver. Driver A expects also that these other drivers will attempt by various subtle cues and signals to prevent his acquisition of the advantage if they feel they have the greater competitive strength. If such cues and signals are forthcoming, A may either reassert his prerogative or relinquish his claim and allow B to proceed first. If an immediate satisfactory competitive adjustment by both cannot be worked out on this "automatic" level of orderly nonverbal communication, then both drivers, in their mutual confusion, will slow down, and they will then have to bring a more conscious and deliberate appraisal of the situation into play. The typical Boston driver has no intention to be *overly* competitive. His motive for engaging in the competitive interplay is to comprehend and react to the ongoing events in as "automatic" a manner as possible. Competition is a workable system when everyone shares its rules: it takes a minimal amount of mental effort, leads to little confusion, and is relatively safe and efficient.

2. Both A and B are Lawrence drivers. Again an efficient, relatively safe system can be observed. Driver A, stopped at the stop-sign, holds the expectation that he must wait at the stop-sign for closely approaching drivers to pass before he even begins to try to enter the intersection. The idea that he, A, might try to assert a competitive prerogative over other drivers appears to him irresponsible. Other Lawrence drivers fully share this expectation of considerateness. Since driver B is also Lawrence driver, without reflection he understands that A certainly must intend to wait and, consequently, B maintains his speed. But if B is far away, both A and B will interpret the situation as one in which B should stop. Thus, A will begin to move into the intersection. Driver A need not hurry, since, by the preexisting rules, he already knows B must intend to stop.

3. Driver A is a Boston driver; B is a Lawrence driver. B is traveling peaceably along the throughway, convinced of his right-of-way. B then sees A, the Boston driver, at first hurriedly stop at the stop-sign, and then, just as hurriedly, dash out into the throughway. Driver A, on the other hand, has clearly signalled to B his greater competitive strength, and A is thus disconcerted to see B keep on coming. Both parties are confused, both feel they have behaved correctly, and both believe the other driver is behaving inappropriately.

4. Driver A is a Lawrence driver; B is a Boston driver. If B is close enough, A simply waits for him to pass. If B is far enough away, A assumes that B intends to stop, and thus A proceeds to enter the intersection. If A enters confidently, B will stop; if A is slow or hesitant, B may interpret A's indecisiveness as a signal for seeking and giving further information of intentions through competitive interaction. B may consequently "automatically" speed up slightly or veer a trifle to the left to try to communicate to A his relative competitive strength. Since A will probably misinterpret these subtle communications, confusion generally results.

**Illustration II.: The Entering Heavy Traffic Situation. An unending line of traffic is moving along a main thoroughfare. On a side street, leading into the thoroughfare, is a car driven by A. Driver A wishes to enter the line of traffic.**

A parallel set of four permutations of Boston or Lawrence norms may be described.

1. Driver A is a Bostonian in Boston. Driver A will slowly creep out into the thoroughfare as each car passes until someone is forced to let him enter. Before A is finally allowed to enter, however, he causes himself to become more and more of an obstacle to the advancing line of traffic. On account of A, the advancing line of traffic is consequently forced to slow down and veer further out to the center of the roadway to pass. Eventually, A becomes so much of an obstacle in the advancing line of traffic, and it has slowed down so much anyway, that someone finds it easier to allow A to enter rather than to pass him by. Driver A must carefully time the process so as to take as much competitive advantage as possible with each passing car, and yet not to move out so fast as to create a danger.

2. Driver A is a Lawrencian in Boston. Driver A is at a disadvantage because unending lines of traffic are such an uncommon occurrence in his rural location that his normative expectations are ill-equipped to deal with them efficiently. The Lawrence driver in Boston is overwhelmed by the unending line of traffic, and when no driver shows him the least courtesy he feels indignant at the selfishness. When, inevitably, a reasonably large opening does present itself, the Lawrence driver expects that other drivers will finally have to allot him the right-of-way, and are thus preparing to stop. Boston drivers, however, share no such expectations; in Boston, right-of-way is achieved competitively. Armed with his erroneous expectation, the Lawrence driver either moves leisurely into the intersection or dashes quickly out into the opening. If the Lawrence driver moves into the intersection leisurely, he finds the next car advancing toward him with undiminished speed and trying to cut off his progress. If, on the other hand, the Lawrence driver dashes quickly out into the intersection, the approaching Boston driver is suddenly confronted with a dangerous, unexpected obstacle. In Lawrence, the opening between cars is itself a mutually understood signal to let the waiting car enter; in Boston, it means no such thing.

When the unending traffic situation does occur (rarely) in Lawrence, we again find confusions only when driving norms clash.

3. Driver A is a Lawrence driver in Lawrence. Driver A just waits patiently at the intersection until, shortly, someone courteously allows him to enter.

4. Driver A is a Boston driver in Lawrence. Driver A's competitive scramble calls forth emergency reactions in the Lawrence drivers, and A's behavior is interpreted as gross rudeness.

## E. HOW THE NEW DRIVER LEARNS THE NORMS

The new automobile driver learns the social norms through example, in the process of actual interplays with other drivers. The new driver has only a dim conception at first of what to expect from, and how to communicate with, other drivers and pedestrians. The new driver's indecisiveness, however, is often expressively communicated to experienced drivers, who then appropriately readjust their expectations and behavior to allow the new driver to proceed unmolested. Occasionally, however, the new driver's lack of understanding results in a confusion serious enough to supply raw material for his slowly dawning understanding of the social norms, as is illustrated in the following example.

> Two cars enter a city rotary at the same time and speed but from different roads. Driver A, an inexperienced driver, enters on a roadway to the right of driver B, an experienced driver. Inexperienced A hesitates momentarily and experienced B "illegally," but properly, monopolizes A's legal right-of-way, to A's consternation.

Driver A knew that he had the legal right-of-way, but because of his inexperience A was somewhat hesitant in his driving behavior. Because actual driving decisions depend upon the complex of particular circumstances and signals rather than upon abstract legal rules, driver B was watching inexperienced A's movements for signals. Driver B saw A hesitating and–legal right-of-way notwithstanding–properly interpreted A's hesitation as a yielding of competitive initiative. Driver B had no wish to violate A's prerogative. B did not care who entered the rotary first, and he would have freely honored A's right-of-way had A appropriately asserted it. Provided driver B knows what driver A plans to do, it is irrelevant to B who gets the right-of-way. If, at the last moment and without sufficient signaling, inexperienced A asserts his legal right-of-way, B's failure to honor it will incorrectly seem to inexperienced A as the act of an irresponsible, selfish driver who has little regard for legal rules. In time, however, an unverbalized awareness of the true variables slowly tends to develop out of just such urgencies.

Some new drivers never become proficient in the social norms, however. As a consequence, they remain overcautious, with low official accident records, and yet are a constant source of harassment and confusion (e.g., the so-called "woman driver" of either sex). It is our suspicion that, except for the sporadic driver, these are often individuals who have hardly ever been forced to drive when fatigued or preoccupied with other considerations. Only then, would we suspect, is the new driver apt to allow his conscious deliberations to relax enough for expressive communications to register and evolve into appropriate nonverbal conceptual understandings.

## F. SUMMARY

In the scientific literature on automobile driving, little attention has been devoted to how drivers interpret nonverbally the locomotive intentions of other drivers, and how they communicate their own intentions in return. The view presented in this brief discussion is that mutually understood patterns of social expectations (norms) develop out of the realities of the driving situation. These shared expectations then serve as the basis of nonverbal communication. Examples are given of how confusions result when normative expectations are not shared, and of the process by which new drivers learn the norms.

## REFERENCES

1. **DESILVA, H. R.** *Why we have automobile accidents.* New York: Wiley, 1942.

2. **FORBES, T. W.** Procedural task factors and performance decrement in automobile driving. Paper presented at the American Psychological Association Convention, 1960.

3. **GIBSON, J. J., & CROOKS, L. E.** A theoretical field-analysis of automobile driving. *Amer. J. Psychol.*, 1938, **51**, 453-471.

4. **LAUER, A. R.** Learning to drive safely. Minneapolis: Burgess, 1949.

5. **MATSON, T. M., SMITH, W. S., & HURD, F. W.** Traffic engineering. New York: McGraw-Hill, 1955.

6. **McFARLAND, R. A.** Human variables in motor vehicle accidents. Boston: Harvard School of Public Health, 1955.

7. **PRESIDENT'S COMMITTEE FOR TRAFFIC SAFETY.** Special report on the Williamsburg conference. *Traffic Safety Res. Rev.*, 1958, **2**, 2-11.

8. **ROSS, H. L.** Schematic analysis of the driving situation. Unpublished manuscript, 1960.

9. ————. Ignorance of collision course as a factor in traffic accidents. Unpublished manuscript, 1960.

10. **VAN LENNEP, D. J.** Psychological factors in driving. *Traffic Quart.*, 1952, **6**, 483-498.

# TOWARD A SOCIOLOGY OF PUBLIC TRANSIT*

MORRIS DAVIS
*University of Illinois*

SOL LEVINE
*Johns Hopkins University*

Short trips on public transit frequently exhibit stressful sociological characteristics. Passengers tend to view the vehicles as mono-instrumental conveyances and to evince a pronounced exit-orientation; but transit arrangements rarely facilitate an equitable order in departing. Severe limits on what one can see and whom one can look at further reduce the joy of riding. The folklore of public transit reinforces its situational deficiencies. Some unusual modes of transit do escape these difficulties; in the main, though, transit riders engage in various small conflicts and in low-level, but persistent and focused, games of anticipation.

Despite the great amount of aggregate time that people in modern industrial society spend on short-run public transit, there is relatively little sociological understanding of the phenomenon or of the meaning it has for its participants. There is also no readily available theoretical framework in which to embed a transit study.[1] Longer trips such as ocean voyages and cross-country train rides are inherently more amenable to customary sociological analysis, since they rapidly embody dimensions of on-going systems and permit the transfer of social status from the encompassing society. Not only are first class and tourist accomodations generally consonant with previous status positions, but also efforts are made, often successfully, to approximate the full sweep of daily living. This is most manifest on ocean liners, where wants like dining, dancing, relaxation, and entertainment are amply provided for; but long-haul airlines, too, attempt to duplicate more familiar environments and to provide "all the benefits of home."[2] Under such circumstances behavior tends to be socially structured and governed by a repertoire of normative prescriptions. In addition, during lengthy journeys various relationships develop which further define and circumscribe interpersonal activity. These have been described closely and vividly by novelists like Somerset Maugham and Katherine Anne Porter and could themselves fruitfully be the object of sociological inquiry.

The focus of this paper, though, is on relatively brief transport situations and, correlatively, on vehicles that do not contain or make available facilities sufficient to provide a daily living environment for most passengers. Accordingly, we include intra-city and shorter inter-city buses, but exclude long distance buses which make regular stops for eating and "resting." Commuter railroad trains are also included, for although soft drinks and sandwiches may be sold on them and they may contain some minimal washroom facilities, they do not seriously provide for the bodily needs of their passengers to the extent typical of cross-country trains. Methods of vertical transport like elevators and escalators are encompassed by the public transit category; and so are planes flying short routes, especially those on shuttle service. Brief ferry rides are included, but overnight trips like those between Oslo and Copenhagen are not. In brief, the vehicle situations to be discussed constitute only short trips that would be specifically labeled public transit and not those longer ones which might come under the more generic designation of public transportation.[3]

The literature of sociology offers little guidance for understanding behavior on public transit. People in such settings can hardly be viewed as constituting social groups, for they are not in established relationships with one another and their behavior is often little dictated by their social status in the outside society. Nor can one turn to the field of collective behavior for illumination, since its focus is generally on

*This article stems from research by the first named author that was supported by U.S. Public Health Service Grant CH 00201 from the Division of Community Health Services.

[1] See Morris Davis, Robert Seibert, and Warren Breed, "Interracial Seating Patterns on New Orleans Public Transit," *Social Problems*, 13 (Winter, 1966), pp. 298-306, esp. pp. 304-5.

[2] The airlines labor under severe limitations of time and space. The emphasis in their advertising on gourmet meals, smiling attendants, and in-flight movies, however, testifies to the pattern they are trying to establish.

[3] Vehicles such as automobiles, motor scooters, and taxis have been omitted for being insufficiently "public."

dramatic and unusual events such as "riots, crazes, lynchings, panics, and revolutions."[4]

To be sure, temporary aggregations on public transit may possess a potential for developing established ties. People do meet each other on buses, trains, and shuttle flights, and there are many romantic accounts in story and song and in daily parlance attesting to how these chance meetings blossomed into more enduring liaisons. Less dramatically, repetitive trips may help persons develop meaningful acquaintances with bus drivers, streetcar conductors, and airline personnel, as well as with fellow passengers. Then too, a casual collection of riders may, under certain conditions and appropriate stimuli, be converted into an active crowd or even a raging mob. All these, however, constitute exceptional activities for public transit participants.

What one tends to observe on transit vehicles is a large number of persons in very close physical proximity, but not in social interactions save for the occasional exchange of amenities emerging out of, and required by, their close physical presence.[5] Although they act uniformly, their behavior is only slightly affected by signs or cues communicated to one another. It is governed instead more by the rhythms and requirements of the vehicles themselves. Lack of social structure is especially evident on short "local" trips, since they are characterized by frequent rearrangements and redistributions of passenger complements as riders enter and depart.

The "co-acting group" described by Doob comes closest perhaps to the kind of behavior considered in this paper. According to Doob:

> A co-acting group consists of a small number of persons who are simultaneously seeking approximately the same goal without competing or cooperating but who have an awareness of one another. Although the participants may come from the same culture and even from the same social class, they do not as a group apparently possess a body of traditions or a formal organization that regulates their behavior. Their incidental contacts are culturally prescribed but little or no co-ordination exists. Each person who is taking a written examination or waiting for a bus in the presence of others is concerned only with himself and not with his relations to the small group.[6]

But even this description would be somewhat misleading. For competition and, to a lesser degree, cooperation are salient characteristics of many transit situations. As a result, even a person "concerned only with himself" must consider at least a few of "his relations to the small group."

## EXIT ORIENTATION

Public transit is ordinarily not valued for its own sake, but is merely instrumental to the specific end of going from one place to another. Accordingly, passengers tend to be "exit-oriented." They get on to get off. The less time a trip takes, the more the vehicle tends to be viewed instrumentally, and the more its passengers, from their moment of boarding, are oriented toward leaving.

Some vehicles are so constructed that the entrance-exit process can be continuous and equitable. Thus, for escalators, the first person on is the first person off. The same tends to be true of double-ended ferries. On many vehicles, however, the physical properties of the setting work otherwise. Then, like cans on a grocery shelf, the last one on is likely to be the first one off. The last person to enter a crowded elevator has the easiest time leaving it, and the same holds for many streetcars and buses.

In vehicle situations where first on does not automatically involve eligibility to be first off, passengers must either anticipate logistical problems or experience difficulty and frustration in exiting at an appropriate time. Their intensity of exit-orientation may well seem disproportionate to the actual cost of a few seconds or minutes, even given the harried pace of modern society and the actual possibility of missing a stop or destination. But no matter, transit riders do play a continual game to avoid being foiled in their exiting maneuvers.

Consider, for example, a person waiting in a busy convention hotel for an up elevator to the fourth floor. If he boards too quickly he may be swept along to the back of the car and then have to squeeze his way out. If he delays too much, he may not get on at all or he may have to step outside momentarily on the second and third floors to let others off. Furthermore, persons boarding on the mezzanine level may upset all his advance calculations.

Or again, suppose you intend to ride only one stop on a subway train and have delayed entering until just before the door closes in order to be right by it when it next opens. The door stays open ten seconds more, though, and a dozen people are now rushing along the platform. Should you move in only to push past them a minute or two later? Or will you remain by the

---

[4] Roger Brown, *Social Psychology*, New York: Free Press, 1965, p. 709. Compare also the substantive content of Neil J. Smelser, *Theory of Collective Behavior*, New York: Free Press, 1963.

[5] The rich meanings of these exchanges have, of course, been expertly burnished in the writings of Erving Goffman.

[6] Leonard W. Doob, *Social Psychology*, New York: Holt, 1952, p. 195.

door, perhaps turning sideways, and let *them* shove past?

Because of their extreme exit orientation, passengers on public transit are exceedingly eager to leave a vehicle at the earliest feasible moment. They frequently begin the exiting process before that moment has arrived. Derring-do may sometimes be implicated, as in jumping off a London omnibus before it has fully stopped. Technical difficulties also may have an effect; for unless one moves to a tactically advantageous position on a subway car before it stops, those rushing on board may make exiting nearly impossible. Many instances, however, could be cited that are explainable only in terms of sheer exit-orientation.

An airplane has just landed and the stewardess asks everyone to remain seated until it has come to a complete stop at the ramp. Her words are scarcely heeded. Passengers begin standing, pulling clothes down from overhead racks, and gathering up small bundles. As they struggle into their coats, they move forward quickly to prevent anyone further back from getting ahead of them in the line. Since the steps have not yet been wheeled into position, people continue to stand, packages in their arms and heavy coats on, in a rapidly warming craft for three, four, five minutes. Finally, the door opens and the lead passengers now scurry to the baggage claim section where they will again wait.[7]

Although exiting from a transit situation may mean simply leaving a vehicle–e.g., getting off a bus or trolley–often one does not feel he has truly departed until he has passed through a number of ancillary settings and reestablished some sort of symbolic contact with the outside world. A commuter pushes off a train at Pennsylvania Station, crowds along a dark platform, elbows his way up a narrow stairway, and strides across the concourse. He stops at a telephone booth to make a call. Only then perhaps does he feel that he has truly left the transit setting. Similarly, many passengers feel they complete their airline flight not on landing but on receiving their luggage; and not until they have passed through all the outbuildings and gangways of the ferry slip have most riders finished that journey either. This attitude may help explain the impatience and uneasiness that people exhibit during even quite short delays at terminals.

[7]If our view is correct, the major advantage in the newer high-level, telescoping exits at airports is not that they protect passengers from the elements–a breath of fresh air is not necessarily all that unpleasant–or even that they eliminate clambering down steps, but that they permit more rapid egress and so obviate much purposeless cuing.

## LIMITS ON DIVERSIONS

Public transit ordinarily provides its passengers with a paucity of things to do. Often they have nothing, or almost nothing, to view outside, while inside they are frequently inhibited from looking too closely or obviously at their fellow passengers. The diversionary dearth tends to be greatest on relatively short trips.

Consider an elevator in an office building. There is virtually nothing to read except a little card about weight limits and speed, and there is little to look at except a succession of lighted numbers and a door opening and closing. One cannot talk to strangers or even hide behind a newspaper. One simply stands there, facing front like everyone else. A ride of a minute or two is certainly tolerable; a ride of an hour under such circumstances would be distinctly unpleasant.

A subway train offers more variety. There are facilities for sitting as well as standing. Papers are read. A succession of light bulbs studs the tunnel walls. Subway ad cards offer oases of visual interest. Stations flash by. Riders depart and are replaced by newcomers. An elevated train, whatever its deleterious effect on neighborhoods, provides even more to see and, because of reduced noise, a greater opportunity for talk among acquaintances.

In general one can look at inanimate objects within a transit vehicle–advertisements, newspapers, station listings, the floor–and any items, inanimate or not, outside it, so long as they are not assimilated to an internal status. Passengers in one train, for example, can look at passengers in another as it goes by in the opposite direction. But should both trains stop, the staring becomes progressively more uncomfortable and tends to be extinguished. Two trains, let us say, are stopped on adjacent tracks in Union Station. Some small children in one train have fixed their gaze on two occupants of the dining car in the other. The couple glares back in annoyance. The parents then try to distract the children with candy and a magazine. The longer the cars remain side by side, the more awkward the situation becomes.

Similar reasons explain the more pleasant ambiance of escalators in department stores. Since the machinery often criss-crosses as it goes from floor to floor, the up and down ramps forming an "x" pattern, vistas may suddenly open, with passengers gliding upward able to see, and be seen by, those moving downward. Many glances occur between the two streams. Their tone is gentle and mildly curious, as if the participants were watching a series of mannikins gradually slipping by. One can safely gaze and be gazed upon, for by definition the two arrays are separate, outside each other's immediate vehicle space, and unlikely ever to meet.

Passengers on public transit may be likened to an audience at a theater in which no play is ever given. Sometimes, as in an elevator, it is like an audience before a proscenium arch; other times, as in a train or bus, it is more like one in the round. Since there is nothing much to see or hear, people fasten on the color of the curtain and the placement of spotlights or they look at a printed program. If they have arrived in small clusters, they may retreat into dyadic and triadic conversations, rarely anything larger, and so make the waiting more endurable. Even that solace is rather limited since dyads often become inhibited in this setting; and besides, it is often difficult to hear what is said.

## IMAGERY, NEGATIVE AND POSITIVE

The mono-instrumental character of most public transit, revealed in its dearth of diversions and its exit orientation, is reinforced by a folklore that is almost wholly negative and by interactive patterns with a potential for compounding awkwardness. In the folklore passengers are packed in like sardines; the ride is slow and dirty and exhausting; the vehicles are places of crime and hooliganism. Improbable disasters also seem to weigh heavily on many persons' minds. The elevator may plummet to the ground; the train may break down under the East River; the airplane engine is going to fall off.

Even a "safe" vehicle, though, may present irritating problems. If you do not stay alert, you will miss your stop. Someone unpleasant—a tough juvenile or a fat lady—will choose an adjacent seat. You will not be able to find any change, will offer a large bill to the bus driver, and besides his insults, will have delayed a long line of impatient people. During the rush hour a pregnant woman laden with bundles will choose to strap-hang nearby. A group of school kids will get on the train and begin talking loudly and horsing around.

Expectations and behavior depart from these patterns, however, on those exceptional public transit vehicles that are not chiefly instrumental and whose passengers do not deem exiting of paramount concern. The more pleasurable or thrilling a ride is in itself, the more frequently participant interactions tend to occur and the more commonly riders focus on the process and not on the conclusion of their journey. Unusual sorts of public transit—the ascenseur to the top of Montmartre, the inclined railway in Chattanooga, the aerial tramways between Switzerland and Italy, the cable cars in San Francisco—have a particularly enjoyable character to them.[8] Some regular passengers may become blasé and bored, but they are usually outnumbered by enthusiastic tourists and sojourners. Furthermore, since many of these modes of transit are slower than alternative public facilities, the regular riders, too, are often persons who *prefer* this way of moving about.

A ferry normally exhibits characteristics that lie between the two extremes of purely instrumental and purely entertaining. Even a trip across a narrow river has an aura of excitement. The vessels are often archaic, and they chug and groan picturesquely. A longer trip across a harbor or down a canal has even more tang and visual interest. Some passengers, it is true, read their newspapers oblivious to gulls and shipping activity; but others, even staid businessmen, customarily stand at the bow of the vessel and enjoy the spray and the wind.

Technological developments may rapidly convert a type of transit from instrumental to affective. New Orleans, which once had dozens of streetcar routes, now has only one, the St. Charles line. It follows a slow, round-about, but visually beautiful course between the far uptown area and lower Canal Street. Other transit lines are far more direct and rapid. The streetcar sways and jerks. Its steps are high and its acceleration rate low. But the windows open wide on the open air; and the wooden seats, the unshaded lights, the standing motorman with a hand-operated rheostat, and the constant ringing in of fares all have a nostalgia and charm about them that makes the regular patron a perpetual tourist. Among a considerable number of New Orleanians the motto is "Streetcars Desired." They simply find the ride pleasant.[9]

## CONCLUSIONS

Behavior in public transit situations exemplifies a range of human conduct that obtains when, aside from general cultural prescriptions, individuals are not guided in their actions by established and reciprocal

[8] Vehicles that in effect do not go anywhere exemplify the furthest extreme of non-instrumental fun. For some observations about merry-go-rounds see Erving Goffman, *Encounters*, Indianapolis: Bobbs-Merrill, 1961, pp. 97-99 and 105-110.

[9] Unusual variations in familiar kinds of public transit may produce a similar effect. Consider, for example, the glass elevator on the outside of the Fairmont Hotel in San Francisco.

role relationships. More than spectator crowds, which are bound together by a common if temporary interest, individuals on transit vehicles appear to be in a state of suspension from the larger social system. We have, of course, barely begun to scratch the surface of this topic, and our observations derive from unplanned participant observation. Hopefully, they may serve to stimulate systematic research on this rather neglected but increasingly important subject.

To this end the simultaneous employment of a variety of approaches would be most useful. Though polls and other attitudinal instruments clearly have their place, greater emphasis might well be put on direct and nonreactive observations.[10] Attention could be focused on the preferences and behavior patterns of different socio-economic and occupational groupings in transit situations, or on a comparison between these and the assumptions made by the owners and managers of the transit vehicles.

What is especially needed is comparative and cross-cultural research. Our observations were made largely in the United States and in Western Europe. For the most part, they did not reach persons below the lower middle class. Performances and outlooks in other countries and among other strata may exhibit very different patterns. The variability among transit populations has sometimes been held to argue against research in this setting. "Thus, for a comparison of attitudes between New York and Los Angeles, conversation sampling in buses and commuter trains would tap such different segments of the communities as to be scarcely worth doing."[11] From our point of view, though, it would be interesting to know whether such differential tapping yields markedly different transit behavior in the two cities.

The focus in this paper has been on situational attributes of transit vehicles. Research in a variety of locales and among differing population types would make it possible to ascertain the additional contributions to transit phenomena of general cultural forces, class characteristics, and individual predispositions. This kind of comparative and multi-variate analysis should provide a better understanding of present-day public transit. It should also facilitate more successful planning of transit facilities for the future.

---

[10] See Eugene J. Webb, Donald T. Campbell, Richard D. Schwartz, and Lee Sechrest, *Unobtrusive Measures*, Chicago: Rand McNally, 1966.

[11] *Ibid.*, p. 27.

# NAME INDEX

Page numbers in *italic* indicate references in text.


Abelson, R. P., 205-206, 208-215, *214*, 257, 289
Adams, J. S., 209, *214*
Adorno, T., *305*
Agnew, S. T., 205
Allen, H., 8-9, 22-33, 120, 205
Allport, F. H., *81*
Allport, G. W., *81*, 119, *121*, 171, *172*
Allyn, J., *218*, *224*, 269, *274*
Alper, T. G., *201*
Altman, I., 173, *179*
American Association of University Women, 130
Americans for Democratic Action, 130
Appelbaum, A. S., 3, *6*
Ardrey, R., 173, *179*
Argyle, M., *181*
Argyris, C., 4, *6*
Arnhoff, F. N., 54, *55*
Aronson, E., 2, *6*, 119, *121*, 210, *214*, *217*, 259, *263*
Asch, S. E., 71, *77*, 198, *198*

Back, K., 264, *267*
Backman, C. W., *104*
Bandura, A., 12, 15, *17*, 18, *21*, 71, 77
Barch, A. M., 58, 68-70, 95
Barker, C. H., 71, *77*
Baumrind, D., 171, *172*
Bayley, G. A., 108-109, 111, *112*
Becker, F. D., 171, 173-180, 289
Bem, D. J., 24, *33*
Berkowitz, L., 11-12, 15, *17*, 28, 30, *33*, 163, *169*, 172, 196-198
Berkowitz, W. R., 206, *207*
Berscheid, E., 34, *42*, 59, *59*, 209, *214*
Bevan, W., 187, 194, *195*
Bickman, L., 8-9, *10*, 58, *59*, 95-96, 102-104, 120, 162-169, *169*, 172, 196-198, 206, 289
Bigart, H., *83*
Birdwhistell, R. L., *181*
Black, D. J., 39, *42*
Blake, P., 172, *172*
Blake, R. R., 8, 12, *17*, 18, *21*, 58, *59*, *69*, *70*, 78-81, *81*, *83*, 95-96, *104*, 105-107, *107*, 108, *112*
Bogardus, E. S., *201*
Bowerman, M., 250
Bowerman, W., 250
Breed, W., 120, 155-161, 171, *324*
Brehm, J. W., 172, 206, *207*, *237*, 238, 257, *258*, 267, *267*, 269-274, *274*
Brock, T. C., 257, 264-268
Brodsky, C., *67*
Brotzman, E., 57-58, 60-67, 171
Brown, J. D., *285*
Brown, R., *325*
Brownlee, K. A., *152*
Bruner, J., 71, *77*, 187, *195*
Brunswick, E., 4, *6*
Bryan, J. H., 7-9, 11-17, *17*, 18, *21*, 28, *33*, 34-35, *42*, 163, *169*
Buckhout, R., 279, *279*
Bullock, R. P., *67*
Burgess, M., *101*
Burnett, S. A., 58, 82-83
Burnstein, E., 264, 267, *267*
Burtt, H. E., *300*, 301
Buss, A. H., *101*
Buzbee, W., *83*
Byrne, D., 264, *267*

Campbell, A., 226, *236*
Campbell, D. T., 2-4, *6*, *101*, 108, *112*, 120, 129, *129*, 146-154, *146*, *150*, 163, 223, 251, *255*, *328*
Carlsmith, J. M., 71, *77*, 210, *214*, *217*, *237*, 257, 259-263
Carriger, B. K., *236*
Catton, B., 119, *121*
Chandler, P. J., 12, *17*, *69*, *107*, 108, *112*
Chesler, M., 288, 302-308, *302*, *303*, *307*
Chiang Kai-shek, 245-, 249-250
Christori, F., *285*
Clausen, A., *304*
Cohen, A. R., *101*, 120, *121*, 206, *207*, 208-209, 214, *214*, 226, *236*, *237*, 267, *267*
Cohen, J., *33*
Cole, A. H., *274*
Coleman, J. S., 196, 198, *198*, 208, *214*
Collins, M. E., 128, *129*, *139*
Committee on Civil Rights in East Manhattan, 130, 132-138
Conolly, E. S., 198, *198*
Converse, P. E., 226, *236*, *304*
Cook, S. W., 1, *6*, *139*
Crane, A. R., 113, *117*
Crook, J. H., *183*, 184
Crooks, L. E., 319, *323*
Cuzzort, R. P., *152*

Dalrymple, S., 57-58, 60-67, 171
Daniels, L., 11-12, 15, *17*, 28, 30, *33*, 163, *169*
Danzig, D., *307*
Darley, J. D., 8, *10*, 16, 24, *33*, 34-35, 40-42, *42*
Darlington, R. B., 11, *17*
Davis, M., 95, 120, 155-161, 171, 289, 324-328, *324*
Dean, J., *181*
Desilva, H. R., *323*
Deutsch, K., *157*
Deutsch, M., 1, *6*, 71, *77*, 128, *129*, *139*
Dollard, J., 120, *121*
Doob, A. N., 95-96, 98-101, 257, 259-263
Doob, L. W., *325*
Douty, H., *104*
Droba, D. D., *122*
Duby, G., 290
Duncan, B., *152*, *157*, *161*
Duncan, G., *285*
Duncan, O. D., *140*, *152*, *157*, *161*
Dunn, R. E., 264, *268*
Durkin, D., 113, *117*

Eachus, H. T., *104*
Esser, A. H., 173, *179, 182*

Federal Bureau of Investigation, 248
Feldman, R. E., 7, 9, 44-55, *55*, 96, 206
Felipe, N., 171-173, *179*, 181-186, 289
Feshbach, S., 226, 233-235, *236*, 269, *274*
Festinger, L., 1, 4, *6*, 71, *77*, 171, *218, 224, 237*, 259, *263*, 264, 267, *267, 268*, 269, *274*
Fillenbaum, S., 4, *6*
Fine, B. J., 209, *215, 217*
Firestone, I., 206, *207*
Fisch, E., 7-8, 18-21
Fischer, A., *67*
Fitch, J. M., 174
Fleming, W. H., *237*
Forbes, T. W., *323*
Frager, R., 249
Fraser, R., *285*
Fraser, S. C., 58, 71-77
Freed, A. M., 12, *17, 69, 107*, 108, *112*
Freedman, J. L., 58, 71-77, *224*, 257, 259-263
Freeman, L. C., *152*
French, J. R. P., Jr., 4, *6*
Frenkel-Brunswick, E., *305*
Frey, R., 4, *6*
Friedman, P., 11, 15, *17*
Fuller, J. G., *83*

Gaertner, S., 9, 120, 162-169, 206
Gaito, J., 198, *198*
Gallup, G., 253, 254, *255*
Garfinkle, H., *181*
Genovese, K., 34, 168
Gerard, H. B., 71, *77*, 198, *198, 259, 263, 264, 268*
Gibson, J. J., 319, *323*
Gilbert, E., *139*
Goffman, E., 173, 179, *179, 181, 327*
Goldblatt, R. G., 276, *279*
Golding, S., 3, *6*
Goldman, R., 258, 275, *279*, 280-285, *285*
Goldstein, A. P., 3-4, *6*
Goldstein, M., 226, *236*
Goldwasser, A., 113, *117*
Goldwasser, M., 113, *117*
Goldwater, B., 248, 304
Goodman, C., 187, *195*
Goodman, L. A., 21, *21*
Goranson, R., 15, *17*
Gordon, A., 275, *279*, 280, *285*
Gore, P. M., 11, *17*
Gouldner, A., 11, *17*
Grace, T., 279, *279*
Graves, N., 57-58, 60-67, 171
Greenbaum, C. W., 264, *268*
Greenwood, E., *181*
Grinker, R. R., 30, *33*
Gross, A. E., 95-96, 98-101
Gross, L., 275, *279*, 280, 283, *285*
Gross, P., 11, *17*
Gunther, J., *203*
Gurevitch, M., 291

Haefner, D. P., 226, *236*
Hain, J. D., 58, *59, 81*
Hall, E. T., 173, *179, 181, 185*
Hamid, P., *104*
Handlon, B. J., 11, *17*
Harari, H., 95-96, 113-117
Harding, J., *139*
Harris, L., *129*
Harris, R., 12, *17*, 163, *169*
Harter, S., 46, *55*, 245
Hartman, G. W., 59, 84-93
Harvey, O. J., *201*
Hashim, S. A., 283, *285*
Haythorn, W. W., 173, *179*
Hediger, H., 173, 179, *179*
Heider, F., *104*, 120, *121, 237*
Heller, K., 3-4, *6*
Helson, H., 8, 58, 78-81, *81*, 105, *107*, 187, 194, *195*
Henchy, T., 163, *169*
Hiller, E. T., *200*
Hillmer, M. L., Jr., 264, *268*
Hochbaum, G. M., 234, *236*
Hoffer, E., *306*
Hofling, C. K., 57-58, 60-67, 171
Hogrefe, R., *139*
Hokanson, J. E., *101*
Hollander, P., 33, *33*, 96, 168, *169*
Holmes, D. S., 3, *6*
Holmes, M., 7-8, 18-21
Homans, G., 30, *33*, 209, *214*
Honan, W. H., *83*
Hood, W. R., *200, 201*
Hornstein, H. A., 7-8, 18-21, 206
Horowitz, E. L., *201*
Hovland, C. I., 71, *77*, 208, *215, 217*, 218, *223*, 224, 226, *236*, 267, *268*
Humphrey, H., 251-255
Hurd, F. W., *323*
Hyman, H. H., 150
Hyman, R., 267, *268*

Inkeles, A., 44, *55*

Jacob, P. E., *157*
Jacobs, J., 290
Jaffa, M., 258, 275, *279*, 280-285
Jahoda, M., 1, *6, 139*
James, J., 196, 198, *198*
Janis, I. L., 208, *215, 223*, 226, 233-235, *236*, 269, *274*
Jinson, W., *285*
John Birch Society, The, 302, 303, 305-307
Johnson, L. B., 248, 250
Johnson, M., *67*
Jones, C. B., *237*
Jones, R. A., 269, *274*
Jourard, S. M., 2, *6*

Kanouse, D. E., 257, 275-279
Katz, D., 1, *6*, 172, *172*, 264, 267, *268*
Katz, E., 264, 267, *268*
Kay, J., 58, 82-83
Kefauver, E., *303*, 305
Kelley, H. H., 30, *33*, 120, *121*, 208-209, 213, *215*, 226, *236*
Kelman, H. C., 2, 6, 71, *77*, 267, *268*
Kipnis, D., *238*
Klanderman, S. B., 12, *17*, 163, *169*
Klapper, J. T., 226, *236*
Koch, C., 275, *279*, 280, 285, *285*
Kochen, M., 291, 293
Kogan, N., 24, *33*
Kohn, M. L., 95, 288, 289, 309-318,
Kormann, L. A., 2, *6*
Korte, C., 8, *10*, 297
Krebs, D. L., 7, *10*
Kruskal, W. H., 120, 146-154

Lafoutaine, E., 283, *285*
Landa, P., *131*
Landauer, T. K., 257, 259-263
Landis, C., 287-288, 300-301
Landis, M. H., *300*, 301
LaPiere, R. T., *101*, 119-120, 122-129, *129*
Laplante, R., 283, *285*
Latané, B., 8, *10*, 16, 24, *33*, 34-35, 40-42, *42, 43*
Lavernhe, J., 283, *285*
Lazarsfeld, P. F., 264, 267-268
Lee, D., 54, *55*
Lefkowitz, M., 12, *17, 70*, 95-96, *104*, 105-107
Leon, H. F., 54, *55*
Lerner, M. J., 34, 42, *43*, 168, *169*
Lev, J., *140*, 228, *236, 255*
Leventhal, H., 205-206, 226-236, *236*, 264, 267, *268*
Levin, J., *303*, 305
Levin, L. A., *104*
Levine, S., 120, 289, 324-328
Levinson, D. J., 44, *55, 305*
Levy, B. H., 205-206, *207*, 216-225, *225*, 257
Levy, K., 3, *6*
Levy, L. H., 119, *121*
Lewin, K., 1, *6, 238*
Lichtenstein, E., 3, *6*
Lindzey, G., 119, *121*
Linn, L. S., 120, *121*, 206
Lipman, A., 173, *179*
Lipset, S., *307*
Little, K. B., *181*
Littman, G., *131*
Loeb, M. B., *67*
Loh, W. D., *104*
Lorenz, K., 171, *172*
Lorge, I., 54, *55*
Lubetsky, J., *223*
Lupfer, M., 58, 82-83
Luria, Z., 113, *117*
Lyman, S. M., 173, *179*

McBride, G., *185*
McCarthy, E., 250, 252
McCarthy, J., 254
McClintock, C., 172, *172*
McCloskey, H., *305*
Maccoby, N., *218, 224*
McDavid, J. W., 95-96, 113-117
McEvoy, J., 288, 302-308, *303, 305*
McFarland, R. A., *323*
McGrew, J. M., 119, 128-129
McGuigan, F. J., *219*, 221

McGuire, W. J., 1, *6*, 208, *215*, 257-258, *258*, 269, *274*
Macker, C. E., 11, *17*
McLuhan, H. M., 3, *6*
McNemar, Q., 226, *236*
MacRae, D. A., 113, *117*
Maier, R., 187, 194, *195*
Mann, L., 46, *55*, 171-172, 187-195, *195*, 209, *215*, 245
Mannheim, K., *309*
Mao-Tse-tung, 245, 249-250
Martin, H., *67*
Marx, G., 162, *169*
Marx, M. A., *145*
Mason, R., *238*
Mathewson, G. C., 259, *263*
Matson, T. M., *323*
Matthews, M. W., 35, *43*, 168, *169*
Maugham, S., 324
Mauksch, H., *67*
Merton, R. K., 120, *121*
Metropolitan Life Insurance Company, 281-282, *285*
Midlarsky, E., 11, *17*
Milgram, S., 33, *33*, 46, *55*, 57, 59, 168, *169*, 171-172, *172*, 194, *195*, 196-198, *198*, 206-207, 245-250, 287, 290-299
Miller, F. B., *201*
Miller, J. C., 205-206, 208-215, 257, 289
Miller, N., 205, 209, 216-225, *216*, *223*, *224*, 257
Miller, R. G., Jr., 21, *21*
Miller, W. E., 226, *236*, *304*
Mills, J., 259, *263*
Moore, H. T., *300*, 301
Moore, M. E., 276, *279*
Moran, P. A. P., *153*, *154*
Mouton, J. S., 8, 12, *17*, 58, *59*, *69*, *70*, 78-81, *81*, *83*, 95-96, *104*, 105-107, *107*, 108, *112*
Murata, T., 248
Murphy, G., *200*
Myrdal, G., 128-129, *129*

Nangle, J., 58, 68-70
Nassiakou, M., 44, 53-54, *55*
National Association for the Advancement of Colored People, 315-317
National Biological Research Society, 227
Natsoulas, T., 264, 267, *268*
Newton, M. E., *67*
Niles, P., 205-206, 226-236, *236*
Nisbett, R. E., 257, 275-279, *279*, 280, 282-284, *285*
Nixon, R., 251-255
Noble, G. K., 179, *180*

O'Ballance, E., 54, *55*
O'Connell, E. J., *223*
Orne, M. T., 1-2, *6*, 16, *17*, 163, *169*, 221
Osgood, C. E., *237*

Page, M. M., 2, *6*
Parker, J. H., 120, 139-145
Pastore, N., *101*
Pear, T. H., *200*
Pepitone, A., 57, 96, *97*
Perloe, S. I., 264, 267, *268*
Peryam, D. R., *239*
Peterson, F. K., *67*
Piaget, J., 113, *117*
Pierce, C. M., 57-58, 60-67, 171
Pilger, J., *152*
Pilgrim, F. J., *239*
Piliavin, I. M., 8-9, 34-43, 120, 163, *169*
Piliavin, J. A., 8-9, 34-43, 120, 163, *169*
Pirenne, H., 290
Pitts, J. R., 54, *55*
Pool, I. de S., 291, 293
Porter, K. A., 324
Pritzker, H. A., 71, *77*
Pulsifer, D. H., *285*

Rabbie, J. M., *237*
Radloff, R., 234-235, *236*
Rankin, R. E., *150*
Regan, J. W., 172, 257, 269-274
Reiss, A. J., 39, *42*
Richardson, L. F., 199
Riecken, H. W., 96, *97*, *104*
Ring, K., 1, *6*, 257, *258*
Roberts, H. V., *140*, *154*
Rockefeller, N., 298
Rodin, J., 8-9, 34-43, *43*, 120, 163, *169*
Roos, P. D., 173, *180*
Rosenbaum, M., 12, *17*, 18, *21*, *70*
Rosenberg, M. J., 2, *6*, 221, 226, *236*
Rosenhan, D., 12, *17*, 18, *21*, 31, *33*
Rosenstock, I. M., *236*
Rosenthal, R., 1, 4, *6*, 22, *33*, *219*, 221, 252, *255*
Rosnow, R. L., 4, *6*
Ross, D., 15, *17*, 71, *77*
Ross, H. L., *323*
Ross, S., 15, *17*, 71, *77*
Rotter, J. B., 11, *17*
Ruesch, J., *67*
Rushing, W. A., *67*

Saenger, G., *139*
Salvation Army, The, 9, 13-14
Sanders, I. T., 54, *55*
Sanford, N., *305*
Sarnoff, I., 172, *172*
Schachter, S., 42, *43*, *217*, 258, 267, *268*, 275, 279, *279*, 280-285, *285*, 288-289, *289*
Scheffé, H., 21, *21*
Schein, E. H., 71, *77*
Schmuck, R., 288, 302-308, *302*, *303*, *307*
Schneier, I., 71, *77*
Schopler, J., 35, *43*, 168, *169*
Schultz, D. P., 2, 4, *6*, *104*, 163, *169*
Schwartz, R. D., 2, *6*, *101*, *146*, 163, 251, *255*, *328*
Scollon, R. W., *238*
Scotch, N. A., 276, *279*
Scott, M. B., 173, *179*
Scott, W. A., 205, *207*
Sears, D. O., *224*
Sechrest, L. B., 2-4, *6*, *101*, 163, 251, *255*, *328*
Secord, P. F., xiii-xiv, *104*
Seibert, R., 120, 155-161, 171, *324*
Selltiz, C., 1, *6*, 119, 120, 130-138
Sensenig, J., 269, *274*
Sheatsly, P. B., *150*
Sherif, C. W., *199*, *201*
Sherif, M., 120, 171-172, 199-204, *199*, *200*, *201*, 205, *217*, 218, *224*
Shor, R. E., 95, 289, 319-323
Shulman, A., 3, *6*
Sidman, M., 3, *6*
Siegel, S., 114, *117*, *129*
Sigall, H., 2, *6*
Silverman, I., 3, *6*
Simmons, C. H., 34, 42, *43*, 168, *169*
Singer, J. E., *217*, 288-289, *289*
Sloane, L., *83*
Smith, E. E., 206, 237-244
Smith, W. S., *323*
Snedecor, G. W., *81*
Sommer, R., 171, 173-180, *179*, *180*, 181-186, *181*, 289
Spiegel, J. P., 30, *33*
Stanley, J. C., 3-4, *6*
Stokes, D. E., 226, *236*
Stotland, E., 42, *43*, 264, 267, *267*, *268*
Stricker, L., 3, *6*
Stunkard, A. J., 275-276, *279*, 280, 285, *285*
Sumner, W. G., 128, *129*
Sussman, L., *303*

Tannenbaum, P. H., *237*
Taves, E. H., 194, *195*
Taylor, K. F., 171-172, 187-195
Terry, J. I., *237*
Test, M. A., 7-9, 11-18, *21*, 28, *33*, 34-35, *42*, 163, *169*
Thibaut, J., 30, *33*, 96, *97*, *104*
Thielens, W., *303*, 305
Thorndike, E. L., *93*
Thrasher, F. M., *200*
Thurstone, L. L., *81*
Tinbergen, N., 171, *172*
Toch, H., 171, *172*, 194, *195*, 196, *198*
Tom, S., Jr., 257, 259-263
Torrance, E. P., *238*, *240*, 244
Toscano, J. V., *157*
Travers, J., 293
Triandis, H. C., 44, 53-54, *55*, *104*
Trumbo, D., 58, 68-70
Turner, E., 187, 194, *195*
Turner, J. A., *217*

Ugurel-Semin, R., 11, *17*
United Nations Educational, Scientific and Cultural Organization, 200
University Dormitory Council, 282, *285*
Uptown Chamber of Commerce, 130

Van Hoose, T., 2, *6*
Van Itallie, T. B., 283, *285*
Van Lennep, D. J., *323*
Vassiliou, V., 44, 53-54, *55*
Vidulich, R. N., 96, 108-112, *112*
Volkhart, E. H., 209, *215*

Wagner, C., 8, *10*
Walker, H. M., *140*, 228, *236*, *255*
Walkley, R., *139*
Wallace, G., 251-255
Wallace, W. P., 57, 120, 146-154
Wallach, M. A., 24, *33*
Wallis, W. A., *140*, *154*
Walster, E., 34, *42*, 59, *59*
Walters, R. H., 12, *17*
Wapner, S., *201*
Wartenberg, H., *303*, 305
Webb, E. J., 2, *6*, *101*, *146*, 163, 251, *255*, *328*
Weick, K., 5, *6*
Weisenberg, M., 206, *207*
Weiss, W., 209, *215*, *217*
Welch, R., 303, 305, 307
Welfare and Health Council of New York City, 130
West, P., *139*
Westie, F., *139*
Westie, M., *139*
Wheeler, L., 8, *10*, 12, 16, *17*
White, B. J., *201*
White, G. M., 12, *17*, 18, *21*, 31, *33*
White, H., 295
Wicker, A. W., 120, *121*, 163, *169*
Wicklund, R. A., 257, *258*, 273, *274*
Wiesenthal, D. L., 3, *6*
Wilhelmy, R. A., 198, *198*
Wilks, S. S., *152*
Willerman, B., 267, *268*
Williams, J. L., *181*
Williams, R. M., Jr., *203*, 288-289, 309-318
Wilner, D. M., *139*
Wilson, D. J., 96, 108-112
Wong, T. J., 264, *267*
Woodruff, C. L., 213, *215*
Wright, B. A., 11, *17*
Wrightsman, L. S., 206-207, 251-255
Wyant, R., *304*

Zander, A., 264, 267, *267*
Zimbardo, P. G., 206, *207*, 221, *223*, *224*, *238*

# SUBJECT INDEX


Adaptation level theory:
 and consumer behavior, 257, 262
 in experimental design, 105
Advertising, 71, 77, 84
 (*See also* Compliance)
Age differences:
 in honesty, 104
 in interracial interaction, 120, 141, 159
 between subject populations, 100, 104
Aggregation:
 definition, 146
 index: derivation, 152-154
  uses, 152
 racial: changes over time, 150
  in different schools, 148-150
  and sex, 150
 (*See also* Interracial interaction; Seating patterns)
Aggression:
 definition, 99
 and helping behavior, 168
 and status, 95, 98-100
 (*See also* Automobiles; Frustration)
Alienation, 22
 communication patterns, small-world problem, 299
 (*See also* Helping behavior)
Altruism (*see* Helping behavior)
Amusement influence, measurement of, 108-111
Anomie, 22
 (*See also* Helping behavior)
Anonymity, 103
 questionnaire on religious fasting, 281
Antisemitism (*see* Intergroup conflicts; Prejudice)
Anxiety:
 and attitude change, 226
 and compliance recommendations, 234
Attention, status of communicator and, 103
Attitude change, 71
 after-only design, 205-206, 218, 226-228
 applause, 213
 communicator credibility, 212, 217-218
  inverse relationship, 218
 communicator defamation, 220-225
 communicator presence, 208-214
 communicator status, 219, 222
 consumer behavior: decision change, 264
  hedonic scale, 239
 countercommunication, 235
 dissonance theory: authority figure, 238-244
  balance, 237
  cognitive dissonance, 237
  communicator credibility, 217, 222
  congruity, 237
  consumer behavior, 237-244
  freedom of choice, 242-244
  two-step inducement, 242-243
 distraction, 218, 224
 emotional arousal, 216-225
 extremity of communication, 220-225
  relative to previous communication, 223-224
 extremity of initial attitude, dissonance theory, 238, 241, 243-244
 extremity of subject-communicator discrepancy, 217
 fear arousal, 226-236
  anxiety, 226
  convenience of recommendation, 226-227
  defensive reactions, 226, 234
  degree of, 228-234
Attitude change:
 forewarning against, 269
 group pressure, 235
 "imagined supporter" hypothesis, 209-214
 instructions, evaluative set, 218-225
 insults, 206, 208-214, 217-225
  extremity of attitude, 289
  permanence of change, 214
 intergroup conflict, superordinate goal, 199-204
 by interview, 208-214
 leader influence, military organizations, 238-244
 legislation, 128-129, 137, 155
 military organizations, objectives, 237
 negative change (boomerang effect), 209-214
 persuasibility, and low self-esteem, 223
 picketing, 82-83
 race prejudice, 135-138
 reward, dissonance theory, 238
 social bargaining, 214
 social equity theory, 209-214
 social judgment theory, 217-218, 222-225
 by written communication, 218-220
 (*See also* Communication; Communicator)
Attitude measurement:
 ceiling effect, 229
 content analysis, political letter writing, 302-308
 field research and, 83, 149, 162, 205
 interview, disadvantages, 245-246
 lost-letter technique: anonymity of, 246
  proper use, 250
 rating scales, 210
 reactivity, 225
 seating patterns, 142-144, 146-154

Attitude measurement:
wrong-number technique, 162-165
restrictive response categories, 164
(*See also* Aggregation; Questionnaires; Research methods; Verbal behavior)
Attitudes:
behavioral referents, 120
definition of social, 122, 126-127
racial, 119, 128-129, 135-138, 163
helping behavior, 162
seating patterns, 146
relationship to behavior, 58, 122, 171, 226
cognitive dissonance, 71
competing motives, 120
concerning race, 119, 128-129, 135-138, 163
contiguity, 206, 235
after fear arousal, 231-235
intervening mechanisms, 120
normative prescriptions, 120
prior compliance, 74, 124
reactivity in measurement, 205
(*See also* Predicted versus actual behavior; Prejudice; Verbal behavior)
Authority:
defiance of, and political preference, 207
dissonance theory, attitude change, 238-244
obedience of, in nurse-physician relationship, 60-67
(*See also* Social status)
Automobile driving:
competence, definition, 319
and conformity, 68-69, 95
horn-honking, frustration and, 95, 98-100
sex-role stereotype, "woman driver," 322
social norms: competitive norms, 289, 319
in conflict, 320-323
cooperative norms, 289, 319
learning, 322
multiple cues, 319-320
and traffic conditions, 320
in unpatterned situations, 289
stop-sign violation, and political preference, 207, 254
turn signalling, 68-69
(*See also* Helping behavior; Transportation)
Automobiles, definition of status, 95, 98-99, 253

Brainwashing, Korean tactics, 71
(*See also* Compliance, foot-in-the-door technique)

Cognitive dissonance theory:
definition, 237-238
drive characteristics, 237-238
external pressure, amount of, 71
predictions from, 259
Collective behavior:
and population density, 171
quantification, and crowd size, 194, 196
and territorial behavior, 171
(*See also* Crowds; Waiting lines)
Communication:
content, emotional versus rational, 85-93
conversation content: national differences, 300-301
sex differences, 300-301
in hierarchies, 120
mass media, and intergroup conflict, 200
retention of information in political leaflets, 91-92
Communication patterns:
cross-cultural, 287, 296
ethnic differences, 287, 296
interracial interaction, proposed study, 297-298
mathematical social structure, 290-292
small-world problem: definition, 287, 290
experimental study of message transmission, 292-293
intergroup relations, 298-299
kinship systems, 296
mathematical model, 291-292
number of intermediaries, 295, 297
philosophical views, 291
sex of intermediaries, 296
target persons, 293
social structure, measurement of, 296
Communicator:
credibility: and attitude change, 208
experience of communicator, 264-267
in fear-arousing communication, 228-231
insults, negative attitude change, 208-214
negative, and dissonance theory, 238-244
similarity to recipient: cognitive theory of identification, 264, 267
and decision change, 264-267
social comparison theory, 264
status, 71, 103, 219, 222-225
Compliance, 57-59
and conformity, 71-72, 80-81
external pressure, 71
to fear-arousing communication, 228-235
foot-in-the-door technique, applications of, 71, 77
explanations of, 72-77
and suspicion of manipulation, 74
(*See also* Obedience; Social influence)
Conflict:
resolution, in unpatterned situations, 289, 314-315
and superordinate goal, 120, 144
(*See also* Intergroup conflict)
Conformity, 71
and ambiguity, 71-72
attitudes toward civil rights demonstrations, 214
and crowd formation, activity of stimulus group, 198
and group size, 196-198
imitation and, 68
measurement, *A-S* Reaction Study, 80-81
and personality, 80
petition-signing, 58, 78-81
and prohibitions, 105-107
and status, 95-96, 105-107
and traffic laws, 68-69, 95
pedestrians, 105-107
Consumer behavior:
adaptation level theory, 257, 262
attitude change, in military organizations, 237-244
cognitive dissonance theory, and brand loyalty, 259-263
decision change, price level, 264-267
dissonance theory, 237-244, 257, 259-263
eating stimuli: food deprivation, 275, 280-285
food quality, 282-285
meal time, 283-285
impulse buying, obese versus normal individuals, 277-279
initial product selling price: adaptation level theory, 257, 262
cognitive dissonance theory, 259-263
military organizations, dissonance theory, 237-244
monetary inducement, 270-274
new foods, 238-243
hedonic scale, 239
obese versus normal individuals:
dormitory food, 282-285
food deprivation, 275-285
money spent grocery shopping, 275-279
religious fasting, 280-282, 284-285
time spent grocery shopping, 275-279
time-zone changes, 283-285
and picketing against toy guns, 82-83
reactance theory: boomerang effect, 273
compliance in buying, 273
religious fasting, and eating stimuli, 280-282, 284-285
verbal inducement, 270-274
Content analysis:
conversations, 287-288, 300-301
letters to the editor, 288, 302
demographic variables of writers, 303
hostility and affect, 303
personal versus general values expressed, 303
remarks of helping experiment bystanders, 39-40

Control:
in experimental design, 119
in field experiments, 98, 116
Conversation:
ethics of recording, 288
national differences, 287-288, 300-301
sex differences, 287-288, 300-301
uses of, 288, 300-301
Cross-cultural research, 9, 287
problems of, 249
Crowding (*see* Territorial behavior; Territorial behavior, of animals)
Crowds:
crowd dispersion, 172
crowd formation, 172, 196
activity and size of initial crowd, 196-198
contagion assumption, 196
estimation of numbers: and crowd control, 194
political behavior, 194
in waiting lines, 187-194
supportive function, and attitude change, 212-213
(*See also* Collective behavior; Waiting lines)
Cultural bias, intelligence tests, 287, 300

Debriefing in field experiments, 96-97
Deception, 2, 3
(*See also* Field research)
Demand characteristics, 2, 119, 163
and attitude change, presence of experimenter, 214
in field research, 98, 205
Deprivation, food (*see* Consumer behavior; Obesity)
Deviance as subject for study, 181, 186
(*See also* Territorial behavior)
Discriminatory behavior:
blacks toward whites, 120, 166-168
definition, 131
and economic insecurity, 139
in employment, 130, 139, 210
in helping, 9, 11, 15-16, 34-43, 162-169
in housing, 128-130, 139
index of social measurement, 120, 155-161
judgment of occurrence, 133-134
and legislation, 128-129, 137, 155, 315
in public accommodations, 130-138, 310-318
reduction of, 135-138
community education, 135
by restaurant employees, 131, 134, 137
price range of restaurants, 131-132, 134, 137
visibility hypothesis, 119
situational norms, 309
via telephone, 162, 166-169
whites toward blacks, 120, 128-129, 134, 137, 166-168, 310-318
whites toward Chinese, 123-124
(*See also* Integration; Interracial interaction; Prejudice; Race)
Dissonance theory:
and attitude change, 217, 222-224
consumer behavior, 237-244
balance theory, 237
cognitive dissonance, drive characteristics of, 237-238
congruity, 237
in field situations, 206
negative communicator, 238-244
versus reactance theory, 257
reward, and attitude change, 238
Distance, interpersonal: conversational, 181
social, 123-124, 200-202
Dominance and territorial behavior, 176
in animals, 185
Dress as status-indicator, 96, 102, 109, 155

Economic theories of behavior, 30
Education and propaganda, 93
Emotional arousal:
insults, and attitude change, 216-225
relevance to attitude, and attitude change, 216
Emotions, labeling physiological arousal, 288
Empathy and helping behavior, 11, 38
Ethics (*see* Field research)
Ethnic differences, 44, 48-55
Ethnocentrism, 19-21, 44, 48-55
group norms, 200
(*See also* Discriminatory behavior; Interracial interaction; Prejudice; Race)
Evaluation apprehension, 2
interviews and questionnaires, 245
Experimenter variables, 265
experimenter bias, 119
in content analysis of conversations, 301
in perception, 189, 191, 207, 254
experimenter influence: demand characteristics, 214
difficulty in eliminating, 205, 225
precautions against, 220*n*.
sex, 102, 133
similarity to subject, educational and socioeconomic, 132
status, 96, 108
(*See also* Dress as status-indicator)

Fear arousal and behavior, 232-236, 269
Field research:
case studies of deviance, 181
collective behavior, 171-172
confounding factors in context: election results, 92
picketing, 82
contrast to laboratory results, 37
control, 128, 181, 191
dangers to experimenter, 95, 182
debriefing subjects, 96-97, 116
deception, complexity of, 213
demand characteristics, 205, 214
ecological tradition, 171, 173
Field research:
ethics of, 5, 96-97, 116, 171
invasions of privacy, 288
in mental hospitals, 182
participant-observation, 309
experimenter bias, 189, 191, 207, 254, 257, 301
field experiments versus field studies, 4
frequency of, 1, 287
need for, 1
on public transit, 328
unpatterned situations, 309
pilot survey, 131-132
problems of administration, 132
problems of attitude measurement, 83, 164
problems of data collection: age estimates, 155
social class estimates, 155
problems of letter distribution, 247-248
problems of standardization of situation, 189, 266
control of subject's situation, 164
intervention of bystanders, 104
number of bystanders, 23, 98-99
time of day, 13, 98, 213, 225
problems of standardized procedure, 60-61, 213, 225
problems of subject selection: experimenter differences, 225
random selection, 148, 163-164
self-selection, 189
and questionnaires, 171
reaction of subjects to participation, 64-65, 271-273
reactivity, 205, 309
realism versus control, 98, 104, 171
statistical techniques, 257-258
"tempered naturalness," 5
territorial behavior, 171
as theory verification, 257
uses of, 1, 171
variables in natural context, 4
Foreigners (*see* Ethnocentrism; National character)
Frustration:
aggression, 98
frustration-aggression hypothesis, and hostile communication in attitude change, 217, 224
tension-reduction, 98

Generalizability, 3-4, 33
attitude measurement in field research, 206
Gestalt theory, 85
Groups:
cohesiveness, 30
definition, 199
group formation, status hierarchy, 202
group size: and diffusion of responsibility, 24
and modeling helping behavior, 35, 40
leadership, in resolution of intergroup conflict, 203-204
norms, 199, 202
helping behavior, 30
social distance, 200

Groups:
peer group, 113-116
reference group, in unpatterned situations, 317
Guilt and attitude change, 209, 217, 219-225

Helping behavior:
ambiguity of situation, 32, 168
anonymity of bystander, 168
apathy, 32
avoidance mechanism: denial of situation, 33, 42
"matter of principle" refusal, 74, 76
projection of blame, 33
rationalization, 33, 35, 42
in children, 12
and conformity, 16
cost-reward matrix, 42
cross-cultural study of, 9, 44, 48-55
diffusion of responsibility and, 8, 16, 22-25, 29-34, 40-42
in emergency situations, 8-9, 16, 24
same-race helping, 163
visual cues, 34-43
empathy and, 11, 38
guilt and, 11, 16-17
as habit, 31
latency, 31-32, 34-43
modeling, 12-17, 28-43
consequence to model, 7, 18-21
model-recipient interaction, 8, 14-16, 38
model-subject similarity, 7, 18
negative models, 8, 17
strength of, 31
norm of reciprocity, 11
race and, 9, 11, 15, 16, 34-43
and reactance theory, 269-270
request versus demand for help, 169
role of subject, 53
self-image of helper, 58, 76-77
sex and, 9, 13, 38, 40-42, 166-167
social context of, 44-55
social responsibility norm, 12, 16, 30, 32
anonymity of bystander, 168
presence of others, 168
and race, 163, 166-168
social status and, 9, 44-55
sympathy arousal, 13, 38
task dimensions: honesty versus special favor, 53
monetary versus personal exchange, 53
threat to bystander and, 22, 25-28, 30-33, 35, 42
as arousal, 27
embarrassment, 26-27
"freezing" under stress, 31
physical, 26-27
in the urban environment, 33
victim characteristics, 22, 34-43, 48-55, 168
deservingness, 28-33
responsibility for plight, 35, 42
Honesty:
and anonymity, 103
with money, 51-53
and social status, 51-53, 96, 103
Humor, 108-111

Identification, cognitive theory, 264
Imitation, 68, 71
(*See also* Conformity; Modeling)
Ingroup-outgroup distinction:
attribution of qualities, 200
foreigners and compatriots, 53-55
labor and management, 200
Insults (*see* Attitude change)
Integration:
church setting: seating patterns, 139
social functions, 140-142
legislation, 128-129, 137, 155, 199, 315
racial balance, 158
of social classes, 139
voluntary, 139
(*See also* Aggregation; Discriminatory behavior; Interracial interaction)
Intelligence tests:
cultural bias, 287, 300
sex differences, 300
Intergroup conflict:
appeal to moral ideals, 199
communication, 202-204
mass-media, 200
competition, 202
and group solidarity, 199-202
ethnocentrism, 200
functional intergroup relations, 200
and group leadership, 203
with superordinate goals, 204
insults, 205
and intragroup relations, 202
legislation and, 199
polarization, 205
boomerang effect, 208
and release of frustration, 199
social contact, 199
deleterious effects, 203
and social-distance norms, 200
superordinate goals, 199-204
cumulative effect, 203
definition, 199
territorial invasions, urban gangs, 200
(*See also* Integration; Interracial interaction)
Intergroup relations in unpatterned situations, 288, 309-318
Interpersonal attraction in helping behavior, 11, 15-16, 28
Interracial interaction:
age differences, 120, 141-142, 159
aggregation index, uses of, 152
church setting: active group members, 139, 143-144
pre- versus post-integration members, 141-142
self-selectivity, 144
superordinate goal, 145
communication patterns, proposed study, 297-298
community norms, 144
Interracial interaction:
convenience of action versus threat of integration, crowded buses, 159
conversation, 139-142
frequency, 140
interracial experience, 144-145
leadership, 145
lost-letter technique, 248
as means of attitude change, 139
political party dinner, superordinate goal, 314
seating patterns, 139-144, 148-152, 314
methods of measurement, 156-161
sex differences, 159
situational norms, 309-318
social class, 139-141
in unpatterned situations, 288, 309-318
conflicting definitions, 314-315
modification of reaction, 316-317
voluntary integration, 139-146
(*See also* Discriminatory behavior; Integration; Intergroup conflict; Prejudice; Race)
Interracial marriage, discrimination, 128-129
Involvement:
and emotional arousal, 216, 224
fear of, 22, 31
(*See also* Helping behavior)

Laboratory research:
advantages, 267
contrast to field research, 100, 104
in attitude change, 209
generalizability, 1
problems of, 2, 7, 34, 95-96
reactivity in measurement, 98
subject cooperativeness, 98
Law, legislation and integration, 128-129, 137, 155, 199, 315
Leadership:
attitude change, in military organizations, 238-244
definition of appropriate behavior, in unpatterned situations, 313, 315-317
Lines, waiting (*see* Waiting lines)
Locations of research (geographic):
Allentown, Pennsylvania, voting wards, 87
Athens, Greece: Omonia Square metro stop, 46
pastry shops, 47
taxies, 48
Venizelou and Stadiou Streets, 45, 47
Austin, Texas: commercial district intersection, 105
University of Texas, hallways, 79
Bangkok, Thailand, streets, 249
Baton Rouge, Louisiana, Louisiana State University, 109
coffee shop and lounge, 109
library, 109
Boston, Massachusetts: parked automobiles, 248
pastry shops, 47
taxies, 48
traffic, 321-322

Locations of research (geographic):
Boston, Massachusetts: Washington Street, 45, 47
Washington Street transit station, 46
work place of target person, 293
Brooklyn, New York, telephone calls to, 162-169
Buffalo, New York, apartment dwellings, 128
Cambridge, Massachusetts, residence of target person, 293
Chicago, Illinois, First Baptist Church, 139
Columbus, Ohio, streets, 300-301
Davidson County, Tennessee, parking lots, 252
Durham, North Carolina, supermarkets, 269
an Eastern city, paint department of chain store, 264
Hong Kong, China, streets, 249
Lansing, Michigan, intersections, 68
Lawrence, Kansas, traffic, 321-322
London, England, Oxford and Regent Streets, 300-301
Los Angeles, California, highway, 12
Melbourne, Australia: Collingwood Football Club, 189-190
Grosvernor theatre (downtown), 190-191
Melbourne Cricket Ground, 187-188
small coeducational high school, 191-194
Memphis, Tennessee, department store, 82
Mendocino State Hospital, 182-183
Menlo Park, California, intersections, 98
Midwest, General Hospital, 60-61
New Haven, Connecticut: parked automobiles, 246
phone booths, 246
shopping plazas, 219
shops, 246
sidewalks, 246
supermarket, 276
New Orleans, Louisiana, Public Transit, 155
New York, New York: Broadway, 300-301
City University and New York University, psychology and social sciences classes, 281
Columbia University, dining halls, 282
East Manhattan restaurants, 130
Forty-second Street, 197
Grand Central Station, phone booths, 102
Kennedy Airport, phone booths, 102
midtown Manhattan street, 19
New York Coliseum, 1961 Health Exposition, 227
subways, 23, 35
Washington Square Park, benches, 210-211
New York state, restaurants and taverns, 310

Locations of research (geographic):
North Carolina, tobacco towns: black neighborhoods, 248
white neighborhoods, 248
Omaha, Nebraska, letters mailed to residents, 293
Palo Alto, California: households, 72, 75
intersections, 98
Paris, France: Air France medical department records, 283
Boulevard Haussmann, 45, 47
Chausee D'Antin metro stop, 46
Havre Caumartin metro stop, 46
pastry shops, 47
taxies, 48
Princeton, New Jersey, department store entrance, 13
Sharon, Massachusetts, residence of target person, 293
Singapore, Malaysia, streets, 249
Trenton, New Jersey, shopping center, 14-16
Wichita, Kansas, letters mailed to residents, 293
Worcester, Massachusetts, streets, 247
Locations of research (geography not specified):
boys' camp, 204
discount store chain, 259-262
dormitory study hall, 176
junior high school history classes, 113
library study halls, 173, 176-178, 183-184
motels, hotels, and restaurants, 123
national magazine, 302
northern colleges, 147
soda fountain, 175
U.S. Army Reserve unit, 238-244

Mental hospitals, 182
Military organizations, consumer behavior, 237-244
(*See also* War)
Modeling:
age of model, 108-109
and automobile driving, turn-signalling, 68-69
minimal subject-model interaction, 68-69
model-recipient interaction, 8, 14-16, 38
model-subject similarity, 7, 18, 264
negative model, 8, 17, 78-81
petition-signing, 78-81
propriety-defining activity, 12
sex of model, 69, 108-109
status of model, 105-111
and traffic law, 105-107
(*See also* Helping behavior; Imitation)
Moral development, moral realism and relativism, 113

National character, 44
helping behavior, 48-55
lost-letter technique, 206
(*See also* Ethnocentrism)
Nonreactive research (*see* Reactivity)

Norms:
for automobile driving: competitive norms, 289, 319
conflicting norms, 320-323
cooperative norms, 289, 319
learning of, 201, 322
peer-group, 113-116
prohibitions, 108, 111
situational: automobile driving and traffic conditions, 319
discriminatory behavior, 309
social distance, and intergroup conflict, 200
for unpatterned situations, definition of appropriate behavior, 288-289, 309-318
(*See also* Deviance; Groups)
Nurse-physician relationships, 60-67
major characteristics, 65-67
reaction-formation, 67
transference, 67

Obedience:
attribution of responsibility, 57
efficiency and, 65
to illegitimate orders, 60-67
to law, 68-69
civil rights legislation, 128-129, 137, 155, 199, 315
and political preference, 206-207, 251-255
respect and, 65
threat and, 71
trust and, 65
uniforms and, 58, 96
in war, 57
(*See also* Compliance: Conformity; Dress as status-indicator)
Obesity:
consummatory data, disadvantages of, 275
criteria: deviation from national norms, 281, 282
observer judgment, 276
and dormitory food, 282-285
eating stimuli: external, 275, 280-285
internal, 275, 280-285
guilt-arousal by insult, and attitude change, 209, 217, 219-225
and religious fasting, 275, 280-282, 284-285
(*See also* Consumer behavior)
Overt behavior (*see* Verbal behavior, versus overt behavior)

Peer-group norms, 113-116
(*See also* Groups)
Person perception:
and race, 165
via tape recordings, 165-166
Personality characteristics:
and emotional political literature, 92
perceived via tape recordings, 165-166
tendency to conform, 80-81
and territorial behavior, 176
conversational distance, 181

Physical appearance, 25, 28, 123, 128
(*See also* Dress as status-indicator; Interpersonal attraction; Uniforms)
Placebo effects, 3
Police behavior:
crowd estimates, and crowd control, 194
as indicator of norms, 111
prejudice toward blacks, 39
Political behavior:
anti-war demonstrations, influence on public opinion, 206
bumper sticker display, and 1968 election results, 207
campaign expenditures, and efficiency in vote-getting, 84, 91
civil rights demonstrations, attitudes toward, 210
conformity to John Birch Society Bulletin, and demographic and personality factors, 306-307
crowd estimates, influence on public opinion, 194
extremism: anti-Communist protest letters, 302-308
conservatism, 302
nationalism, 302
and religious fundamentalism, 307-308
leafletting: efficiency in vote-getting, 91
emotional versus rational, 59, 85-93
letter writing, and 1964 election results, 304
letters to the editor, 288, 302-308
demographic factors, 306
group salience, 305-306
lost-letter technique, and election results, 248
petition-signing, 58, 78-81
picketing, 58-59
effectiveness of, 82-83
polarization, boomerang effect, 208
political preference: and obedience of law, 207, 251-255
and social class, 253
sign display, 75-77
voter registration, 87
voting, 84-93
Political psychology, as scientific inquiry, 84-85
Population density, 171-172
Predicted versus actual behavior, 80, 178-179
obese versus normal grocery shoppers, 277
racial discrimination, 128-129
reaction to discrimination, 316
and self-deception, 65
(*See also* Questionnaires)
Prejudice:
blacks toward whites, 162
internalized group norms, in children, 201
reduction of intergroup conflict, 172, 199-204
and social desirability, 119
in white police officers, 39
Prejudice:
whites toward blacks, 162, 210
(*See also* Attitudes; Discriminatory behavior; Ethnocentrism; Integration; Intergroup conflict; Interracial interaction)
Prohibition:
cognitive norms, 111
strength of, 108
(*See also* Conformity; Obedience)
Propaganda, 71, 77, 84, 93
socialist, 85-93
(*See also* Political behavior)
"Psychopathology of everyday life," 63-67

Questionnaires:
as attitude measurement, 206
disadvantages, 122-123, 126-127, 162
and behavioral measures, 61-67, 100, 103-104, 226-235
for development of hypotheses, 171
evaluation apprehension, 245
fear arousal measure, 234
reactivity, 251
recording data of participant-observers, 131
social desirability, 146
(*See also* Predicted versus actual behavior; Verbal behavior)
Queues (*see* Waiting lines)

Race:
and dialect, 164-165
and helping behavior, 9, 11, 15-16, 34-43, 162-169
identification of, 148
by residential area, 164
skin color, 132
voice characteristics, 162, 164
(*See also* Discriminatory behavior; Interracial interaction; Prejudice)
Racism (*see* Discriminatory behavior; Intergroup conflict; Integration; Interracial interactions; Prejudice)
Reactance theory:
boomerang effect, 257, 273
coercion, 269
and consumer behavior, 269-274
derogation of threat source, 273
explanation, 257, 269, 273
and helping behavior, 269-270
importance of freedom, 273
and insults, 257
recommendations by peer, 269
reward, 269
social pressure, 269
Reaction-formation in nurse-physician relationships, 67
Reactivity, 3, 5, 98, 146, 162
in attitude measurement, 205
in field research, 205
Reference group in unpatterned situations, 317
(*See also* Groups)
Reliability (*see* Validity, internal)
Religion:
and ethnocentrism, 200
fasting on Yom Kippur, obese versus normal individuals, 280-282, 284-285
and political extremism, 302, 306-308
the True Believer, and mimetic behavior in protest letters, 306-308
Research, locations of (*see* Locations of research)
Research methods:
amusement influence, 109-110
asking directions, 22-33, 45-46
charity donations, 13-16
content analysis: conversations, 139-142
letters to the editor, 302-308
crowd formation, 197
dissonance techniques, 238-243, 260-261
fear arousal, 226-228
foot-in-the-door technique, 71-77
interviews, 75-76, 91-92, 178-179, 187-194, 219-220, 271-273
invasion of personal space, 175-179, 182-184
lost dime in telephone booth, 102
lost-letter technique, 245, 250
lost money on sidewalk, 47
lost-wallet technique, 19-20
by mail, 19-20, 46, 245, 292-294
in New York subway, limitations, 33
overpayment of shop clerks, 47-48
participant-observation, 128, 131-134, 140-141, 175-178, 310-312, 328
personal insults, 208-214, 217-225
petition-signing, 78-79
picketing, 82-83
political leafletting, 85-87
seating patterns, 142-143, 146-148, 152-161
small-world problem, 292-294
sociometric ratings, 204
by telephone, 60-61, 72-73, 129, 163-165
in traffic: blocking intersection, 98-99
changing a flat tire, 12-13
waiting line formation, 191-192
wrong-number technique, 163-165
(*See also* Field research; Laboratory research; Modeling; Questionnaires)
Risk-taking and territorial behavior, 176
Role:
and group relationships, 199
nurse-physician relationships, 57, 60-67
southern Negro female-white male relationships, 159, 167

Seating patterns:
crowding, 159
interracial, 142-144, 148-152
aggregation index, 146-147, 151-154
other methods of measurement, 156-161
prior acquaintance opportunity, 146
sex, 150

Segregation (*see* Aggregation; Discriminatory behavior; Integration; Interracial interaction)
Sex aggregation, seating patterns, 150
Sex differences:
agents of social change, 159
in aggression, 100
in amusement influence, 110
in automobile horn-honking, 100
communication patterns, sex of intermediaries, 296
in compliance in consumer behavior, 271-272
in compliance with pickets, 83
in conformity to traffic law, 69
in conversation content, 300-301
in helping behavior, 9, 13, 38, 166-167
in honesty, 104
interracial seating patterns, 146, 150, 159
and race differences in helping behavior, 166-167
in rating experimenters, 265
in sociometric status, 114-115
in territorial behavior, 175-176
violation of segregation precedence, 120, 159
Sex role stereotypes:
in conversation, 288
"woman driver," 322
Snobs, effete, 205
Social action, racial discrimination in restaurants, 130-138
Social change:
agents of: age differences, 159
sex differences, 159
in unpatterned situations, 288, 309
Social comparison theory and communicator-recipient similarity, 264, 267
Social desirability, 7, 119, 146, 163, 251
Social distance:
as indicator of attitude, 123-124
and intergroup conflict, 200-202
and wrong-number technique, 167
Social influence:
authority figures and, 57-58, 111
without awareness, 58
definition, 57
emotional versus rational appeal, 84-93
and environmental setting: library, 96, 109-111
student union, 109-111
fear-arousing communication, 226
overt response, 232-233
group size, 108, 196-198
petition-signing: as compliance, 75-81
conformity and, 58, 78-81
modeling and, 58, 78-81
situational factors, 78-81
on prohibitions, 83, 105-107
via protest, 58, 82-83
and status: in experiments, 57-58
in field situations, 96, 105-111
unanimity, 108
(*See also* Attitude change; Compliance; Conformity; Modeling; Obedience)
Social judgment theory and attitude change, 217-218, 222-225
Social responsibility norm (*see* Helping behavior)
Social status:
and attribution of causality, 96
and communication, 120
and communication patterns, 292
definitions: automobile (make and year), 95, 98-99, 253
dress, 95-96, 102, 105, 109, 155
occupation, 303
sociometric ratings, 95
writing implement and stationery, 303
exercise of sanctions, 98
and "finking," 113-116
sex differences, 115
hierarchy in groups, 202
idiosyncrasy, credit, 96
inhibitor of response, 98-100
and political preference, 253
and prohibitions, 105-107
and public transportation, 324
sex differences, 114
Social structure:
mathematical, in communication patterns, 290-292
measurement of, by communication patterns, 296
Socialist party (1935 Pennsylvania election):
political leafletting, 85-93
and social class, 91-92
Sociology:
experimental, 181
of public transit, 324-328
Sociometric technique:
and intergroup conflict, 201
and status, 96, 114
Space, personal (*see* Territorial behavior)
Stereotypes, 45
intergroup conflict, 199-204
sex-role, 288, 322
Subject population:
homogeneous, for intergroup conflict study, 202
problems of selection: experimenter differences, 225
representation of national trends, 245
self-selection, 144, 189
volunteers, 4

Telephone (*see* Research methods)
Territorial behavior:
acquaintance, 181
active defense versus retreat, 173-175
of animals: in confinement, avoidance movements, 185
markers, 175
spacing mechanisms in birds, 184
and attribution of sexual motives, 185
Territorial behavior:
conversational distance: personality factors, 181
situational factors, 181
and culture, 181
defense: avoidance, 173-175, 184
measurement of, 181, 184-186
offensive ownership, 173-175
public area, 173-179
definition of terms, 173, 179
core areas, 173
defense, 173
home, 173
jurisdiction, 173
personalization, 173
range, 173
territory, 173
deviance, measurement of, 181
dominance, 176, 185
ecological tradition, 171
invasions: adaptation to, 185
arrival distance, 184-185
intergroup conflict, 200
personal space, 175, 181
settled distance, 184-185
sex difference, 175-176
and law, 179
locations: library, 173-179, 183-184
mental hospital, 182-183
public areas, 173, 179
soda fountains, 175-176
markers: defender's presence, 175
discussion, 179
of humans, visual, 175
neighbors, 173, 176-179
personal, 173-179
ownership, 173
physical barriers, 173-175
and risk-taking, 176
room density, 173-178, 181
temporary territories, 179
territoriality, criteria, 182
(*See also* Seating patterns)
Theft, 113-116
Transference in nurse-physician relationships, 67
Transportation:
automobile driving, 68-69, 98-100, 254, 319-323
buses, interracial seating patterns, 155-157
pedestrians, 105
public, and social status, 324
public transit: "co-acting group," 325
versus collective behavior, 324-325
definition, 324
diversions, 289, 326-327
exit orientation, 325-326
personal space, 289
sociology: of public transit, 120, 160, 324-328
of public transportation, lengthy journeys, 324
subways, 8, 22-33, 34-43
taxicabs, 48, 52-55
Trust:
and helping behavior, 38
in laboratory situations, 4
and obedience, 65

Uniforms and status, 58, 96
(*See also* Dress as status-indicator; Obedience)
Urban planning, 172

Validity:
external (*see* Generalizability)
internal, 3
Verbal behavior:
versus overt behavior, 171
attitude measurement, 205
compliance, 72-75
concerning race, 119-120, 123, 128-129, 162-163
Verbal behavior:
response to hypothetical situations, 125-126, 206
inadequacies, 309
racial discrimination, 316

Waiting lines:
attitudes toward, and place in line, 193
for chocolate bars, 191-194
attitudes toward chocolate, 193-194
estimation of place in line: critical point, 187-194
Waiting lines:
estimation of place in line: explanations of errors, 189, 191, 193
psychophysical factors, 189, 191
and racial aggregation index, 152
reactance motivation, 171-172
(*See also* Crowds)
War:
anti-war demonstrations, influence on public opinion, 206
and intergroup relations: the British Empire, 199-200
effects on intragroup relations, 202